Silver Burdett Ginn

Mathematics

Answer Key

Practice

Reteach

Extend

Daily Review

Practice Workbook

2

Silver Burdett Ginn

Parsippany, NJ • Needham, MA

Atlanta, GA • Deerfield, IL • Irving, TX • Santa Clara, CA

Silver Burdett Ginn
A Division of Simon & Schuster
299 Jefferson Road, P.O. Box 480
Parsippany, NJ 07054-0480

ISBN 0-382-37342-1

2 3 4 5 6 7 8 9-M-00 99 98 97

Contents

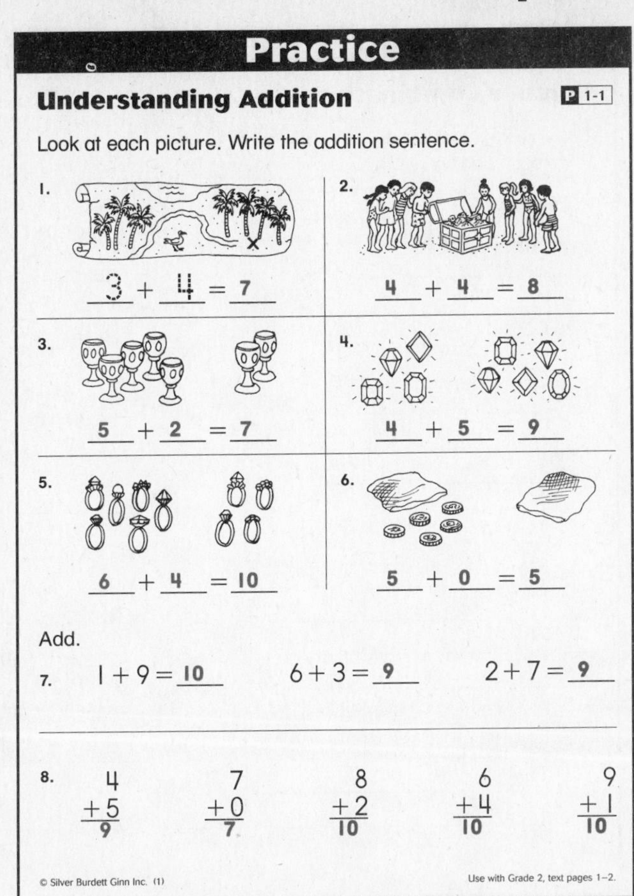

Practice

Understanding Addition

P 1-1

Look at each picture. Write the addition sentence.

1. 3 + 4 = 7
2. 4 + 4 = 8
3. 5 + 2 = 7
4. 4 + 5 = 9
5. 6 + 4 = 10
6. 5 + 0 = 5

Add.

7. 1 + 9 = 10   6 + 3 = 9   2 + 7 = 9

8.

4	7	8	6	9
+5	+0	+2	+4	+1
9	7	10	10	10

© Silver Burdett Ginn Inc. (1)

Use with Grade 2, text pages 1–2.

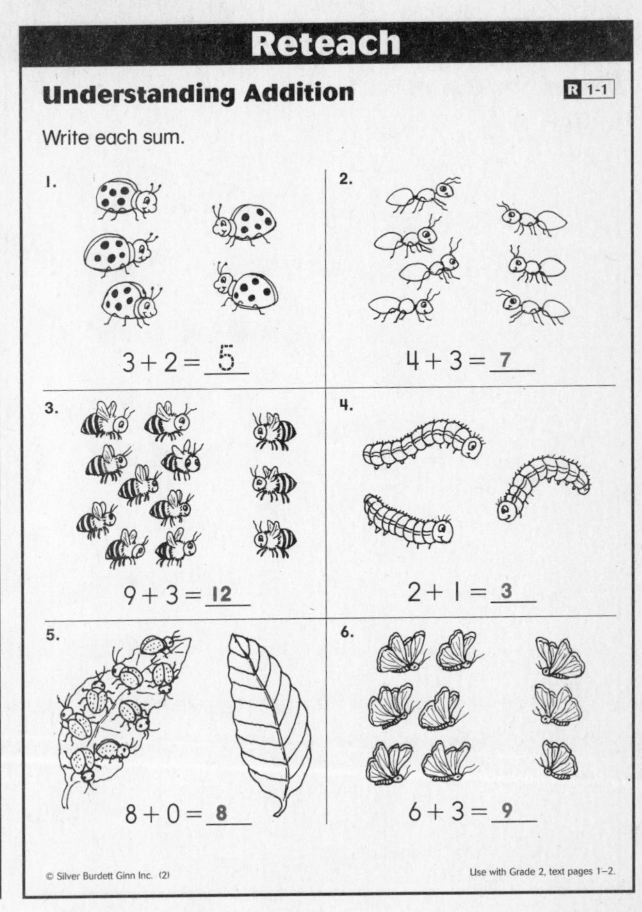

Reteach

Understanding Addition

R 1-1

Write each sum.

1. 3 + 2 = 5
2. 4 + 3 = 7
3. 9 + 3 = 12
4. 2 + 1 = 3
5. 8 + 0 = 8
6. 6 + 3 = 9

© Silver Burdett Ginn Inc. (2)

Use with Grade 2, text pages 1–2.

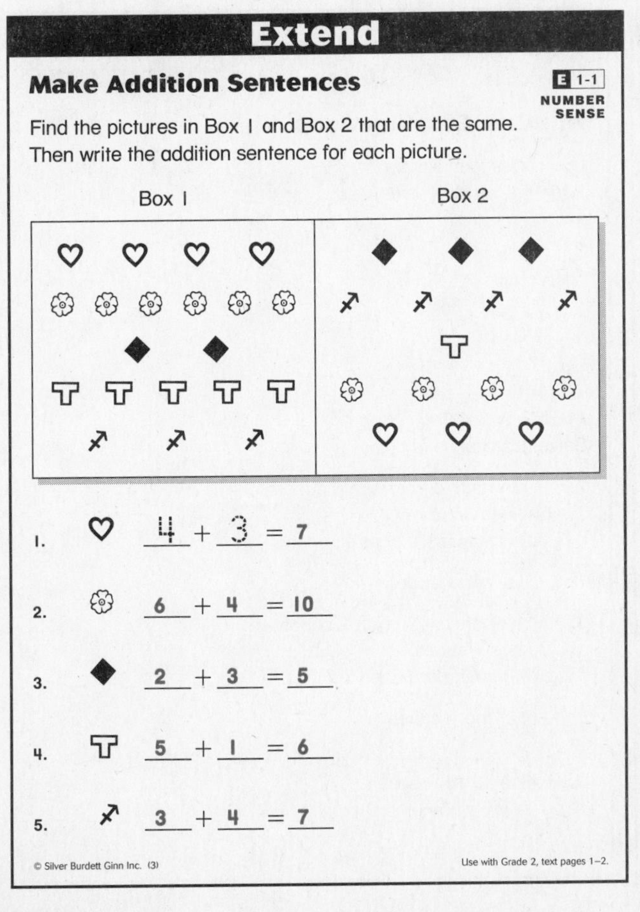

Extend

Make Addition Sentences

E 1-1 NUMBER SENSE

Find the pictures in Box 1 and Box 2 that are the same. Then write the addition sentence for each picture.

Box 1   Box 2

1. ♡ 4 + 3 = 7
2. ✿ 6 + 4 = 10
3. ◆ 2 + 3 = 5
4. T 5 + 1 = 6
5. ↗ 3 + 4 = 7

© Silver Burdett Ginn Inc. (3)

Use with Grade 2, text pages 1–2.

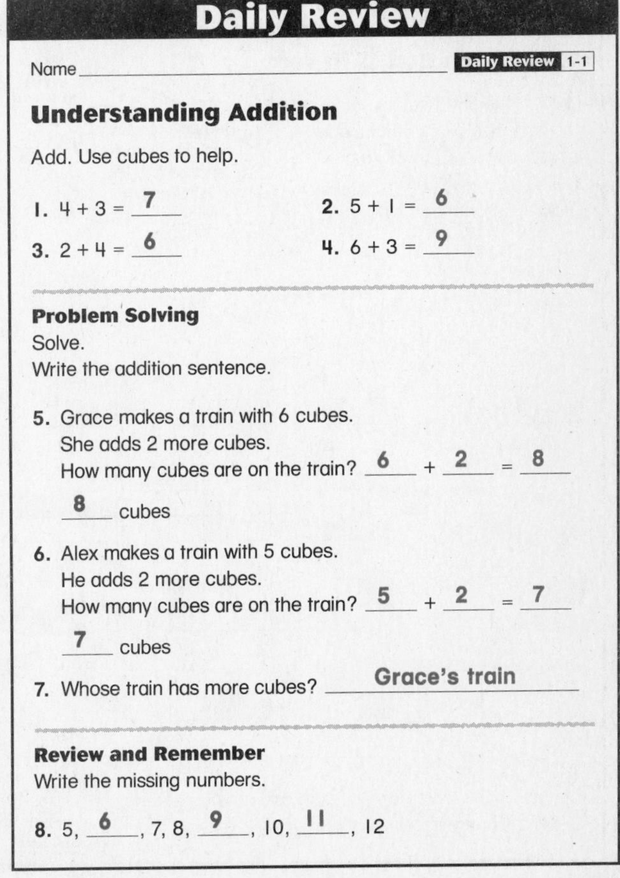

Daily Review

Name ____________________

Daily Review 1-1

Understanding Addition

Add. Use cubes to help.

1. 4 + 3 = 7
2. 5 + 1 = 6
3. 2 + 4 = 6
4. 6 + 3 = 9

Problem Solving

Solve.

Write the addition sentence.

5. Grace makes a train with 6 cubes.
   She adds 2 more cubes.
   How many cubes are on the train? 6 + 2 = 8
   8 cubes
6. Alex makes a train with 5 cubes.
   He adds 2 more cubes.
   How many cubes are on the train? 5 + 2 = 7
   7 cubes
7. Whose train has more cubes? Grace's train

Review and Remember

Write the missing numbers.

8. 5, 6, 7, 8, 9, 10, 11, 12

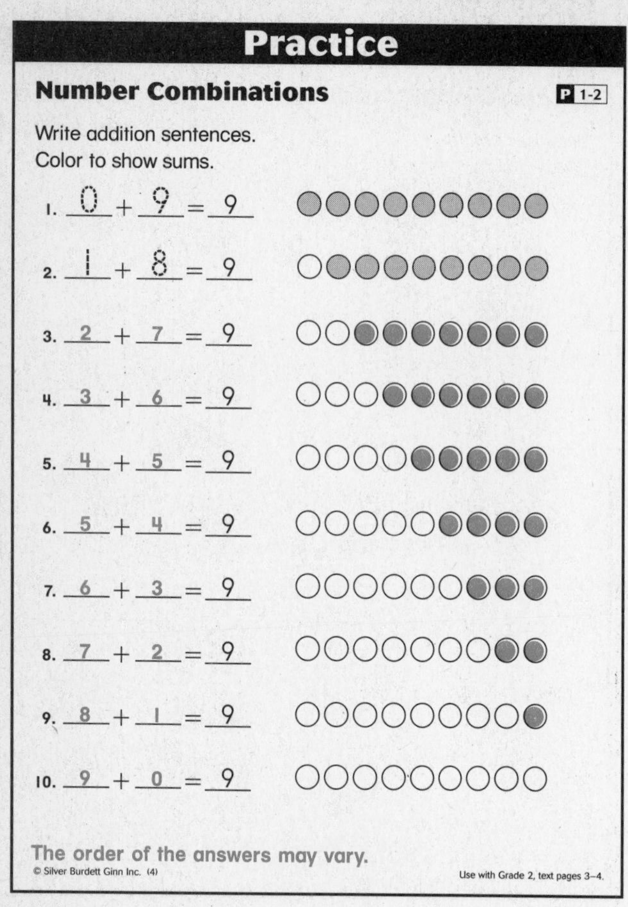

Practice

Number Combinations

P 1-2

Write addition sentences.
Color to show sums.

1. 0 + 9 = 9
2. 1 + 8 = 9
3. 2 + 7 = 9
4. 3 + 6 = 9
5. 4 + 5 = 9
6. 5 + 4 = 9
7. 6 + 3 = 9
8. 7 + 2 = 9
9. 8 + 1 = 9
10. 9 + 0 = 9

The order of the answers may vary.

 Use with Grade 2, text pages 3–4.

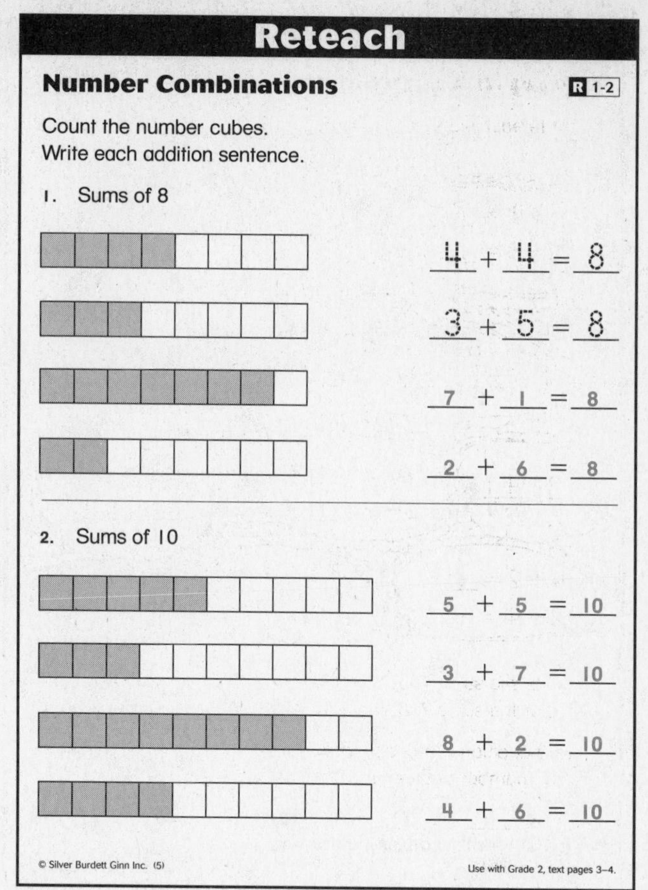

Reteach

Number Combinations

R 1-2

Count the number cubes.
Write each addition sentence.

1. Sums of 8

4 + 4 = 8
3 + 5 = 8
7 + 1 = 8
2 + 6 = 8

2. Sums of 10

5 + 5 = 10
3 + 7 = 10
8 + 2 = 10
4 + 6 = 10

 Use with Grade 2, text pages 3–4.

Extend

Make Each Box Different

E 1-2 VISUAL THINKING

Look at the first two boxes.
In each, two blocks are shaded and four blocks are white.
Color to show different ways to make the same combination.

Remember, always have two blocks shaded and four blocks white.

Did you find 15 different ways to color the boxes?
Order of answers will vary.

 Use with Grade 2, text pages 3–4.

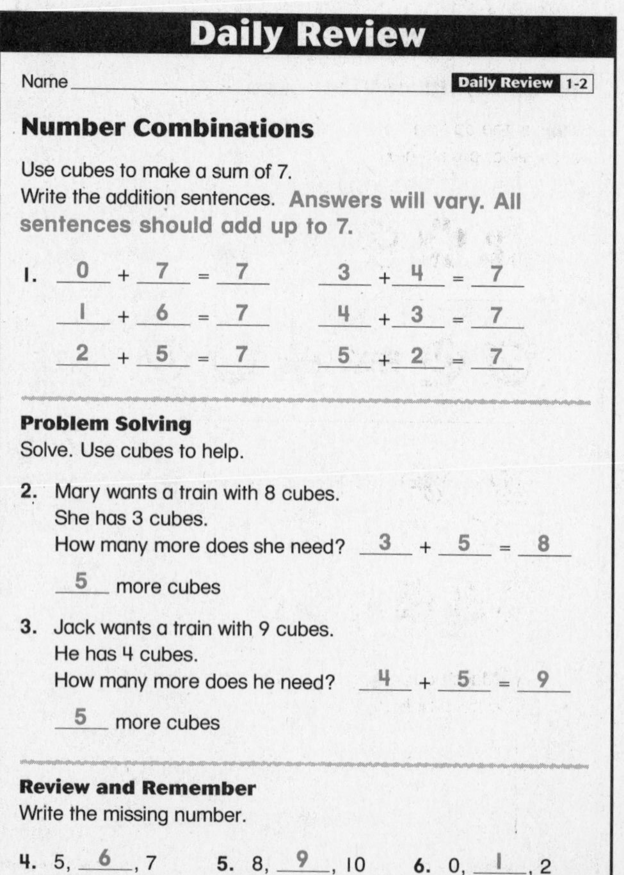

Daily Review

Name__________ Daily Review 1-2

Number Combinations

Use cubes to make a sum of 7.
Write the addition sentences. Answers will vary. All sentences should add up to 7.

1. 0 + 7 = 7 3 + 4 = 7
1 + 6 = 7 4 + 3 = 7
2 + 5 = 7 5 + 2 = 7

Problem Solving
Solve. Use cubes to help.

2. Mary wants a train with 8 cubes.
She has 3 cubes.
How many more does she need? 3 + 5 = 8
5 more cubes

3. Jack wants a train with 9 cubes.
He has 4 cubes.
How many more does he need? 4 + 5 = 9
5 more cubes

Review and Remember
Write the missing number.

4. 5, 6, 7 5. 8, 9, 10 6. 0, 1, 2

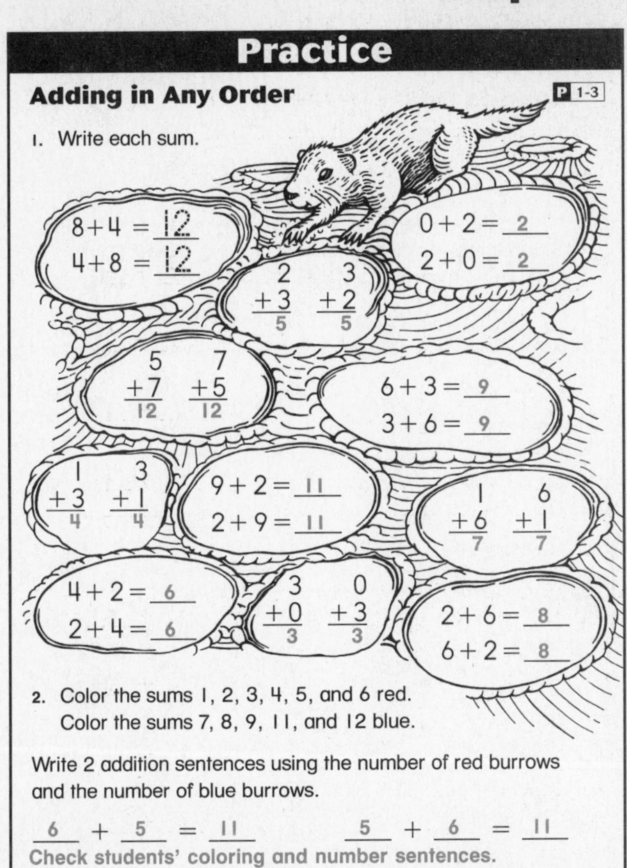

Practice

Adding in Any Order

P 1-3

1. Write each sum.

8 + 4 = 12
4 + 8 = 12

0 + 2 = 2
2 + 0 = 2

$\begin{array}{r}2\\+3\\\hline 5\end{array}$ $\begin{array}{r}3\\+2\\\hline 5\end{array}$

$\begin{array}{r}5\\+7\\\hline 12\end{array}$ $\begin{array}{r}7\\+5\\\hline 12\end{array}$

6 + 3 = 9
3 + 6 = 9

$\begin{array}{r}1\\+3\\\hline 4\end{array}$ $\begin{array}{r}3\\+1\\\hline 4\end{array}$

9 + 2 = 11
2 + 9 = 11

$\begin{array}{r}1\\+6\\\hline 7\end{array}$ $\begin{array}{r}6\\+1\\\hline 7\end{array}$

4 + 2 = 6
2 + 4 = 6

$\begin{array}{r}3\\+0\\\hline 3\end{array}$ $\begin{array}{r}0\\+3\\\hline 3\end{array}$

2 + 6 = 8
6 + 2 = 8

2. Color the sums 1, 2, 3, 4, 5, and 6 red.
Color the sums 7, 8, 9, 11, and 12 blue.

Write 2 addition sentences using the number of red burrows and the number of blue burrows.

6 + 5 = 11   5 + 6 = 11

Check students' coloring and number sentences.

 Use with Grade 2, text pages 5–6.

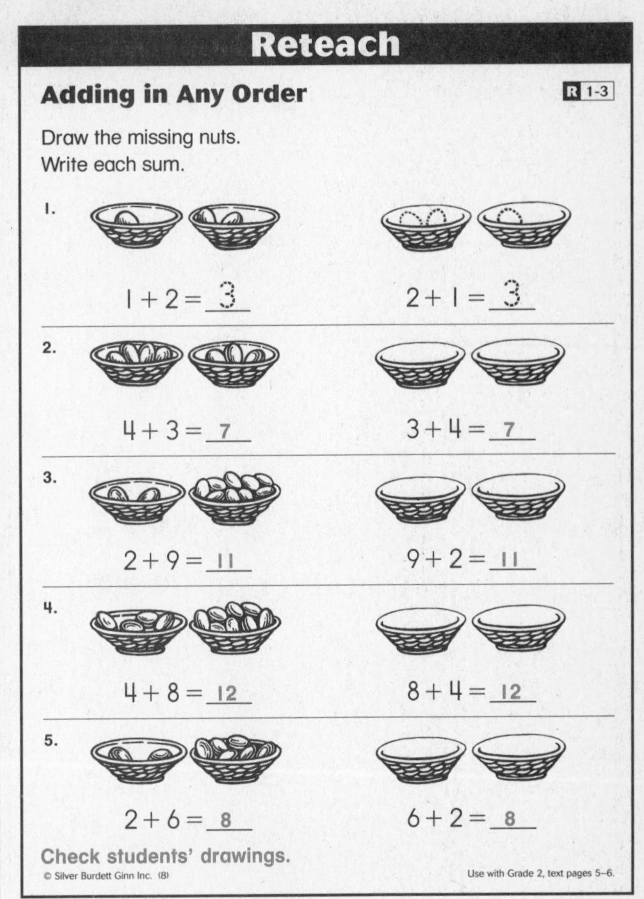

Reteach

Adding in Any Order

R 1-3

Draw the missing nuts.
Write each sum.

1. 1 + 2 = 3   2 + 1 = 3

2. 4 + 3 = 7   3 + 4 = 7

3. 2 + 9 = 11   9 + 2 = 11

4. 4 + 8 = 12   8 + 4 = 12

5. 2 + 6 = 8   6 + 2 = 8

Check students' drawings.

 Use with Grade 2, text pages 5–6.

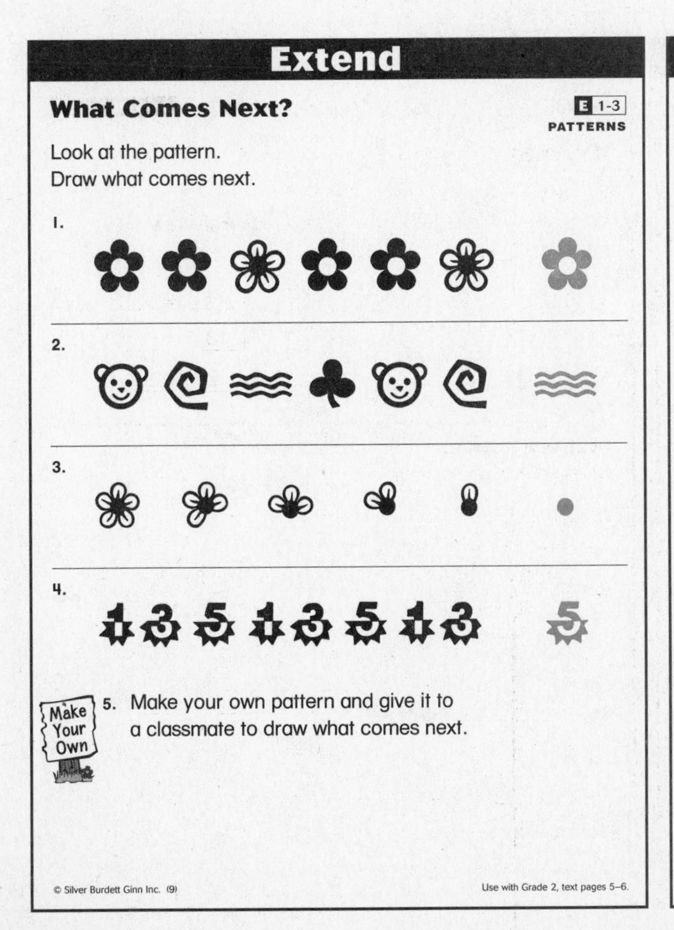

Extend

What Comes Next?

E 1-3
PATTERNS

Look at the pattern.
Draw what comes next.

1.

2.

3.

4. 1 3 5 1 3 5 1 3 5

5. Make your own pattern and give it to a classmate to draw what comes next.

Make Your Own

 Use with Grade 2, text pages 5–6.

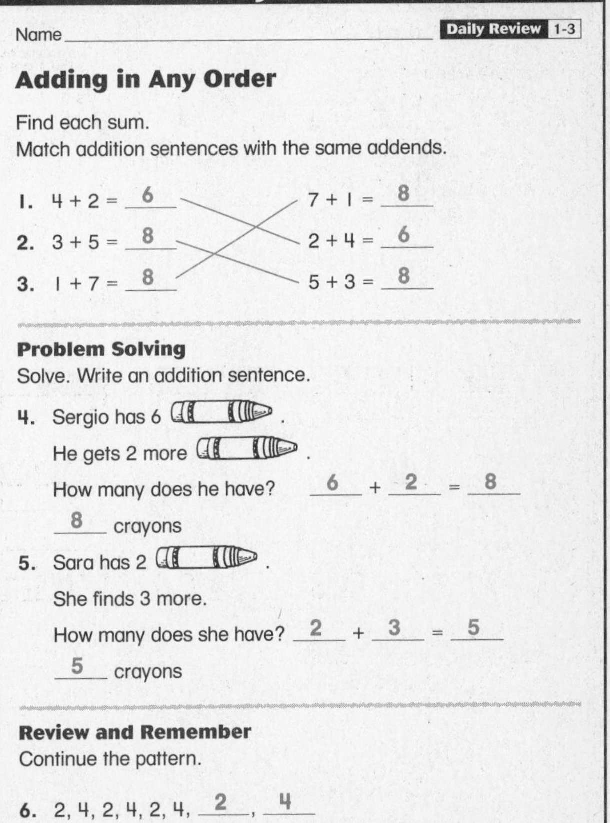

Daily Review

Name __________ Daily Review 1-3

Adding in Any Order

Find each sum.
Match addition sentences with the same addends.

1. 4 + 2 = 6   7 + 1 = 8
2. 3 + 5 = 8   2 + 4 = 6
3. 1 + 7 = 8   5 + 3 = 8

Problem Solving

Solve. Write an addition sentence.

4. Sergio has 6 .
He gets 2 more .
How many does he have? 6 + 2 = 8
8 crayons

5. Sara has 2 .
She finds 3 more.
How many does she have? 2 + 3 = 5
5 crayons

Review and Remember

Continue the pattern.

6. 2, 4, 2, 4, 2, 4, 2, 4

Chapter 1 • Lesson 4

Practice

Counting On

P 1-4

Count on to add.
Write each sum.

1 2 3 4 5 6 7 8 9 10 11 12

1. 4 + 2 = 6
2. 1 + 3 = 4
3. 3 + 5 = 8
4. 9 + 2 = 11
5. 2 + 8 = 10
6. 7 + 3 = 10
7. 3 + 8 = 11
8. 3 + 2 = 5
9. 10 + 2 = 12
10. 2 + 5 = 7
11. 1 + 2 = 3
12. 3 + 6 = 9

Use with Grade 2, text pages 7–8.

Reteach

Counting On

R 1-4

5 + 3 = ?

Start with the greater number.
Think 5.

Say 6, 7, 8.

5 + 3 = 8

Circle the greater number. Then count on.
Draw or use cubes if you like.

1. (8) + 2 = ?
Think 8 Say 9, 10
8 + 2 = 10

2. 1 + (6) = ?
Think 6 Say 7
1 + 6 = 7

3. 2 + (9) = ?
Think 9 Say 10, 11
2 + 9 = 11

Use with Grade 2, text pages 7–8.

Extend

Spin and Count

E 1-4
PROBABILITY

What You Need
a paper clip
a pencil

① Spin the paper clip.
② Write the number.
③ Count on to find the sum.
④ Play again.

1
2
3

1. 7 + ___ = ___
2. 9 + ___ = ___
3. ___ + 8 = ___
4. 6 + ___ = ___
5. 5 + ___ = ___
6. ___ + 8 = ___
7. ___ + 6 = ___
8. ___ + 9 = ___

9. Which number comes up most often?
Explain why you think this happens.
Three should come up most often because it makes up half the spinner.

Check students' methods.

Use with Grade 2, text pages 7–8.

Daily Review

Name ________________

Daily Review 1-4

Counting On

Count on to add.

1.

2	5	4	7	0	3
+ 2	+ 1	+ 2	+ 2	+ 8	+ 2
4	6	6	9	8	5

Problem Solving
Add.
Write addition sentences to continue the pattern.

2. 6 + 1 = 7
6 + 2 = 8
6 + 3 = 9
6 + 4 = 10
6 + 5 = 11

3. 4 + 3 = 7
4 + 4 = 8
4 + 5 = 9
4 + 6 = 10
4 + 7 = 11

Review and Remember
Match.

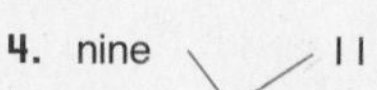

4. nine — 11
5. eleven — 8
6. eight — 9

7. six — 5
8. four — 6
9. five — 4

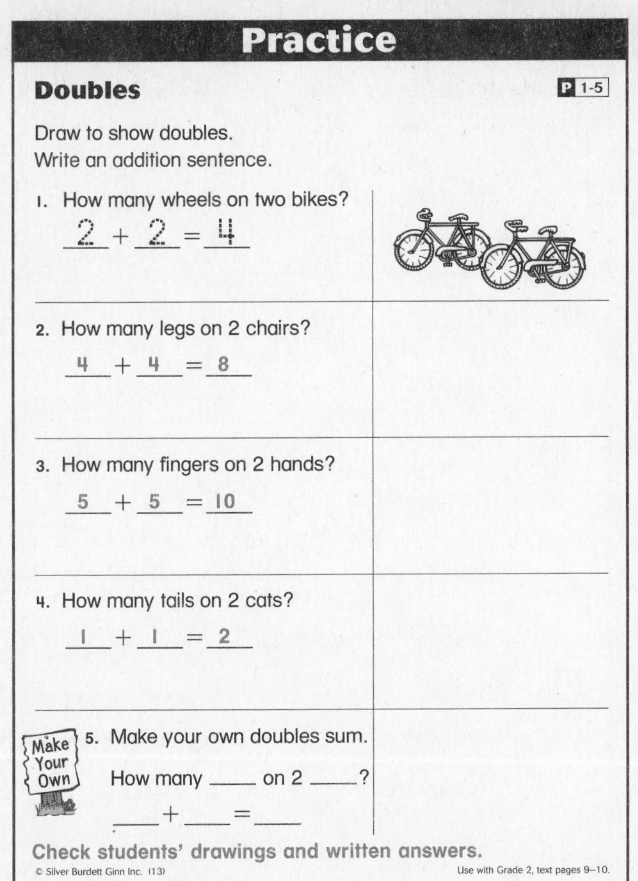

Practice

Doubles

P 1-5

Draw to show doubles.
Write an addition sentence.

1. How many wheels on two bikes?
   2 + 2 = 4
2. How many legs on 2 chairs?
   4 + 4 = 8
3. How many fingers on 2 hands?
   5 + 5 = 10
4. How many tails on 2 cats?
   1 + 1 = 2
5. Make your own doubles sum.
   How many ____ on 2 ____?
   ____ + ____ = ____

Make Your Own

Check students' drawings and written answers.

 Use with Grade 2, text pages 9–10.

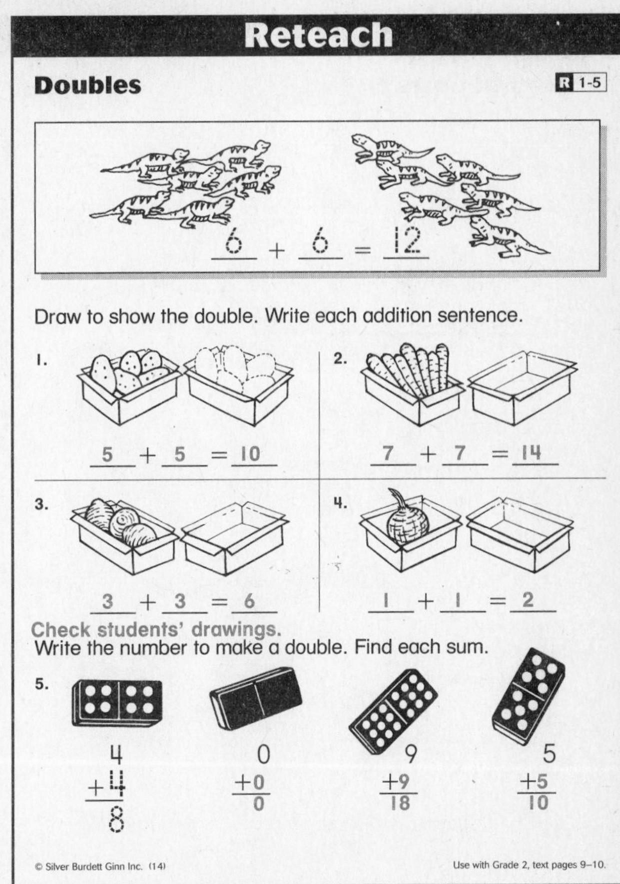

Reteach

Doubles

R 1-5

6 + 6 = 12

Draw to show the double. Write each addition sentence.

1. 5 + 5 = 10
2. 7 + 7 = 14
3. 3 + 3 = 6
4. 1 + 1 = 2

Check students' drawings.

Write the number to make a double. Find each sum.

5. 4 + 4 = 8   0 + 0 = 0   9 + 9 = 18   5 + 5 = 10

 Use with Grade 2, text pages 9–10.

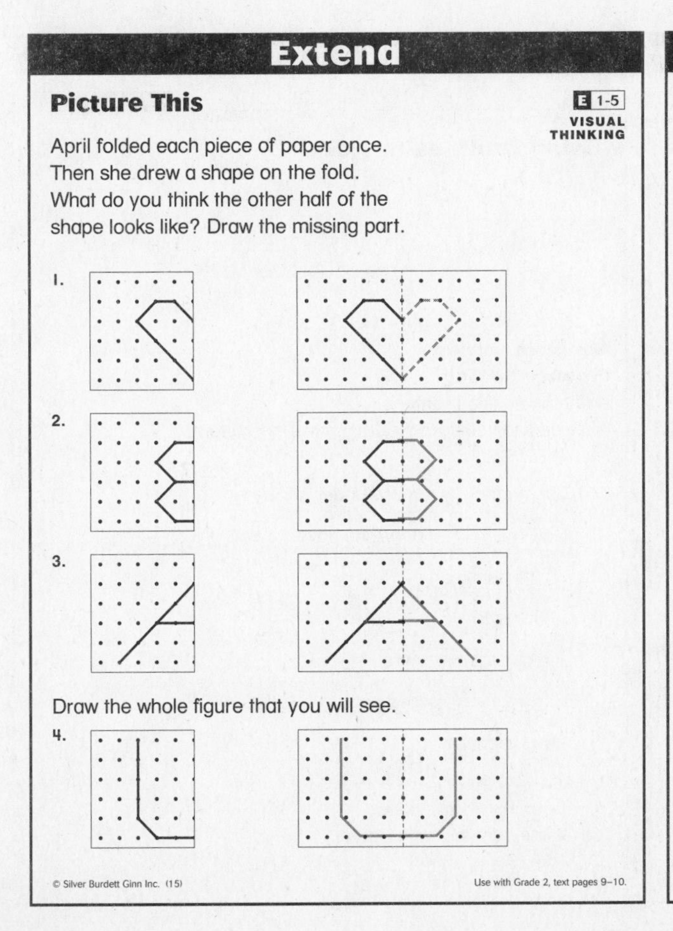

Extend

Picture This

E 1-5
VISUAL THINKING

April folded each piece of paper once. Then she drew a shape on the fold. What do you think the other half of the shape looks like? Draw the missing part.

1.

2.

3.

Draw the whole figure that you will see.

4.

 Use with Grade 2, text pages 9–10.

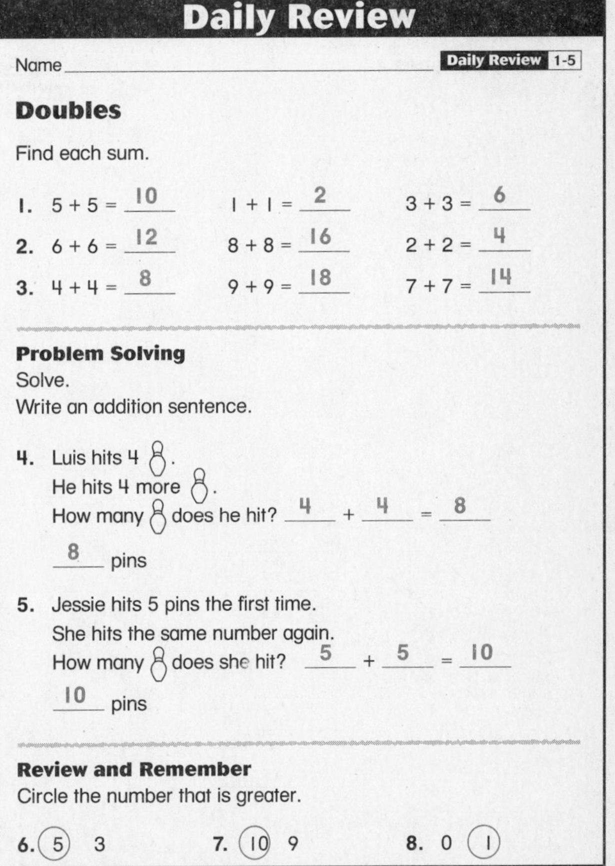

Daily Review

Name ____________________

Daily Review 1-5

Doubles

Find each sum.

1. 5 + 5 = 10   1 + 1 = 2   3 + 3 = 6
2. 6 + 6 = 12   8 + 8 = 16   2 + 2 = 4
3. 4 + 4 = 8   9 + 9 = 18   7 + 7 = 14

Problem Solving

Solve.
Write an addition sentence.

4. Luis hits 4 pins.
   He hits 4 more pins.
   How many pins does he hit? 4 + 4 = 8
   8 pins
5. Jessie hits 5 pins the first time.
   She hits the same number again.
   How many pins does she hit? 5 + 5 = 10
   10 pins

Review and Remember

Circle the number that is greater.

6. (5) 3   7. (10) 9   8. 0 (1)

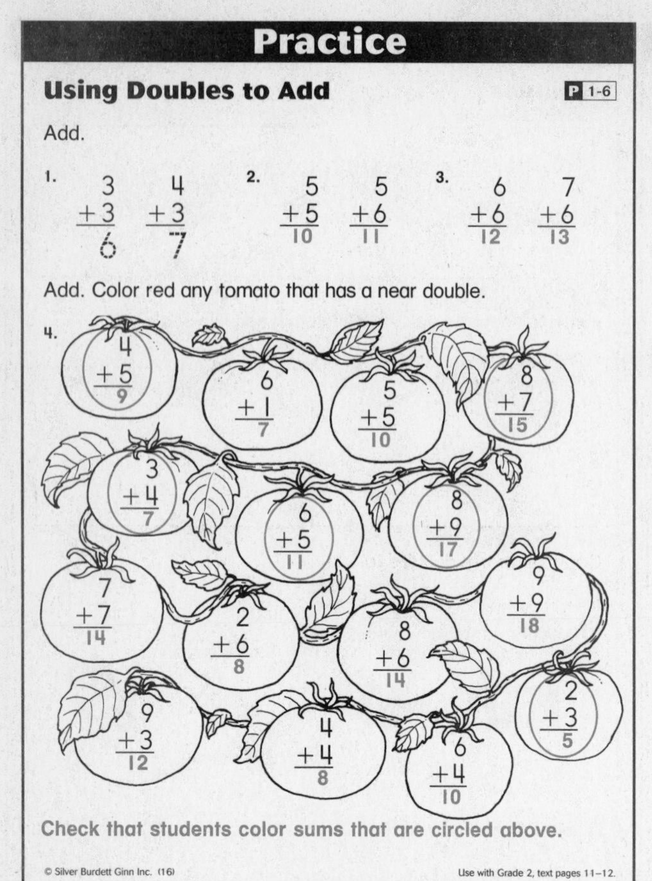

Practice

Using Doubles to Add

P 1-6

Add.

1. 3 + 3 = 6   4 + 3 = 7
2. 5 + 5 = 10   5 + 6 = 11
3. 6 + 6 = 12   7 + 6 = 13

Add. Color red any tomato that has a near double.

4. 4 + 5 = 9; 6 + 1 = 7; 5 + 5 = 10; 8 + 7 = 15; 3 + 4 = 7; 6 + 5 = 11; 8 + 9 = 17; 7 + 7 = 14; 2 + 6 = 8; 8 + 6 = 14; 9 + 9 = 18; 9 + 3 = 12; 4 + 4 = 8; 6 + 4 = 10; 2 + 3 = 5

Check that students color sums that are circled above.

 Use with Grade 2, text pages 11–12.

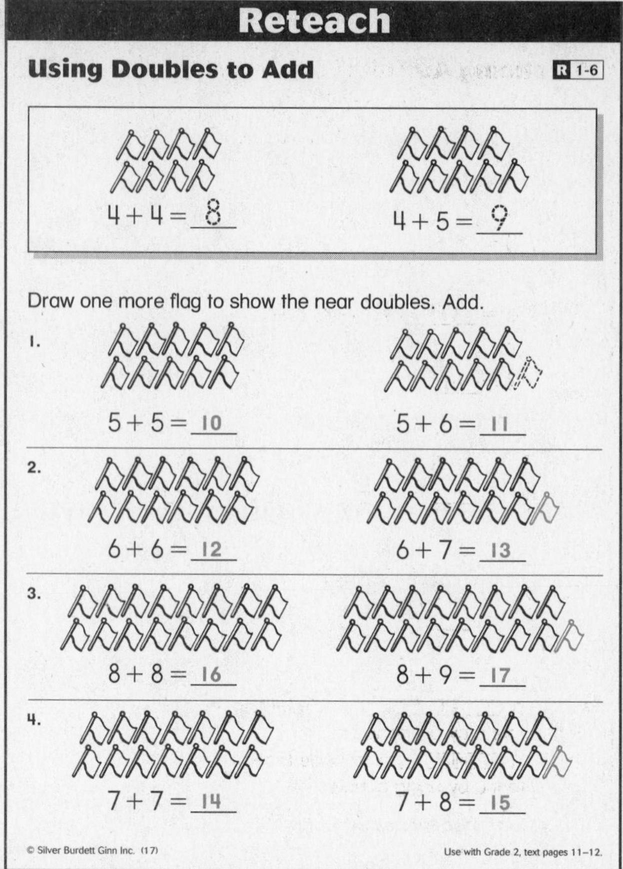

Reteach

Using Doubles to Add

R 1-6

4 + 4 = 8   4 + 5 = 9

Draw one more flag to show the near doubles. Add.

1. 5 + 5 = 10   5 + 6 = 11
2. 6 + 6 = 12   6 + 7 = 13
3. 8 + 8 = 16   8 + 9 = 17
4. 7 + 7 = 14   7 + 8 = 15

 Use with Grade 2, text pages 11–12.

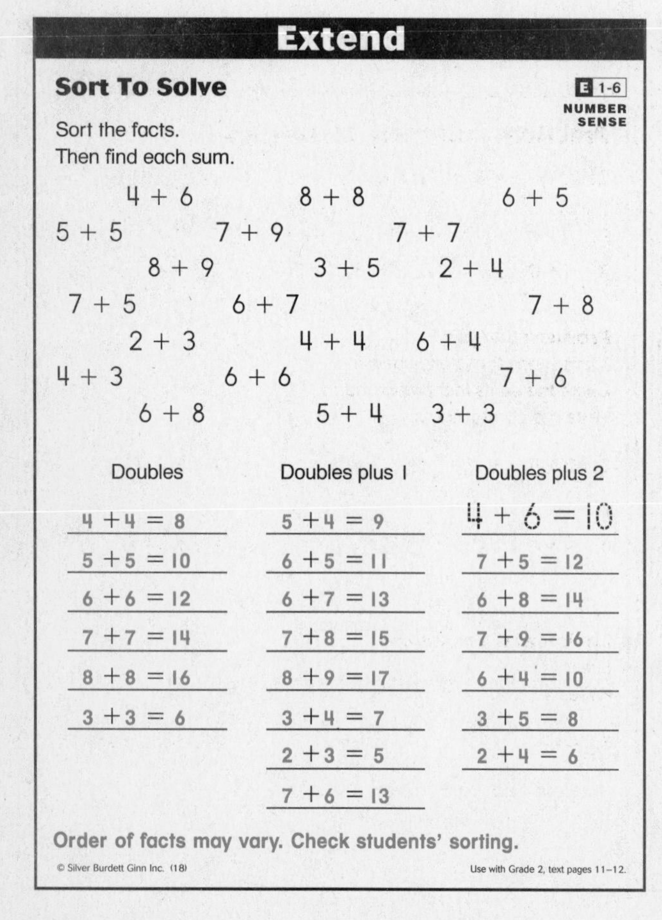

Extend

Sort To Solve

E 1-6 NUMBER SENSE

Sort the facts.
Then find each sum.

4 + 6   8 + 8   6 + 5
5 + 5   7 + 9   7 + 7
8 + 9   3 + 5   2 + 4
7 + 5   6 + 7   7 + 8
2 + 3   4 + 4   6 + 4
4 + 3   6 + 6   7 + 6
6 + 8   5 + 4   3 + 3

Doubles	Doubles plus 1	Doubles plus 2
4 + 4 = 8	5 + 4 = 9	4 + 6 = 10
5 + 5 = 10	6 + 5 = 11	7 + 5 = 12
6 + 6 = 12	6 + 7 = 13	6 + 8 = 14
7 + 7 = 14	7 + 8 = 15	7 + 9 = 16
8 + 8 = 16	8 + 9 = 17	6 + 4 = 10
3 + 3 = 6	3 + 4 = 7	3 + 5 = 8
	2 + 3 = 5	2 + 4 = 6
	7 + 6 = 13	

Order of facts may vary. Check students' sorting.

 Use with Grade 2, text pages 11–12.

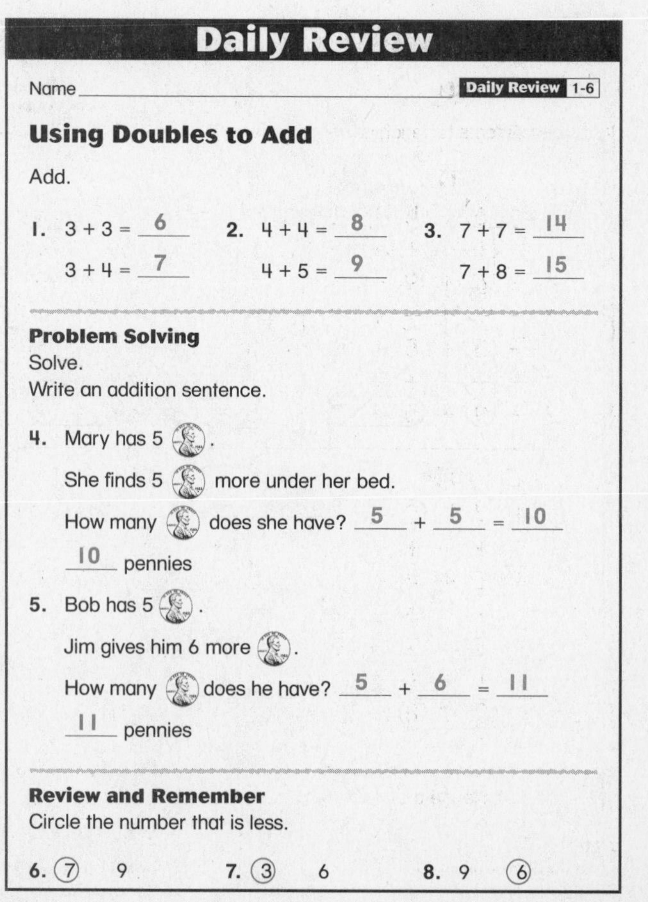

Daily Review

Name ____________________ Daily Review 1-6

Using Doubles to Add

Add.

1. 3 + 3 = 6   3 + 4 = 7
2. 4 + 4 = 8   4 + 5 = 9
3. 7 + 7 = 14   7 + 8 = 15

Problem Solving
Solve.
Write an addition sentence.

4. Mary has 5 pennies.
She finds 5 more under her bed.
How many does she have? 5 + 5 = 10
10 pennies

5. Bob has 5 pennies.
Jim gives him 6 more.
How many does he have? 5 + 6 = 11
11 pennies

Review and Remember
Circle the number that is less.

6. (7) 9   7. (3) 6   8. 9 (6)

Chapter 1 • Lesson 7

Practice

Practicing Addition Strategies
P 1-7

Count on or use doubles when you can.

Add.

1. $9 + 8 = \underline{17}$ $2 + 6 = \underline{8}$ $5 + 6 = \underline{11}$

2. $3 + 6 = \underline{9}$ $4 + 3 = \underline{7}$ $8 + 7 = \underline{15}$

3. $6 + 7 = \underline{13}$ $8 + 1 = \underline{9}$ $4 + 5 = \underline{9}$

4.
$\begin{array}{r} 7 \\ +2 \\ \hline 9 \end{array}$
$\begin{array}{r} 5 \\ +3 \\ \hline 8 \end{array}$
$\begin{array}{r} 8 \\ +9 \\ \hline 17 \end{array}$
$\begin{array}{r} 7 \\ +8 \\ \hline 15 \end{array}$
$\begin{array}{r} 3 \\ +6 \\ \hline 9 \end{array}$
$\begin{array}{r} 8 \\ +3 \\ \hline 11 \end{array}$

5.
$\begin{array}{r} 8 \\ +2 \\ \hline 10 \end{array}$
$\begin{array}{r} 9 \\ +3 \\ \hline 12 \end{array}$
$\begin{array}{r} 7 \\ +3 \\ \hline 10 \end{array}$
$\begin{array}{r} 6 \\ +5 \\ \hline 11 \end{array}$
$\begin{array}{r} 1 \\ +7 \\ \hline 8 \end{array}$
$\begin{array}{r} 2 \\ +9 \\ \hline 11 \end{array}$

6. Use a ⬤red✏ to circle three sums you found by counting on.
 Use a ⬤blue✏ to circle three sums you found by using doubles.

Check that students color sums as directed.

© Silver Burdett Ginn Inc. (19) Use with Grade 2, text pages 13–14.

Reteach

Practicing Addition Strategies
R 1-7

When you see 1, 2, or 3 added to a number — count on!

When you see a number added to 1 more or 1 less than itself — use doubles!

$3 + 5$ $5 + 6$

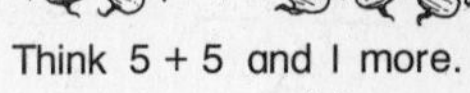

Start with the greater number. Think 5, and count on 3. Say 6, 7, 8.

$3 + 5 = \underline{8}$

Think $5 + 5$ and 1 more.

$5 + 5 = \underline{10}$

and one more is $\underline{11}$

$5 + 6 = \underline{11}$

Count on or use doubles to add.

1. $4 + 3 = \underline{7}$ $5 + 2 = \underline{7}$ $7 + 1 = \underline{8}$

2. $8 + 9 = \underline{17}$ $6 + 7 = \underline{13}$ $4 + 5 = \underline{9}$

3.
$\begin{array}{r} 7 \\ +6 \\ \hline 13 \end{array}$
$\begin{array}{r} 9 \\ +8 \\ \hline 17 \end{array}$
$\begin{array}{r} 0 \\ +8 \\ \hline 8 \end{array}$
$\begin{array}{r} 7 \\ +8 \\ \hline 15 \end{array}$
$\begin{array}{r} 6 \\ +3 \\ \hline 9 \end{array}$
$\begin{array}{r} 2 \\ +8 \\ \hline 10 \end{array}$

4.
$\begin{array}{r} 4 \\ +2 \\ \hline 6 \end{array}$
$\begin{array}{r} 5 \\ +1 \\ \hline 6 \end{array}$
$\begin{array}{r} 9 \\ +3 \\ \hline 12 \end{array}$
$\begin{array}{r} 9 \\ +0 \\ \hline 9 \end{array}$
$\begin{array}{r} 5 \\ +6 \\ \hline 11 \end{array}$
$\begin{array}{r} 2 \\ +9 \\ \hline 11 \end{array}$

© Silver Burdett Ginn Inc. (20) Use with Grade 2, text pages 13–14.

Extend

Sum Search
E 1-7
NUMBER SENSE

Circle the facts for each sum.

1. **12**

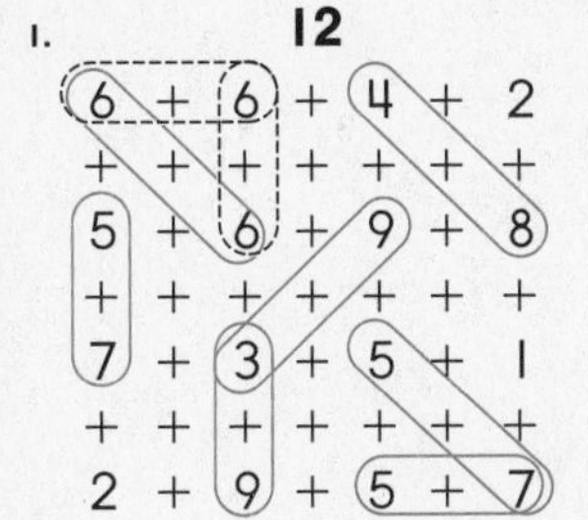

2. **13**

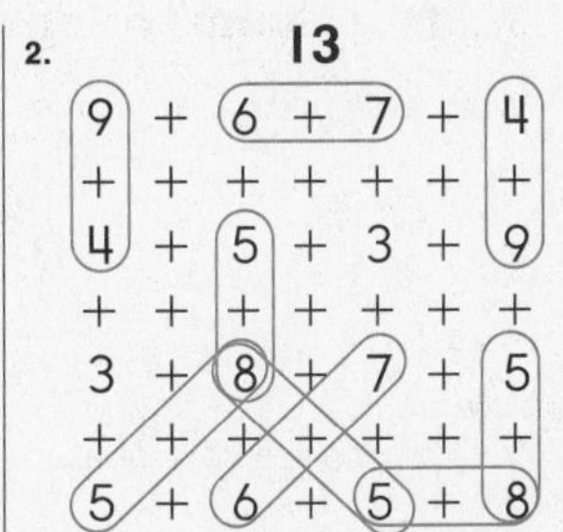

3. **10**

4. **14**

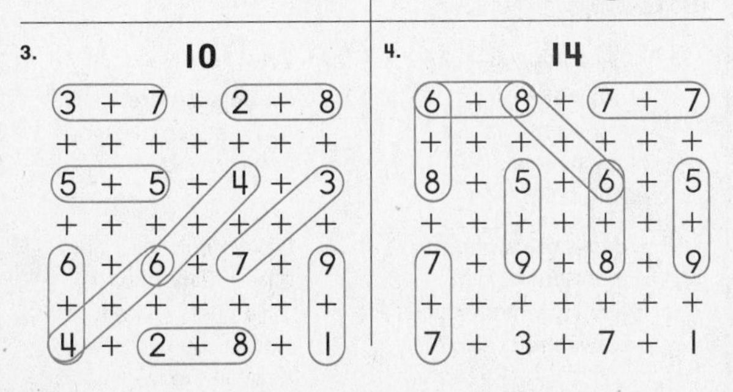

5. Make your own sum search on the back of this page. Challenge a classmate to circle the facts.

© Silver Burdett Ginn Inc. (21) Use with Grade 2, text pages 13–14.

Daily Review

Name _____
Daily Review 1-7

Practicing Addition Strategies

Count on or use doubles to add.

1. $1 + 3 = \underline{4}$ $2 + 5 = \underline{7}$ $3 + 4 = \underline{7}$

2. $5 + 0 = \underline{5}$ $7 + 6 = \underline{13}$ $2 + 6 = \underline{8}$

Problem Solving

Maria made 2 mistakes below.
Circle the sums that are wrong.
Write the correct sums.

3. $0 + 4 = 4$ $5 + 2 = ⑥$ $7 + 3 = 10$
 7

4. $6 + 6 = 12$ $2 + 7 = 9$ $5 + 3 = ⑨$
 8

Review and Remember

Draw 1 more.
Write the number.

5. ○○○○○○ 6. ○○○○ 7. ○○○○○○○

 $\underline{6}$ $\underline{4}$ $\underline{7}$

Practice

Problem Solving P 1-8

Write a Number Sentence

Read the story and write the addition sentences.

1. Sarah and Matt took a walk.
They saw 3 birds on the ground
and 2 birds in the tree.
How many birds in all?

3 + 2 = 5

2. They saw 1 spider start to make a web.
They saw 4 spiders on their webs.
How many spiders in all?

1 + 4 = 5

3. Matt showed Sarah 2 caterpillars.
Sarah found 6 more.
How many caterpillars in all?

2 + 6 = 8

4. They saw 5 squirrels come out of a nest.
Then 3 more squirrels came out.
How many squirrels in all?

5 + 3 = 8

5. At the pond they counted turtles.
Matt counted 6. Sarah counted 5.
How many turtles in all?

6 + 5 = 11

 Use with Grade 2, text pages 15–16.

Reteach

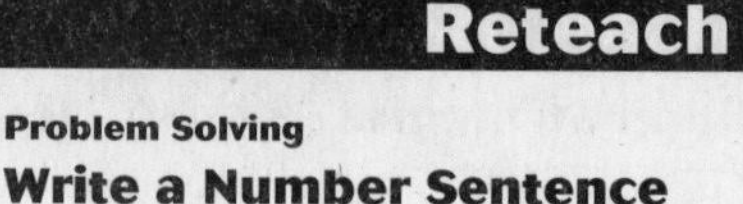

Problem Solving R 1-8

Write a Number Sentence

Write addition sentences.

1. How many on the tree? 6
How many on the ground? 7
How many in all? 13 — 6 + 7 = 13

2. How many on the log? 5
How many on the shore? 4
How many in all? 9 — 5 + 4 = 9

3. How many on the stump? 3
How many on the ground? 4
How many in all? 7 — 3 + 4 = 7

 Use with Grade 2, text pages 15–16.

Extend

Number Trees

E 1-8 REASONING

Complete each addition sentence tree.

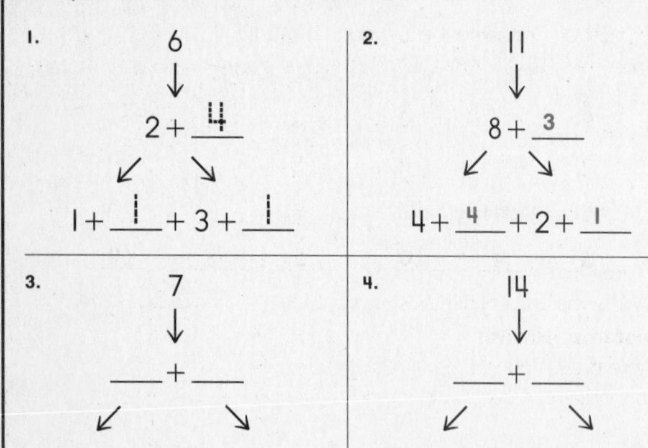

1. 6 → 2 + 4 → 1 + 1 + 3 + 1

2. 11 → 8 + 3 → 4 + 4 + 2 + 1

3. 7 → ___ + ___ → ___ + ___ + ___ + ___

4. 14 → ___ + ___ → ___ + ___ + ___ + ___

5. 15 → ___ + ___ → ___ + ___ + ___ + ___

6. Make your own.
___ → ___ + ___ → ___ + ___ + ___ + ___

Check students' methods.

 Use with Grade 2, text pages 15–16.

Daily Review

Name ______________ Daily Review 1-8

Problem Solving

Write a Number Sentence

Write each addition sentence.

1. 9 + 4 = 13

2. 8 + 7 = 15

Solve. Write the numbers.

3. 6 ponies are eating grass in the field. 5 more join them. How many ponies are eating now? 6 + 5 = 11

4. A dog has 3 bones. He gets 7 more. How many bones does the dog have now? 3 + 7 = 10

5. 8 ducks are swimming. 6 more ducks join them. How many ducks are swimming now? 8 + 6 = 14

6. 4 birds build nests in a tree. 8 more birds build nests in the tree. How many birds build nests in the tree? 4 + 8 = 12

Review and Remember

Add.

7. 4 + 4 = 8 8. 3 + 3 = 6 9. 8 + 8 = 16

Practice

Sums of 10

P 1-9

Find each sum.
Color each sentence that makes a sum of 10.

4 + 6 = 10	7 + 1 = 8	5 + 2 = 7
5 + 5 = 10	3 + 7 = 10	2 + 8 = 10

1. Write how many sums of 10. 4
2. Write a sum of 10 with this number. 4 + 6 = 10

5 + 5 = 10	1 + 9 = 10	3 + 7 = 10
7 + 3 = 10	8 + 2 = 10	4 + 8 = 12

3. Write how many sums of 10. 5
4. Write a sum of 10 with this number. 5 + 5 = 10

 Use with Grade 2, text pages 17–18.

Reteach

Sums of 10

R 1-9

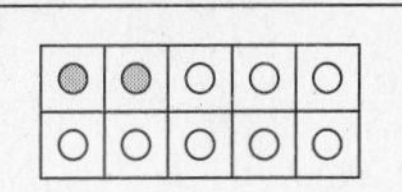
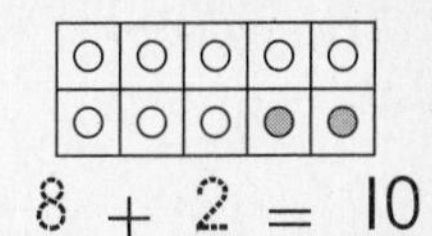

2 + 8 = 10 8 + 2 = 10

Draw to show different ways to make 10.
Write each number sentence in two ways.

1.
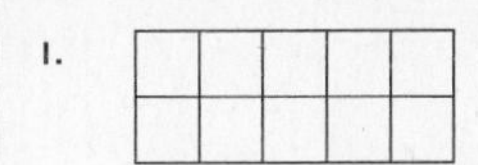

6 + 4 = 10 4 + 6 = 10

2.
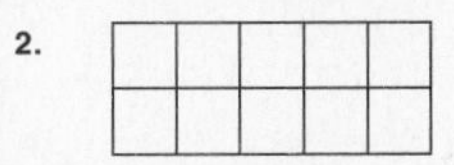

7 + 3 = 10 3 + 7 = 10

3.
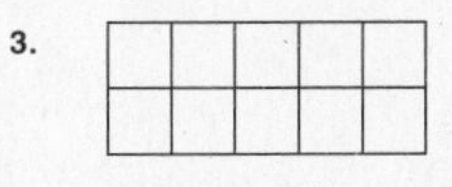
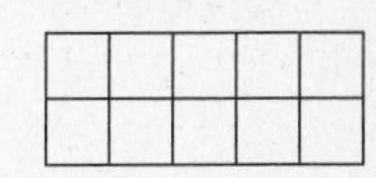

9 + 1 = 10 1 + 9 = 10

Check students' methods. Order of answers will vary.

 Use with Grade 2, text pages 17–18.

Extend

Seeing Double

E 1-9 VISUAL THINKING

Look at the top picture. Then look at the bottom picture to see how it is different. Circle each difference.

I can circle 8 things, can you?

 Use with Grade 2, text pages 17–18.

Daily Review

Name ____________ Daily Review 1-9

Sums of 10

Use counters.
Find different ways to make 10.
Write the number sentences. Answers may vary.

1. 9 + 1 = 10 5 + 5 = 10
   8 + 2 = 10 4 + 6 = 10
   7 + 3 = 10 3 + 7 = 10
   6 + 4 = 10 2 + 8 = 10

Problem Solving
There are 10 bugs in each group.
How many are under each rock?

2.
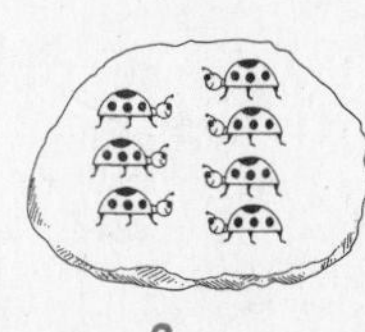
3

3.
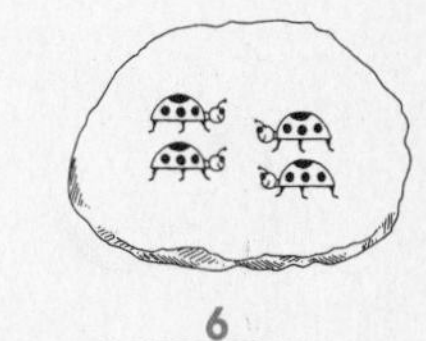
6

Review and Remember
Write the number that comes just before.

4. 5, 6 5. 9, 10 6. 11, 12

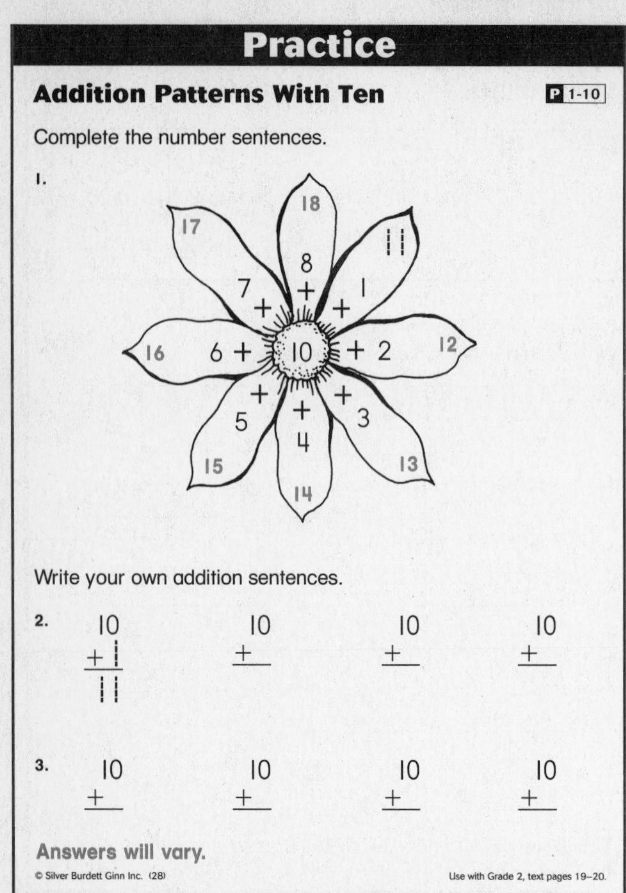

Practice

Addition Patterns With Ten

P 1-10

Complete the number sentences.

1.

Write your own addition sentences.

2. 10 + 1 = 11   10 + ___   10 + ___   10 + ___

3. 10 + ___   10 + ___   10 + ___   10 + ___

Answers will vary.

Use with Grade 2, text pages 19–20.

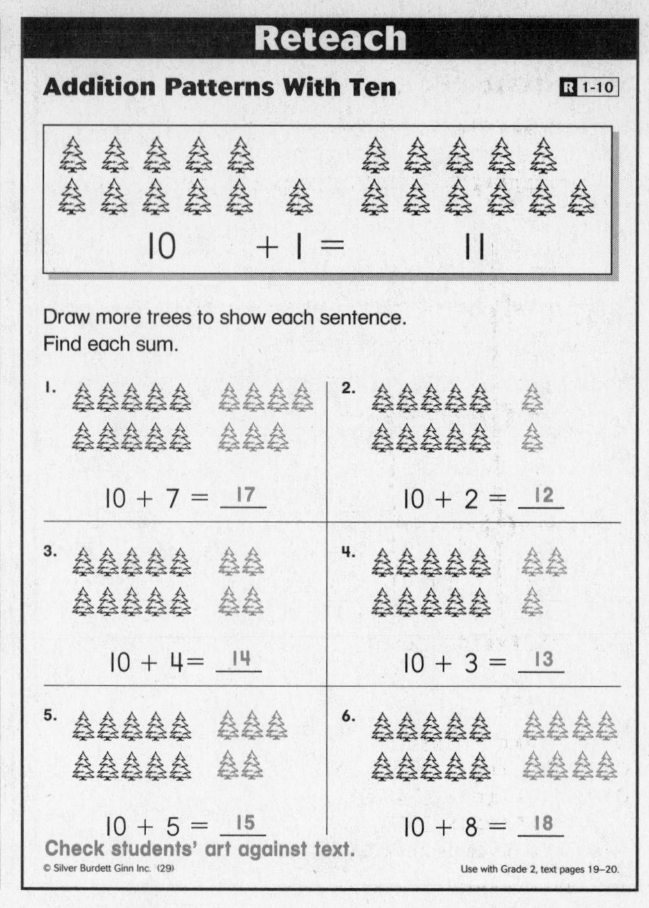

Reteach

Addition Patterns With Ten

R 1-10

10 + 1 = 11

Draw more trees to show each sentence.
Find each sum.

1. 10 + 7 = 17
2. 10 + 2 = 12
3. 10 + 4 = 14
4. 10 + 3 = 13
5. 10 + 5 = 15
6. 10 + 8 = 18

Check students' art against text.

Use with Grade 2, text pages 19–20.

Extend

Treasure Hunt

E 1-10
REASONING

Step 1 Check the sum on each rock. Make an X on the rocks that have wrong sums. Then write the correct sum.

Step 2 Find the path to the treasure. You can only jump to a rock that has a sum that is 1 more than the rock you are on.

Start here.

Use with Grade 2, text pages 19–20.

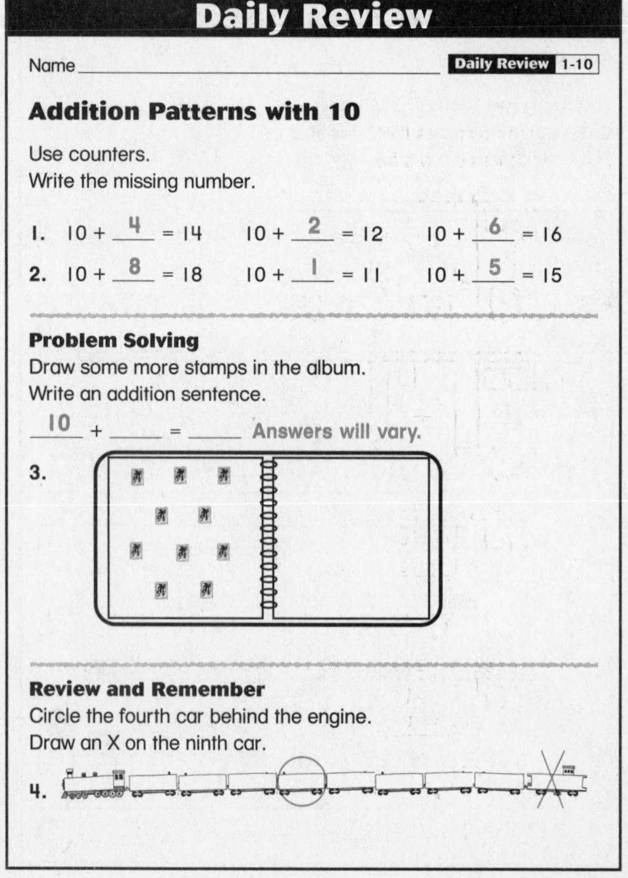

Daily Review

Name ______________________ Daily Review 1-10

Addition Patterns with 10

Use counters.
Write the missing number.

1. 10 + 4 = 14   10 + 2 = 12   10 + 6 = 16
2. 10 + 8 = 18   10 + 1 = 11   10 + 5 = 15

Problem Solving

Draw some more stamps in the album.
Write an addition sentence.

10 + ___ = ___ Answers will vary.

3.

Review and Remember

Circle the fourth car behind the engine.
Draw an X on the ninth car.

4.

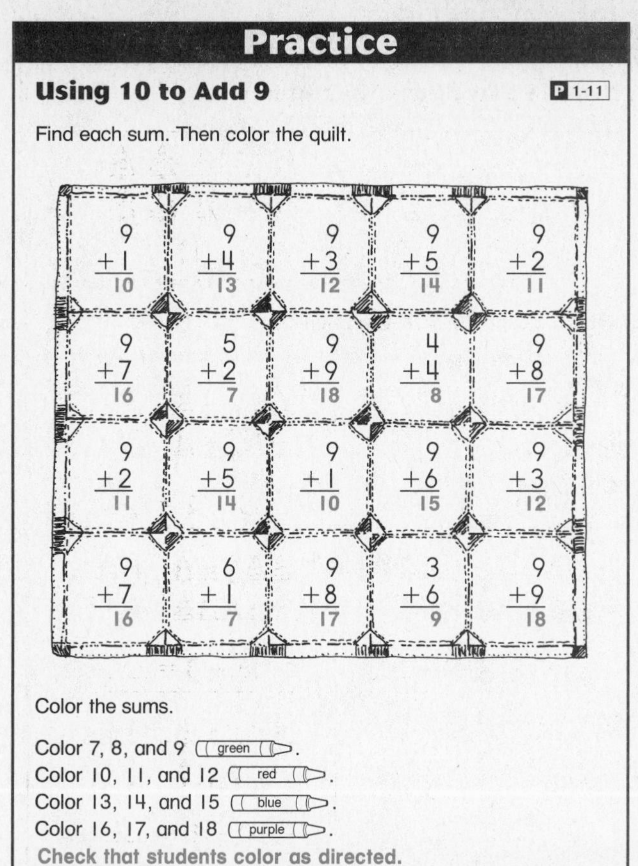

Practice

Using 10 to Add 9

P 1-11

Find each sum. Then color the quilt.

9 + 1 = 10	9 + 4 = 13	9 + 3 = 12	9 + 5 = 14	9 + 2 = 11
9 + 7 = 16	5 + 2 = 7	9 + 9 = 18	4 + 4 = 8	9 + 8 = 17
9 + 2 = 11	9 + 5 = 14	9 + 1 = 10	9 + 6 = 15	9 + 3 = 12
9 + 7 = 16	6 + 1 = 7	9 + 8 = 17	3 + 6 = 9	9 + 9 = 18

Color the sums.

Color 7, 8, and 9 green.
Color 10, 11, and 12 red.
Color 13, 14, and 15 blue.
Color 16, 17, and 18 purple.

Check that students color as directed.

 Use with Grade 2, text pages 21–22.

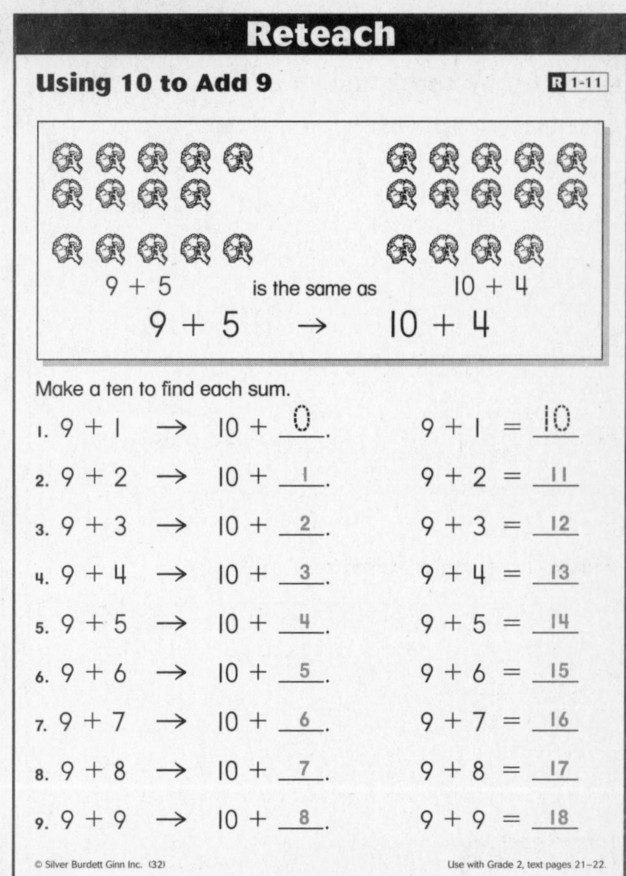

Reteach

Using 10 to Add 9

R 1-11

9 + 5 is the same as 10 + 4

9 + 5 → 10 + 4

Make a ten to find each sum.

1. 9 + 1 → 10 + 0. 9 + 1 = 10
2. 9 + 2 → 10 + 1. 9 + 2 = 11
3. 9 + 3 → 10 + 2. 9 + 3 = 12
4. 9 + 4 → 10 + 3. 9 + 4 = 13
5. 9 + 5 → 10 + 4. 9 + 5 = 14
6. 9 + 6 → 10 + 5. 9 + 6 = 15
7. 9 + 7 → 10 + 6. 9 + 7 = 16
8. 9 + 8 → 10 + 7. 9 + 8 = 17
9. 9 + 9 → 10 + 8. 9 + 9 = 18

 Use with Grade 2, text pages 21–22.

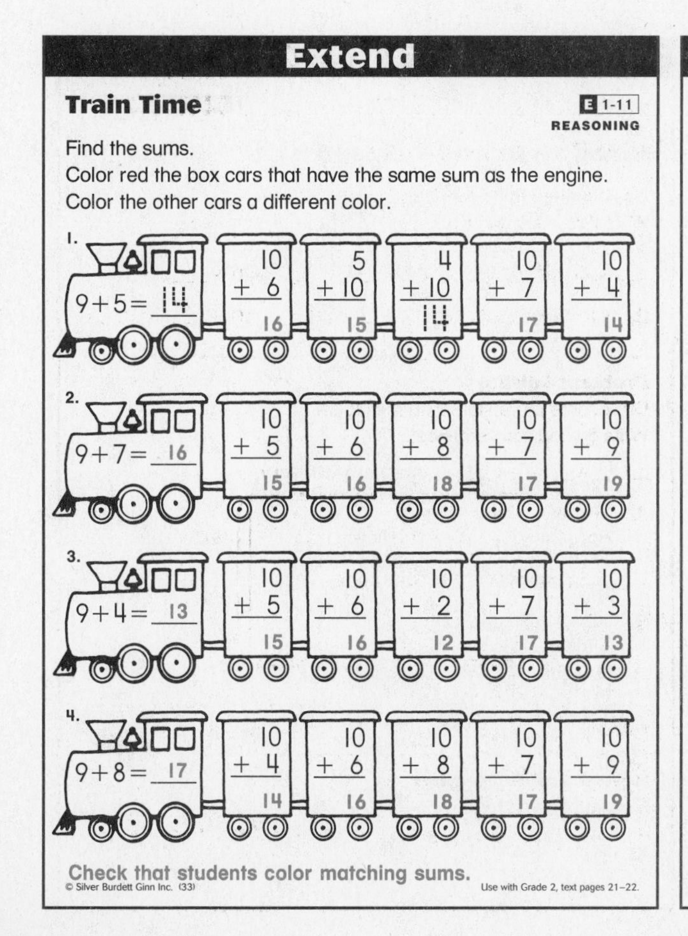

Extend

Train Time

E 1-11 REASONING

Find the sums.
Color red the box cars that have the same sum as the engine.
Color the other cars a different color.

1. 9+5= 14 | 10 + 6 = 16 | 5 + 10 = 15 | 4 + 10 = 14 | 10 + 7 = 17 | 10 + 4 = 14
2. 9+7= 16 | 10 + 5 = 15 | 10 + 6 = 16 | 10 + 8 = 18 | 10 + 7 = 17 | 10 + 9 = 19
3. 9+4= 13 | 10 + 5 = 15 | 10 + 6 = 16 | 10 + 2 = 12 | 10 + 7 = 17 | 10 + 3 = 13
4. 9+8= 17 | 10 + 4 = 14 | 10 + 6 = 16 | 10 + 8 = 18 | 10 + 7 = 17 | 10 + 9 = 19

Check that students color matching sums.

 Use with Grade 2, text pages 21–22.

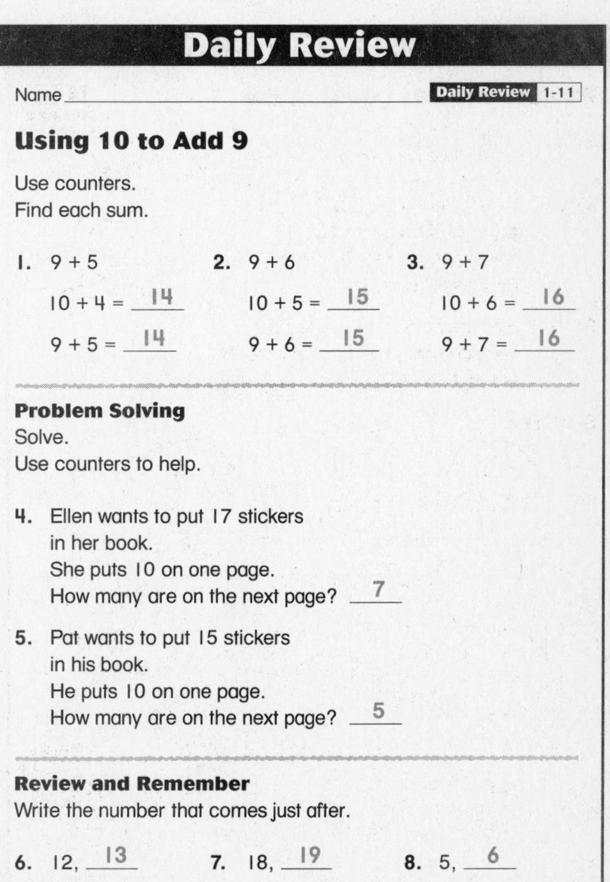

Daily Review

Name ______ Daily Review 1-11

Using 10 to Add 9

Use counters.
Find each sum.

1. 9 + 5
   10 + 4 = 14
   9 + 5 = 14
2. 9 + 6
   10 + 5 = 15
   9 + 6 = 15
3. 9 + 7
   10 + 6 = 16
   9 + 7 = 16

Problem Solving
Solve.
Use counters to help.

4. Ellen wants to put 17 stickers in her book. She puts 10 on one page. How many are on the next page? 7
5. Pat wants to put 15 stickers in his book. He puts 10 on one page. How many are on the next page? 5

Review and Remember
Write the number that comes just after.

6. 12, 13
7. 18, 19
8. 5, 6

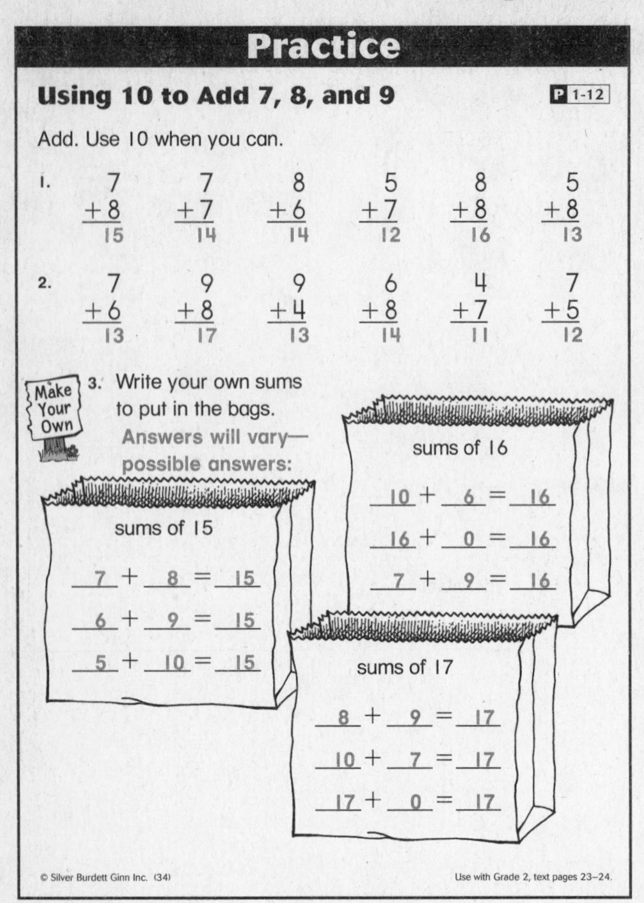

Practice

Using 10 to Add 7, 8, and 9 (P 1-12)

Add. Use 10 when you can.

1. $7 + 8 = 15$ $7 + 7 = 14$ $8 + 6 = 14$ $5 + 7 = 12$ $8 + 8 = 16$ $5 + 8 = 13$

2. $7 + 6 = 13$ $9 + 8 = 17$ $9 + 4 = 13$ $6 + 8 = 14$ $4 + 7 = 11$ $7 + 5 = 12$

Make Your Own

3. Write your own sums to put in the bags. **Answers will vary—possible answers:**

sums of 15
7 + 8 = 15
6 + 9 = 15
5 + 10 = 15

sums of 16
10 + 6 = 16
16 + 0 = 16
7 + 9 = 16

sums of 17
8 + 9 = 17
10 + 7 = 17
17 + 0 = 17

 Use with Grade 2, text pages 23–24.

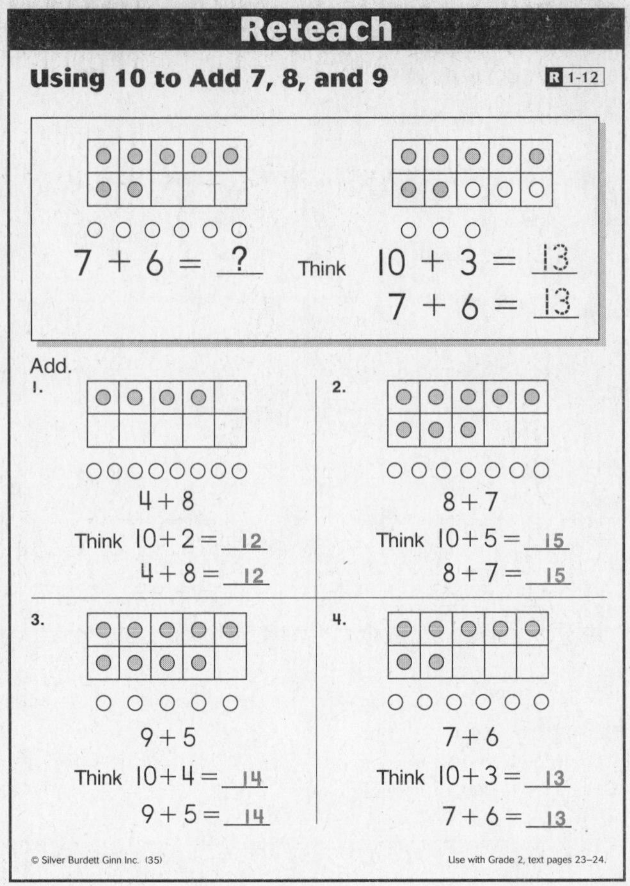

Reteach

Using 10 to Add 7, 8, and 9 (R 1-12)

$7 + 6 = ?$ Think $10 + 3 = 13$
$7 + 6 = 13$

Add.

1. $4 + 8$
Think $10 + 2 = 12$
$4 + 8 = 12$

2. $8 + 7$
Think $10 + 5 = 15$
$8 + 7 = 15$

3. $9 + 5$
Think $10 + 4 = 14$
$9 + 5 = 14$

4. $7 + 6$
Think $10 + 3 = 13$
$7 + 6 = 13$

 Use with Grade 2, text pages 23–24.

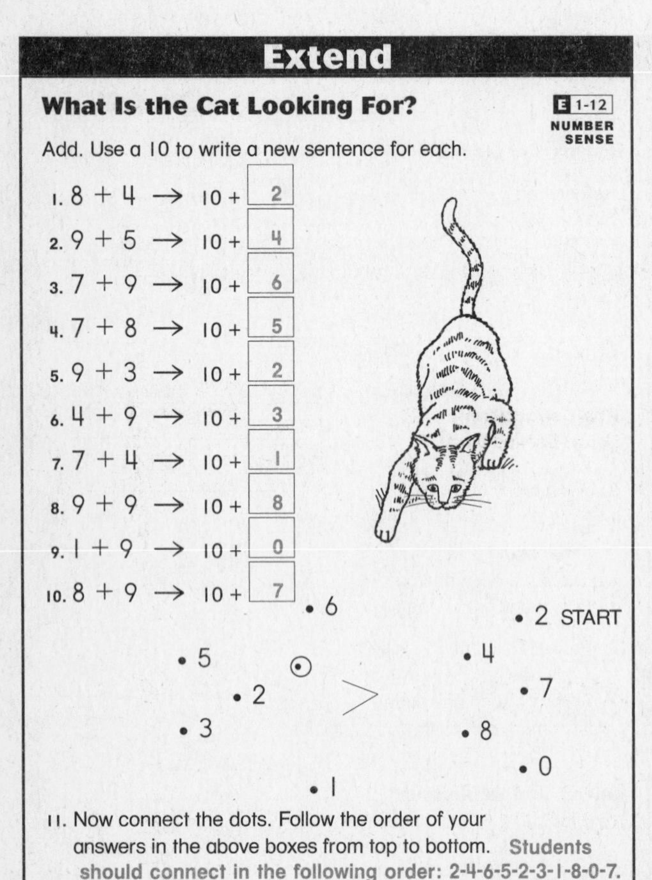

Extend

What Is the Cat Looking For? (E 1-12, NUMBER SENSE)

Add. Use a 10 to write a new sentence for each.

1. 8 + 4 → 10 + 2
2. 9 + 5 → 10 + 4
3. 7 + 9 → 10 + 6
4. 7 + 8 → 10 + 5
5. 9 + 3 → 10 + 2
6. 4 + 9 → 10 + 3
7. 7 + 4 → 10 + 1
8. 9 + 9 → 10 + 8
9. 1 + 9 → 10 + 0
10. 8 + 9 → 10 + 7

11. Now connect the dots. Follow the order of your answers in the above boxes from top to bottom. **Students should connect in the following order: 2-4-6-5-2-3-1-8-0-7.**

 Use with Grade 2, text pages 23–24.

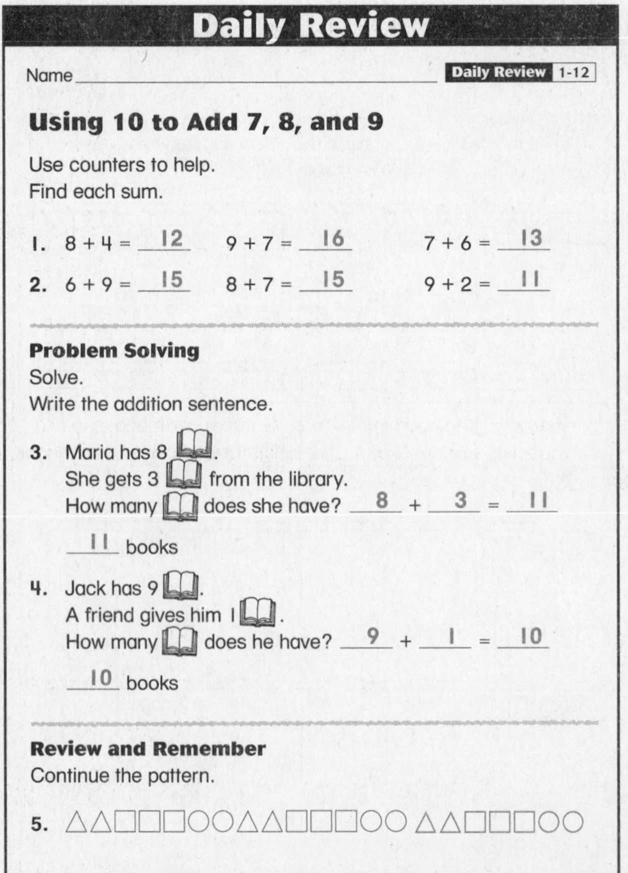

Daily Review

Name ______________________ Daily Review 1-12

Using 10 to Add 7, 8, and 9

Use counters to help.
Find each sum.

1. $8 + 4 = 12$ $9 + 7 = 16$ $7 + 6 = 13$
2. $6 + 9 = 15$ $8 + 7 = 15$ $9 + 2 = 11$

Problem Solving

Solve.
Write the addition sentence.

3. Maria has 8 📖.
She gets 3 📖 from the library.
How many 📖 does she have? 8 + 3 = 11
11 books

4. Jack has 9 📖.
A friend gives him 1 📖.
How many 📖 does he have? 9 + 1 = 10
10 books

Review and Remember

Continue the pattern.

5. △△□□□○○△△□□□○○△△□□□○○

Practice

Three Addends
P 1-13

Add. Try different ways.
Circle in red if you use a double to add.
Circle in blue if you use a sum of 10.

1.
$$\begin{array}{r} 8 \\ 3 \\ +2 \\ \hline 13 \end{array} \quad \begin{array}{r} 6 \\ 4 \\ +0 \\ \hline 10 \end{array} \quad \begin{array}{r} 3 \\ 3 \\ +6 \\ \hline 12 \end{array} \quad \begin{array}{r} 2 \\ 5 \\ +4 \\ \hline 11 \end{array} \quad \begin{array}{r} 5 \\ 5 \\ +2 \\ \hline 12 \end{array} \quad \begin{array}{r} 1 \\ 5 \\ +1 \\ \hline 7 \end{array}$$

2.
$$\begin{array}{r} 7 \\ 6 \\ +4 \\ \hline 17 \end{array} \quad \begin{array}{r} 3 \\ 3 \\ +2 \\ \hline 8 \end{array} \quad \begin{array}{r} 6 \\ 0 \\ +4 \\ \hline 10 \end{array} \quad \begin{array}{r} 9 \\ 1 \\ +5 \\ \hline 15 \end{array} \quad \begin{array}{r} 2 \\ 2 \\ +7 \\ \hline 11 \end{array} \quad \begin{array}{r} 6 \\ 2 \\ +5 \\ \hline 13 \end{array}$$

3.
$$\begin{array}{r} 2 \\ 7 \\ +0 \\ \hline 9 \end{array} \quad \begin{array}{r} 8 \\ 8 \\ +3 \\ \hline 19 \end{array} \quad \begin{array}{r} 1 \\ 9 \\ +6 \\ \hline 16 \end{array} \quad \begin{array}{r} 2 \\ 3 \\ +4 \\ \hline 9 \end{array} \quad \begin{array}{r} 5 \\ 0 \\ +2 \\ \hline 7 \end{array} \quad \begin{array}{r} 7 \\ 7 \\ +1 \\ \hline 15 \end{array}$$

4. $4 + 4 + 3 = \underline{11}$ $5 + 1 + 6 = \underline{12}$ $2 + 6 + 6 = \underline{14}$

5. $9 + 1 + 9 = \underline{19}$ $7 + 0 + 3 = \underline{10}$ $4 + 3 + 5 = \underline{12}$

Check that students circle as directed.

© Silver Burdett Ginn Inc. (37) Use with Grade 2, text pages 25–26.

Reteach

Three Addends
R 1-13

$$\begin{array}{r} 4 \\ 4 \\ +6 \\ \hline 14 \end{array}$$
doubles
sum of 10
any order

You could start with a double: $4 + 4 = 8$

You could start with a sum of 10: $6 + 4 = 10$

Add. Circle the numbers you added first.
Then circle the way.

1.
$$\begin{array}{r} 4 \\ 6 \\ +3 \\ \hline 13 \end{array}$$
doubles
sum of 10
any order

2.
$$\begin{array}{r} 2 \\ 2 \\ +6 \\ \hline 10 \end{array}$$
doubles
sum of 10
any order

3.
$$\begin{array}{r} 7 \\ 1 \\ +3 \\ \hline 11 \end{array}$$
doubles
sum of 10
any order

4.
$$\begin{array}{r} 3 \\ 1 \\ +9 \\ \hline 13 \end{array}$$
doubles
sum of 10
any order

5.
$$\begin{array}{r} 3 \\ 8 \\ +3 \\ \hline 14 \end{array}$$
doubles
sum of 10
any order

6.
$$\begin{array}{r} 6 \\ 2 \\ +1 \\ \hline 9 \end{array}$$
doubles
sum of 10
any order

Check students' methods.

© Silver Burdett Ginn Inc. (38) Use with Grade 2, text pages 25–26.

Extend

Choose a Path
E 1-13
PROBLEM SOLVING

Use the map to find the three addends.
Write the number sentence and solve.

1. Go from town to highpoint to lighthouse to town.

 $\underline{5} + \underline{7} + \underline{3} = \underline{15}$

2. Go from cliff to cove to highpoint to south beach.

 $\underline{5} + \underline{9} + \underline{11} = \underline{25}$

3. Go from highpoint to cliff to north beach to lighthouse.

 $\underline{9} + \underline{7} + \underline{8} = \underline{24}$

4. Go from south beach to overlook to town to lighthouse.

 $\underline{6} + \underline{4} + \underline{3} = \underline{13}$

5. Go from cliff to cove to highpoint to lighthouse.

 $\underline{5} + \underline{9} + \underline{7} = \underline{21}$

6. Go from north beach to lighthouse to town to overlook.

 $\underline{8} + \underline{3} + \underline{4} = \underline{15}$

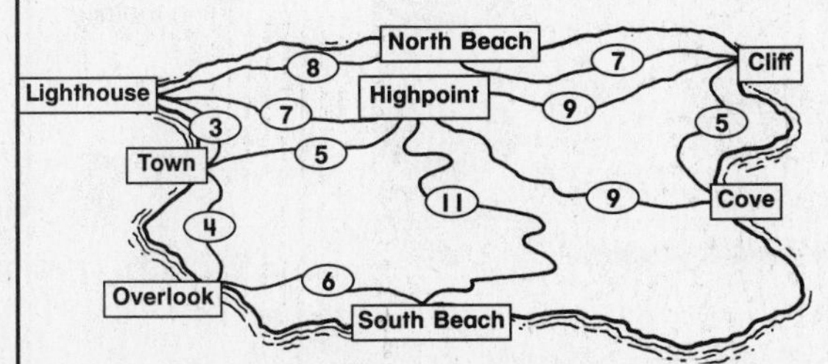

7. Write your own directions on the back of this page to make a sum with three addends.

Answers will vary. Check students' work against map.

© Silver Burdett Ginn Inc. (39) Use with Grade 2, text pages 25–26.

Daily Review

Three Addends

Add.

1.
$$\begin{array}{r} 2 \\ 1 \\ +9 \\ \hline 12 \end{array} \quad \begin{array}{r} 4 \\ 6 \\ +3 \\ \hline 13 \end{array} \quad \begin{array}{r} 1 \\ 8 \\ +1 \\ \hline 10 \end{array} \quad \begin{array}{r} 7 \\ 3 \\ +5 \\ \hline 15 \end{array} \quad \begin{array}{r} 5 \\ 0 \\ +5 \\ \hline 10 \end{array} \quad \begin{array}{r} 4 \\ 7 \\ +4 \\ \hline 15 \end{array}$$

Problem Solving
Solve. Use the graph.

Tickets Sold	
Monday	▯ ▯ ▯ ▯ ▯
Tuesday	▯ ▯ ▯
Wednesday	▯ ▯ ▯ ▯ ▯ ▯
Thursday	▯ ▯ ▯

2. How many tickets were sold on Monday, Tuesday, and Wednesday?

 $\underline{5} + \underline{3} + \underline{6} = \underline{14}$

 $\underline{14}$ tickets

3. How many tickets were sold on Tuesday, Wednesday, and Thursday?

 $\underline{3} + \underline{6} + \underline{3} = \underline{12}$

 $\underline{12}$ tickets

Review and Remember
Draw O to make groups of 12.

4. o o o o o o
 o o o o o o

5. o o o o o o
 o o o o o o

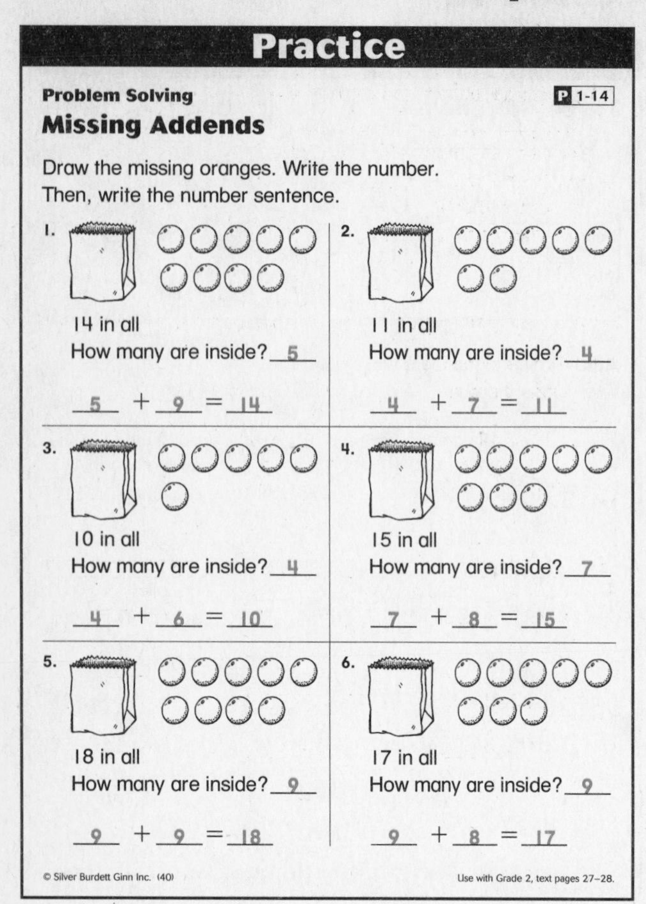

Practice

Problem Solving P 1-14

Missing Addends

Draw the missing oranges. Write the number.
Then, write the number sentence.

1. 14 in all
How many are inside? 5
5 + 9 = 14

2. 11 in all
How many are inside? 4
4 + 7 = 11

3. 10 in all
How many are inside? 4
4 + 6 = 10

4. 15 in all
How many are inside? 7
7 + 8 = 15

5. 18 in all
How many are inside? 9
9 + 9 = 18

6. 17 in all
How many are inside? 9
9 + 8 = 17

 Use with Grade 2, text pages 27–28.

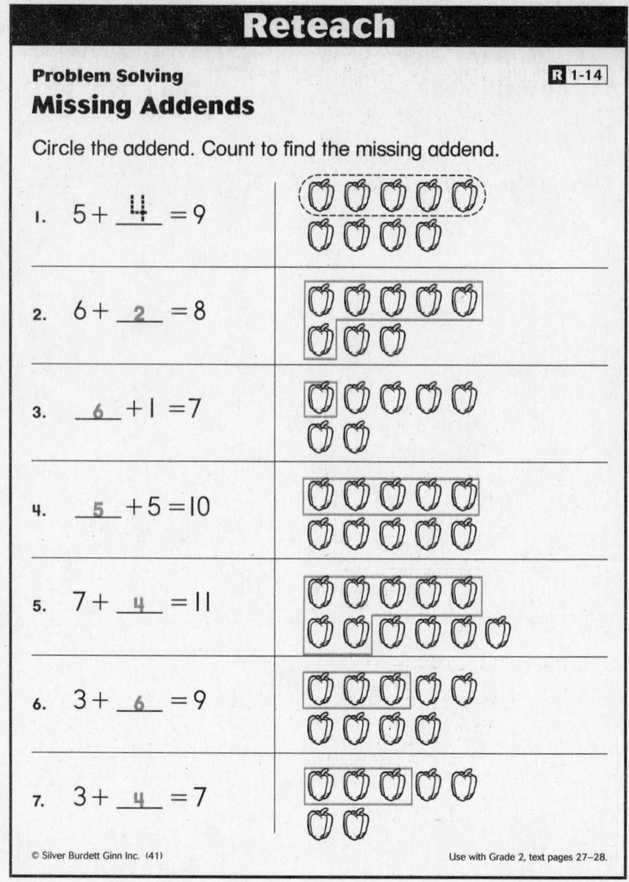

Reteach

Problem Solving R 1-14

Missing Addends

Circle the addend. Count to find the missing addend.

1. 5 + 4 = 9
2. 6 + 2 = 8
3. 6 + 1 = 7
4. 5 + 5 = 10
5. 7 + 4 = 11
6. 3 + 6 = 9
7. 3 + 4 = 7

 Use with Grade 2, text pages 27–28.

Extend

Missing Numbers

E 1-14 NUMBER SENSE

Each problem has some numbers missing.
Fill in the missing numbers.
Use numbers from 0 to 10.

Use counters
or draw pictures
to help you.

1. Nicky has ____ fish.
Kari has ____ fish.
Sondra has ____ fish.
They have 15 fish in all.

2. Miles has ____ toads.
Theo has ____ toads.
Judy has ____ toads.
They have 11 toads in all.

3. Gert has ____ snails.
Alice has ____ snails.
Paul has ____ snails.
They have 9 snails in all.

4. Jo has ____ turtles.
Liz has ____ turtles.
Sara has ____ turtles.
They have 10 turtles in all.

5. Joan has ____ beetles.
Mel has ____ beetles.
Ellen has ____ beetles.
They have 14 beetles in all.

6. Make your own problem.

Answers will vary. Check that 3 addends add up to sum given

 Use with Grade 2, text pages 27–28.

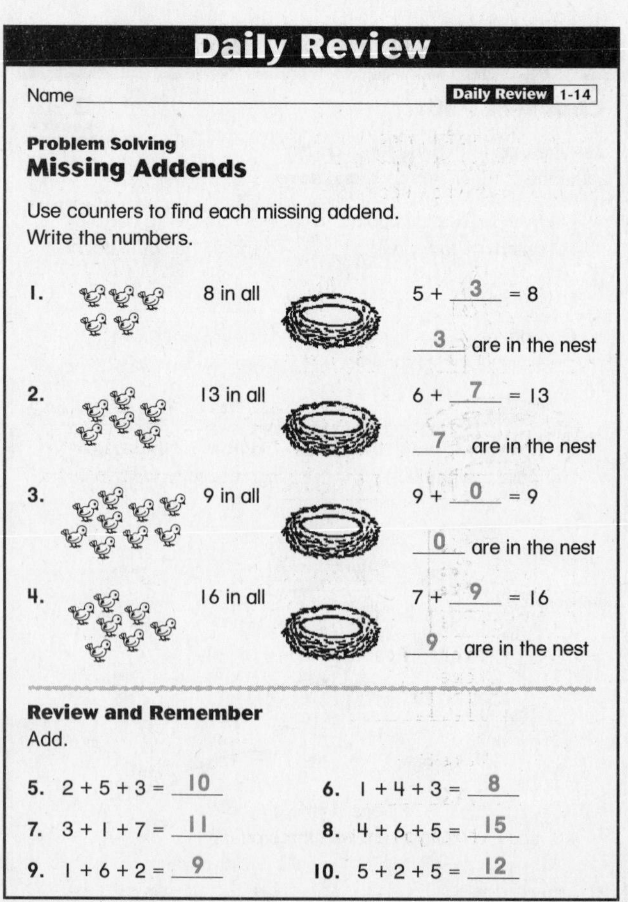

Daily Review

Name ____________________ Daily Review 1-14

Problem Solving

Missing Addends

Use counters to find each missing addend.
Write the numbers.

1. 8 in all — 5 + 3 = 8
3 are in the nest

2. 13 in all — 6 + 7 = 13
7 are in the nest

3. 9 in all — 9 + 0 = 9
0 are in the nest

4. 16 in all — 7 + 9 = 16
9 are in the nest

Review and Remember

Add.

5. 2 + 5 + 3 = 10
6. 1 + 4 + 3 = 8
7. 3 + 1 + 7 = 11
8. 4 + 6 + 5 = 15
9. 1 + 6 + 2 = 9
10. 5 + 2 + 5 = 12

Practice

Understanding Subtraction

P 2-1

Subtract. Draw or use cubes if you like.

1. $10 - 3 = 7$ $\quad 9 - 6 = 3$ $\quad 8 - 2 = 6$ $\quad 7 - 4 = 3$

2. $6 - 1 = 5$ $\quad 7 - 5 = 2$ $\quad 4 - 3 = 1$ $\quad 8 - 2 = 6$

Look at each picture.
Write the subtraction sentence.

3. 

5 – 2 = 3

4. 

9 – 2 = 7

5. 

10 – 4 = 6

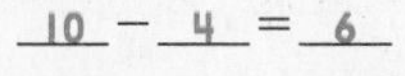

6. 

6 – 4 = 2

 Use with Grade 2, text pages 35–36.

Reteach

Understanding Subtraction

R 2-1

Draw or use cubes to help you subtract.
Start with 7 cubes.
Take away 3 cubes.
How many are left?

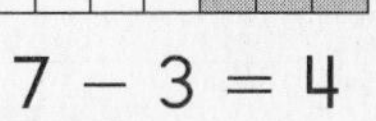

$7 - 3 = 4$

4 is the difference.

Subtract the cubes that are shaded.
Write the difference in the subtraction sentence.

1. 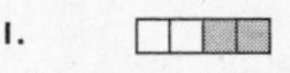 $4 - 2 = 2$ 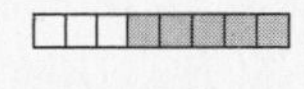 $8 - 5 = 3$ $\quad 3 - 1 = 2$

2. $6 - 4 = 2$ $\quad 5 - 4 = 1$ $\quad 9 - 6 = 3$

3. $2 - 2 = 0$ $\quad 7 - 4 = 3$ $\quad 1 - 0 = 1$

 Use with Grade 2, text pages 35–36.

Extend

Fair Play

E 2-1
DECISION MAKING

Welcome to the fair. Find 4 different ways to use exactly 8 tickets.
Write letters to show each choice.

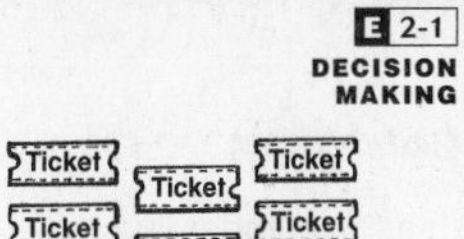
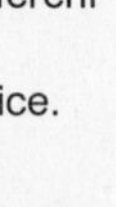

4 Tickets | A

3 Tickets | B

2 Tickets | C

3 Tickets | D

BALLOONS

2 Tickets | E

GO FISH! Every player catches a prize!

4 Tickets | F

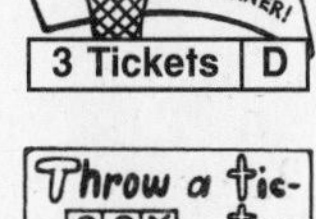
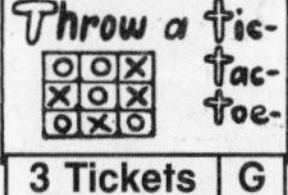

3 Tickets | G

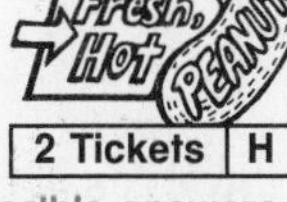

2 Tickets | H

Lemonade

1 Ticket | I

Answers will vary—Possible answers:

Choice 1: B, D, E

Choice 2: A, F

Choice 3: I, A, G

Choice 4: C, G, H, I

Circle the choice you like best.

 Use with Grade 2, text pages 35–36.

Daily Review

Name ____________________

Daily Review 2-1

Understanding Subtraction

Look at each picture. Write the subtraction sentence.

1. 5 – 1 = 4

2. 

7 – 3 = 4

Problem Solving

Write the subtraction sentence.

3. 

4 – 2 = 2

4. 

4 – 1 = 3

Review and Remember

Write the missing numbers.

5. 10, 11, 12, 13, 14, 15, 16

6. 3, 4, 5, 6, 7, 8, 9, 10

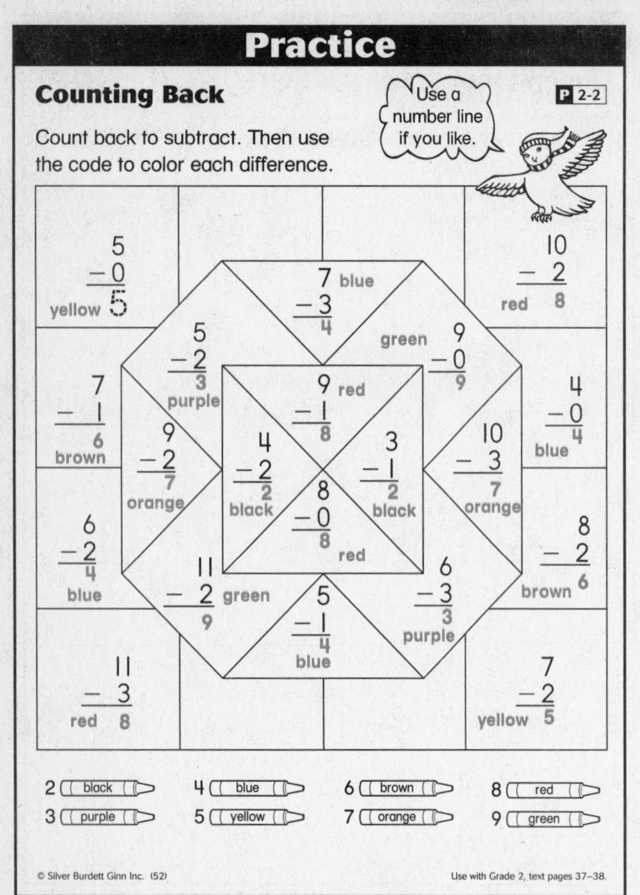

Practice

Counting Back P 2-2

Count back to subtract. Then use the code to color each difference.

5 − 0 = 5 yellow

10 − 2 = 8 red

7 − 3 = 4 blue

5 − 2 = 3 purple

9 − 0 = 9 green

7 − 1 = 6 brown

9 − 1 = 8 red

4 − 0 = 4 blue

9 − 2 = 7 orange

4 − 2 = 2 black

3 − 1 = 2 black

10 − 3 = 7 orange

8 − 0 = 8 red

6 − 2 = 4 blue

8 − 2 = 6 brown

11 − 2 = 9 green

6 − 3 = 3 purple

5 − 1 = 4 blue

11 − 3 = 8 red

7 − 2 = 5 yellow

2 black, 3 purple, 4 blue, 5 yellow, 6 brown, 7 orange, 8 red, 9 green

 Use with Grade 2, text pages 37–38.

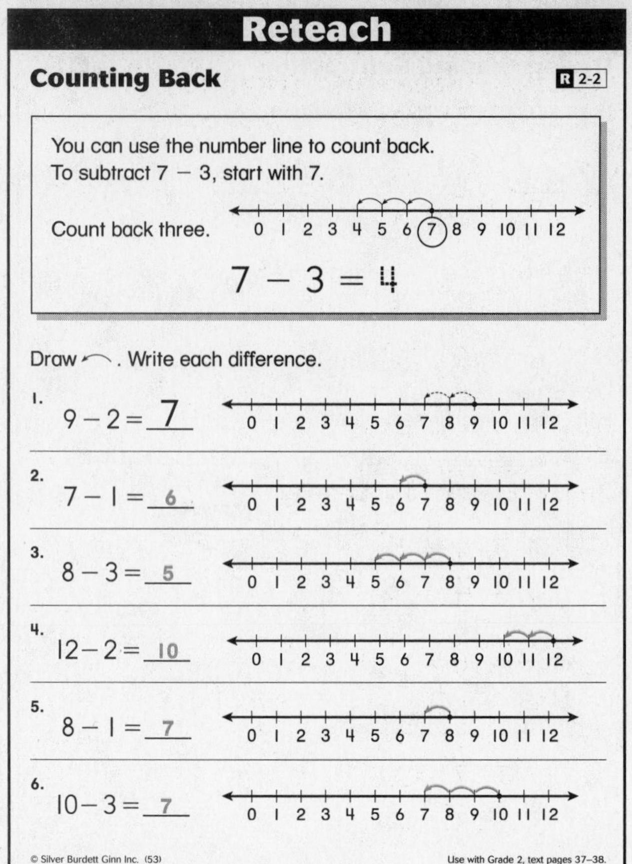

Reteach

Counting Back R 2-2

You can use the number line to count back.
To subtract 7 − 3, start with 7.

Count back three. 0 1 2 3 4 5 6 7 8 9 10 11 12

7 − 3 = 4

Draw ⌒. Write each difference.

1. 9 − 2 = 7
2. 7 − 1 = 6
3. 8 − 3 = 5
4. 12 − 2 = 10
5. 8 − 1 = 7
6. 10 − 3 = 7

 Use with Grade 2, text pages 37–38.

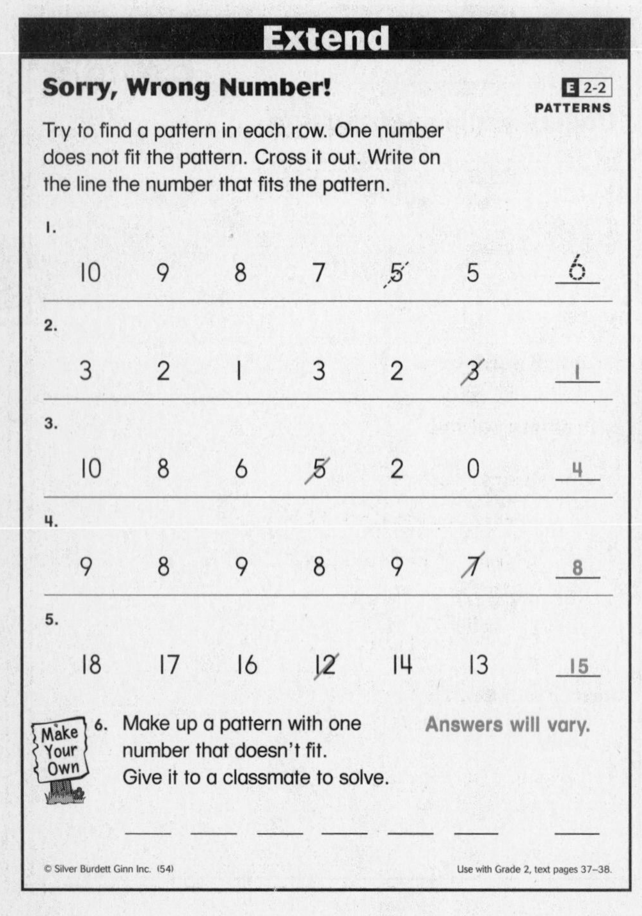

Extend

Sorry, Wrong Number! E 2-2 PATTERNS

Try to find a pattern in each row. One number does not fit the pattern. Cross it out. Write on the line the number that fits the pattern.

1. 10 9 8 7 ~~5~~ 5 ___6___
2. 3 2 1 3 2 ~~3~~ ___1___
3. 10 8 6 ~~5~~ 2 0 ___4___
4. 9 8 9 8 9 ~~7~~ ___8___
5. 18 17 16 ~~12~~ 14 13 ___15___

6. Make up a pattern with one number that doesn't fit. Give it to a classmate to solve. Answers will vary.

___ ___ ___ ___ ___ ___ ___

 Use with Grade 2, text pages 37–38.

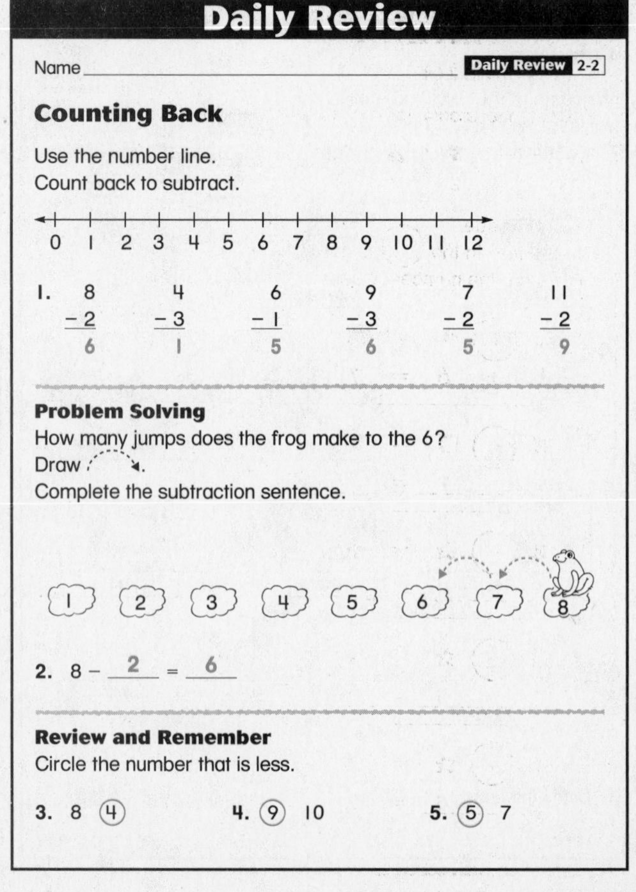

Daily Review

Name ____________ Daily Review 2-2

Counting Back

Use the number line.
Count back to subtract.

0 1 2 3 4 5 6 7 8 9 10 11 12

1. 8 − 2 = 6; 4 − 3 = 1; 6 − 1 = 5; 9 − 3 = 6; 7 − 2 = 5; 11 − 2 = 9

Problem Solving

How many jumps does the frog make to the 6?
Draw ⌒.
Complete the subtraction sentence.

2. 8 − 2 = 6

Review and Remember

Circle the number that is less.

3. 8 (4)   4. (9) 10   5. (5) 7

Practice

Relating Addition and Subtraction

P 2-3

Find each sum and difference.

1. 

5	12
+ 7	− 5
12	7

2. 

4	9
+ 5	− 5
9	4

3.

8	11
+ 3	− 3
11	8

4.

6	10
+ 4	− 6
10	4

5.

5	13
+ 8	− 5
13	8

6.

4	8
+ 4	− 4
8	4

Solve the addition sentence.
Then write a related subtraction fact.

Check that students write related subtraction sentences.

7. 8 + 4 = 12
12 − 4 = 8

8. 7 + 3 = 10
10 − 7 = 3

9. 6 + 5 = 11
11 − 5 = 6

10. 9 + 2 = 11
11 − 9 = 2

11. 5 + 7 = 12
12 − 7 = 5

12. 8 + 3 = 11
11 − 8 = 3

 Use with Grade 2, text pages 39–40.

Reteach

Relating Addition and Subtraction

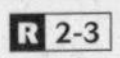
R 2-3

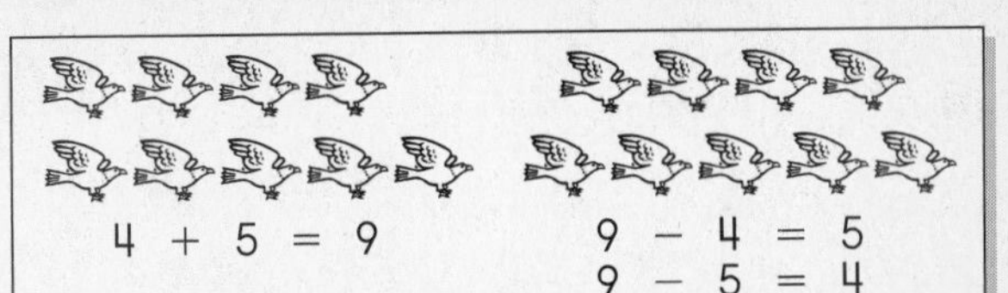

4 + 5 = 9

9 − 4 = 5
9 − 5 = 4

Solve the addition sentence.
Then write one related subtraction sentence.

1. 

3 + 4 = 7
7 − 3 = 4

2. 

6 + 7 = 13
13 − 6 = 7

3. 
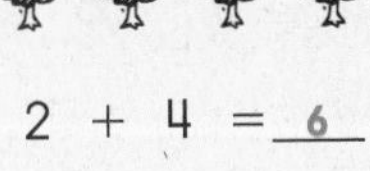

2 + 4 = 6
6 − 2 = 4

4. 

5 + 5 = 10
10 − 5 = 5

 Use with Grade 2, text pages 39–40.

Extend

Code Breaker

E 2-3
NUMBER SENSE

Each symbol stands for a number.

■	✳	♥	▲	❖	☆	✦	❒	❀	✖
0	1	2	3	4	5	6	7	8	9

Read the code.
Write + or − in the ◯ to make a symbol sentence.
Then write the number sentence.

1. ✳ (+) ✦ = ❒
1 + 6 = 7

2. ✖ (−) ✦ = ▲
9 − 6 = 3

3. ✖ (−) ❒ = ♥
9 − 7 = 2

4. ♥ (+) ▲ = ☆
2 + 3 = 5

5. ✖ (−) ☆ = ❖
9 − 5 = 4

6. ❀ (+/−) ■ = ❀
8 +/− 0 = 8

7. ❒ (−) ☆ = ♥
7 − 5 = 2

8. ▲ (−) ▲ = ■
3 − 3 = 0

9. ❖ (+) ☆ = ✖
4 + 5 = 9

10. ✦ (+/−) ■ = ✦
6 +/− 0 = 6

 Use with Grade 2, text pages 39–40.

Daily Review

Name ______________________ Daily Review 2-3

Relating Addition and Subtraction

Add. Write a related subtraction fact.
Use counters to help.

1. 8 + 5 = 13
13 − 5 = 8

2. 6 + 7 = 13
13 − 7 = 6

3. 8 + 1 = 9
9 − 1 = 8

4. 2 + 9 = 11
11 − 9 = 2

Problem Solving

Solve.
Write a number sentence.

5. 5 children are playing ball. 7 more come to play.
How many children are playing? 7 + 5 = 12
12 children

6. 12 children are playing ball. 7 children leave.
How many are still playing? 12 − 7 = 5
5 children

Review and Remember

Find each sum.

7. 4 + 4 = 8   7 + 7 = 14   1 + 1 = 2

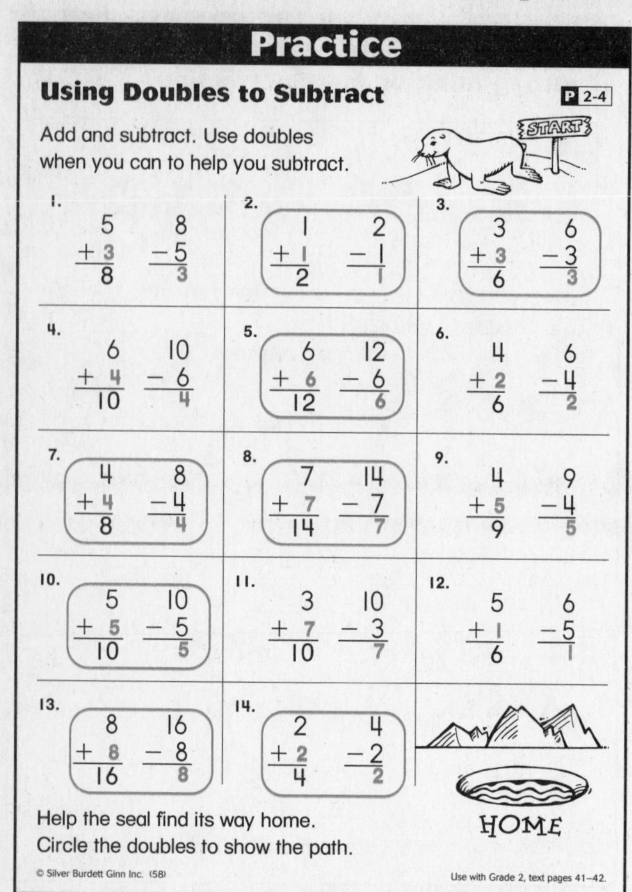

Practice

Using Doubles to Subtract

P 2-4

Add and subtract. Use doubles when you can to help you subtract.

1. $5 + 3 = 8$ $8 - 5 = 3$
2. $1 + 1 = 2$ $2 - 1 = 1$
3. $3 + 3 = 6$ $6 - 3 = 3$
4. $6 + 4 = 10$ $10 - 6 = 4$
5. $6 + 6 = 12$ $12 - 6 = 6$
6. $4 + 2 = 6$ $6 - 4 = 2$
7. $4 + 4 = 8$ $8 - 4 = 4$
8. $7 + 7 = 14$ $14 - 7 = 7$
9. $4 + 5 = 9$ $9 - 4 = 5$
10. $5 + 5 = 10$ $10 - 5 = 5$
11. $3 + 7 = 10$ $10 - 3 = 7$
12. $5 + 1 = 6$ $6 - 5 = 1$
13. $8 + 8 = 16$ $16 - 8 = 8$
14. $2 + 2 = 4$ $4 - 2 = 2$

Help the seal find its way home.
Circle the doubles to show the path.

Use with Grade 2, text pages 41–42.

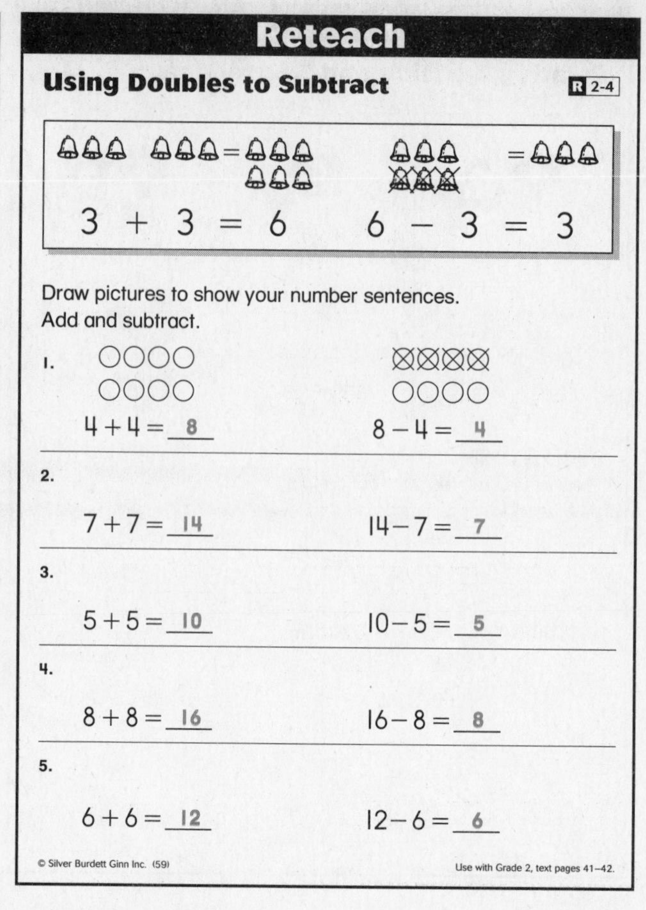

Reteach

Using Doubles to Subtract

R 2-4

$3 + 3 = 6$ $6 - 3 = 3$

Draw pictures to show your number sentences.
Add and subtract.

1. $4 + 4 =$ 8 $8 - 4 =$ 4
2. $7 + 7 =$ 14 $14 - 7 =$ 7
3. $5 + 5 =$ 10 $10 - 5 =$ 5
4. $8 + 8 =$ 16 $16 - 8 =$ 8
5. $6 + 6 =$ 12 $12 - 6 =$ 6

Use with Grade 2, text pages 41–42.

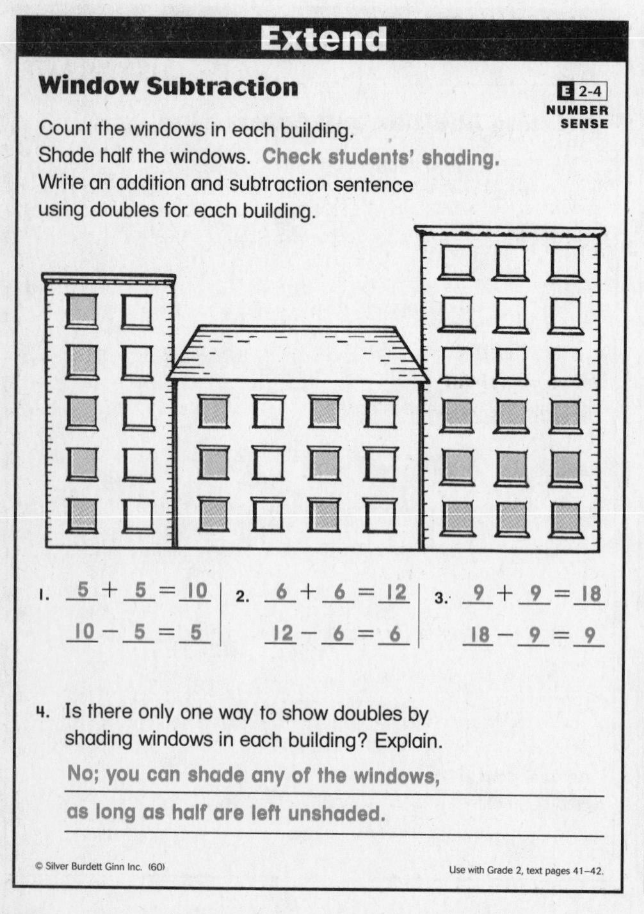

Extend

Window Subtraction

E 2-4
NUMBER SENSE

Count the windows in each building.
Shade half the windows. **Check students' shading.**
Write an addition and subtraction sentence using doubles for each building.

1. $5 + 5 = 10$ $10 - 5 = 5$
2. $6 + 6 = 12$ $12 - 6 = 6$
3. $9 + 9 = 18$ $18 - 9 = 9$

4. Is there only one way to show doubles by shading windows in each building? Explain.
No; you can shade any of the windows, as long as half are left unshaded.

Use with Grade 2, text pages 41–42.

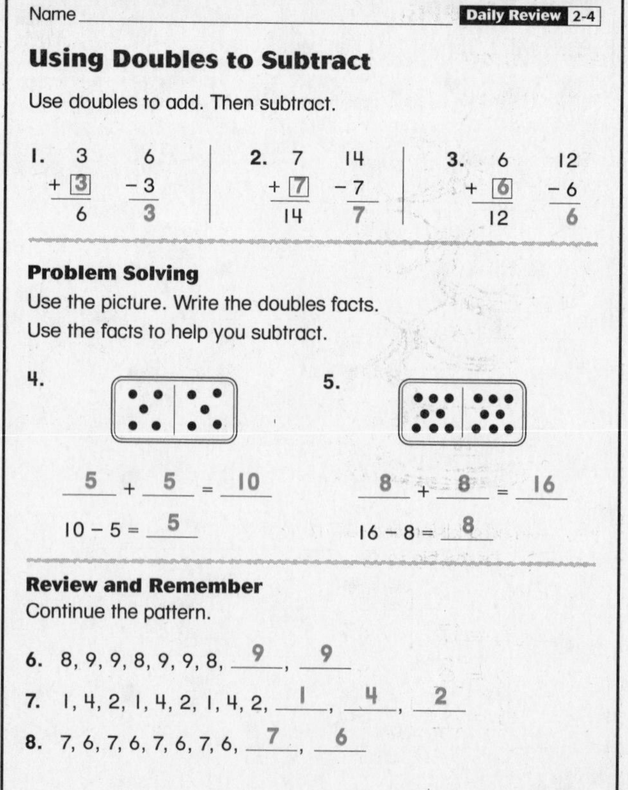

Daily Review

Name ____________________ Daily Review 2-4

Using Doubles to Subtract

Use doubles to add. Then subtract.

1. $3 + 3 = 6$ $6 - 3 = 3$
2. $7 + 7 = 14$ $14 - 7 = 7$
3. $6 + 6 = 12$ $12 - 6 = 6$

Problem Solving

Use the picture. Write the doubles facts.
Use the facts to help you subtract.

4. $5 + 5 = 10$ $10 - 5 = 5$
5. $8 + 8 = 16$ $16 - 8 = 8$

Review and Remember

Continue the pattern.

6. 8, 9, 9, 8, 9, 9, 8, 9, 9
7. 1, 4, 2, 1, 4, 2, 1, 4, 2, 1, 4, 2
8. 7, 6, 7, 6, 7, 6, 7, 6, 7, 6

Practice

Using Addition to Subtract

P 2-5

What You Need

pencil
paper clip

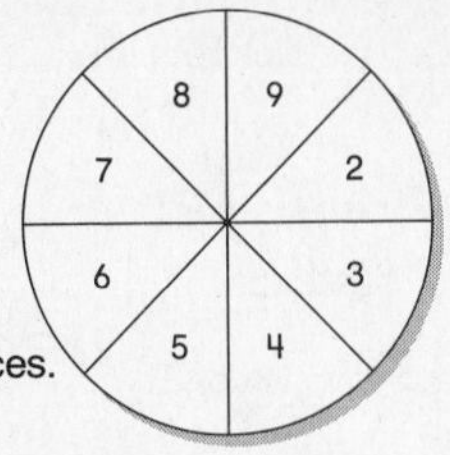

① Spin and write the number.
② Spin again and write the number.
③ Find the sum of the two numbers.
④ Write 2 related subtraction sentences.
⑤ Play again.

Answers will vary. Check students' methods.

GAME 1	GAME 2	GAME 3
___ + ___ = ___	___ + ___ = ___	___ + ___ = ___
___ − ___ = ___	___ − ___ = ___	___ − ___ = ___
___ − ___ = ___	___ − ___ = ___	___ − ___ = ___
GAME 4	**GAME 5**	**GAME 6**
___ + ___ = ___	___ + ___ = ___	___ + ___ = ___
___ − ___ = ___	___ − ___ = ___	___ − ___ = ___
___ − ___ = ___	___ − ___ = ___	___ − ___ = ___

 Use with Grade 2, text pages 43–44.

Reteach

Using Addition to Subtract

R 2-5

Draw. Use the related addition fact to help you subtract.

1. 6 + 7 = 13

13 − 7 = 6   13 − 6 = 7

2. 9 + 8 = 17

17 − 8 = 9   17 − 9 = 8

3. 8 + 4 = 12

12 − 4 = 8   12 − 8 = 4

4. 5 + 7 = 12

12 − 7 = 5   12 − 5 = 7

5. 8 + 6 = 14

14 − 8 = 6   14 − 6 = 8

6. 9 + 7 = 16

16 − 7 = 9   16 − 9 = 7

7. 5 + 6 = 11

11 − 5 = 6   11 − 6 = 5

8. 8 + 7 = 15

15 − 7 = 8   15 − 8 = 7

9. 5 + 8 = 13

13 − 5 = 8   13 − 8 = 5

 Use with Grade 2, text pages 43–44.

Extend

Follow the Path

E 2-5
NUMBER SENSE

Add or subtract.

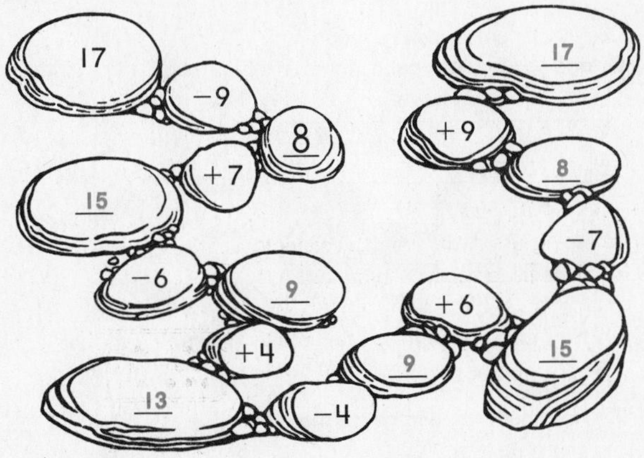

Write related addition and subtraction sentences for the big rocks.

1.	2.	3.
8 + 9 = 17	6 + 9 = 15	9 + 4 = 13
17 − 9 = 8	15 − 9 = 6	13 − 4 = 9
17 − 8 = 9	15 − 6 = 9	13 − 9 = 4

 Use with Grade 2, text pages 43–44.

Daily Review

Name ____________________

Daily Review 2-5

Using Addition to Subtract

Add.
Write the related subtraction facts.

1. 3 + 7 = 10
10 − 7 = 3
10 − 3 = 7

2. 4 + 8 = 12
12 − 8 = 4
12 − 4 = 8

3. 3 + 8 = 11
11 − 3 = 8
11 − 8 = 3

Problem Solving

Complete the number sentences.
Write + or −.

4. 6 (+) 5 = 11
11 (−) 5 = 6

5. 13 (−) 9 = 4
9 (+) 4 = 13

Review and Remember

Write the number.

6. 
7

7. 
10

8. 
8

Practice

Problem Solving P 2-6

Make a Graph

Pick 5 different colors. Write their names under the graph.
Ask some classmates which color they like best.
Color a box for each answer. Check students' methods.

Favorite Colors

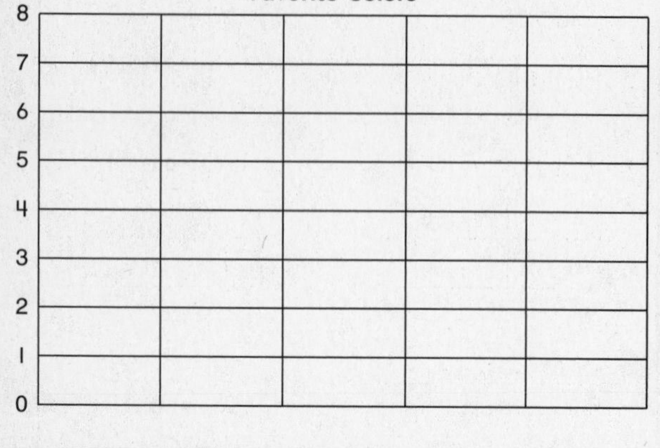

______ ______ ______ ______ ______

1. How many people did you ask? ____
2. What is the favorite color? ____
3. What is the least favorite color? ____

 Use with Grade 2, text pages 45–46.

Reteach

Problem Solving R 2-6

Make a Graph

Use the picture to make a graph.

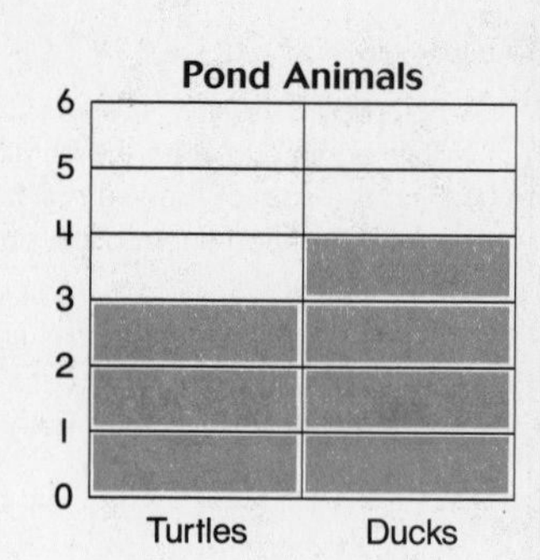

1. Circle each turtle.
   Now color a box for each turtle.
   How many boxes did you color? 3
2. Circle each duck.
   Now color a box for each duck.
   How many boxes did you color? 4
3. How many turtles are there? 3
4. How many ducks are there? 4
5. How many more ducks than turtles are there? 1

 Use with Grade 2, text pages 45–46.

Extend

Poor Little U, Poor Little I!

E 2-6
REASONING

Which vowel is used most often?
Make a guess. ____
Then do a test. Look at this page from the title to the last problem at the bottom.
How many a's can you count?
How many e's?

You could use tally marks to keep track. 卌

Fill in the chart for all the vowels used.

a	卌 卌 卌 卌 卌 ||
e	卌 卌 卌 卌 卌 卌 卌 卌 卌 卌 |
i	卌 卌 卌 卌 ||||
o	卌 卌 卌 卌 卌 卌 卌 卌 ||
u	卌 卌 ||||

1. Which vowel did you find most often? e
2. Which vowel did you find least often? u

On the back of this page, write a sentence that tells your name and how old you are.

3. Which vowel is used most in the sentence? ____
4. Which vowel is used least in the sentence? ____

 Use with Grade 2, text pages 45–46.

Daily Review

Name ______________________ Daily Review 2-6

Problem Solving

Make a Graph

Use the picture to make a graph.
Color a box for each pet.

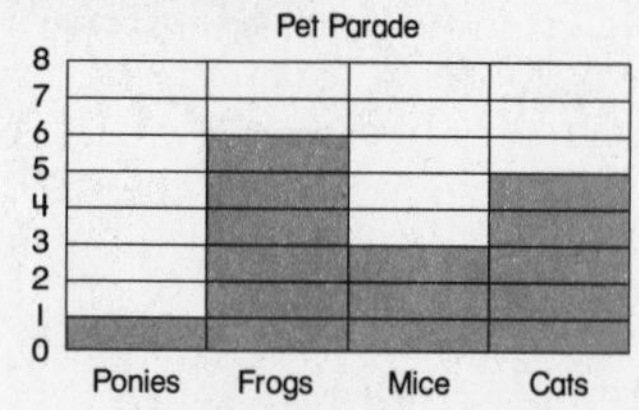

1. How many fewer mice are there than cats?
   2 fewer mice
2. How many more frogs are there than ponies?
   5 more frogs
3. What if there were 4 more mice? How many would there be?
   7 mice

Review and Remember

Count back to subtract.

4. $6 - 1 = 5$ 5. $8 - 2 = 6$ 6. $5 - 1 = 4$
7. $4 - 1 = 3$ 8. $6 - 2 = 4$ 9. $7 - 3 = 4$

Practice

Using 10 to Subtract 9

P 2-7

Subtract. Look for the pattern.

1. 18 − 9 = 9 | 18 − 10 = 8
2. 17 − 9 = 8 | 17 − 10 = 7
3. 16 − 9 = 7 | 16 − 10 = 6
4. 15 − 9 = 6 | 15 − 10 = 5
5. 14 − 9 = 5 | 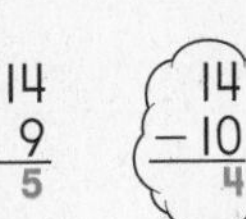 14 − 10 = 4
6. 13 − 9 = 4 | 13 − 10 = 3
7. 12 − 9 = 3 | 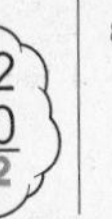 12 − 10 = 2
8. 11 − 9 = 2 | 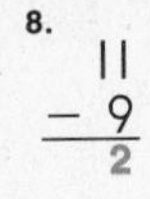 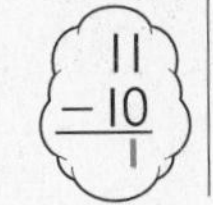 11 − 10 = 1
9. 10 − 9 = 1 | 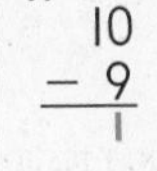 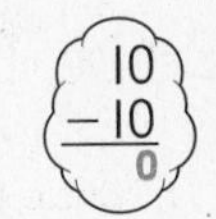 10 − 10 = 0

Write how many are left.

10. 16 − 9 = 7; 12 − 8 = 4; 18 − 7 = 11; 15 − 9 = 6; 10 − 9 = 1

11. 14 − 6 = 8; 11 − 9 = 2; 17 − 9 = 8; 13 − 8 = 5; 9 − 9 = 0

 Use with Grade 2, text pages 47–48.

Reteach

Using 10 to Subtract 9

R 2-7

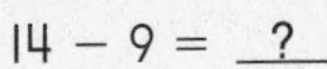
14 − 9 = ?

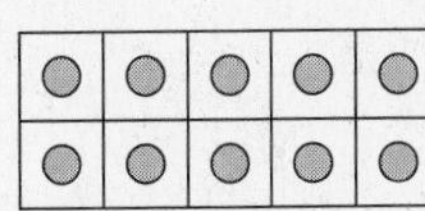
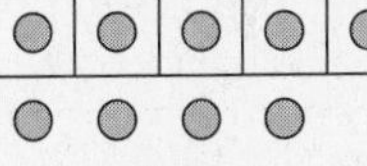
Show 14
How many are left?

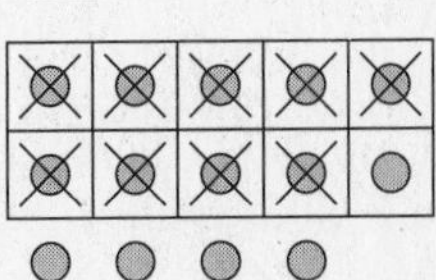
Subtract 9
14 − 9 = 5

Draw ● to show how many. Cross out to subtract.

1. 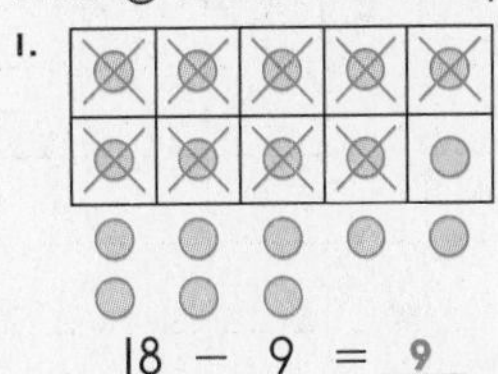
18 − 9 = 9

2. 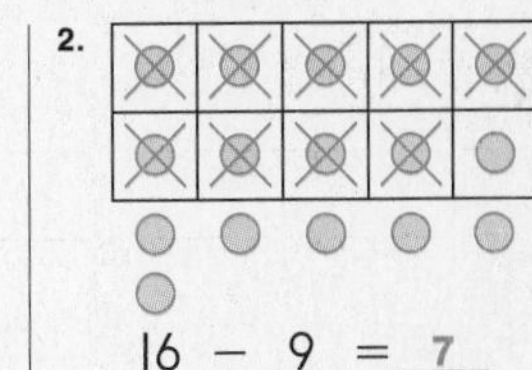
16 − 9 = 7

3. 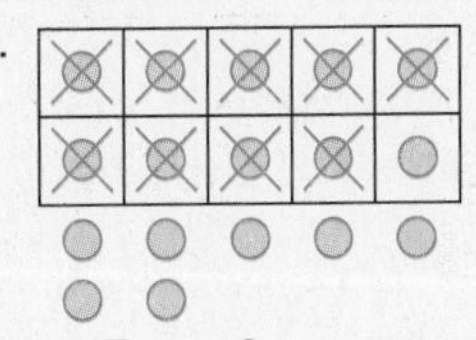
17 − 9 = 8

4. 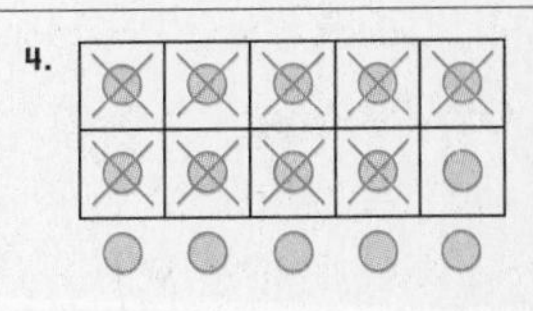

15 − 9 = 6

 Use with Grade 2, text pages 47–48.

Extend

Building Blocks

E 2-7
VISUAL THINKING

Color to show how many blocks to take away to make the wall in the box.
Write how many.

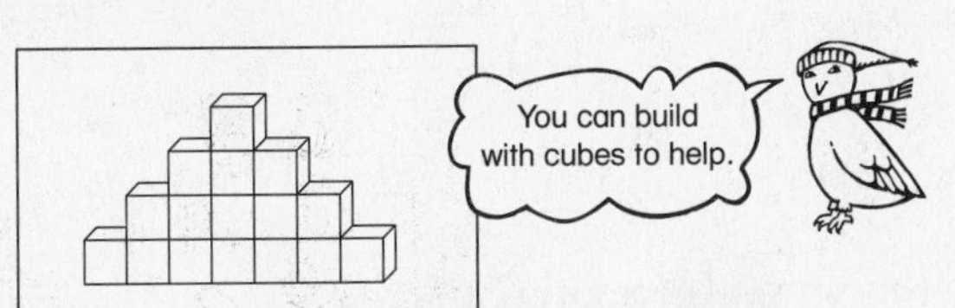

1. 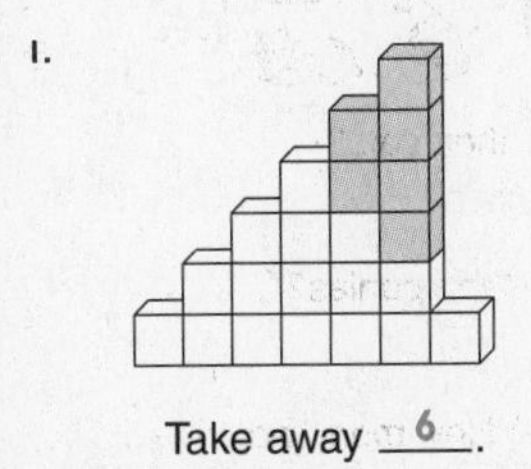
Take away 6.

2. 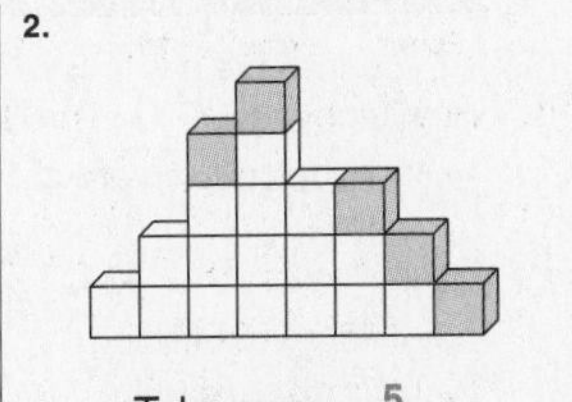
Take away 5.

3. 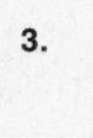 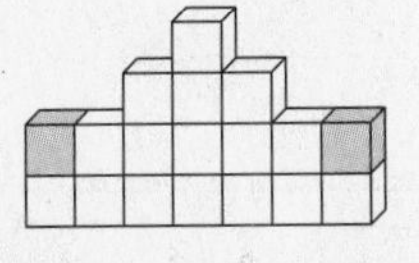 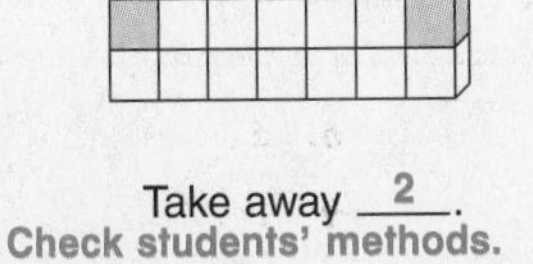
Take away 2.

4. 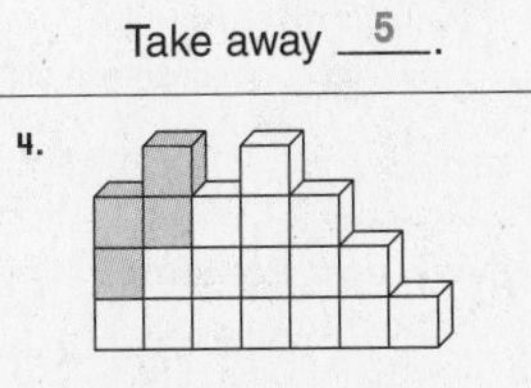
Take away 4.

Check students' methods.

 Use with Grade 2, text pages 47–48.

Daily Review

Name ____________________

Daily Review 2-7

Using 10 to Subtract 9

Subtract.
Use counters to help.

1. 10 − 9 = 1; 14 − 9 = 5; 12 − 9 = 3; 16 − 9 = 7; 13 − 9 = 4; 15 − 9 = 6

Problem Solving
Complete the subtraction sentences.
Then continue the pattern.

2. 15 − 9 = 6
3. 14 − 9 = 5
4. 13 − 9 = 4
5. 12 − 9 = 3
6. 11 − 9 = 2
7. 10 − 9 = 1

Review and Remember
Add.

8. 3 + 8 = 11   1 + 4 = 5   9 + 3 = 12

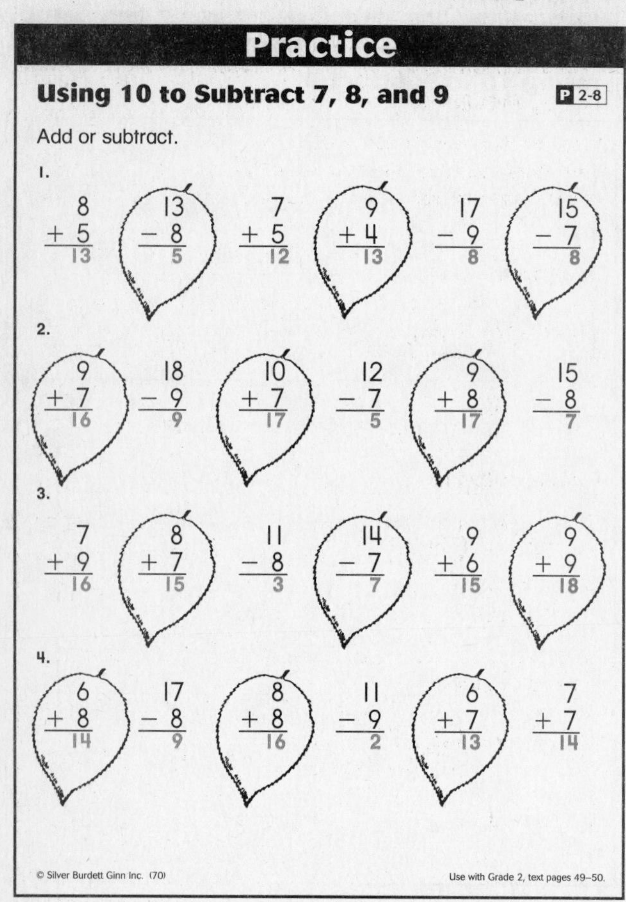

Practice

Using 10 to Subtract 7, 8, and 9

P 2-8

Add or subtract.

1. 8 + 5 = 13 | 13 − 8 = 5 | 7 + 5 = 12 | 9 + 4 = 13 | 17 − 9 = 8 | 15 − 7 = 8

2. 9 + 7 = 16 | 18 − 9 = 9 | 10 + 7 = 17 | 12 − 7 = 5 | 9 + 8 = 17 | 15 − 8 = 7

3. 7 + 9 = 16 | 8 + 7 = 15 | 11 − 8 = 3 | 14 − 7 = 7 | 9 + 6 = 15 | 9 + 9 = 18

4. 6 + 8 = 14 | 17 − 8 = 9 | 8 + 8 = 16 | 11 − 9 = 2 | 6 + 7 = 13 | 7 + 7 = 14

 Use with Grade 2, text pages 49–50.

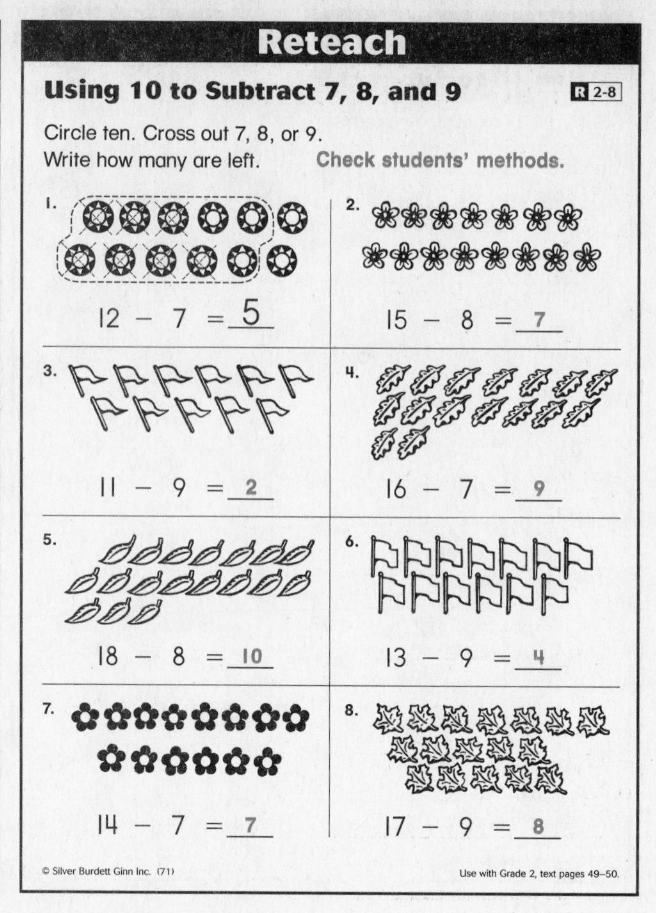

Reteach

Using 10 to Subtract 7, 8, and 9

R 2-8

Circle ten. Cross out 7, 8, or 9.
Write how many are left. Check students' methods.

1. 12 − 7 = 5
2. 15 − 8 = 7
3. 11 − 9 = 2
4. 16 − 7 = 9
5. 18 − 8 = 10
6. 13 − 9 = 4
7. 14 − 7 = 7
8. 17 − 9 = 8

 Use with Grade 2, text pages 49–50.

Extend

Four Little Pigs

E 2-8
REASONING

Help the pigs find their cars.
Color to show which car goes with each pig.

red — My license plate has numbers and letters.

blue — My car is in this lot.

green — The number on my license plate is the same as 9 − 3.

brown — My license plate has only letters.

Help each pig find its house.

red — My house is on this street.

blue — The number on my house is the same as 12 − 3.

green — My house does not have a chimney.

brown — My house is not made of bricks.

Check students' coloring.

 Use with Grade 2, text pages 49–50.

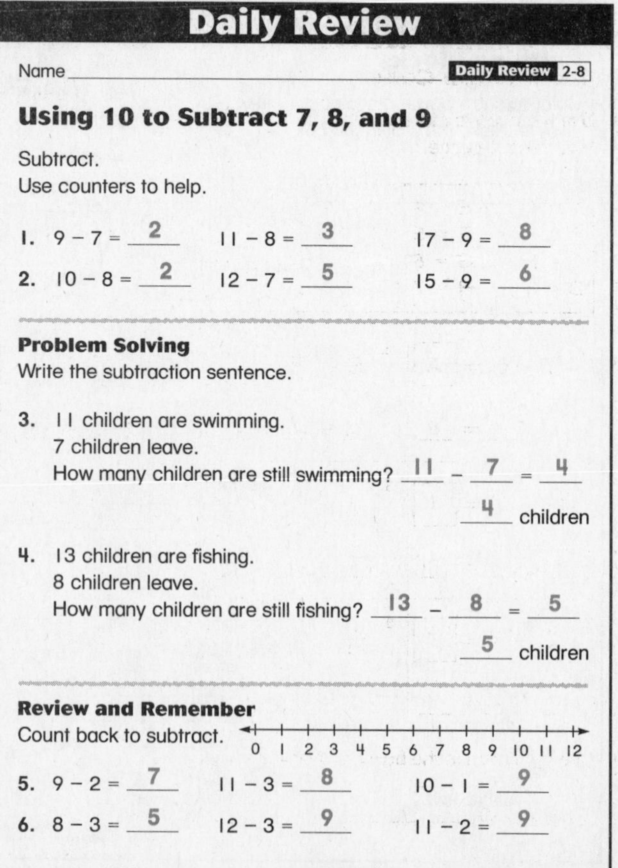

Daily Review

Name ______

Daily Review 2-8

Using 10 to Subtract 7, 8, and 9

Subtract.
Use counters to help.

1. 9 − 7 = 2 | 11 − 8 = 3 | 17 − 9 = 8
2. 10 − 8 = 2 | 12 − 7 = 5 | 15 − 9 = 6

Problem Solving

Write the subtraction sentence.

3. 11 children are swimming.
   7 children leave.
   How many children are still swimming? 11 − 7 = 4
   4 children

4. 13 children are fishing.
   8 children leave.
   How many children are still fishing? 13 − 8 = 5
   5 children

Review and Remember

Count back to subtract.

0 1 2 3 4 5 6 7 8 9 10 11 12

5. 9 − 2 = 7 | 11 − 3 = 8 | 10 − 1 = 9
6. 8 − 3 = 5 | 12 − 3 = 9 | 11 − 2 = 9

Practice

Using Strategies to Subtract

P 2-9

Use the strategies you learned to help you subtract.
For the problems in the seals, write which strategy you used.

Strategies:
Count back 1, 2, or 3. Check students' strategies.
Use an addition fact.
Think of a double.
Use 10 to subtract 7, 8, or 9.

1. 

15	12	16	9	10
− 9	− 7	− 7	− 3	− 5
6	5	9	6	5

Strategy ____________

2. 

14	11	15	8	18
− 7	− 1	− 7	− 6	− 9
7	10	8	2	9

Strategy ____________

3. 

18	12	9	13	18
− 3	− 6	− 7	− 8	− 7
15	6	2	5	11

Strategy ____________

 Use with Grade 2, text pages 51–52.

Reteach

Using Strategies to Subtract

R 2-9

There are many ways to subtract.
Look at the example. Then solve the problems next to it using the same way.

Count back.

5 − 3 = ? (Think 4, 3, 2)

5 − 3 = 2

1. 11 − 2 = 9
2. 5 − 3 = 2
3. 9 − 1 = 8
4. 7 − 2 = 5

Use an addition fact.

5 − 4 = ? (Think 4 + 1 = 5)

5 − 4 = 1

5. 14 − 8 = 6
6. 13 − 4 = 9
7. 7 − 5 = 2
8. 9 − 6 = 3

Think of a double.

8 − 4 = ? (Think 4 + 4 = 8)

8 − 4 = 4

9. 16 − 8 = 8
10. 12 − 6 = 6
11. 6 − 3 = 3
12. 14 − 7 = 7

 Use with Grade 2, text pages 51–52.

Extend

Subtraction Code

E 2-9
ALGEBRA

Use the code to make problems.
Find the difference.

A = 0	E = 4	I = 8	M = 12	Q = 16
B = 1	F = 5	J = 9	N = 13	R = 17
C = 2	G = 6	K = 10	O = 14	S = 18
D = 3	H = 7	L = 11	P = 15	T = 19

1. G − G = A
   6 − 6 = 0
2. S − H = L
   18 − 7 = 11
3. Q − F = L
   16 − 5 = 11
4. N − F = I
   13 − 5 = 8
5. J − D = G
   9 − 3 = 6
6. P − P = A
   15 − 15 = 0
7. T − A = T
   19 − 0 = 19
8. Q − C = O
   16 − 2 = 14
9. S − B = R
   18 − 1 = 17

Use the letters in the boxes to finish the saying:

See you later, A L L I G A T O R!

 Use with Grade 2, text pages 51–52.

Daily Review

Name ____________ Daily Review 2-9

Using Strategies to Subtract

Subtract.
Draw a line to the strategy you used.

1. 14 − 8 = 6
2. 11 − 6 = 5
3. 10 − 5 = 5
4. 11 − 2 = 9
5. 12 − 5 = 7

Strategies
Count back.
Use an addition fact.
Think of a double.
Use 10 to subtract.
Answers will vary.

Problem Solving
Look at the number on each cup.
How many balls are still in the cup?

6. 

9

7. 

9

Review and Remember
Write the number that comes just before.

8. 18, 19
9. 13, 14
10. 19, 20

Practice

Fact Families to 12

P 2-10

Add or subtract. Circle the fact in each fact family that does not belong.

1.	2.	3.
2 + 1 = 3	3 + 2 = 5	(7 + 4 = 11)
1 + 2 = 3	2 + 3 = 5	3 + 4 = 7
(3 + 2 = 5)	5 − 2 = 3	4 + 3 = 7
3 − 1 = 2	5 − 3 = 2	7 − 4 = 3
3 − 2 = 1	(10 − 5 = 5)	7 − 3 = 4

4.	5.	6.
5 + 4 = 9	7 + 2 = 9	5 + 3 = 8
4 + 5 = 9	2 + 7 = 9	(9 + 1 = 10)
(9 + 5 = 14)	(9 + 2 = 11)	3 + 5 = 8
9 − 5 = 4	9 − 2 = 7	8 − 3 = 5
9 − 4 = 5	9 − 7 = 2	8 − 5 = 3

Use with Grade 2, text pages 53–54.

Reteach

Fact Families to 12

Complete each fact family.
Use cubes or counters if you like.

1.

5 + 6 = 11
6 + 5 = 11
11 − 5 = 6
11 − 6 = 5

2.

8 + 4 = 12
4 + 8 = 12
12 − 4 = 8
12 − 8 = 4

3.

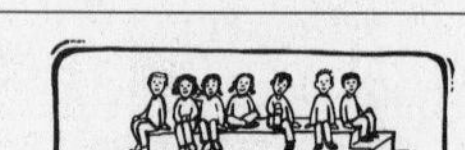

7 + 4 = 11
4 + 7 = 11
11 − 7 = 4
11 − 4 = 7

4.

4 + 6 = 10
6 + 4 = 10
10 − 6 = 4
10 − 4 = 6

Use with Grade 2, text pages 53–54.

Extend

Hide and Seek

E 2-10
VISUAL THINKING

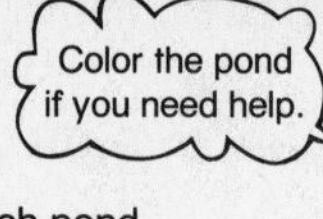

Look at each pond.
Find the fish.
Draw three more fish in each pond.
Draw two flowers outside each pond.

1.

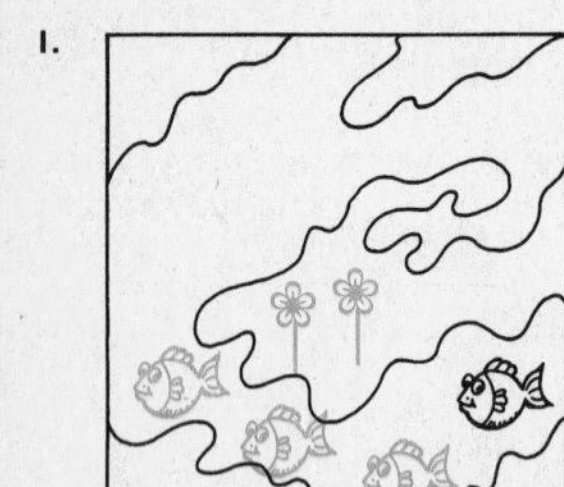

2.

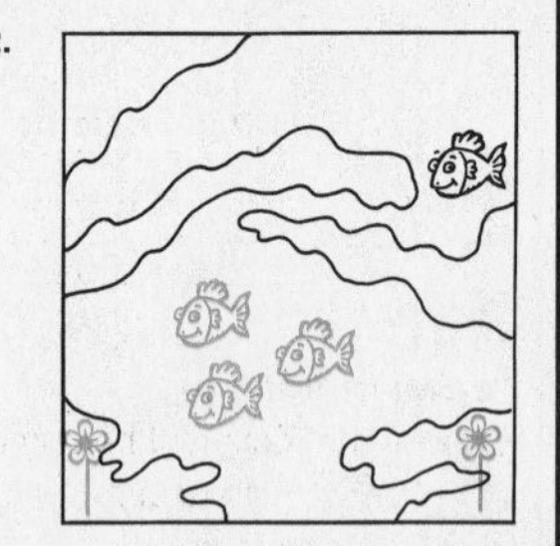

3.

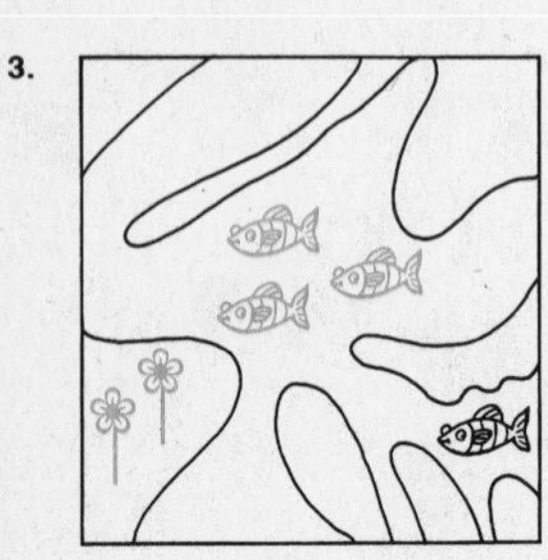

4.

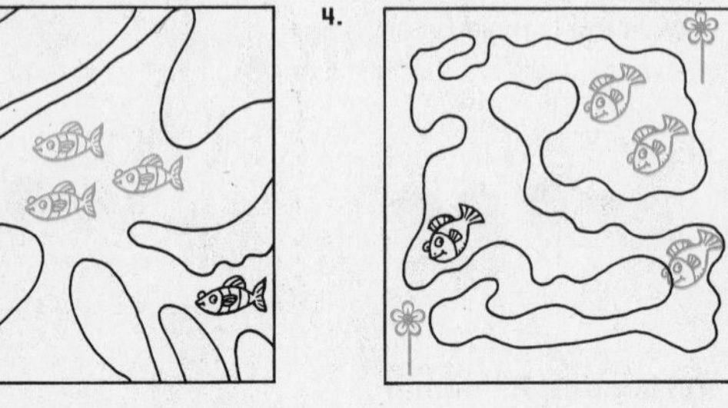

Check students' drawings.

Use with Grade 2, text pages 53–54.

Daily Review

Name ______________________ Daily Review 2-10

Fact Families to 12

Add and subtract.

1. 4 + 7 = 11
   7 + 4 = 11
   11 − 7 = 4
   11 − 4 = 7

2. 4 + 8 = 12
   8 + 4 = 12
   12 − 8 = 4
   12 − 4 = 8

Problem Solving

Add and subtract.
Circle the one that doesn't belong in the fact family.

3. 2 + 8 = 10
   8 + 2 = 10
   (10 − 7 = 3)
   10 − 2 = 8

4. 3 + 9 = 12
   (6 + 6 = 12)
   12 − 9 = 3
   12 − 3 = 9

Review and Remember

Draw 2 more O.
Write the number.

5. O O O O O O
   O O
   8

6. O O O O O O O O

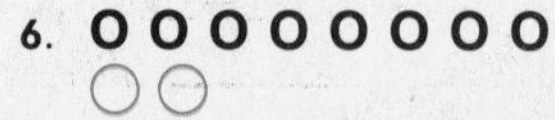

   10

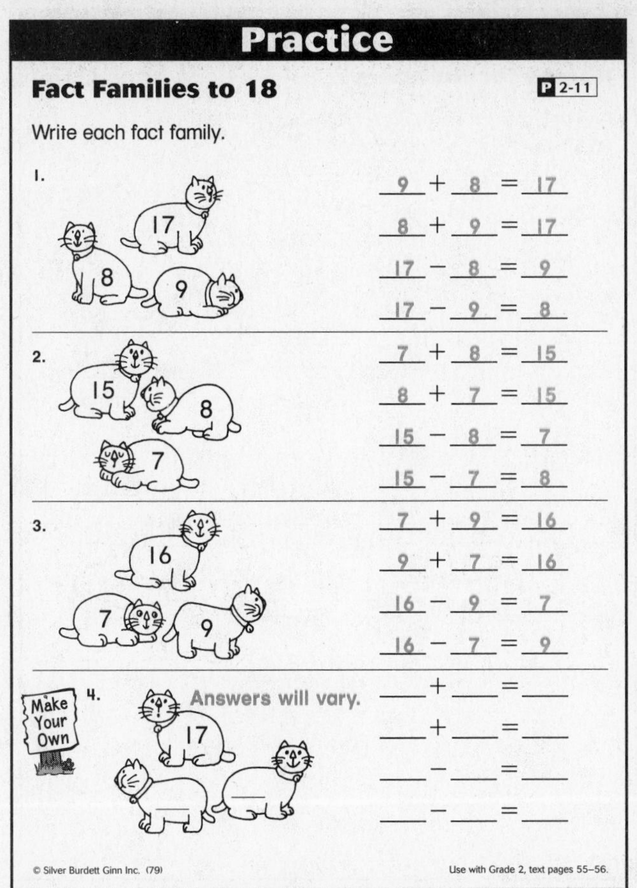

Practice

Fact Families to 18

P 2-11

Write each fact family.

1. 17, 8, 9

9 + 8 = 17
8 + 9 = 17
17 − 8 = 9
17 − 9 = 8

2. 15, 8, 7

7 + 8 = 15
8 + 7 = 15
15 − 8 = 7
15 − 7 = 8

3. 16, 7, 9

7 + 9 = 16
9 + 7 = 16
16 − 9 = 7
16 − 7 = 9

Make Your Own

4. 17 Answers will vary.

___ + ___ = ___
___ + ___ = ___
___ − ___ = ___
___ − ___ = ___

© Silver Burdett Ginn Inc. (79) Use with Grade 2, text pages 55–56.

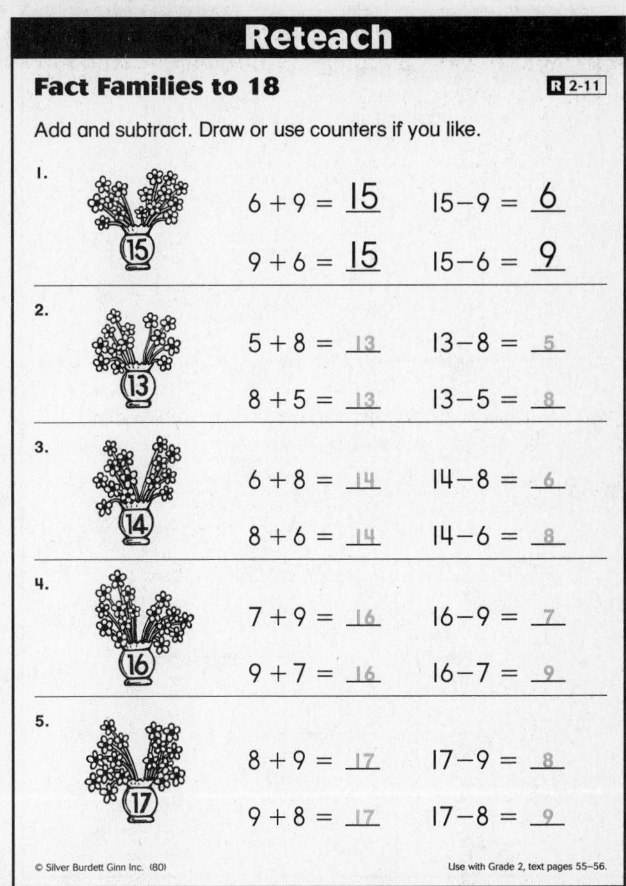

Reteach

Fact Families to 18

R 2-11

Add and subtract. Draw or use counters if you like.

1. 15

6 + 9 = 15 15 − 9 = 6
9 + 6 = 15 15 − 6 = 9

2. 13

5 + 8 = 13 13 − 8 = 5
8 + 5 = 13 13 − 5 = 8

3. 14

6 + 8 = 14 14 − 8 = 6
8 + 6 = 14 14 − 6 = 8

4. 16

7 + 9 = 16 16 − 9 = 7
9 + 7 = 16 16 − 7 = 9

5. 17

8 + 9 = 17 17 − 9 = 8
9 + 8 = 17 17 − 8 = 9

© Silver Burdett Ginn Inc. (80) Use with Grade 2, text pages 55–56.

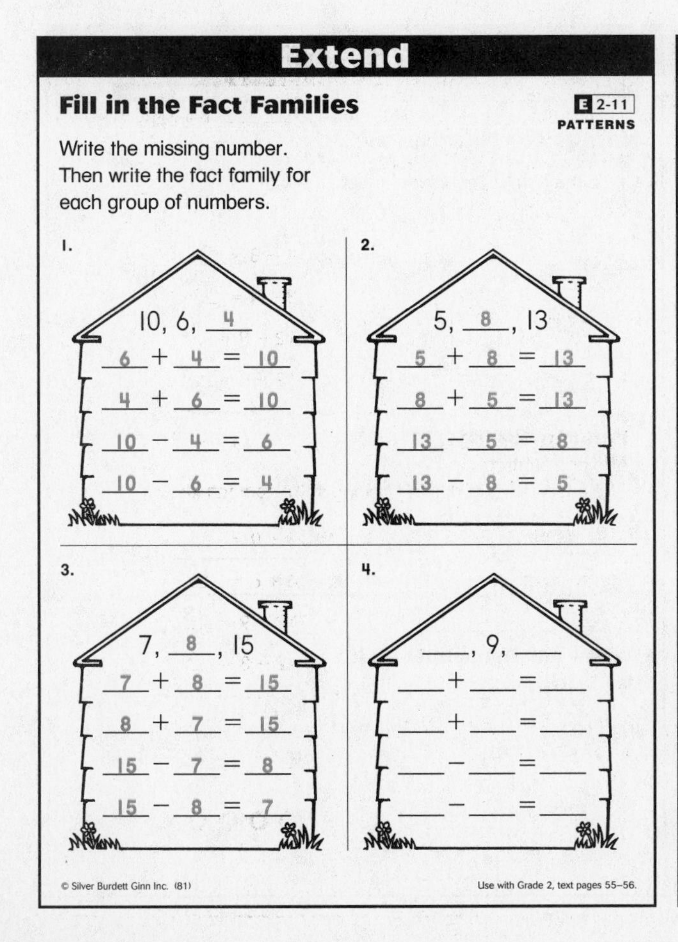

Extend

Fill in the Fact Families

E 2-11
PATTERNS

Write the missing number.
Then write the fact family for each group of numbers.

1. 10, 6, 4

6 + 4 = 10
4 + 6 = 10
10 − 4 = 6
10 − 6 = 4

2. 5, 8, 13

5 + 8 = 13
8 + 5 = 13
13 − 5 = 8
13 − 8 = 5

3. 7, 8, 15

7 + 8 = 15
8 + 7 = 15
15 − 7 = 8
15 − 8 = 7

4. ___, 9, ___

___ + ___ = ___
___ + ___ = ___
___ − ___ = ___
___ − ___ = ___

© Silver Burdett Ginn Inc. (81) Use with Grade 2, text pages 55–56.

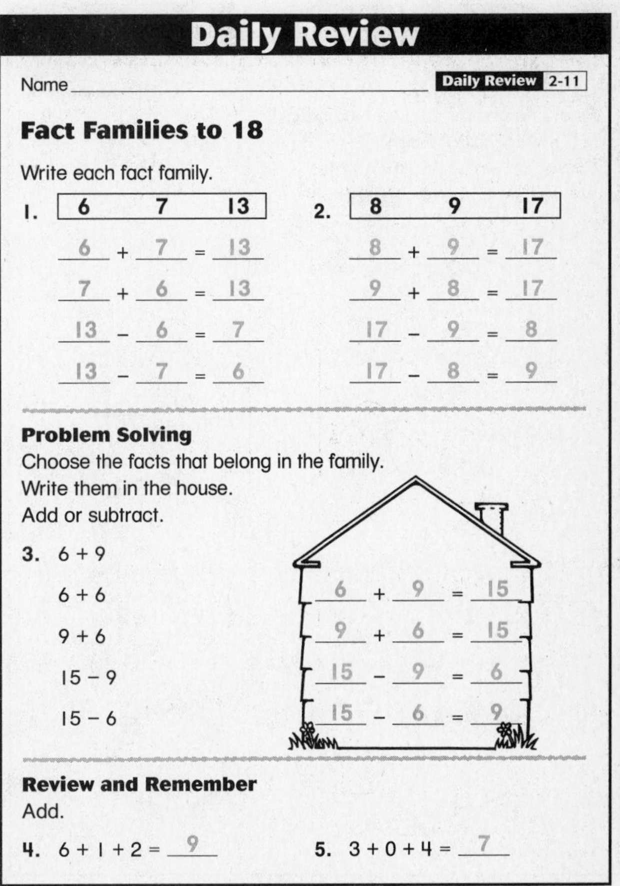

Daily Review

Name ____________________

Daily Review 2-11

Fact Families to 18

Write each fact family.

1. 6 7 13

6 + 7 = 13
7 + 6 = 13
13 − 6 = 7
13 − 7 = 6

2. 8 9 17

8 + 9 = 17
9 + 8 = 17
17 − 9 = 8
17 − 8 = 9

Problem Solving

Choose the facts that belong in the family.
Write them in the house.
Add or subtract.

3. 6 + 9
6 + 6
9 + 6
15 − 9
15 − 6

6 + 9 = 15
9 + 6 = 15
15 − 9 = 6
15 − 6 = 9

Review and Remember

Add.

4. 6 + 1 + 2 = 9

5. 3 + 0 + 4 = 7

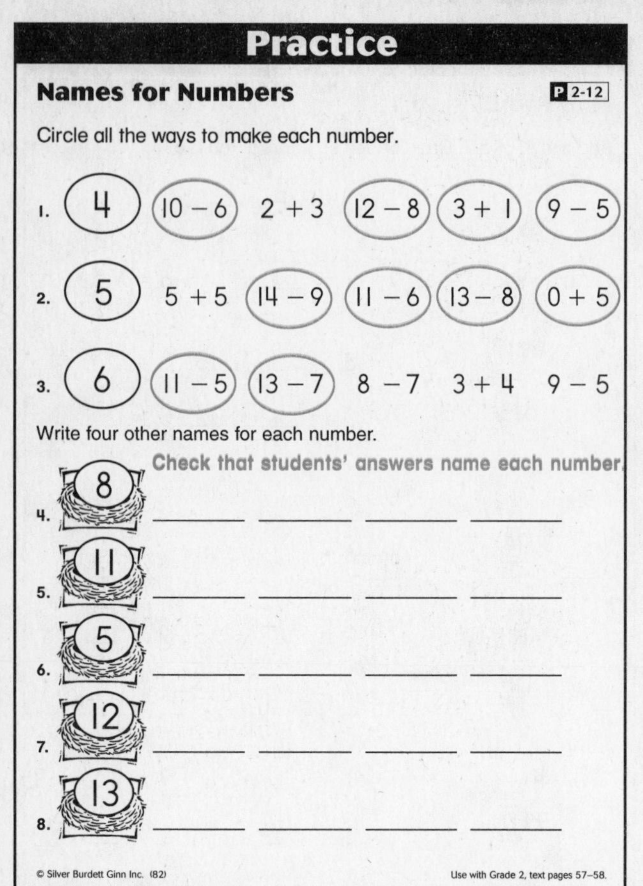

Practice

Names for Numbers

P 2-12

Circle all the ways to make each number.

1. (4) (10 − 6) 2 + 3 (12 − 8) (3 + 1) (9 − 5)
2. (5) 5 + 5 (14 − 9) (11 − 6) (13 − 8) (0 + 5)
3. (6) (11 − 5) (13 − 7) 8 − 7 3 + 4 9 − 5

Write four other names for each number.

Check that students' answers name each number.

4. 8 ______ ______ ______ ______
5. 11 ______ ______ ______ ______
6. 5 ______ ______ ______ ______
7. 12 ______ ______ ______ ______
8. 13 ______ ______ ______ ______

 Use with Grade 2, text pages 57–58.

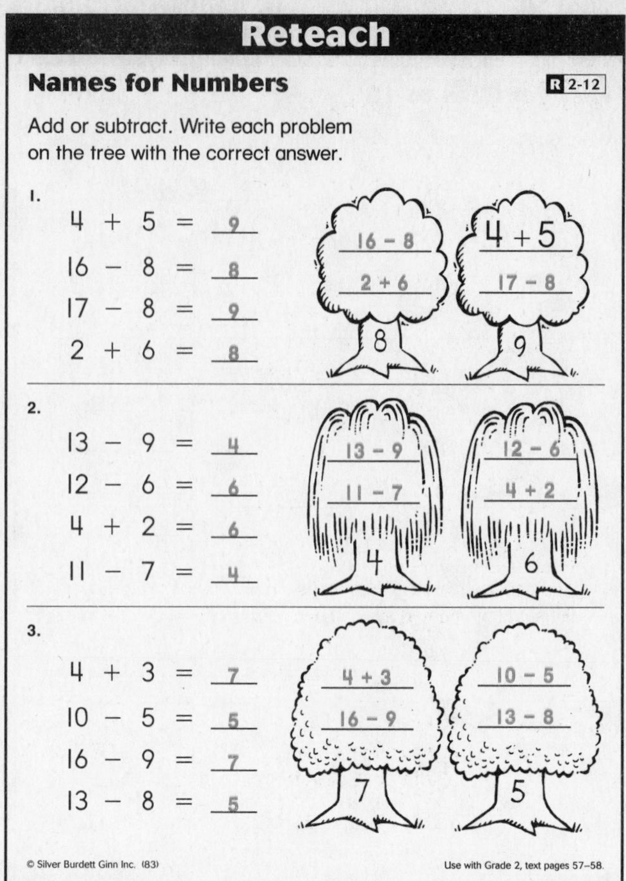

Reteach

Names for Numbers

R 2-12

Add or subtract. Write each problem on the tree with the correct answer.

1.
4 + 5 = 9
16 − 8 = 8
17 − 8 = 9
2 + 6 = 8

2.
13 − 9 = 4
12 − 6 = 6
4 + 2 = 6
11 − 7 = 4

3.
4 + 3 = 7
10 − 5 = 5
16 − 9 = 7
13 − 8 = 5

 Use with Grade 2, text pages 57–58.

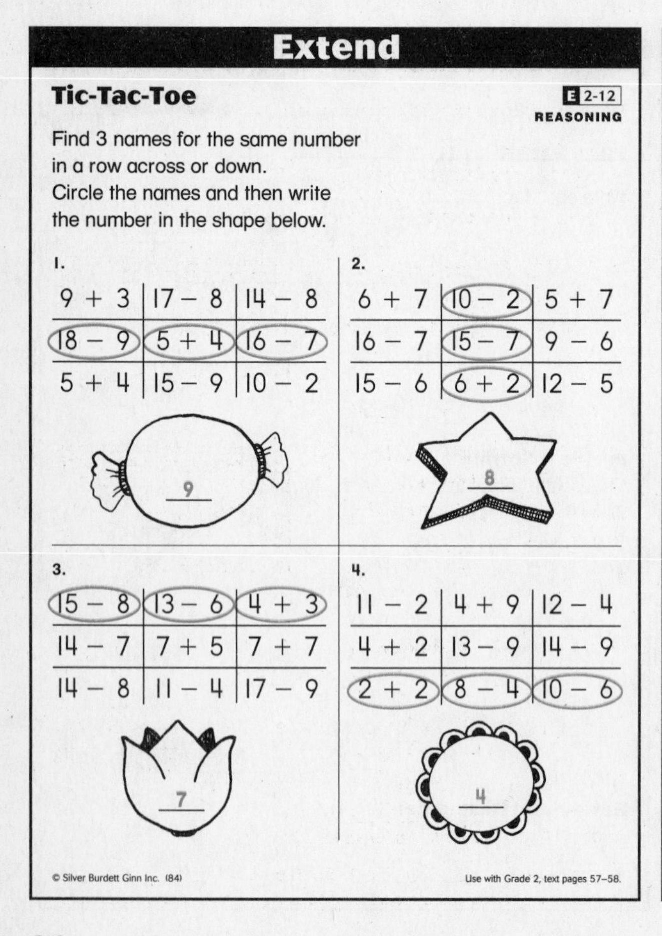

Extend

Tic-Tac-Toe

E 2-12
REASONING

Find 3 names for the same number in a row across or down.
Circle the names and then write the number in the shape below.

1.

9 + 3	17 − 8	14 − 8
(18 − 9)	(5 + 4)	(16 − 7)
5 + 4	15 − 9	10 − 2

9

2.

6 + 7	(10 − 2)	5 + 7
16 − 7	(15 − 7)	9 − 6
15 − 6	(6 + 2)	12 − 5

8

3.

(15 − 8)	(13 − 6)	(4 + 3)
14 − 7	7 + 5	7 + 7
14 − 8	11 − 4	17 − 9

7

4.

11 − 2	4 + 9	12 − 4
4 + 2	13 − 9	14 − 9
(2 + 2)	(8 − 4)	(10 − 6)

4

 Use with Grade 2, text pages 57–58.

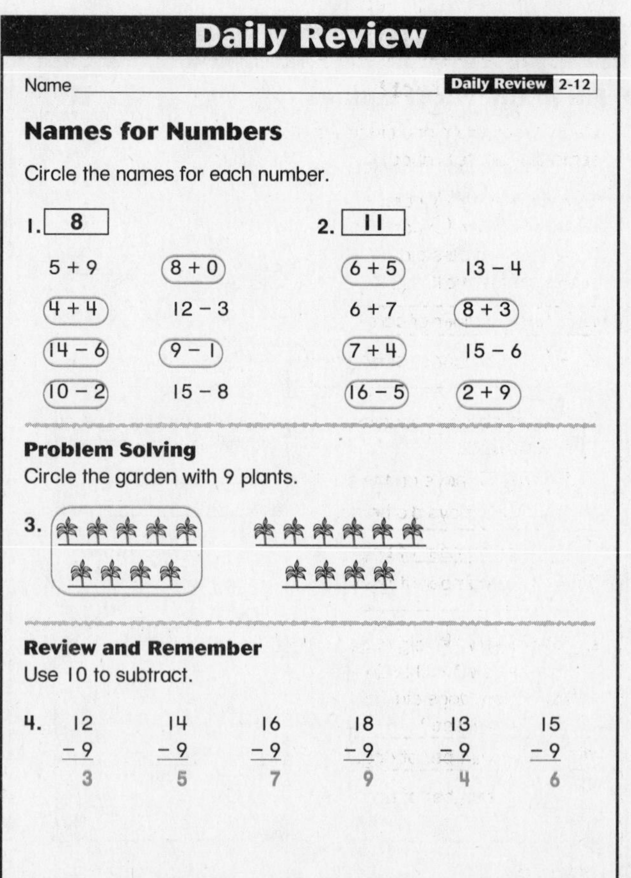

Daily Review

Name ______________ Daily Review 2-12

Names for Numbers

Circle the names for each number.

1. 8

5 + 9	(8 + 0)
(4 + 4)	12 − 3
(14 − 6)	(9 − 1)
(10 − 2)	15 − 8

2. 11

(6 + 5)	13 − 4
6 + 7	(8 + 3)
(7 + 4)	15 − 6
(16 − 5)	(2 + 9)

Problem Solving

Circle the garden with 9 plants.

3.

Review and Remember

Use 10 to subtract.

4.

12	14	16	18	13	15
− 9	− 9	− 9	− 9	− 9	− 9
3	5	7	9	4	6

Practice

Problem Solving P 2-13

Choose the Operation

Circle the operation. Write the sentence.

1. You have 6 fish in your bucket. Your friend puts 2 more fish into the bucket. How many fish are there now?

   (add) subtract

   6 (+) 2 = 8

2. There is a hole in a bucket with 9 fish. 5 fish escape. How many fish are there left?

   add (subtract)

   9 (−) 5 = 4

3. You put your 7 fish into a new bucket. There are already 4 fish in the new bucket. How many fish are there now?

   (add) subtract

   7 (+) 4 = 11

4. You see your brother has no fish in his bucket. You give him 3 fish. How many does he have now?

   (add) subtract

   0 (+) 3 = 3

5. On your way home you imagine your 8 fish are doubled. How many fish would there be?

   (add) subtract

   8 (+) 8 = 16

 Use with Grade 2, text pages 59–60.

Reteach

Problem Solving R 2-13

Choose the Operation

Use counters to act out the story.
Then write the number sentence.

1. 7 squirrels are in a tree. 3 of them jump to the roof. How many are still in the tree?

   7 (−) 3 = 4 squirrels

2. 6 mice hide in a log. 4 more mice join them. How many mice are inside now?

   6 (+) 4 = 10 mice

3. 9 dogs play in the park. 5 of them go home. How many dogs are in the park now?

   9 (−) 5 = 4 dogs

4. 5 cats sleep on the couch. 3 cats sleep on the floor. How many cats are sleeping?

   5 (+) 3 = 8 cats

 Use with Grade 2, text pages 59–60.

Extend

Add or Subtract?

E 2-13 NUMBER SENSE

Read the problem and circle the sentence that tells about it.

1. Rachel drew △ cars. Russell drew ○ cars. How many cars did they draw in all?

   (△ + ○ = number of cars)

   △ − ○ = number of cars

2. Rachel saw □ birds. ▽ birds flew away. How many birds were left?

   □ + ▽ = number of birds

   (□ − ▽ = number of birds)

3. Russell saw ◇ boys on the sidewalk. He saw ☆ boys on the bus. How many boys did he see?

   (◇ + ☆ = number of boys)

   ☆ − ◇ = number of boys

4. Rachel counted ✻ bugs. ⌗ bugs crawled away. How many bugs were left?

   (✻ − ⌗ = number of bugs)

   ⌗ − ✻ = number of bugs

5. Russell saw ✦ big dogs. Rachel saw ☼ little dogs. How many dogs did Rachel and Russell see?

   (✦ + ☼ = number of dogs)

   ✦ − ☼ = number of dogs

6. Russell has ◇ apples. Rachel takes ✲ apples. How many apples does Russell have now?

   ◇ + ✲ = number of apples

   (◇ − ✲ = number of apples)

 Use with Grade 2, text pages 59–60.

Daily Review

Name ____________________ Daily Review 2-13

Problem Solving

Choose the Operation

Circle **add** or **subtract**. Write the number sentence.

1. 6 fish are in the tank. 7 more are put in. How many fish are in the tank?

   (add) subtract

   6 + 7 = 13 fish

2. 10 fish are in the tank. 8 fish are taken out. How many fish are left?

   add (subtract)

   10 − 8 = 2 fish

Problem Solving Review

Use the picture. Color a box for each toy.

7			
6			
5			
4			
3			
2			
1			
0	doll	bear	block

3. Are there more dolls or bears? bears

4. How many fewer dolls are there than blocks? 1

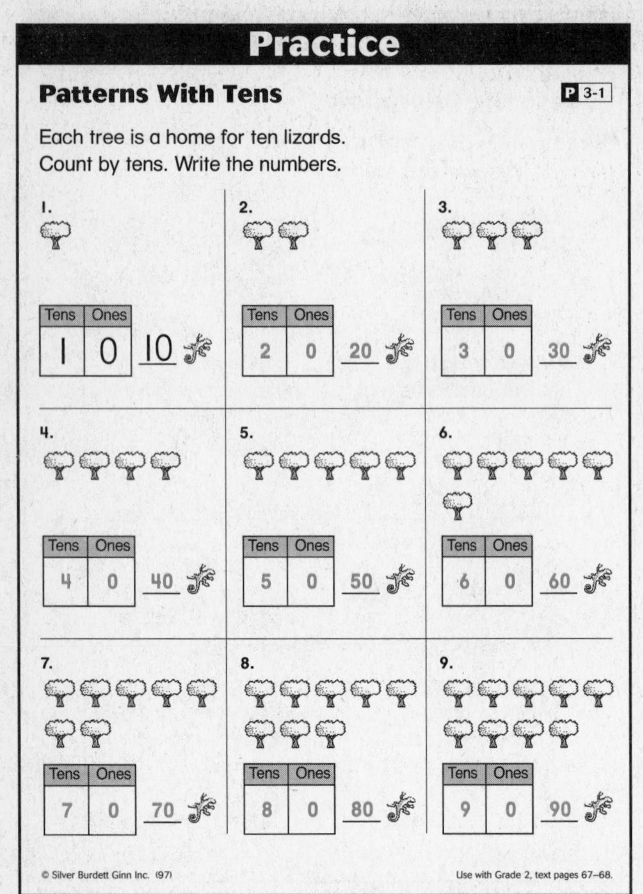

Practice

Patterns With Tens P 3-1

Each tree is a home for ten lizards.
Count by tens. Write the numbers.

1. Tens 1, Ones 0 — 10
2. Tens 2, Ones 0 — 20
3. Tens 3, Ones 0 — 30
4. Tens 4, Ones 0 — 40
5. Tens 5, Ones 0 — 50
6. Tens 6, Ones 0 — 60
7. Tens 7, Ones 0 — 70
8. Tens 8, Ones 0 — 80
9. Tens 9, Ones 0 — 90

 Use with Grade 2, text pages 67–68.

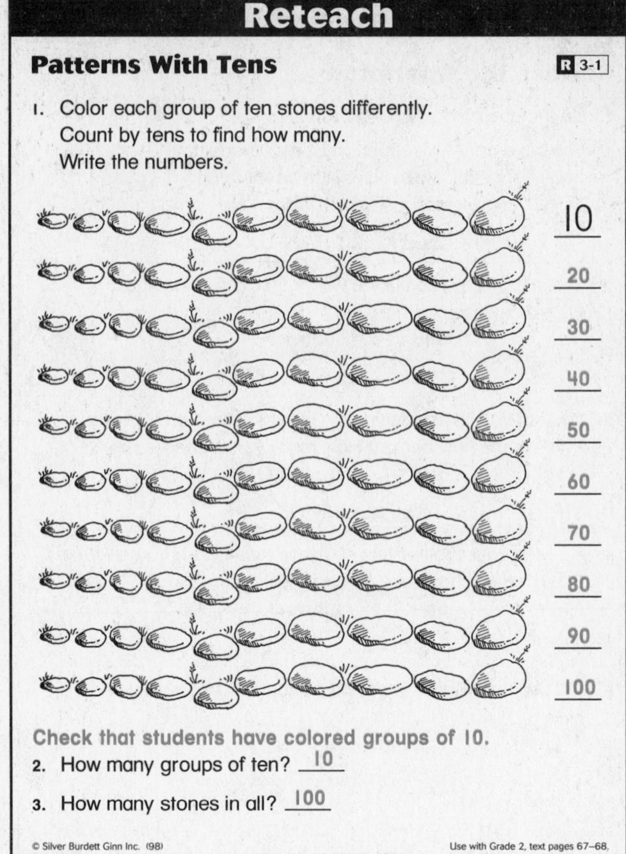

Reteach

Patterns With Tens R 3-1

1. Color each group of ten stones differently.
   Count by tens to find how many.
   Write the numbers.

10
20
30
40
50
60
70
80
90
100

Check that students have colored groups of 10.

2. How many groups of ten? 10
3. How many stones in all? 100

 Use with Grade 2, text pages 67–68.

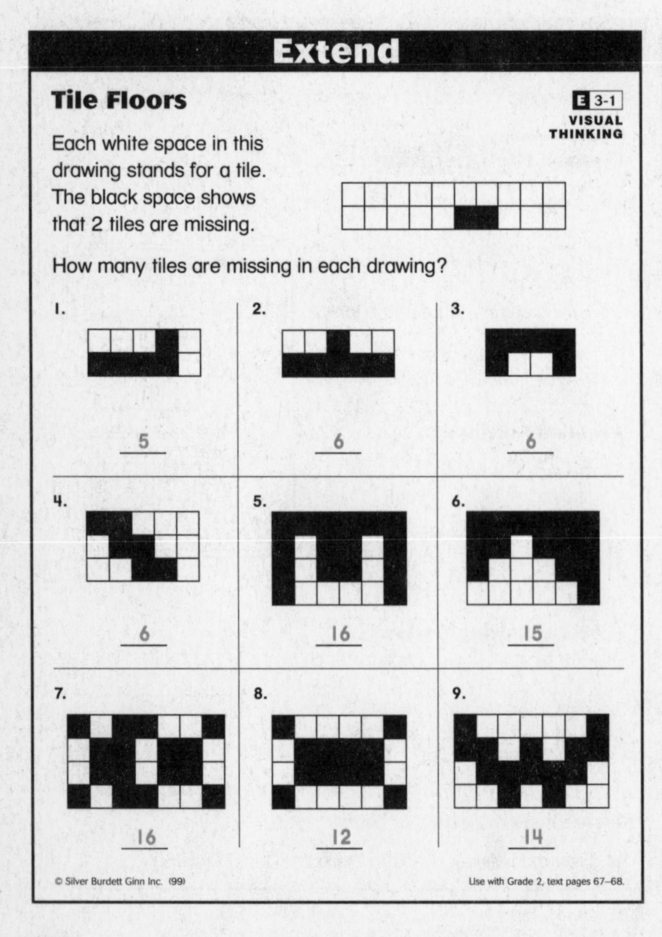

Extend

Tile Floors E 3-1 VISUAL THINKING

Each white space in this drawing stands for a tile. The black space shows that 2 tiles are missing.

How many tiles are missing in each drawing?

1. 5
2. 6
3. 6
4. 6
5. 16
6. 15
7. 16
8. 12
9. 14

 Use with Grade 2, text pages 67–68.

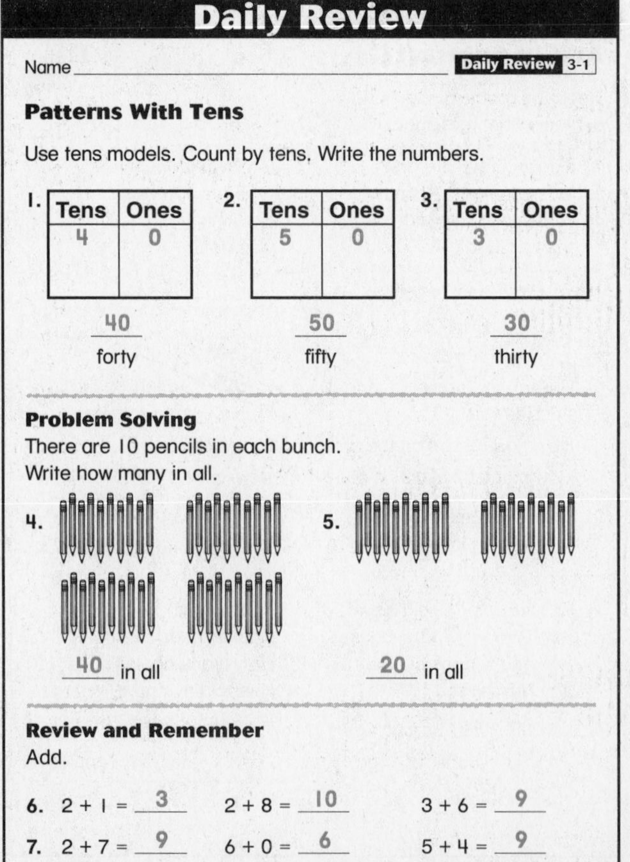

Daily Review

Name ______________________ Daily Review 3-1

Patterns With Tens

Use tens models. Count by tens. Write the numbers.

1. Tens 4, Ones 0 — 40 forty
2. Tens 5, Ones 0 — 50 fifty
3. Tens 3, Ones 0 — 30 thirty

Problem Solving

There are 10 pencils in each bunch.
Write how many in all.

4. 40 in all
5. 20 in all

Review and Remember

Add.

6. 2 + 1 = 3 2 + 8 = 10 3 + 6 = 9
7. 2 + 7 = 9 6 + 0 = 6 5 + 4 = 9

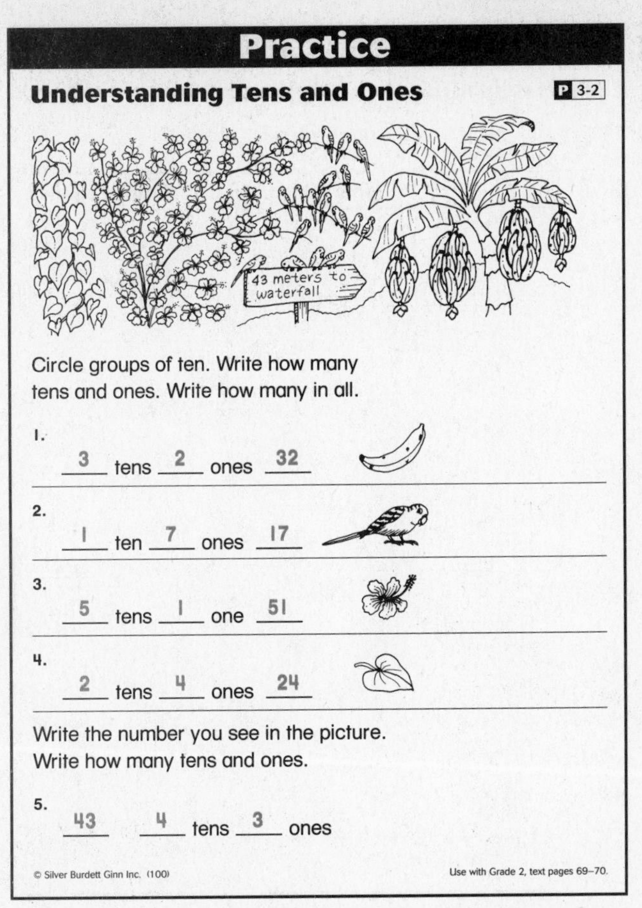

Practice

Understanding Tens and Ones

P 3-2

Circle groups of ten. Write how many tens and ones. Write how many in all.

1. 3 tens 2 ones 32
2. 1 ten 7 ones 17
3. 5 tens 1 one 51
4. 2 tens 4 ones 24

Write the number you see in the picture. Write how many tens and ones.

5. 43 4 tens 3 ones

 Use with Grade 2, text pages 69–70.

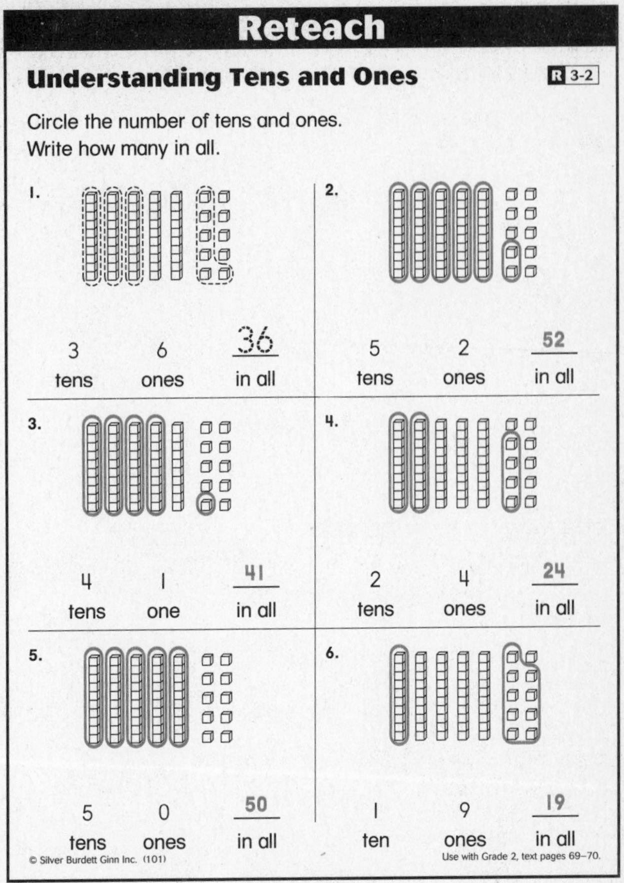

Reteach

Understanding Tens and Ones

R 3-2

Circle the number of tens and ones. Write how many in all.

1. 3 tens 6 ones 36 in all
2. 5 tens 2 ones 52 in all
3. 4 tens 1 one 41 in all
4. 2 tens 4 ones 24 in all
5. 5 tens 0 ones 50 in all
6. 1 ten 9 ones 19 in all

 Use with Grade 2, text pages 69–70.

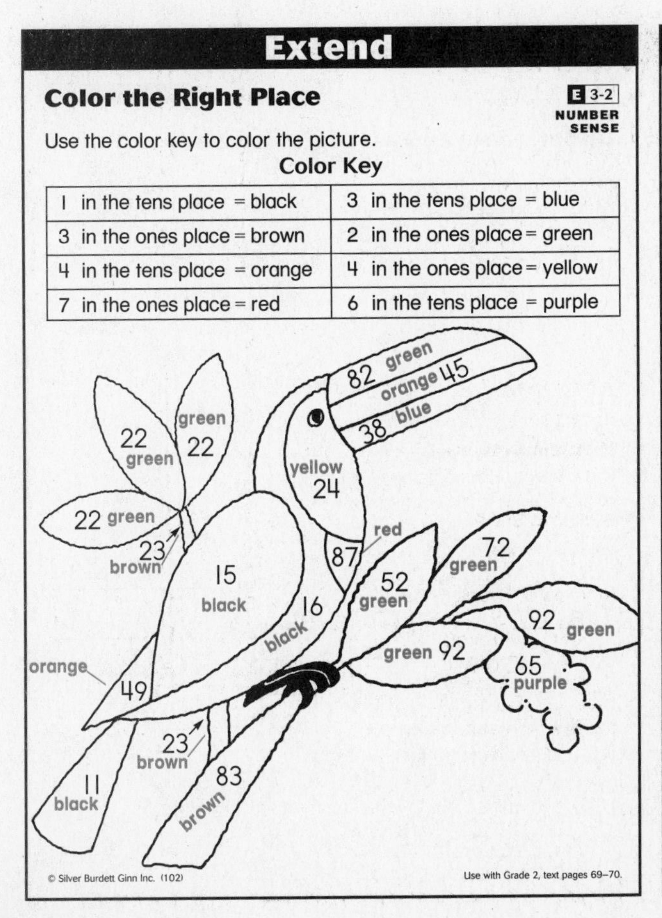

Extend

Color the Right Place

E 3-2 NUMBER SENSE

Use the color key to color the picture.

Color Key

1 in the tens place = black	3 in the tens place = blue
3 in the ones place = brown	2 in the ones place = green
4 in the tens place = orange	4 in the ones place = yellow
7 in the ones place = red	6 in the tens place = purple

 Use with Grade 2, text pages 69–70.

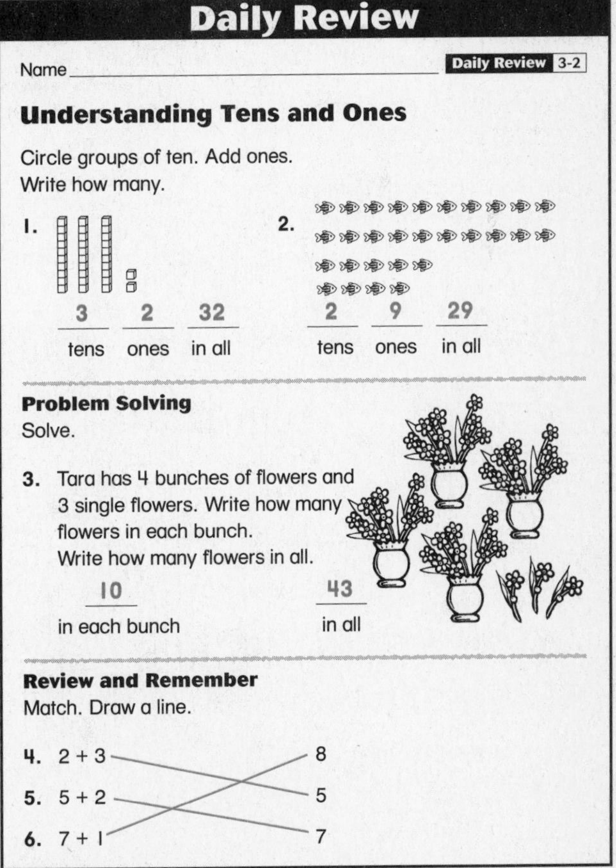

Daily Review

Name ______________________ Daily Review 3-2

Understanding Tens and Ones

Circle groups of ten. Add ones. Write how many.

1. 3 tens 2 ones 32 in all
2. 2 tens 9 ones 29 in all

Problem Solving

Solve.

3. Tara has 4 bunches of flowers and 3 single flowers. Write how many flowers in each bunch. Write how many flowers in all.

10 in each bunch 43 in all

Review and Remember

Match. Draw a line.

4. 2 + 3 — 5
5. 5 + 2 — 7
6. 7 + 1 — 8

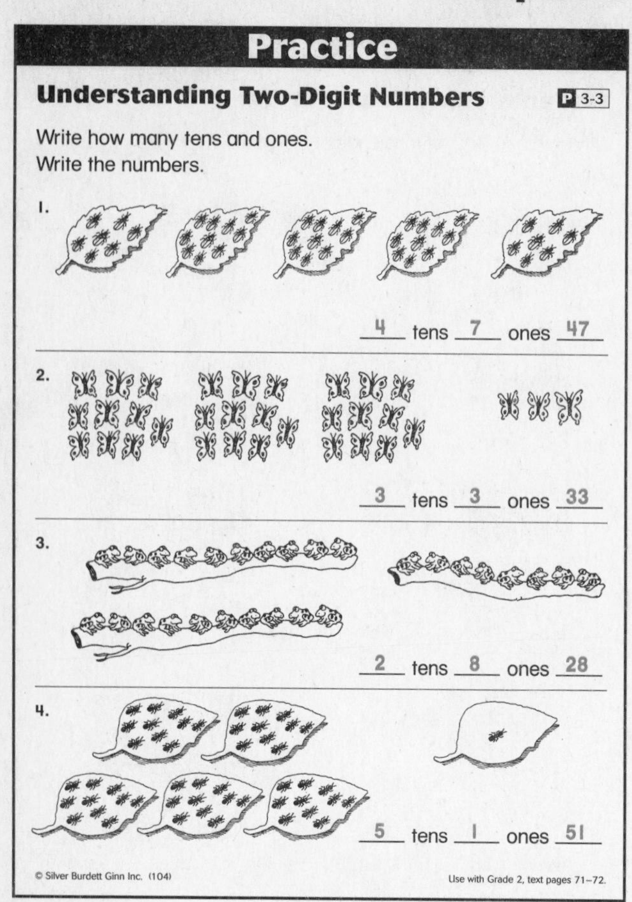

Practice

Understanding Two-Digit Numbers

P 3-3

Write how many tens and ones.
Write the numbers.

1. 4 tens 7 ones 47

2. 3 tens 3 ones 33

3. 2 tens 8 ones 28

4. 5 tens 1 ones 51

Use with Grade 2, text pages 71–72.

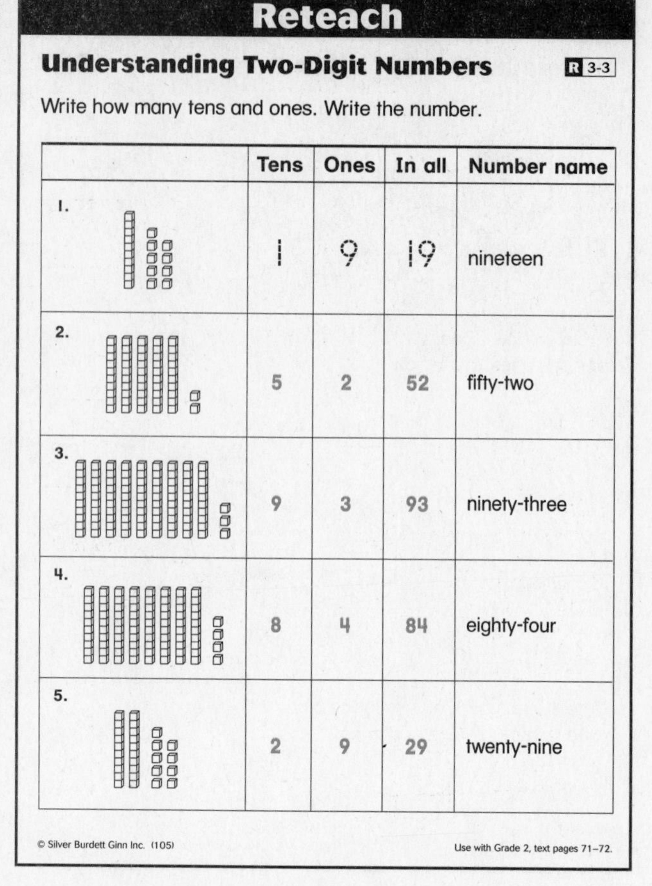

Reteach

Understanding Two-Digit Numbers

R 3-3

Write how many tens and ones. Write the number.

	Tens	Ones	In all	Number name
1.	1	9	19	nineteen
2.	5	2	52	fifty-two
3.	9	3	93	ninety-three
4.	8	4	84	eighty-four
5.	2	9	29	twenty-nine

Use with Grade 2, text pages 71–72.

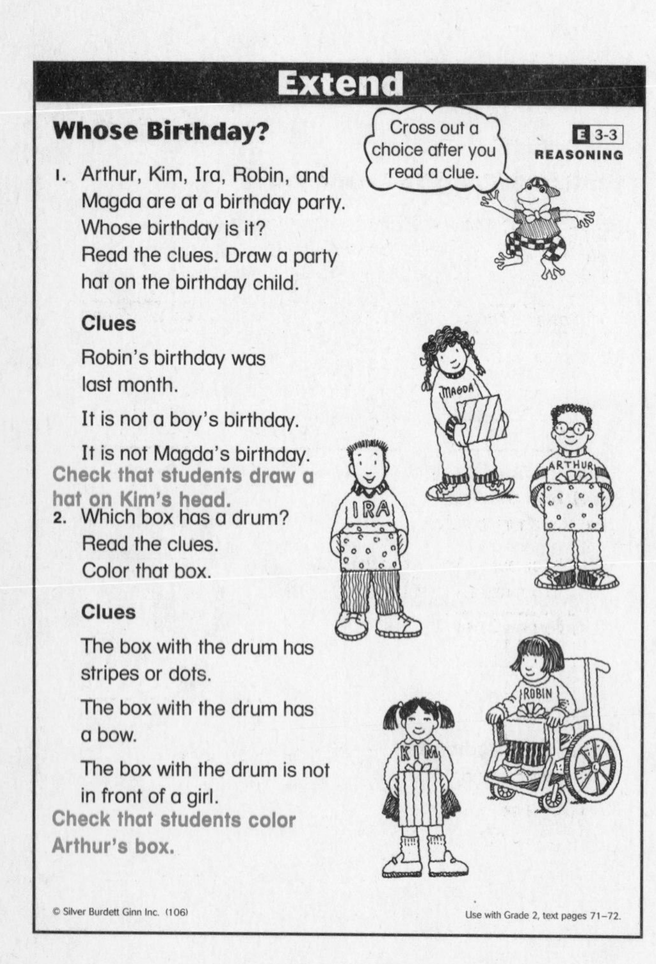

Extend

Whose Birthday?

E 3-3 REASONING

1. Arthur, Kim, Ira, Robin, and Magda are at a birthday party. Whose birthday is it? Read the clues. Draw a party hat on the birthday child.

Clues

Robin's birthday was last month.

It is not a boy's birthday.

It is not Magda's birthday.

Check that students draw a hat on Kim's head.

2. Which box has a drum? Read the clues. Color that box.

Clues

The box with the drum has stripes or dots.

The box with the drum has a bow.

The box with the drum is not in front of a girl.

Check that students color Arthur's box.

Use with Grade 2, text pages 71–72.

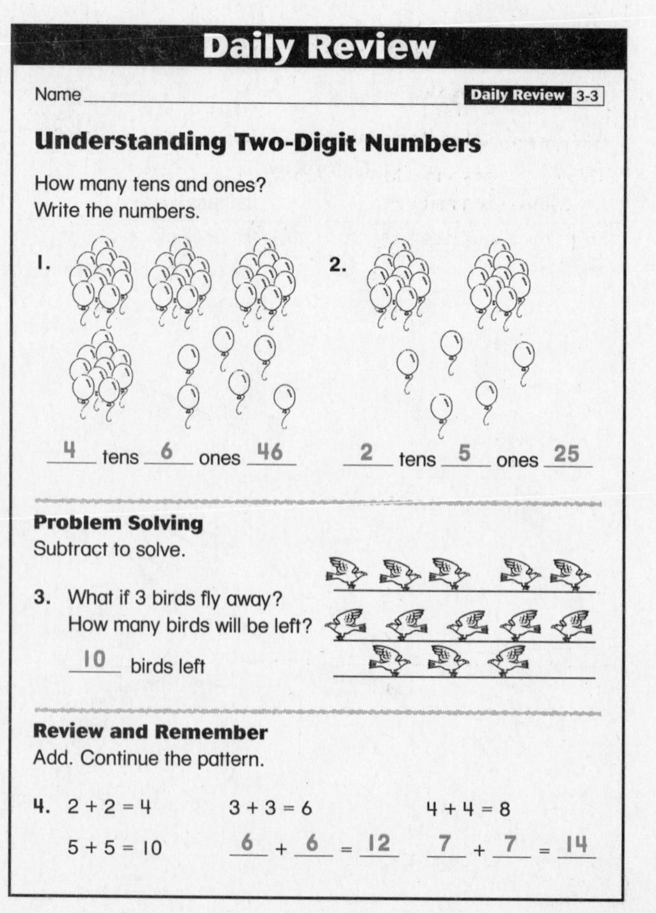

Daily Review

Name ______________________ Daily Review 3-3

Understanding Two-Digit Numbers

How many tens and ones?
Write the numbers.

1. 4 tens 6 ones 46

2. 2 tens 5 ones 25

Problem Solving

Subtract to solve.

3. What if 3 birds fly away? How many birds will be left?

10 birds left

Review and Remember

Add. Continue the pattern.

4. 2 + 2 = 4 3 + 3 = 6 4 + 4 = 8

5 + 5 = 10 6 + 6 = 12 7 + 7 = 14

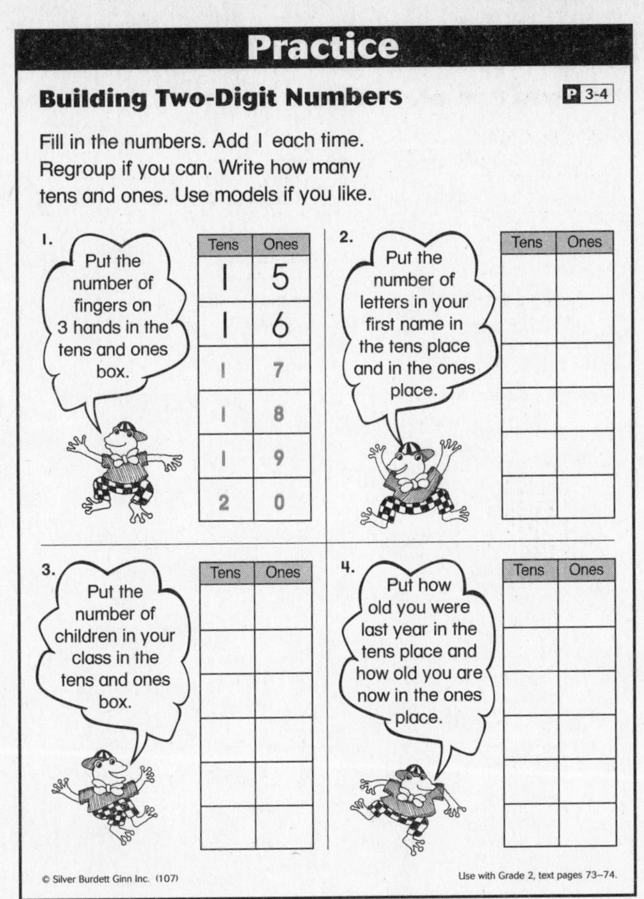

Practice

Building Two-Digit Numbers

P 3-4

Fill in the numbers. Add 1 each time. Regroup if you can. Write how many tens and ones. Use models if you like.

1. Put the number of fingers on 3 hands in the tens and ones box.

Tens	Ones
1	5
1	6
1	7
1	8
1	9
2	0

2. Put the number of letters in your first name in the tens place and in the ones place.

Tens	Ones

3. Put the number of children in your class in the tens and ones box.

Tens	Ones

4. Put how old you were last year in the tens place and how old you are now in the ones place.

Tens	Ones

Use with Grade 2, text pages 73–74.

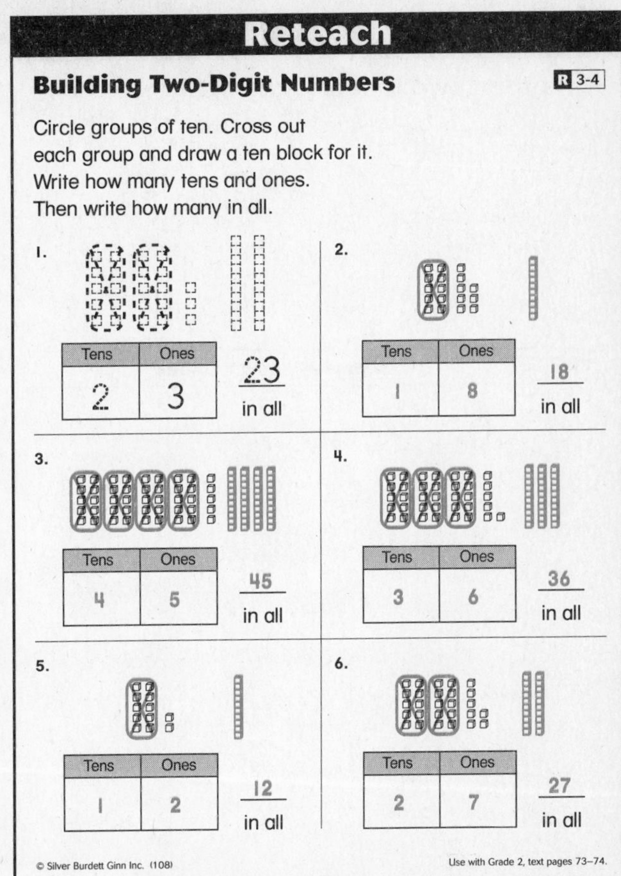

Reteach

Building Two-Digit Numbers

R 3-4

Circle groups of ten. Cross out each group and draw a ten block for it. Write how many tens and ones. Then write how many in all.

1.

Tens	Ones
2	3

23 in all

2.

Tens	Ones
1	8

18 in all

3.

Tens	Ones
4	5

45 in all

4.

Tens	Ones
3	6

36 in all

5.

Tens	Ones
1	2

12 in all

6.

Tens	Ones
2	7

27 in all

Use with Grade 2, text pages 73–74.

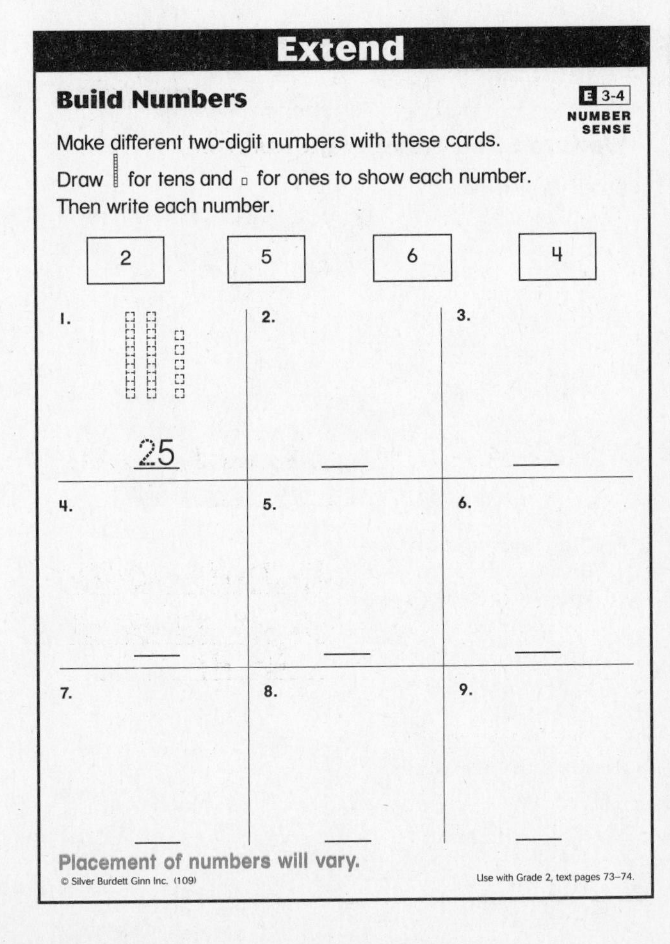

Extend

Build Numbers

E 3-4 NUMBER SENSE

Make different two-digit numbers with these cards.

Draw ▯ for tens and ▫ for ones to show each number. Then write each number.

2 5 6 4

1. 25

2. ____

3. ____

4. ____

5. ____

6. ____

7. ____

8. ____

9. ____

Placement of numbers will vary.

Use with Grade 2, text pages 73–74.

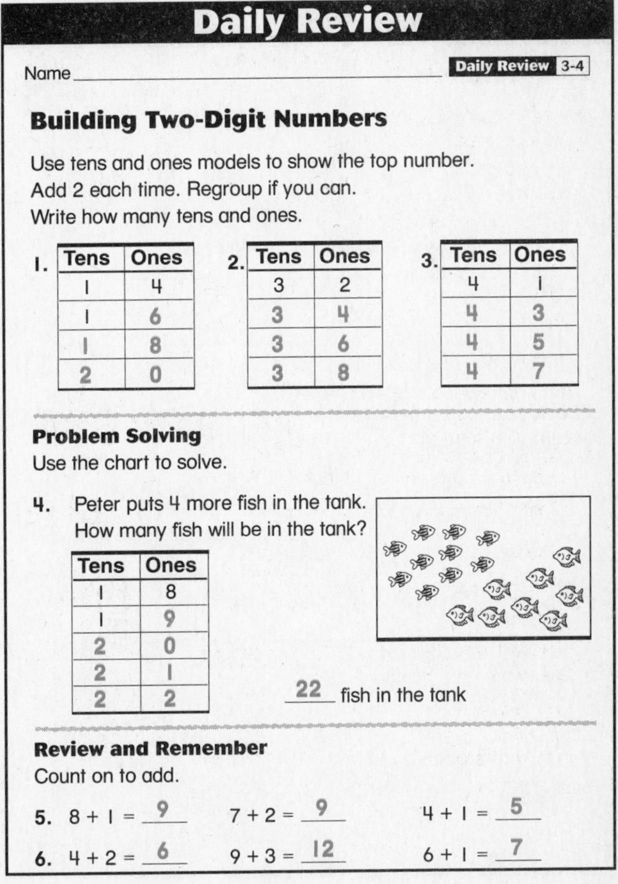

Daily Review

Name ____________________ Daily Review 3-4

Building Two-Digit Numbers

Use tens and ones models to show the top number. Add 2 each time. Regroup if you can. Write how many tens and ones.

1.

Tens	Ones
1	4
1	6
1	8
2	0

2.

Tens	Ones
3	2
3	4
3	6
3	8

3.

Tens	Ones
4	1
4	3
4	5
4	7

Problem Solving

Use the chart to solve.

4. Peter puts 4 more fish in the tank. How many fish will be in the tank?

Tens	Ones
1	8
1	9
2	0
2	1
2	2

22 fish in the tank

Review and Remember

Count on to add.

5. 8 + 1 = 9 7 + 2 = 9 4 + 1 = 5

6. 4 + 2 = 6 9 + 3 = 12 6 + 1 = 7

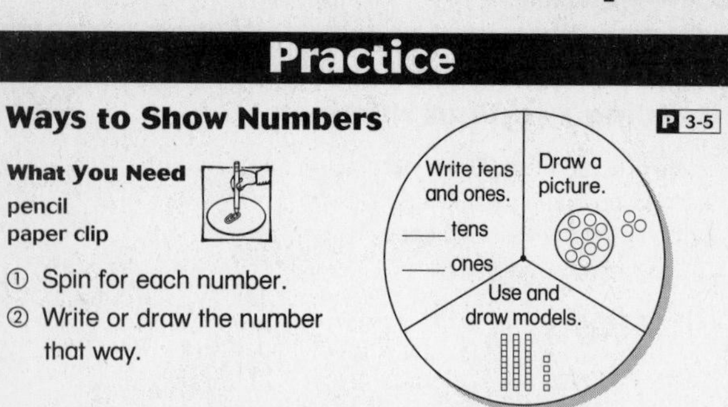

Practice

Ways to Show Numbers P 3-5

What You Need
pencil
paper clip

① Spin for each number.
② Write or draw the number that way.

Number	Ways to show number
1. 53	or or 5 tens 3 ones
2. 29	or or 2 tens 9 ones
3. 16	or or 1 ten 6 ones
4. 67	or or 6 tens 7 ones

 Use with Grade 2, text pages 75–76.

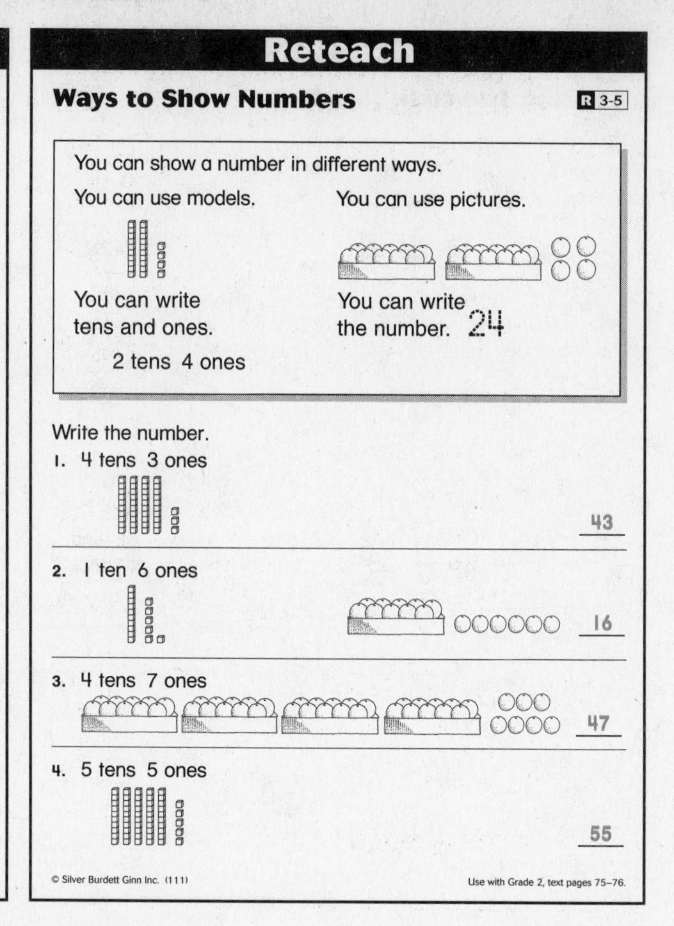

Reteach

Ways to Show Numbers R 3-5

You can show a number in different ways.
You can use models. You can use pictures.
You can write tens and ones. 2 tens 4 ones
You can write the number. 24

Write the number.
1. 4 tens 3 ones — 43
2. 1 ten 6 ones — 16
3. 4 tens 7 ones — 47
4. 5 tens 5 ones — 55

 Use with Grade 2, text pages 75–76.

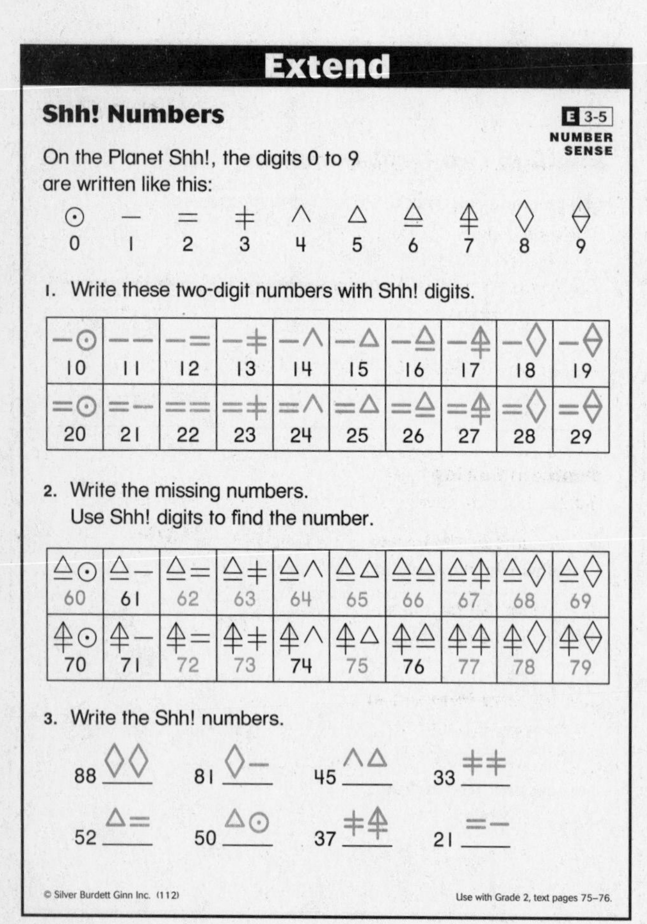

Extend

Shh! Numbers E 3-5 NUMBER SENSE

On the Planet Shh!, the digits 0 to 9 are written like this:

⊙	—	=	ǂ	∧	△	≜	⍋	◇	◇
0	1	2	3	4	5	6	7	8	9

1. Write these two-digit numbers with Shh! digits.

—⊙	——	—=	—ǂ	—∧	—△	—≜	—⍋	—◇	—◇
10	11	12	13	14	15	16	17	18	19
=⊙	=—	==	=ǂ	=∧	=△	=≜	=⍋	=◇	=◇
20	21	22	23	24	25	26	27	28	29

2. Write the missing numbers.
Use Shh! digits to find the number.

≜⊙	≜—	≜=	≜ǂ	≜∧	≜△	≜≜	≜⍋	≜◇	≜◇
60	61	62	63	64	65	66	67	68	69
⍋⊙	⍋—	⍋=	⍋ǂ	⍋∧	⍋△	⍋≜	⍋⍋	⍋◇	⍋◇
70	71	72	73	74	75	76	77	78	79

3. Write the Shh! numbers.

88 ◇◇ 81 ◇— 45 ∧△ 33 ǂǂ
52 △= 50 △⊙ 37 ǂ⍋ 21 =—

 Use with Grade 2, text pages 75–76.

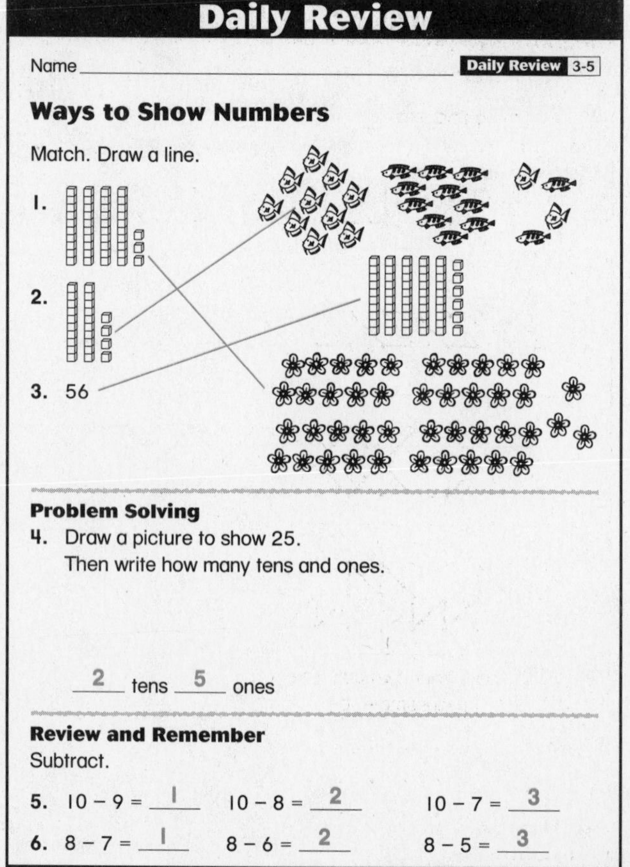

Daily Review

Name ____________ Daily Review 3-5

Ways to Show Numbers

Match. Draw a line.

1.
2.
3. 56

Problem Solving

4. Draw a picture to show 25.
Then write how many tens and ones.

2 tens 5 ones

Review and Remember

Subtract.

5. 10 − 9 = 1 10 − 8 = 2 10 − 7 = 3
6. 8 − 7 = 1 8 − 6 = 2 8 − 5 = 3

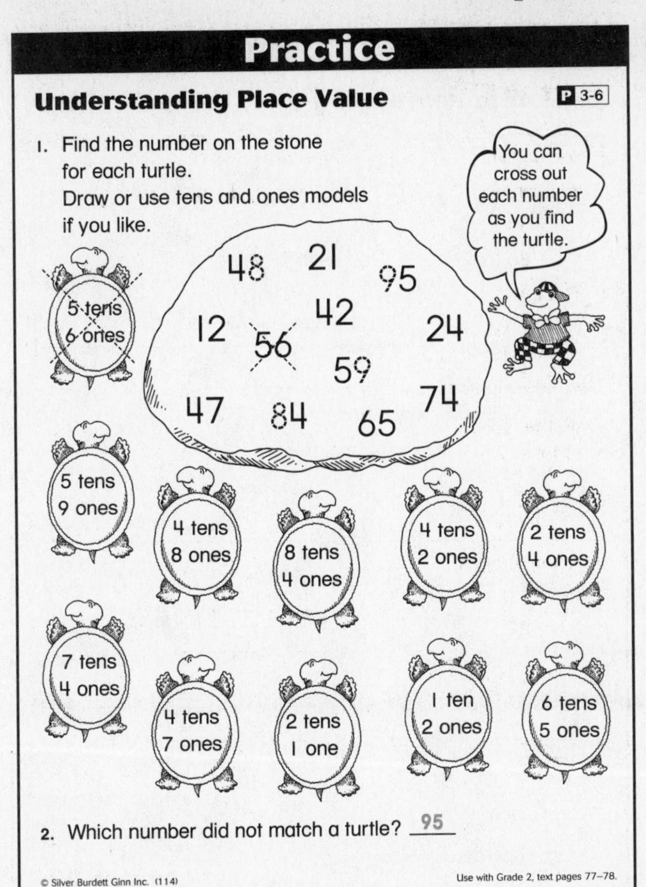

Practice

Understanding Place Value

P 3-6

1. Find the number on the stone for each turtle.
   Draw or use tens and ones models if you like.

2. Which number did not match a turtle? 95

Use with Grade 2, text pages 77–78.

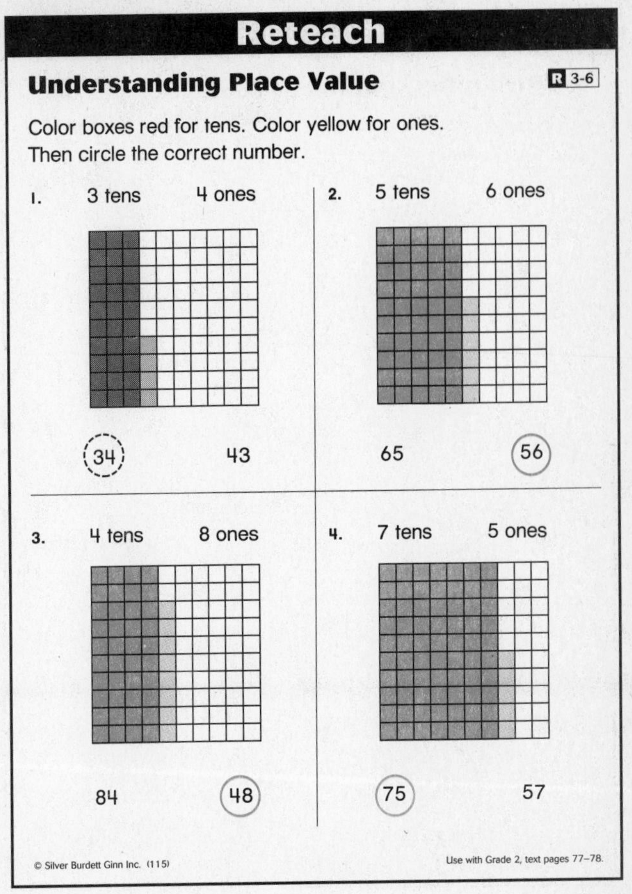

Reteach

Understanding Place Value

R 3-6

Color boxes red for tens. Color yellow for ones.
Then circle the correct number.

1. 3 tens 4 ones — (34) 43
2. 5 tens 6 ones — 65 (56)
3. 4 tens 8 ones — 84 (48)
4. 7 tens 5 ones — (75) 57

Use with Grade 2, text pages 77–78.

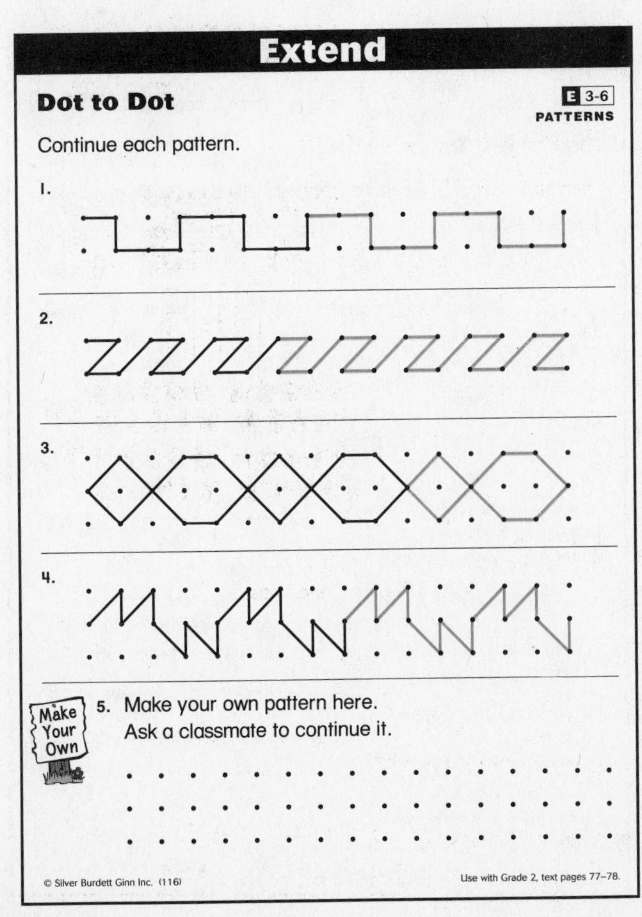

Extend

Dot to Dot

E 3-6
PATTERNS

Continue each pattern.

1.

2.

3.

4.

5. Make your own pattern here.
   Ask a classmate to continue it.

Use with Grade 2, text pages 77–78.

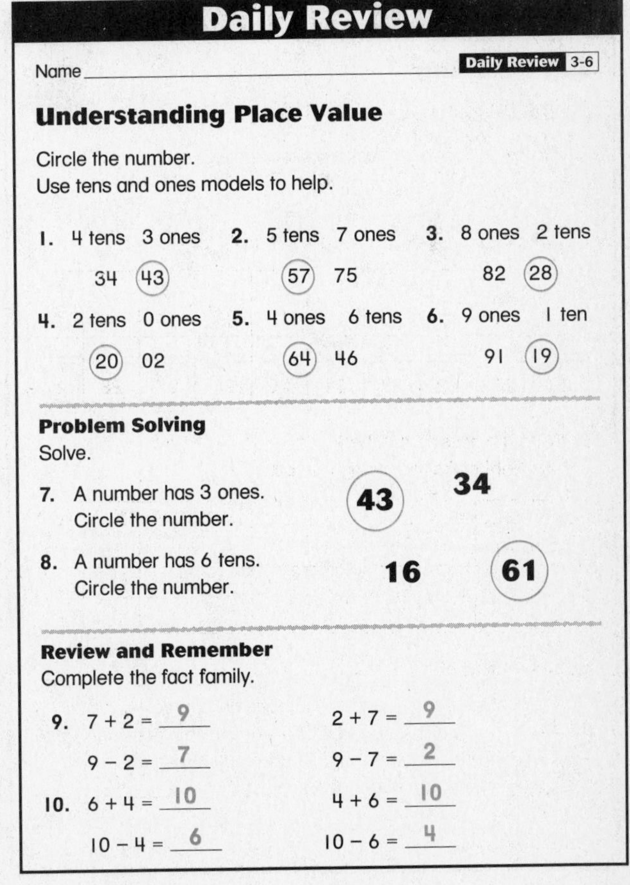

Daily Review

Name ____________________

Daily Review 3-6

Understanding Place Value

Circle the number.
Use tens and ones models to help.

1. 4 tens 3 ones — 34 (43)
2. 5 tens 7 ones — (57) 75
3. 8 ones 2 tens — 82 (28)
4. 2 tens 0 ones — (20) 02
5. 4 ones 6 tens — (64) 46
6. 9 ones 1 ten — 91 (19)

Problem Solving

Solve.

7. A number has 3 ones. Circle the number. — (43) 34
8. A number has 6 tens. Circle the number. — 16 (61)

Review and Remember

Complete the fact family.

9. 7 + 2 = 9　　2 + 7 = 9
   9 − 2 = 7　　9 − 7 = 2
10. 6 + 4 = 10　　4 + 6 = 10
    10 − 4 = 6　　10 − 6 = 4

Chapter 3 • Lesson 7

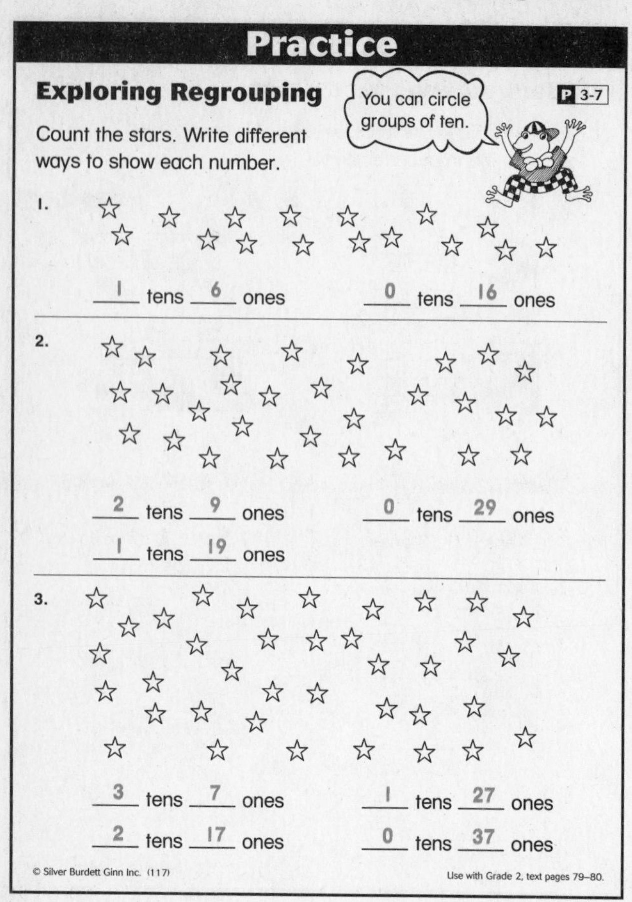

Practice

Exploring Regrouping P 3-7

Count the stars. Write different ways to show each number.

1. 1 tens 6 ones — 0 tens 16 ones

2. 2 tens 9 ones — 0 tens 29 ones
 1 tens 19 ones

3. 3 tens 7 ones — 1 tens 27 ones
 2 tens 17 ones — 0 tens 37 ones

 Use with Grade 2, text pages 79–80.

Reteach

Exploring Regrouping R 3-7

23	2 tens	3 ones
	1 ten	13 ones
	0 tens	23 ones

Use tens and ones models to show each number in different ways.
Draw ▮ for ten. Draw ▫ for one. Record.

1. 15 — 1 tens 5 ones; 0 tens 15 ones

2. 22 — 2 tens 2 ones; 1 tens 12 ones; 0 tens 22 ones

3. 27 — 2 tens 7 ones; 1 tens 17 ones; 0 tens 27 ones

Check students' drawings.

 Use with Grade 2, text pages 79–80.

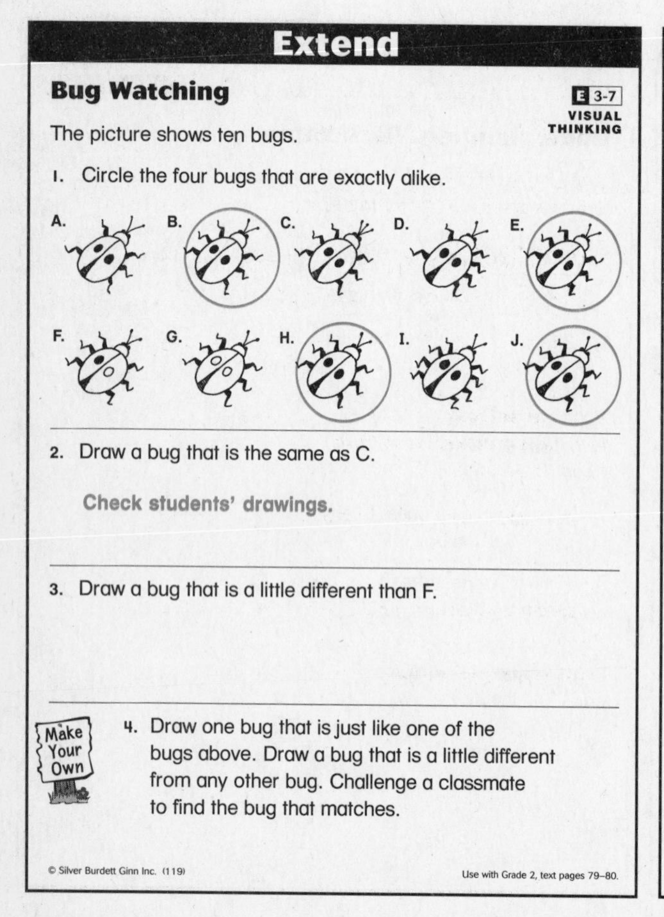

Extend

Bug Watching E 3-7 VISUAL THINKING

The picture shows ten bugs.

1. Circle the four bugs that are exactly alike.

A. B. C. D. E.
F. G. H. I. J.

2. Draw a bug that is the same as C.

Check students' drawings.

3. Draw a bug that is a little different than F.

4. Draw one bug that is just like one of the bugs above. Draw a bug that is a little different from any other bug. Challenge a classmate to find the bug that matches.

 Use with Grade 2, text pages 79–80.

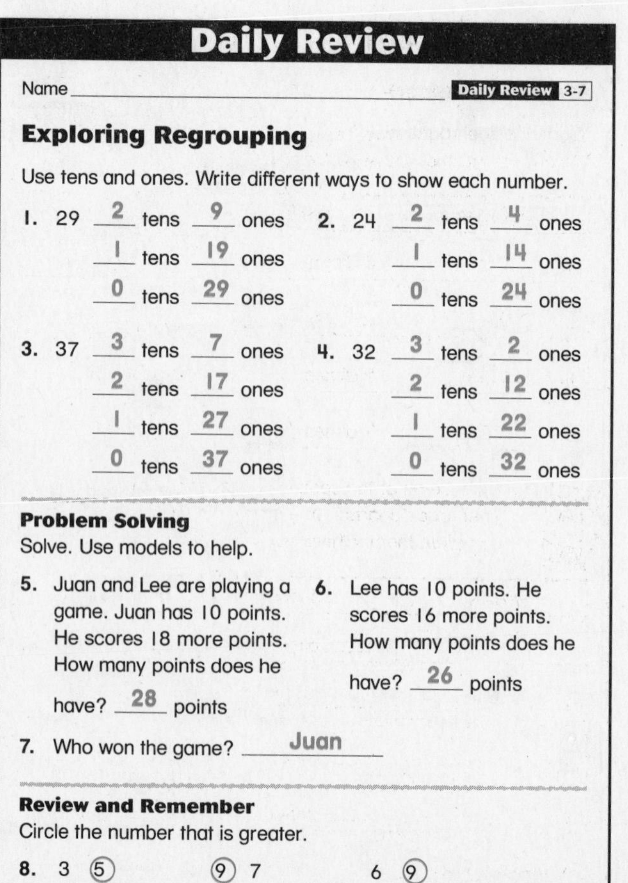

Daily Review

Name ____________________ Daily Review 3-7

Exploring Regrouping

Use tens and ones. Write different ways to show each number.

1. 29 — 2 tens 9 ones; 1 tens 19 ones; 0 tens 29 ones

2. 24 — 2 tens 4 ones; 1 tens 14 ones; 0 tens 24 ones

3. 37 — 3 tens 7 ones; 2 tens 17 ones; 1 tens 27 ones; 0 tens 37 ones

4. 32 — 3 tens 2 ones; 2 tens 12 ones; 1 tens 22 ones; 0 tens 32 ones

Problem Solving

Solve. Use models to help.

5. Juan and Lee are playing a game. Juan has 10 points. He scores 18 more points. How many points does he have? 28 points

6. Lee has 10 points. He scores 16 more points. How many points does he have? 26 points

7. Who won the game? Juan

Review and Remember

Circle the number that is greater.

8. 3 (5) (9) 7 6 (9)

Practice

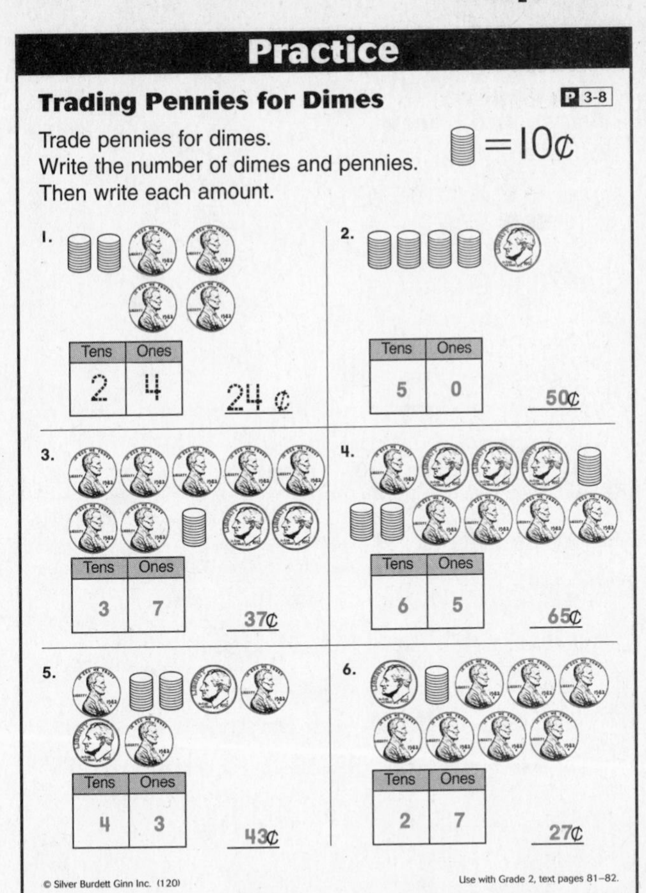

Trading Pennies for Dimes

P 3-8

Trade pennies for dimes.
Write the number of dimes and pennies.
Then write each amount.

(dime stack) = 10¢

1.

Tens	Ones
2	4

24 ¢

2.

Tens	Ones
5	0

50¢

3.

Tens	Ones
3	7

37¢

4.

Tens	Ones
6	5

65¢

5.

Tens	Ones
4	3

43¢

6.

Tens	Ones
2	7

27¢

Use with Grade 2, text pages 81–82.

Reteach

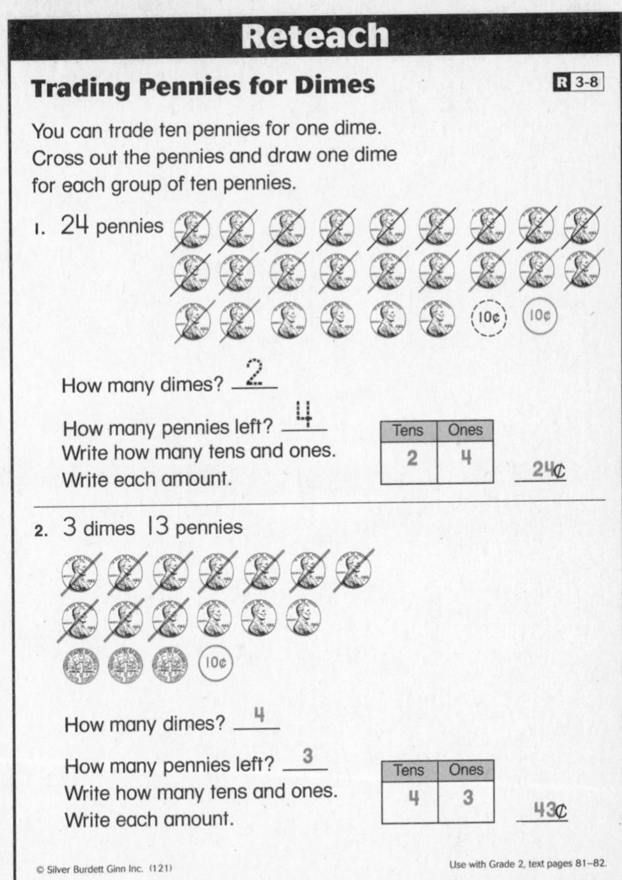

Trading Pennies for Dimes

R 3-8

You can trade ten pennies for one dime.
Cross out the pennies and draw one dime for each group of ten pennies.

1. 24 pennies

10¢ 10¢

How many dimes? 2

How many pennies left? 4

Write how many tens and ones.
Write each amount.

Tens	Ones
2	4

24¢

2. 3 dimes 13 pennies

10¢

How many dimes? 4

How many pennies left? 3

Write how many tens and ones.
Write each amount.

Tens	Ones
4	3

43¢

Use with Grade 2, text pages 81–82.

Extend

Making Change

E 3-8
REASONING

You can trade 10 pennies for 1 dime at the bank.
Fill in the chart that shows the trades.

	Pennies	Dimes	What's left?
1.	36¢	3 dimes	6 pennies
2.	45¢	4 dimes	5 pennies
3.	27¢	2 dimes	7 pennies
4.	41¢	4 dimes	1 penny

Fill in some of the spaces on this chart. Answers will vary.
Then trade charts with a classmate and complete them. Check each other's work.

	Pennies	Dimes	What's left?
5.	¢	____ dimes	____ pennies
6.	¢	____ dimes	____ pennies
7.	¢	____ dimes	____ pennies
8.	¢	____ dimes	____ pennies

Use with Grade 2, text pages 81–82.

Daily Review

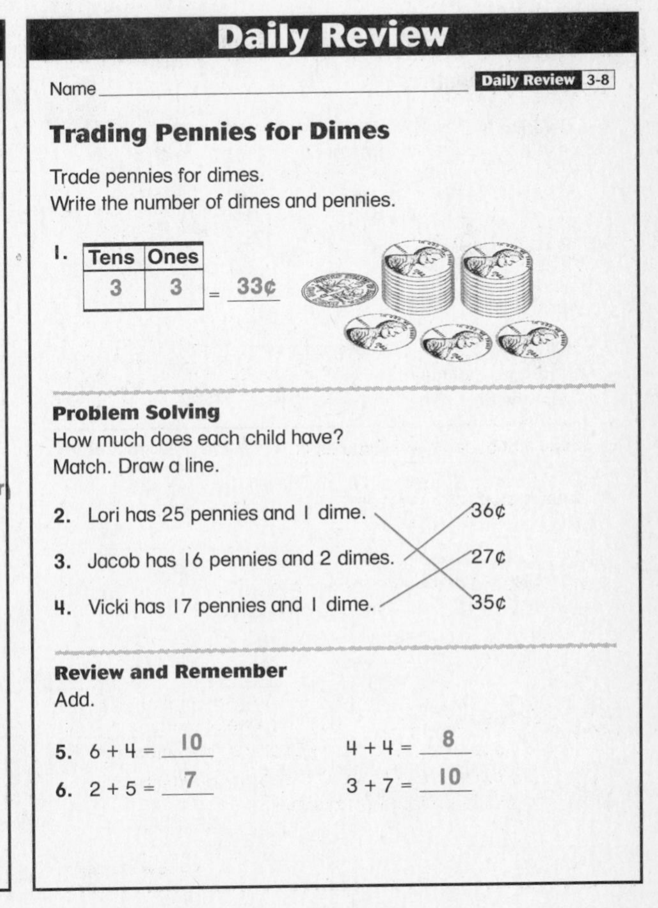

Name ____________________

Daily Review 3-8

Trading Pennies for Dimes

Trade pennies for dimes.
Write the number of dimes and pennies.

1.

Tens	Ones
3	3

= 33¢

Problem Solving

How much does each child have?
Match. Draw a line.

2. Lori has 25 pennies and 1 dime. — 35¢
3. Jacob has 16 pennies and 2 dimes. — 36¢
4. Vicki has 17 pennies and 1 dime. — 27¢

36¢ 27¢ 35¢

Review and Remember

Add.

5. $6 + 4 =$ 10 $\quad 4 + 4 =$ 8

6. $2 + 5 =$ 7 $\quad 3 + 7 =$ 10

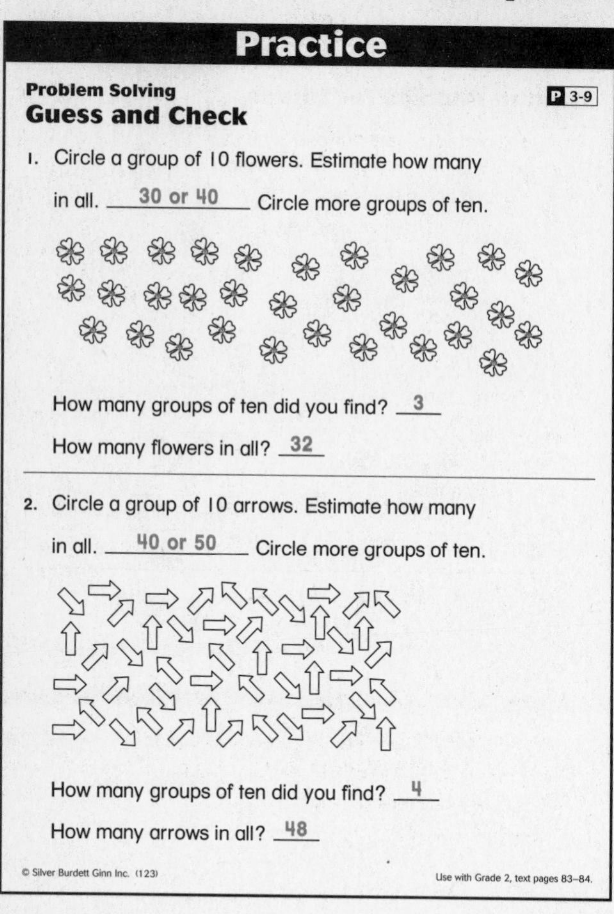

Practice

Problem Solving P 3-9

Guess and Check

1. Circle a group of 10 flowers. Estimate how many in all. 30 or 40 Circle more groups of ten.

How many groups of ten did you find? 3

How many flowers in all? 32

2. Circle a group of 10 arrows. Estimate how many in all. 40 or 50 Circle more groups of ten.

How many groups of ten did you find? 4

How many arrows in all? 48

 Use with Grade 2, text pages 83–84.

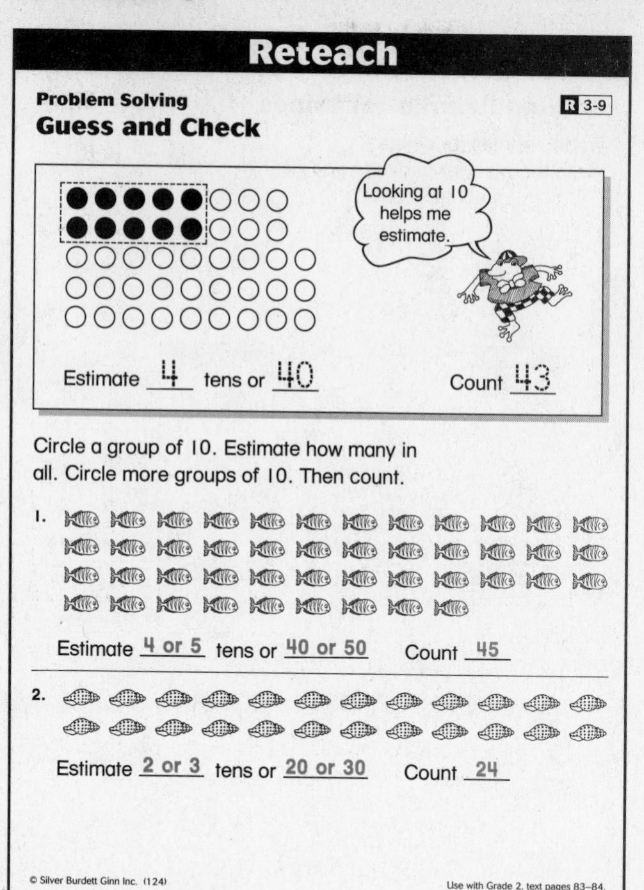

Reteach

Problem Solving R 3-9

Guess and Check

Estimate 4 tens or 40 Count 43

Circle a group of 10. Estimate how many in all. Circle more groups of 10. Then count.

1. Estimate 4 or 5 tens or 40 or 50 Count 45

2. Estimate 2 or 3 tens or 20 or 30 Count 24

 Use with Grade 2, text pages 83–84.

Extend

How Many Beans?

E 3-9 NUMBER SENSE

1. Count ten beans. Then estimate how many beans are in the picture. Record your estimate on the chart.

2. Estimate how many dark beans there are and record that number.
3. Count the dark beans and record the number.

	Total beans	Dark beans	Light beans
Your estimate	50, 60 or 70	20 or 30	30 or 40
Your count	61	23	38

4. Estimate how many light beans there are. Record your estimate. Then count and record.
5. Record how many beans in all.

How close was your estimate? ____________

Draw some dark beans and light beans in this space. Then ask a classmate to estimate how many.

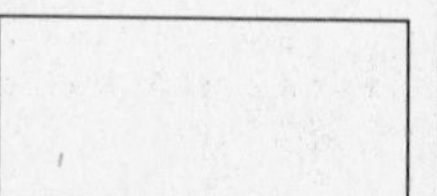

 Use with Grade 2, text pages 83–84.

Daily Review

Name ____________ Daily Review 3-9

Problem Solving

Guess and Check

Circle a group of 10. Estimate. Circle more groups of 10. Then count.

Children may circle different groups.

1. estimate 20 count 23
2. estimate 40 count 38
3. estimate 30 count 34
4. estimate 30 count 31

Review and Remember

Complete.

5. 4 tens 8 ones = 48
6. 2 tens 3 ones = 23
7. 1 ten 9 ones = 19
8. 5 tens 0 ones = 50

Practice

Number Patterns to 99

P 3-10

1. Write the missing numbers.
   Then color to find the hidden message.

0	1	2	3	4	5	6	7	8	9
10	11	12	13	14	15	16	17	18	19
20	21	22	23	24	25	26	27	28	29
30	31	32	33	34	35	36	37	38	39
40	41	42	43	44	45	46	47	48	49
50	51	52	53	54	55	56	57	58	59
60	61	62	63	64	65	66	67	68	69
70	71	72	73	74	75	76	77	78	79
80	81	82	83	84	85	86	87	88	89
90	91	92	93	94	95	96	97	98	99

2. Color all numbers that have 1 in the ones place.
3. Color all numbers that have 3 in the ones place.
4. Color all numbers that have 7 in the ones place.
5. Color all numbers that are more than 40 and less than 44.
6. Color all numbers that are more than 4 and less than 10.
7. Color all numbers that are more than 94 and less than 100.

 Use with Grade 2, text pages 85–86.

Reteach

Number Patterns to 99

R 3-10

1. Write the missing numbers.

0	1	2	3	4	5	6	7	8	9
10	11	12	13	14	15	16	17	18	19
20	21	22	23	24	25	26	27	28	29
30	31	32	33	34	35	36	37	38	39
40	41	42	43	44	45	46	47	48	49
50	51	52	53	54	55	56	57	58	59
60	61	62	63	64	65	66	67	68	69
70	71	72	73	74	75	76	77	78	79
80	81	82	83	84	85	86	87	88	89
90	91	92	93	94	95	96	97	98	99

2. __0__ is the number in the ones place in the numbers you filled in top to bottom.
3. You counted by __10__ to fill in the missing numbers from the top to the bottom.
4. __6__ is the number in the tens place in the numbers you filled in from left to right.
5. You counted by __1__ to fill in the missing numbers from left to right.

 Use with Grade 2, text pages 85–86.

Extend

What's Missing?

E 3-10 PATTERNS

Look for patterns in the chart.
Then complete the sentences.
Add numbers to the chart to help you.

The number 22 is under A and in row H.

	A ↓	B ↓	C ↓	D ↓	E ↓
F →	2	4	6	8	10
G →	12	14	16	18	20
H →	22	24	26	28	30
I →	32	34	36	38	40
J →	42	44	46	48	50
K →	52	54	56	58	60

1. Numbers under D start at 8 and skip count by __10__.
2. Numbers in row H start at 22 and skip count by __2__.
3. You will find 60 under letter __E__.
4. You will find 42 under letter __A__.
5. You will find 44 in row __J__.
6. You will find 52 in row __K__.
7. You will find 50 under letter __E__.
8. You will find 56 under letter __C__.

 Use with Grade 2, text pages 85–86.

Daily Review

Name ______________________

Daily Review 3-10

Number Patterns to 99

1. Write the missing numbers.
   Circle the numbers that have 6 in the ones place.

0	1	2	3	4	5	6	7	8	9
10	11	12	13	14	15	16	17	18	19
20	21	22	23	24	25	26	27	28	29
30	31	32	33	34	35	36	37	38	39
40	41	42	43	44	45	46	47	48	49
50	51	52	53	54	55	56	57	58	59
60	61	62	63	64	65	66	67	68	69
70	71	72	73	74	75	76	77	78	79
80	81	82	83	84	85	86	87	88	89
90	91	92	93	94	95	96	97	98	99

Problem Solving

2. Color all the numbers that have 4.
   What patterns do you see?

   Check students' work. Numbers that go across the page have 4 in the tens place. Numbers that go down the page have 4 in the ones place.

Review and Remember

Subtract.

3. 8 − 4 = __4__ 10 − 5 = __5__ 12 − 6 = __6__

Chapter 3 • Lesson 11

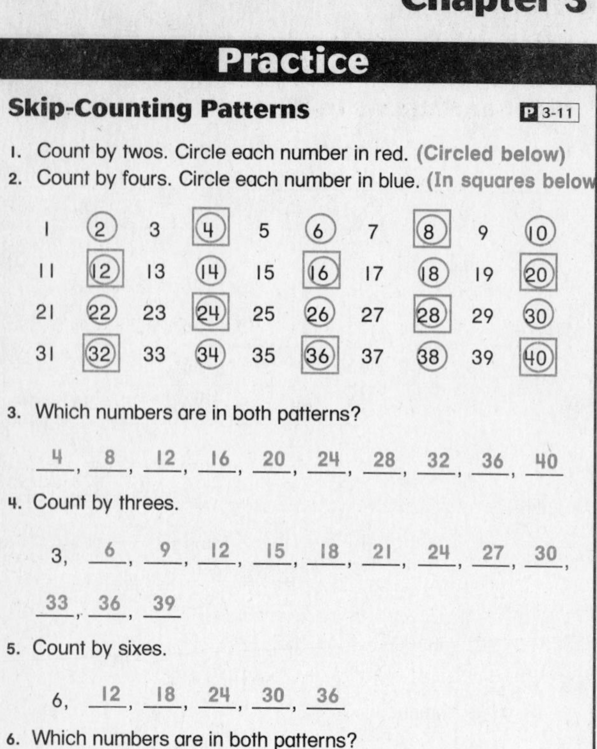

Practice

Skip-Counting Patterns

P 3-11

1. Count by twos. Circle each number in red. **(Circled below)**
2. Count by fours. Circle each number in blue. **(In squares below**

1	(2)	3	[(4)]	5	(6)	7	[(8)]	9	(10)
11	[12]	13	(14)	15	[(16)]	17	(18)	19	[(20)]
21	(22)	23	[(24)]	25	(26)	27	[(28)]	29	(30)
31	[(32)]	33	(34)	35	[(36)]	37	(38)	39	[(40)]

3. Which numbers are in both patterns?

4, 8, 12, 16, 20, 24, 28, 32, 36, 40

4. Count by threes.

3, 6, 9, 12, 15, 18, 21, 24, 27, 30, 33, 36, 39

5. Count by sixes.

6, 12, 18, 24, 30, 36

6. Which numbers are in both patterns?

6, 12, 18, 24, 30, 36

Use with Grade 2, text pages 87–88.

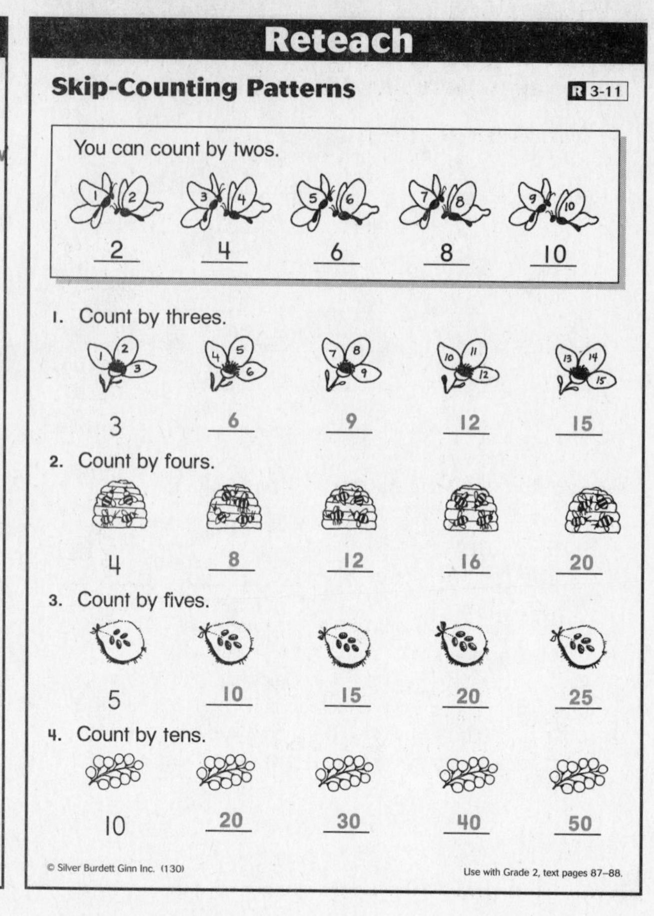

Reteach

Skip-Counting Patterns

R 3-11

You can count by twos.

2 4 6 8 10

1. Count by threes.

3 6 9 12 15

2. Count by fours.

4 8 12 16 20

3. Count by fives.

5 10 15 20 25

4. Count by tens.

10 20 30 40 50

Use with Grade 2, text pages 87–88.

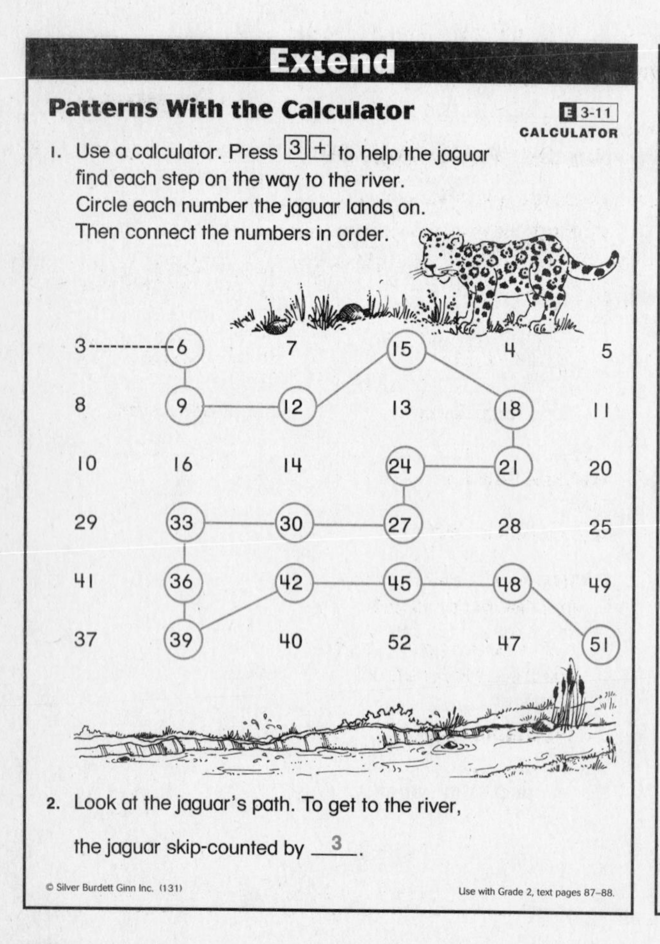

Extend

Patterns With the Calculator

E 3-11
CALCULATOR

1. Use a calculator. Press [3] [+] to help the jaguar find each step on the way to the river. Circle each number the jaguar lands on. Then connect the numbers in order.

3	(6)	7	(15)	4	5
8	(9)	(12)	13	(18)	11
10	16	14	(24)	(21)	20
29	(33)	(30)	(27)	28	25
41	(36)	(42)	(45)	(48)	49
37	(39)	40	52	47	(51)

2. Look at the jaguar's path. To get to the river, the jaguar skip-counted by 3.

Use with Grade 2, text pages 87–88.

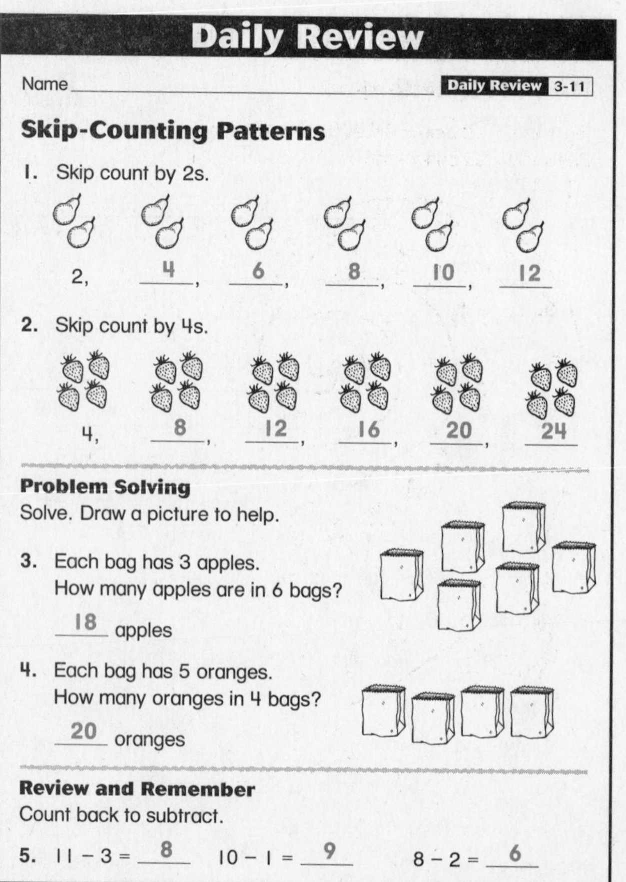

Daily Review

Name ______________________

Daily Review 3-11

Skip-Counting Patterns

1. Skip count by 2s.

2, 4, 6, 8, 10, 12

2. Skip count by 4s.

4, 8, 12, 16, 20, 24

Problem Solving

Solve. Draw a picture to help.

3. Each bag has 3 apples. How many apples are in 6 bags?

18 apples

4. Each bag has 5 oranges. How many oranges in 4 bags?

20 oranges

Review and Remember

Count back to subtract.

5. $11 - 3 =$ 8 $10 - 1 =$ 9 $8 - 2 =$ 6

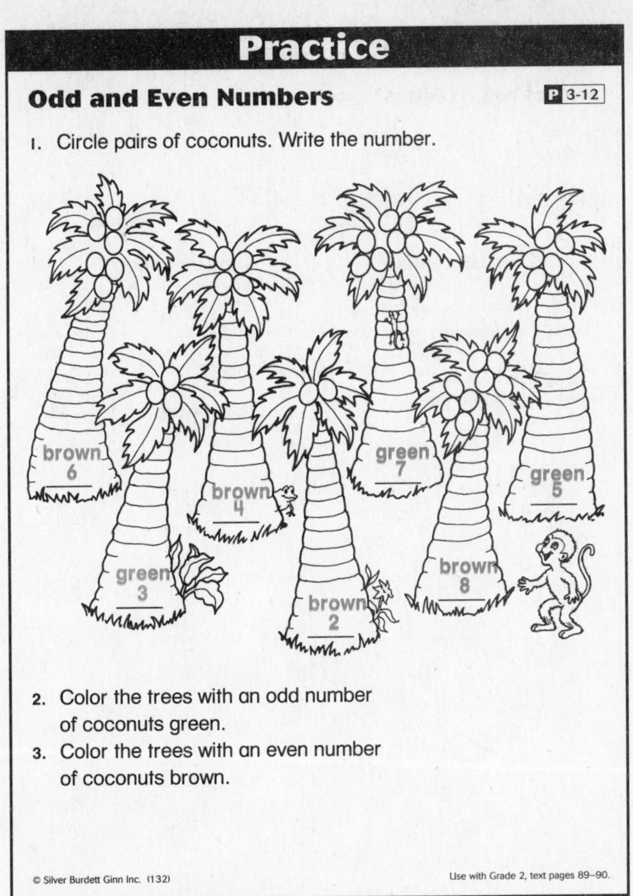

Practice

Odd and Even Numbers

P 3-12

1. Circle pairs of coconuts. Write the number.

2. Color the trees with an odd number of coconuts green.
3. Color the trees with an even number of coconuts brown.

Use with Grade 2, text pages 89–90.

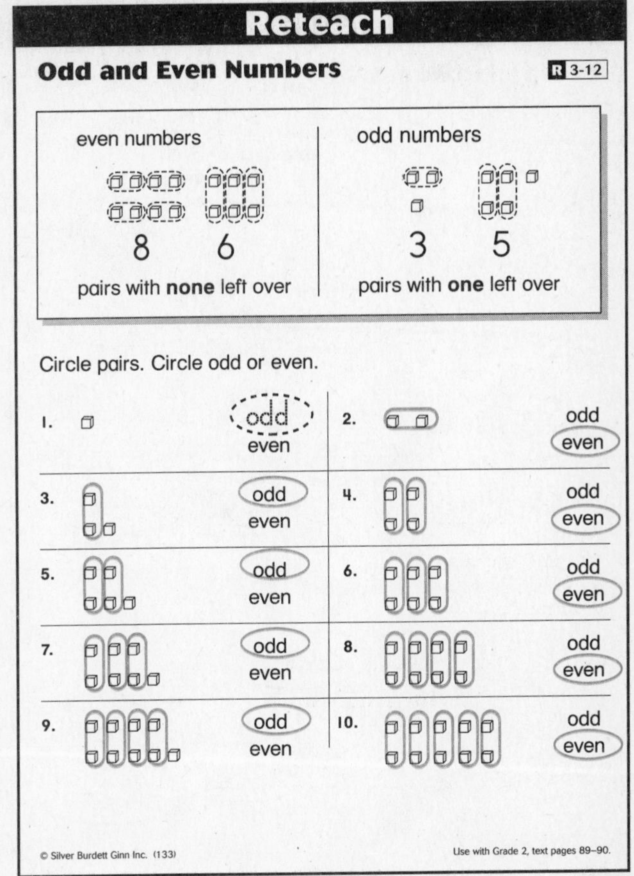

Reteach

Odd and Even Numbers

R 3-12

even numbers		odd numbers	
8	6	3	5
pairs with **none** left over		pairs with **one** left over	

Circle pairs. Circle odd or even.

1. odd / even
2. odd / even
3. odd / even
4. odd / even
5. odd / even
6. odd / even
7. odd / even
8. odd / even
9. odd / even
10. odd / even

Use with Grade 2, text pages 89–90.

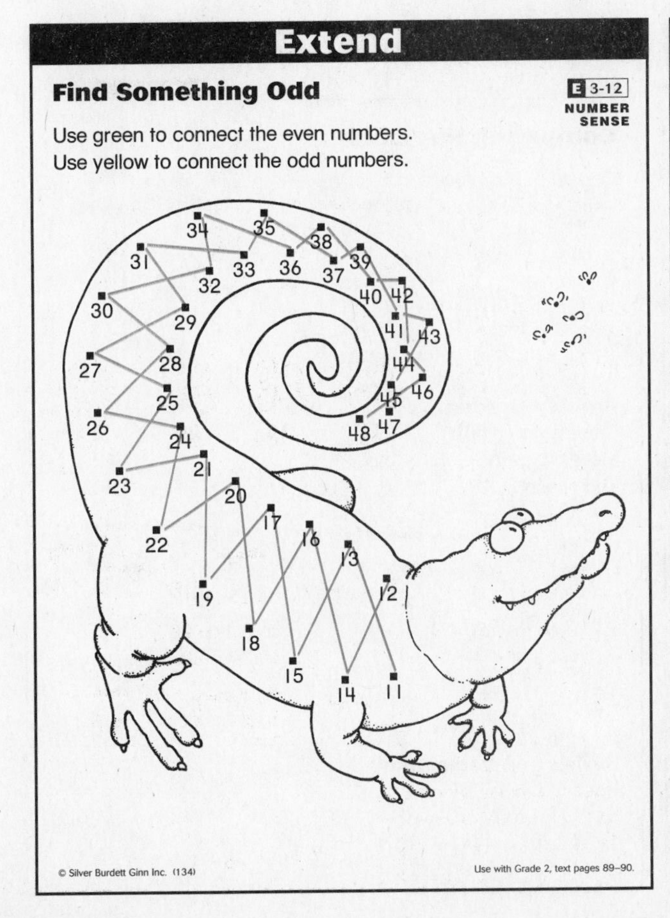

Extend

Find Something Odd

E 3-12
NUMBER SENSE

Use green to connect the even numbers.
Use yellow to connect the odd numbers.

Use with Grade 2, text pages 89–90.

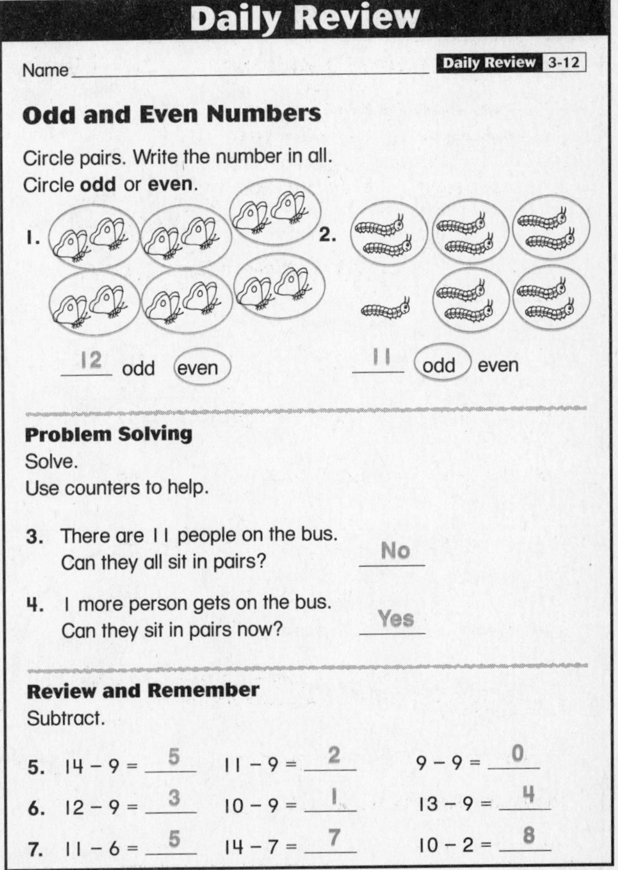

Daily Review

Name ____________________

Daily Review 3-12

Odd and Even Numbers

Circle pairs. Write the number in all.
Circle **odd** or **even**.

1. 12 odd even
2. 11 odd even

Problem Solving

Solve.
Use counters to help.

3. There are 11 people on the bus. Can they all sit in pairs? No
4. 1 more person gets on the bus. Can they sit in pairs now? Yes

Review and Remember

Subtract.

5. 14 − 9 = 5   11 − 9 = 2   9 − 9 = 0
6. 12 − 9 = 3   10 − 9 = 1   13 − 9 = 4
7. 11 − 6 = 5   14 − 7 = 7   10 − 2 = 8

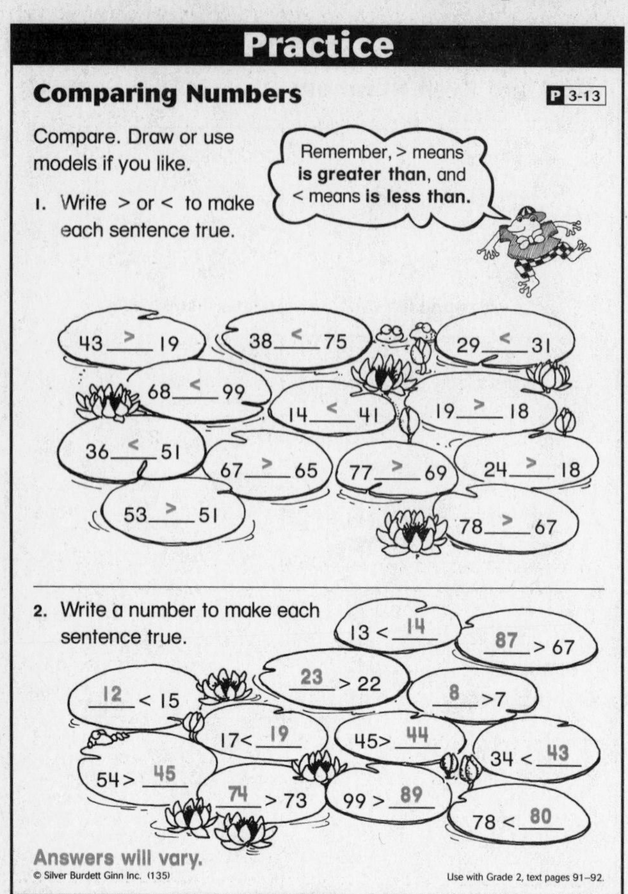

Practice

Comparing Numbers

P 3-13

Compare. Draw or use models if you like.

Remember, > means **is greater than**, and < means **is less than.**

1. Write > or < to make each sentence true.

43 > 19 | 38 < 75 | 29 < 31 | 68 < 99 | 14 < 41 | 19 > 18 | 36 < 51 | 67 > 65 | 77 > 69 | 24 > 18 | 53 > 51 | 78 > 67

2. Write a number to make each sentence true.

13 < 14 | 87 > 67 | 23 > 22 | 12 < 15 | 8 > 7 | 17 < 19 | 45 > 44 | 34 < 43 | 54 > 45 | 74 > 73 | 99 > 89 | 78 < 80

Answers will vary.

 Use with Grade 2, text pages 91–92.

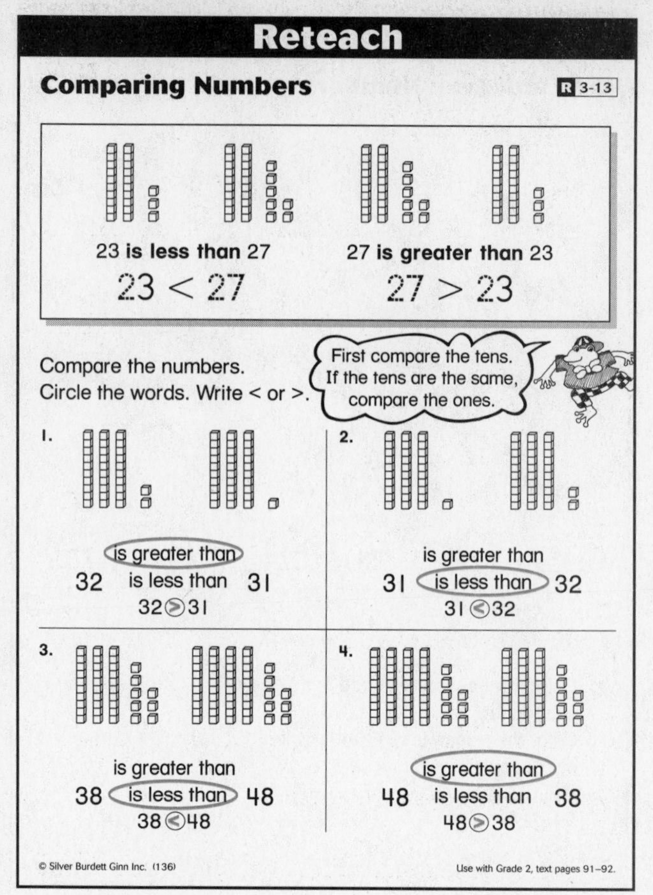

Reteach

Comparing Numbers

R 3-13

23 **is less than** 27

23 < 27

27 **is greater than** 23

27 > 23

Compare the numbers.
Circle the words. Write < or >.

First compare the tens. If the tens are the same, compare the ones.

1. 32 (is greater than) / is less than 31 — 32 > 31
2. 31 is greater than / (is less than) 32 — 31 < 32
3. 38 is greater than / (is less than) 48 — 38 < 48
4. 48 (is greater than) / is less than 38 — 48 > 38

 Use with Grade 2, text pages 91–92.

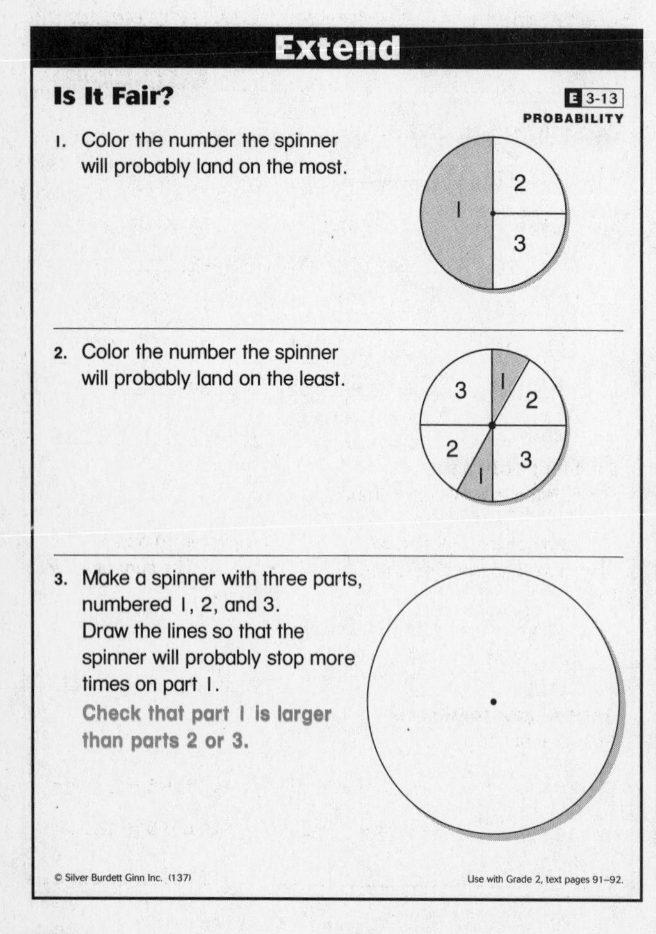

Extend

Is It Fair?

E 3-13
PROBABILITY

1. Color the number the spinner will probably land on the most.

2. Color the number the spinner will probably land on the least.

3. Make a spinner with three parts, numbered 1, 2, and 3. Draw the lines so that the spinner will probably stop more times on part 1.
Check that part 1 is larger than parts 2 or 3.

 Use with Grade 2, text pages 91–92.

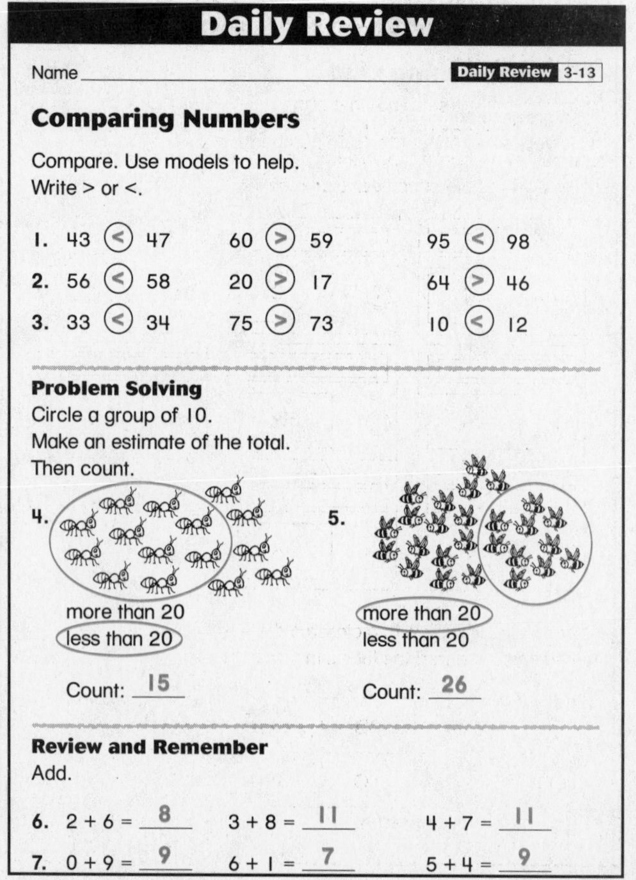

Daily Review

Name ____________________ Daily Review 3-13

Comparing Numbers

Compare. Use models to help.
Write > or <.

1.	43 < 47	60 > 59	95 < 98
2.	56 < 58	20 > 17	64 > 46
3.	33 < 34	75 > 73	10 < 12

Problem Solving

Circle a group of 10.
Make an estimate of the total.
Then count.

4. more than 20 / (less than 20) — Count: 15
5. (more than 20) / less than 20 — Count: 26

Review and Remember

Add.

6.	2 + 6 = 8	3 + 8 = 11	4 + 7 = 11
7.	0 + 9 = 9	6 + 1 = 7	5 + 4 = 9

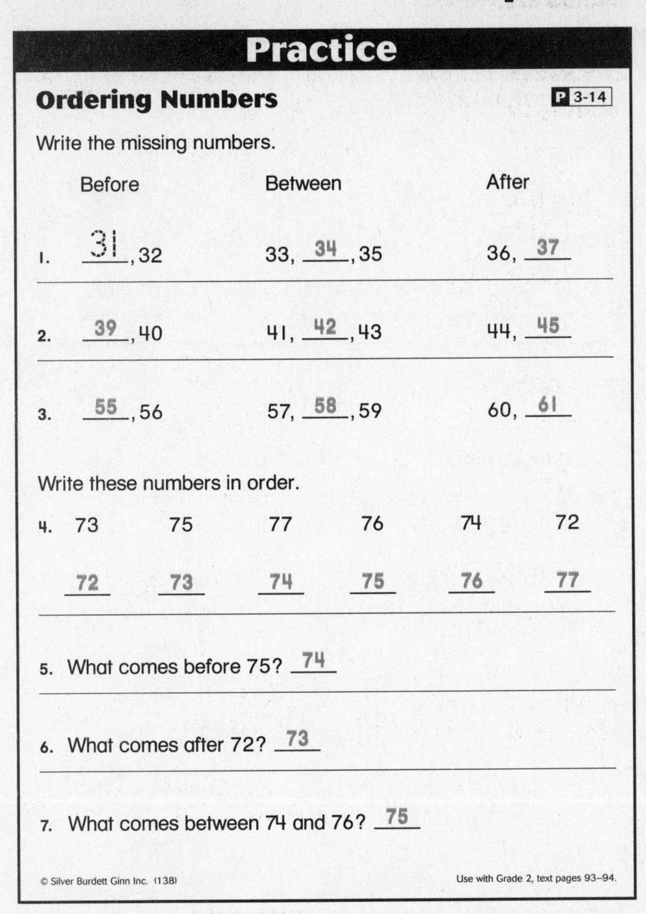

Practice

Ordering Numbers

P 3-14

Write the missing numbers.

	Before	Between	After
1.	31, 32	33, 34, 35	36, 37
2.	39, 40	41, 42, 43	44, 45
3.	55, 56	57, 58, 59	60, 61

Write these numbers in order.

4. 73 75 77 76 74 72

72 73 74 75 76 77

5. What comes before 75? 74

6. What comes after 72? 73

7. What comes between 74 and 76? 75

 Use with Grade 2, text pages 93–94.

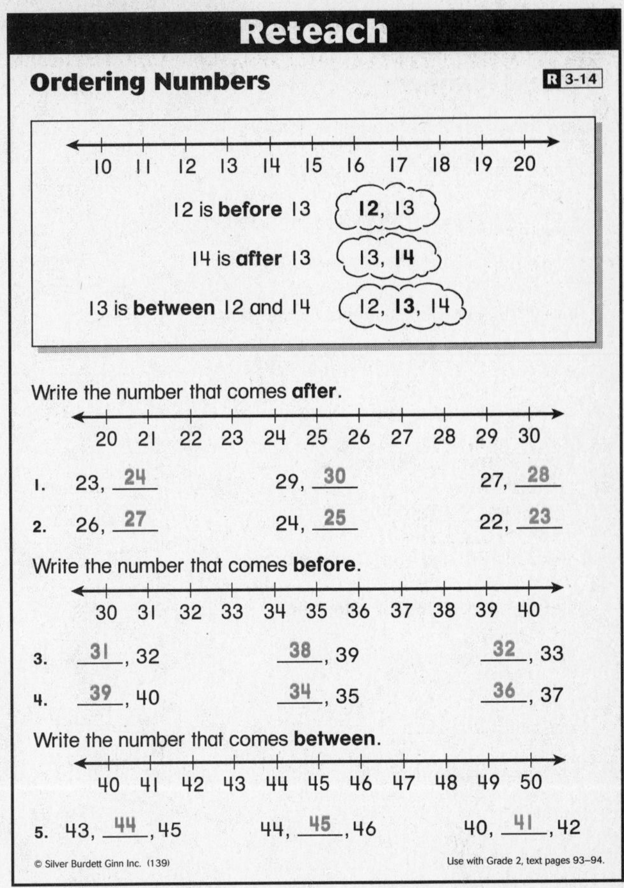

Reteach

Ordering Numbers

R 3-14

10 11 12 13 14 15 16 17 18 19 20

12 is **before** 13 (**12**, 13)

14 is **after** 13 (13, **14**)

13 is **between** 12 and 14 (12, **13**, 14)

Write the number that comes **after**.

20 21 22 23 24 25 26 27 28 29 30

1. 23, 24 29, 30 27, 28
2. 26, 27 24, 25 22, 23

Write the number that comes **before**.

30 31 32 33 34 35 36 37 38 39 40

3. 31, 32 38, 39 32, 33
4. 39, 40 34, 35 36, 37

Write the number that comes **between**.

40 41 42 43 44 45 46 47 48 49 50

5. 43, 44, 45 44, 45, 46 40, 41, 42

 Use with Grade 2, text pages 93–94.

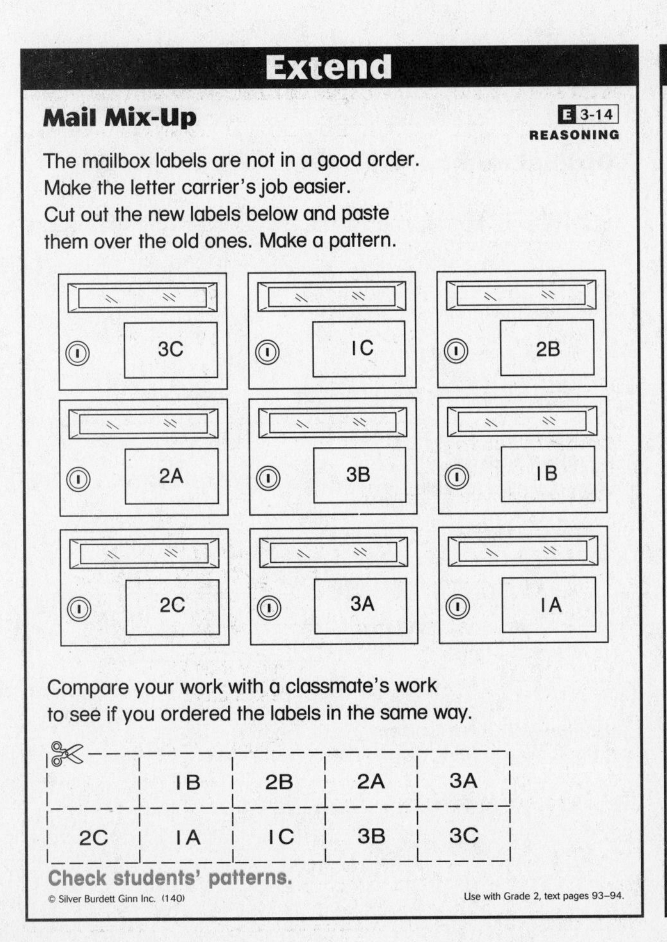

Extend

Mail Mix-Up

E 3-14 REASONING

The mailbox labels are not in a good order. Make the letter carrier's job easier. Cut out the new labels below and paste them over the old ones. Make a pattern.

3C	1C	2B
2A	3B	1B
2C	3A	1A

Compare your work with a classmate's work to see if you ordered the labels in the same way.

	1B	2B	2A	3A
2C	1A	1C	3B	3C

Check students' patterns.

 Use with Grade 2, text pages 93–94.

Daily Review

Name __________ Daily Review 3-14

Ordering Numbers

Write the numbers.

	Before	Between	After
1.	27, 28	35, 36, 37	48, 49
2.	55, 56	69, 70, 71	11, 12
3.	91, 92	85, 86, 87	77, 78
4.	8, 9	50, 51, 52	39, 40

Problem Solving

Solve. Write the mystery number.

5. I am between 64 and 67. I have 5 in the ones place. 65

6. I come after 40 and before 46. The sum of my digits is 9. 45

Review and Remember

Add. Use doubles.

7. $4 + 4 = 8$; $4 + 5 = 9$
8. $3 + 3 = 6$; $3 + 4 = 7$
9. $5 + 5 = 10$; $5 + 6 = 11$

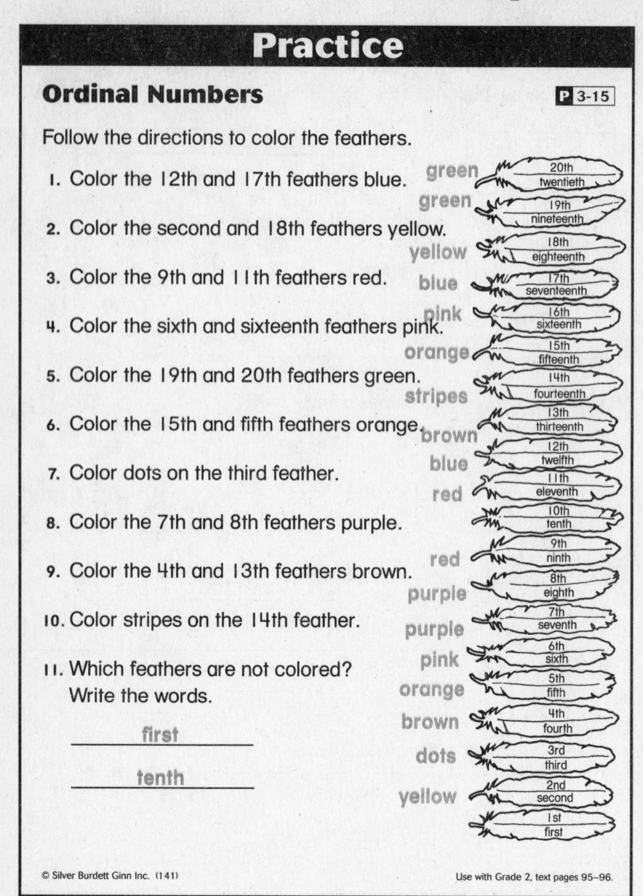

Practice

Ordinal Numbers

P 3-15

Follow the directions to color the feathers.

1. Color the 12th and 17th feathers blue.
2. Color the second and 18th feathers yellow.
3. Color the 9th and 11th feathers red.
4. Color the sixth and sixteenth feathers pink.
5. Color the 19th and 20th feathers green.
6. Color the 15th and fifth feathers orange.
7. Color dots on the third feather.
8. Color the 7th and 8th feathers purple.
9. Color the 4th and 13th feathers brown.
10. Color stripes on the 14th feather.
11. Which feathers are not colored? Write the words.

first

tenth

 Use with Grade 2, text pages 95–96.

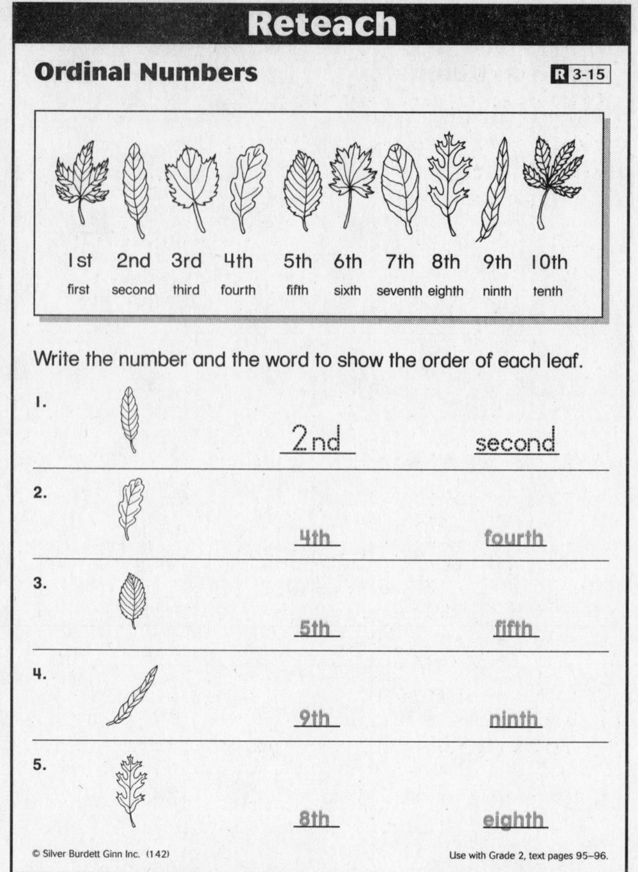

Reteach

Ordinal Numbers

R 3-15

1st	2nd	3rd	4th	5th	6th	7th	8th	9th	10th
first	second	third	fourth	fifth	sixth	seventh	eighth	ninth	tenth

Write the number and the word to show the order of each leaf.

1. 2nd second
2. 4th fourth
3. 5th fifth
4. 9th ninth
5. 8th eighth

 Use with Grade 2, text pages 95–96.

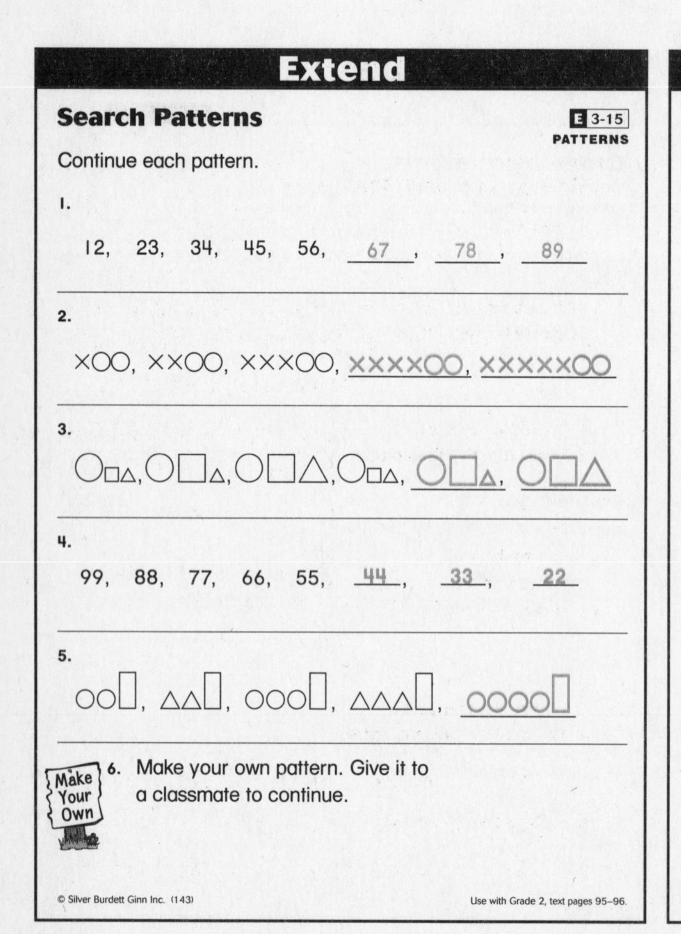

Extend

Search Patterns

E 3-15 PATTERNS

Continue each pattern.

1. 12, 23, 34, 45, 56, 67, 78, 89
2. ×OO, ××OO, ×××OO, ××××OO, ×××××OO
3. O□△, O□△, O□△, O□△, O□△, O□△
4. 99, 88, 77, 66, 55, 44, 33, 22
5. oo▯, △△▯, ooo▯, △△△▯, oooo▯
6. Make your own pattern. Give it to a classmate to continue.

 Use with Grade 2, text pages 95–96.

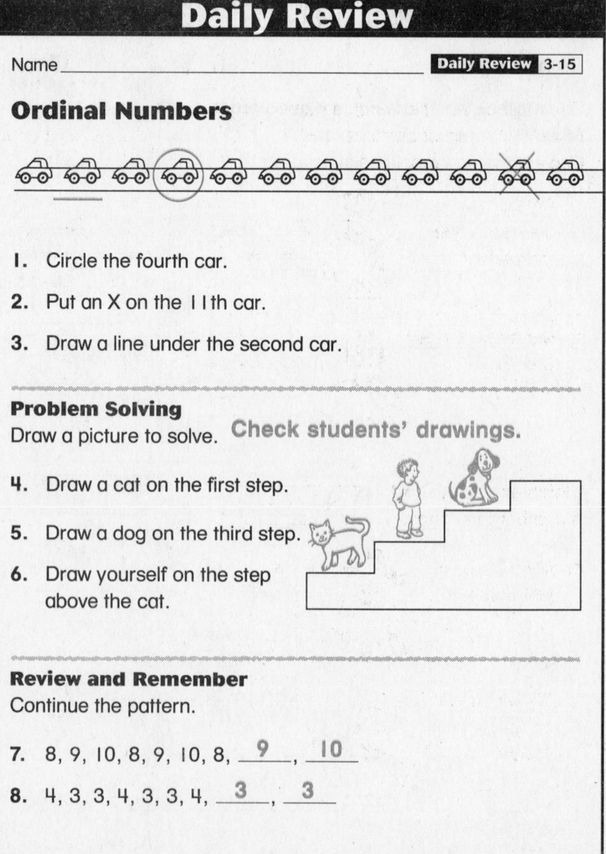

Daily Review

Name ____________

Daily Review 3-15

Ordinal Numbers

1. Circle the fourth car.
2. Put an X on the 11th car.
3. Draw a line under the second car.

Problem Solving

Draw a picture to solve. Check students' drawings.

4. Draw a cat on the first step.
5. Draw a dog on the third step.
6. Draw yourself on the step above the cat.

Review and Remember

Continue the pattern.

7. 8, 9, 10, 8, 9, 10, 8, 9, 10
8. 4, 3, 3, 4, 3, 3, 4, 3, 3

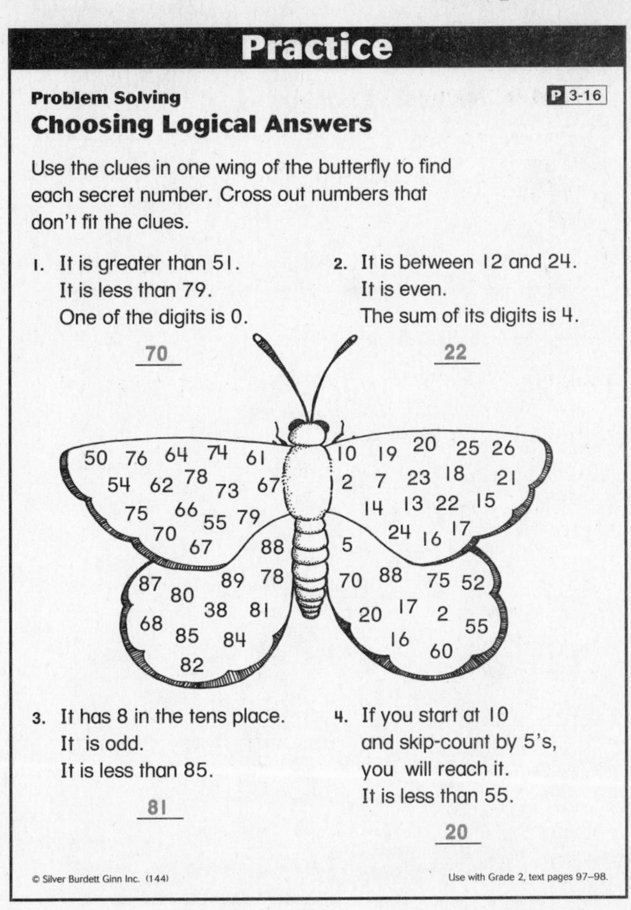

Practice

Problem Solving P 3-16

Choosing Logical Answers

Use the clues in one wing of the butterfly to find each secret number. Cross out numbers that don't fit the clues.

1. It is greater than 51.
   It is less than 79.
   One of the digits is 0.
   70

2. It is between 12 and 24.
   It is even.
   The sum of its digits is 4.
   22

3. It has 8 in the tens place.
   It is odd.
   It is less than 85.
   81

4. If you start at 10 and skip-count by 5's, you will reach it.
   It is less than 55.
   20

 Use with Grade 2, text pages 97–98.

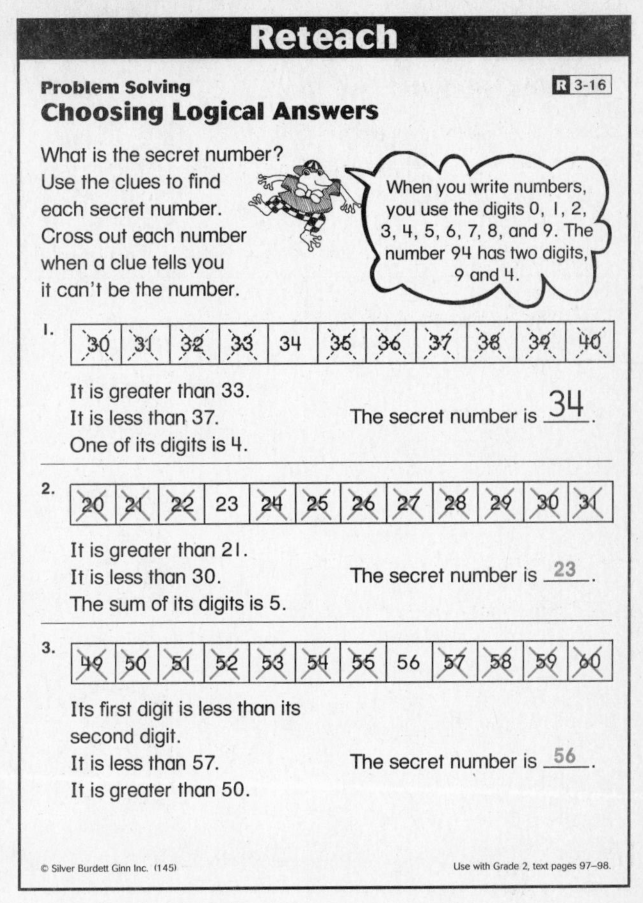

Reteach

Problem Solving R 3-16

Choosing Logical Answers

What is the secret number?
Use the clues to find each secret number.
Cross out each number when a clue tells you it can't be the number.

When you write numbers, you use the digits 0, 1, 2, 3, 4, 5, 6, 7, 8, and 9. The number 94 has two digits, 9 and 4.

1.

30	31	32	33	34	35	36	37	38	39	40

It is greater than 33.
It is less than 37.
One of its digits is 4.
The secret number is 34.

2.

20	21	22	23	24	25	26	27	28	29	30	31

It is greater than 21.
It is less than 30.
The sum of its digits is 5.
The secret number is 23.

3.

49	50	51	52	53	54	55	56	57	58	59	60

Its first digit is less than its second digit.
It is less than 57.
It is greater than 50.
The secret number is 56.

 Use with Grade 2, text pages 97–98.

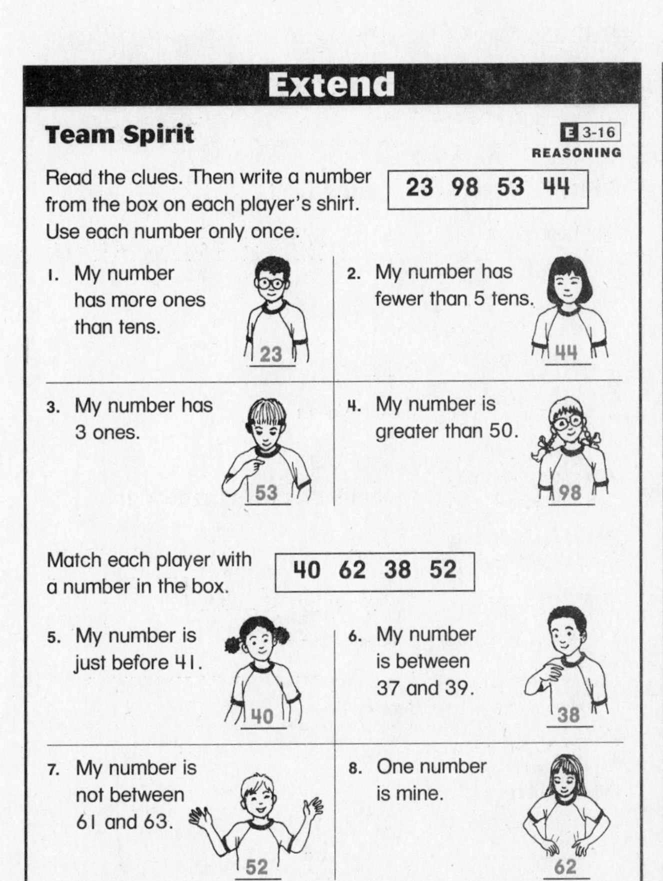

Extend

Team Spirit

E 3-16 REASONING

Read the clues. Then write a number from the box on each player's shirt. Use each number only once.

23 98 53 44

1. My number has more ones than tens. 23
2. My number has fewer than 5 tens. 44
3. My number has 3 ones. 53
4. My number is greater than 50. 98

Match each player with a number in the box.

40 62 38 52

5. My number is just before 41. 40
6. My number is between 37 and 39. 38
7. My number is not between 61 and 63. 52
8. One number is mine. 62

 Use with Grade 2, text pages 97–98.

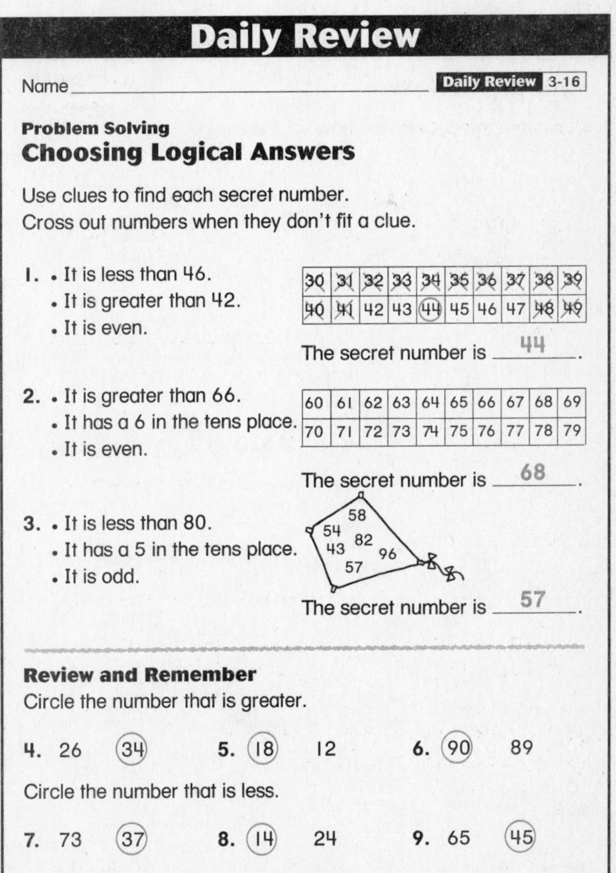

Daily Review

Name__________ Daily Review 3-16

Problem Solving

Choosing Logical Answers

Use clues to find each secret number.
Cross out numbers when they don't fit a clue.

1. • It is less than 46.
   • It is greater than 42.
   • It is even.

30	31	32	33	34	35	36	37	38	39
40	41	42	43	44	45	46	47	48	49

The secret number is 44.

2. • It is greater than 66.
   • It has a 6 in the tens place.
   • It is even.

60	61	62	63	64	65	66	67	68	69
70	71	72	73	74	75	76	77	78	79

The secret number is 68.

3. • It is less than 80.
   • It has a 5 in the tens place.
   • It is odd.

The secret number is 57.

Review and Remember

Circle the number that is greater.

4. 26 (34) 5. (18) 12 6. (90) 89

Circle the number that is less.

7. 73 (37) 8. (14) 24 9. 65 (45)

Practice

Pennies, Nickels, and Dimes

P 4-1

Count on to find the total amount.

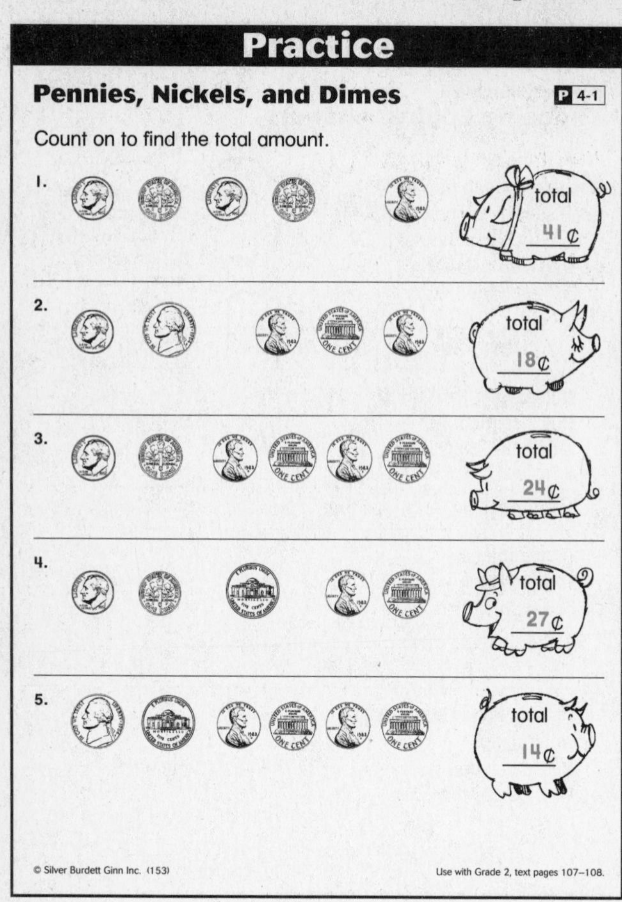

Use with Grade 2, text pages 107–108.

Reteach

Pennies, Nickels, and Dimes

R 4-1

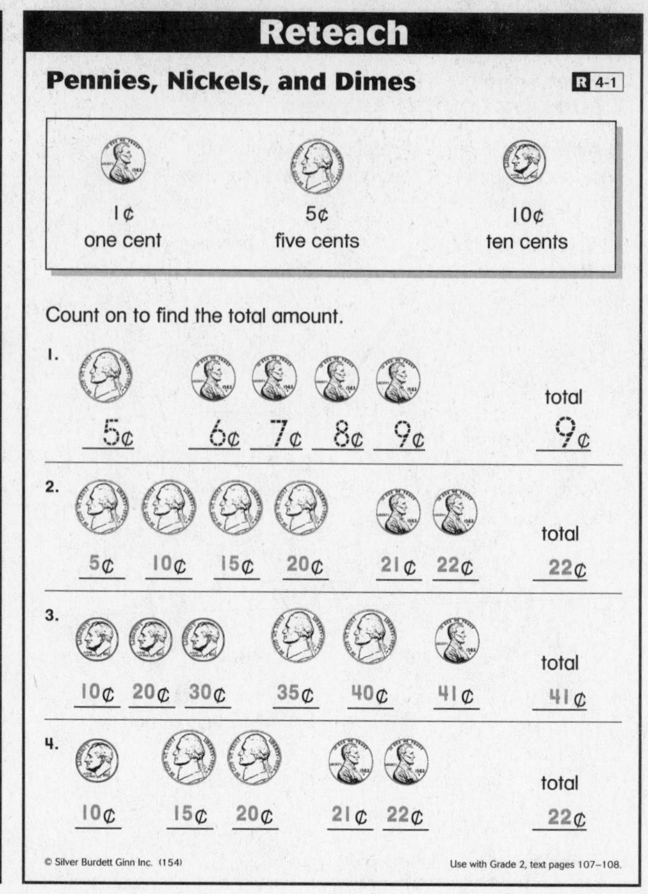

1¢ one cent
5¢ five cents
10¢ ten cents
Count on to find the total amount.
1. 5¢ 6¢ 7¢ 8¢ 9¢ total 9¢
2. 5¢ 10¢ 15¢ 20¢ 21¢ 22¢ total 22¢
3. 10¢ 20¢ 30¢ 35¢ 40¢ 41¢ total 41¢
4. 10¢ 15¢ 20¢ 21¢ 22¢ total 22¢

Use with Grade 2, text pages 107–108.

Extend

Find the Fewest

E 4-1 NUMBER SENSE

Circle the fewest coins to show each amount.
Combinations of coins may vary.

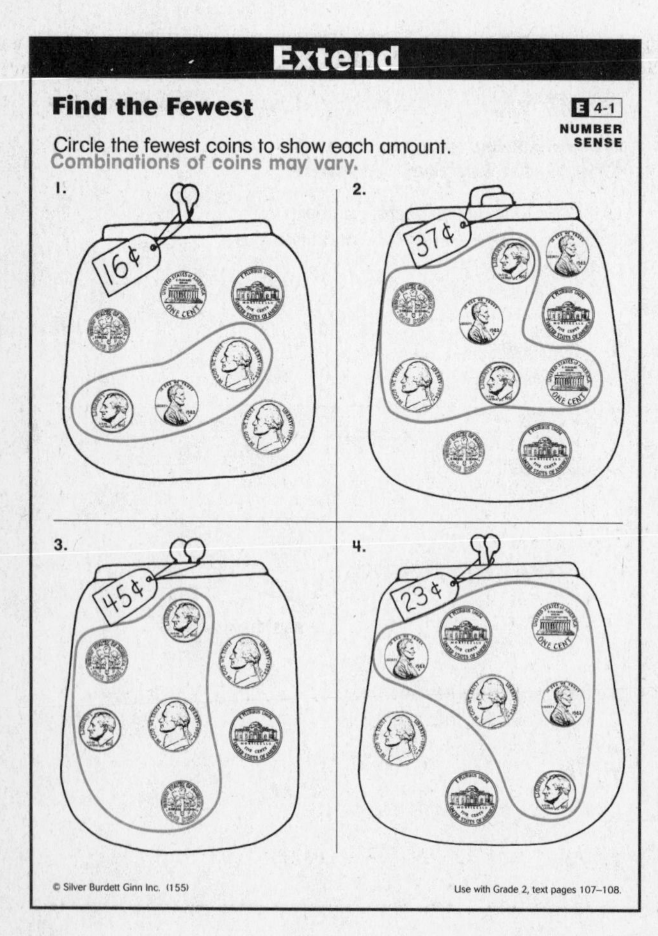

Use with Grade 2, text pages 107–108.

Daily Review

Name ______________________ Daily Review 4-1

Pennies, Nickels, and Dimes

Write each amount.

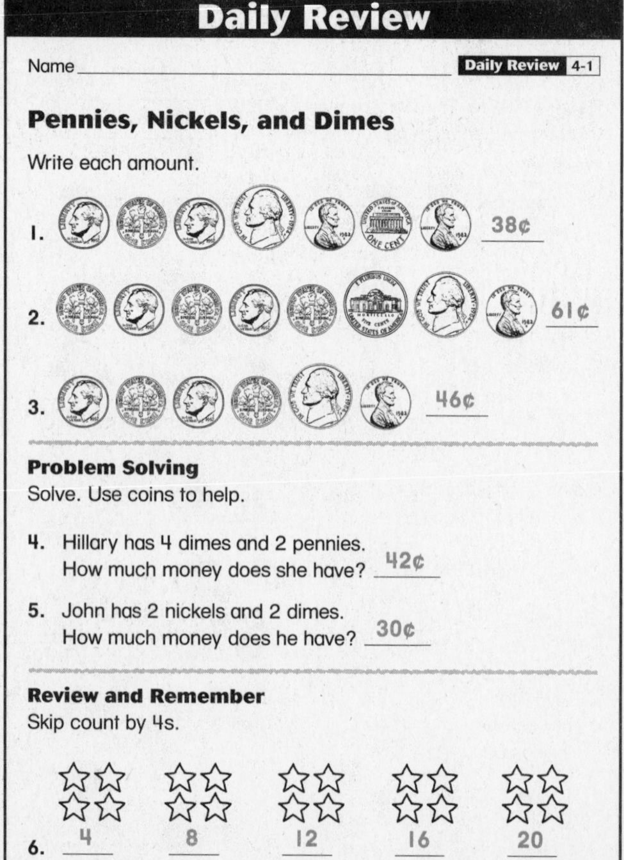

Problem Solving
Solve. Use coins to help.

4. Hillary has 4 dimes and 2 pennies. How much money does she have? 42¢
5. John has 2 nickels and 2 dimes. How much money does he have? 30¢

Review and Remember
Skip count by 4s.

6. 4 8 12 16 20

Practice

Problem Solving P 4-2

Make a List

You have 5 coins. No coin is less than 5¢.
No coin is greater than 10¢.

1. Make a list to show the different possible combinations.

Dimes	Nickels	Amount
5	0	50¢
4	1	45¢
3	2	40¢
2	3	35¢
1	4	30¢
0	5	25¢

2. What is the greatest amount you could have? 50¢
3. What is the least amount you could have? 25¢

 Use with Grade 2, text pages 109–110.

Reteach

Problem Solving R 4-2

Make a List

Look at each amount. Draw it as many ways as you can using nickels and pennies.

Amount	Nickels	Pennies
5¢	5¢	
		1¢ 1¢ 1¢ 1¢ 1¢
6¢	5¢	1¢
		1¢ 1¢ 1¢ 1¢ 1¢ 1¢
11¢	5¢ 5¢	1¢
		1¢ 1¢ 1¢ 1¢ 1¢ 1¢ 1¢ 1¢ 1¢ 1¢ 1¢
	5¢	1¢ 1¢ 1¢ 1¢ 1¢ 1¢

 Use with Grade 2, text pages 109–110.

Extend

Shopping Trip

E 4-2 NUMBER SENSE

Decide if there is enough money to buy both toys.
Then circle yes or no.

1. 

yes
(no)

2.     
yes
(no)

3. 

(yes)
no

4. 

yes
(no)

 Use with Grade 2, text pages 109–110.

Daily Review

Name ______________________ Daily Review 4-2

Problem Solving

Make a List

You have 3 coins for each amount.
No coin is greater than 10¢.
At least one of the coins is a dime.
Complete the chart to show what the coins could be.
Order of answers may vary.

Dimes	Nickels	Pennies	Amount
3	0	0	30¢
2	1	0	25¢
2	0	1	21¢
1	2	0	20¢
1	1	1	16¢
1	0	2	12¢

1. What is the greatest amount you could have? 30¢
2. What is the least amount you could have? 12¢

Review and Remember

3. Circle the second star.
4. Write an X on the fifth star.
5. Circle the seventh star.
6. Write an X on the tenth star.

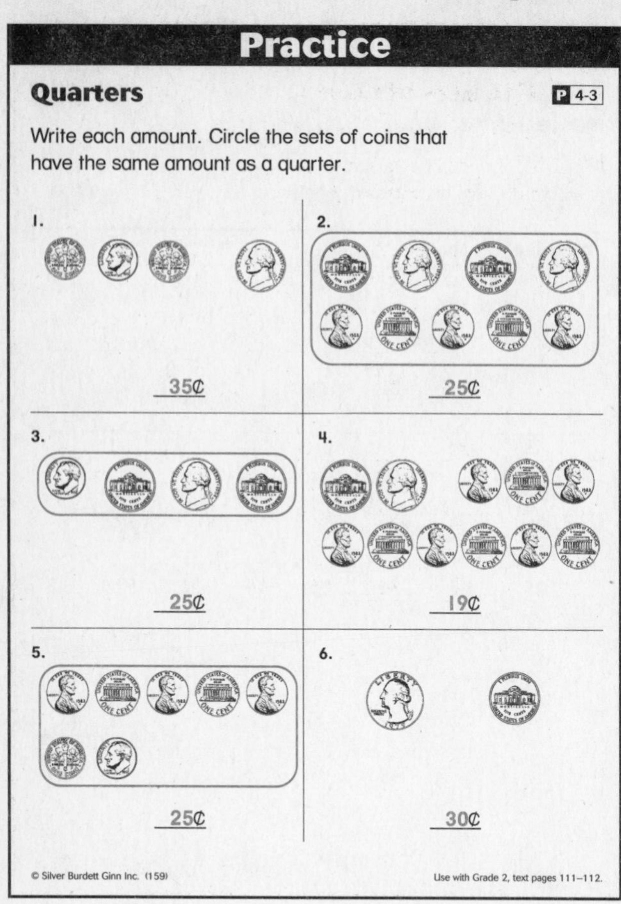

Practice

Quarters

P 4-3

Write each amount. Circle the sets of coins that have the same amount as a quarter.

1. 35¢
2. 25¢
3. 25¢
4. 19¢
5. 25¢
6. 30¢

Use with Grade 2, text pages 111–112.

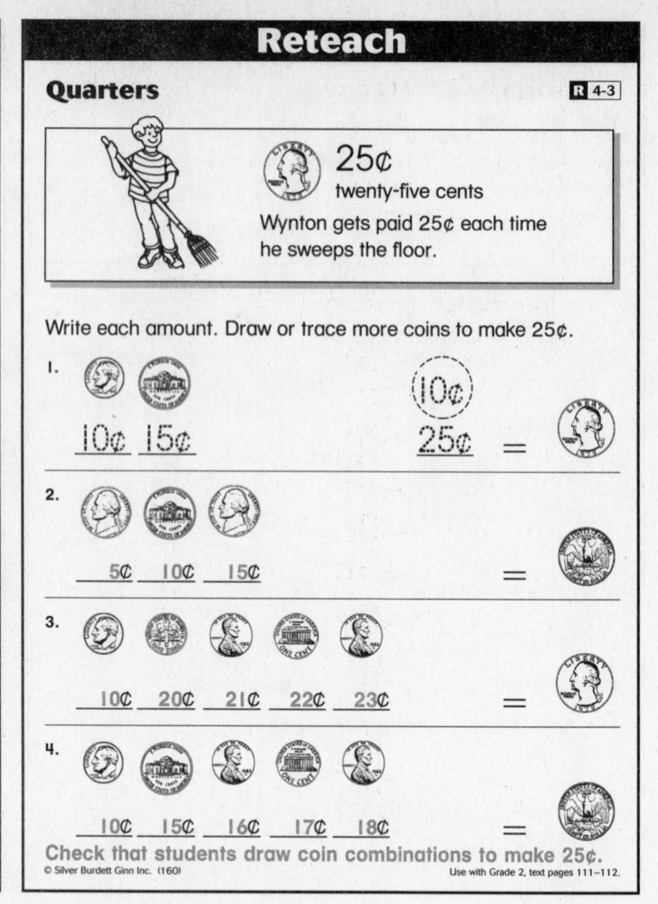

Reteach

Quarters

R 4-3

25¢
twenty-five cents
Wynton gets paid 25¢ each time he sweeps the floor.

Write each amount. Draw or trace more coins to make 25¢.

1. 10¢ 15¢ (10¢) 25¢ =
2. 5¢ 10¢ 15¢ =
3. 10¢ 20¢ 21¢ 22¢ 23¢ =
4. 10¢ 15¢ 16¢ 17¢ 18¢ =

Check that students draw coin combinations to make 25¢.

Use with Grade 2, text pages 111–112.

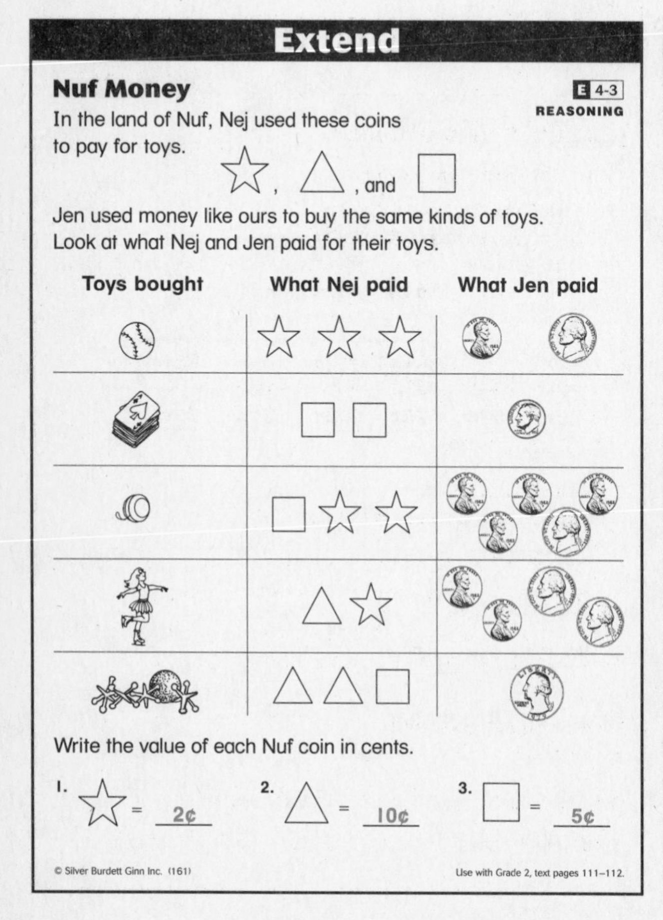

Extend

Nuf Money

E 4-3
REASONING

In the land of Nuf, Nej used these coins to pay for toys. ☆, △, and □

Jen used money like ours to buy the same kinds of toys. Look at what Nej and Jen paid for their toys.

Toys bought	What Nej paid	What Jen paid
	☆ ☆ ☆	
	□ □	
	□ ☆ ☆	
	△ ☆	
	△ △ □	

Write the value of each Nuf coin in cents.

1. ☆ = 2¢
2. △ = 10¢
3. □ = 5¢

Use with Grade 2, text pages 111–112.

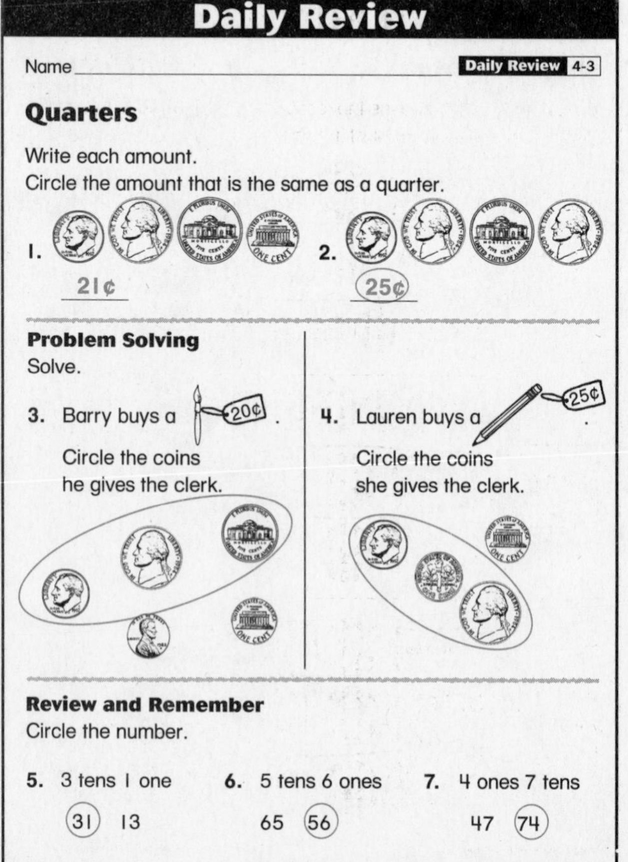

Daily Review

Name ____________

Daily Review 4-3

Quarters

Write each amount.
Circle the amount that is the same as a quarter.

1. 21¢
2. (25¢)

Problem Solving
Solve.

3. Barry buys a [20¢]. Circle the coins he gives the clerk.
4. Lauren buys a [25¢]. Circle the coins she gives the clerk.

Review and Remember
Circle the number.

5. 3 tens 1 one — (31) 13
6. 5 tens 6 ones — 65 (56)
7. 4 ones 7 tens — 47 (74)

Chapter 4 • Lesson 4

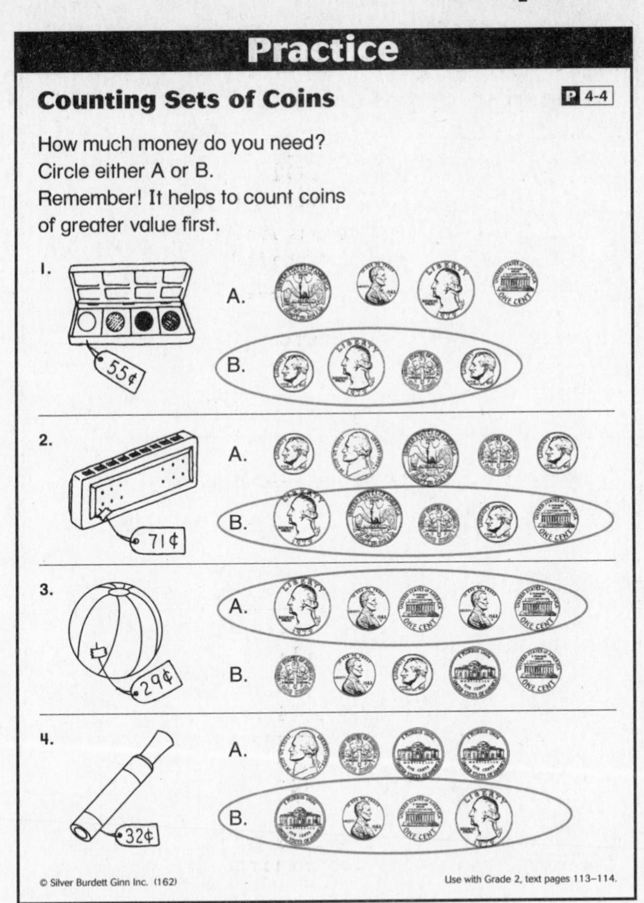

Practice

Counting Sets of Coins

P 4-4

How much money do you need?
Circle either A or B.
Remember! It helps to count coins of greater value first.

1. 55¢ A. B.
2. 71¢ A. B.
3. 29¢ A. B.
4. 32¢ A. B.

© Silver Burdett Ginn Inc. (162) Use with Grade 2, text pages 113–114.

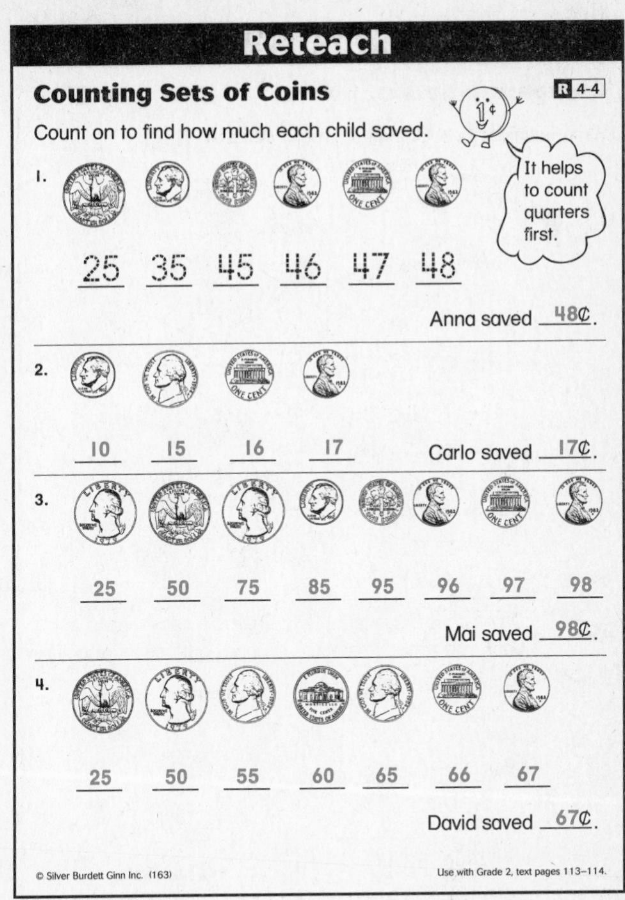

Reteach

Counting Sets of Coins

R 4-4

Count on to find how much each child saved.

1¢
It helps to count quarters first.

1. 25 35 45 46 47 48

Anna saved 48¢.

2. 10 15 16 17

Carlo saved 17¢.

3. 25 50 75 85 95 96 97 98

Mai saved 98¢.

4. 25 50 55 60 65 66 67

David saved 67¢.

© Silver Burdett Ginn Inc. (163) Use with Grade 2, text pages 113–114.

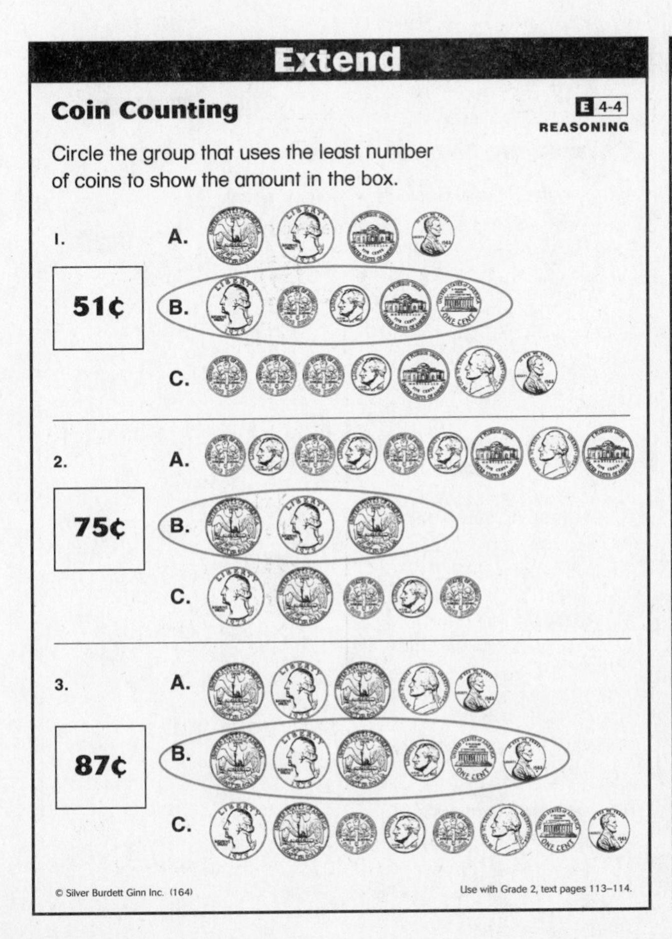

Extend

Coin Counting

E 4-4
REASONING

Circle the group that uses the least number of coins to show the amount in the box.

1. 51¢ A. B. C.
2. 75¢ A. B. C.
3. 87¢ A. B. C.

© Silver Burdett Ginn Inc. (164) Use with Grade 2, text pages 113–114.

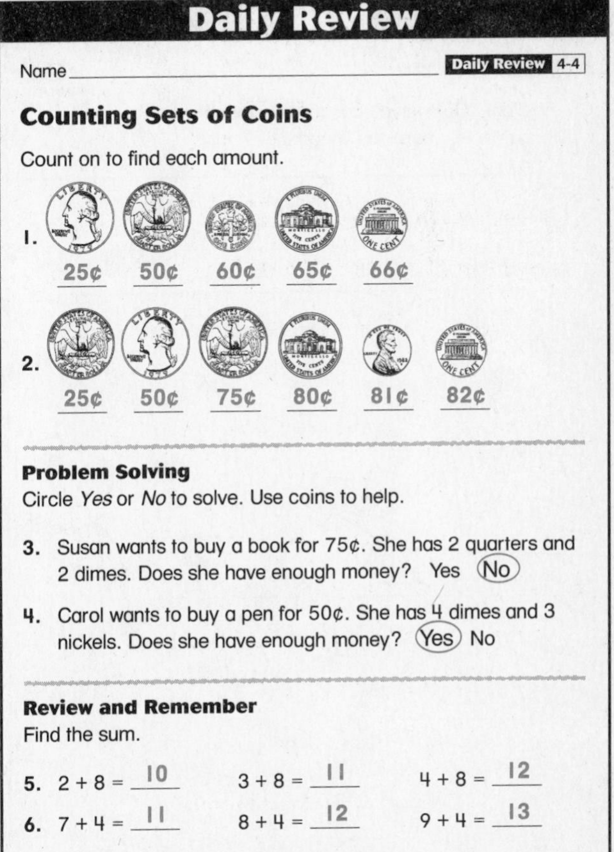

Daily Review

Name ______________________ Daily Review 4-4

Counting Sets of Coins

Count on to find each amount.

1. 25¢ 50¢ 60¢ 65¢ 66¢
2. 25¢ 50¢ 75¢ 80¢ 81¢ 82¢

Problem Solving

Circle *Yes* or *No* to solve. Use coins to help.

3. Susan wants to buy a book for 75¢. She has 2 quarters and 2 dimes. Does she have enough money? Yes No
4. Carol wants to buy a pen for 50¢. She has 4 dimes and 3 nickels. Does she have enough money? Yes No

Review and Remember

Find the sum.

5. 2 + 8 = 10 3 + 8 = 11 4 + 8 = 12
6. 7 + 4 = 11 8 + 4 = 12 9 + 4 = 13

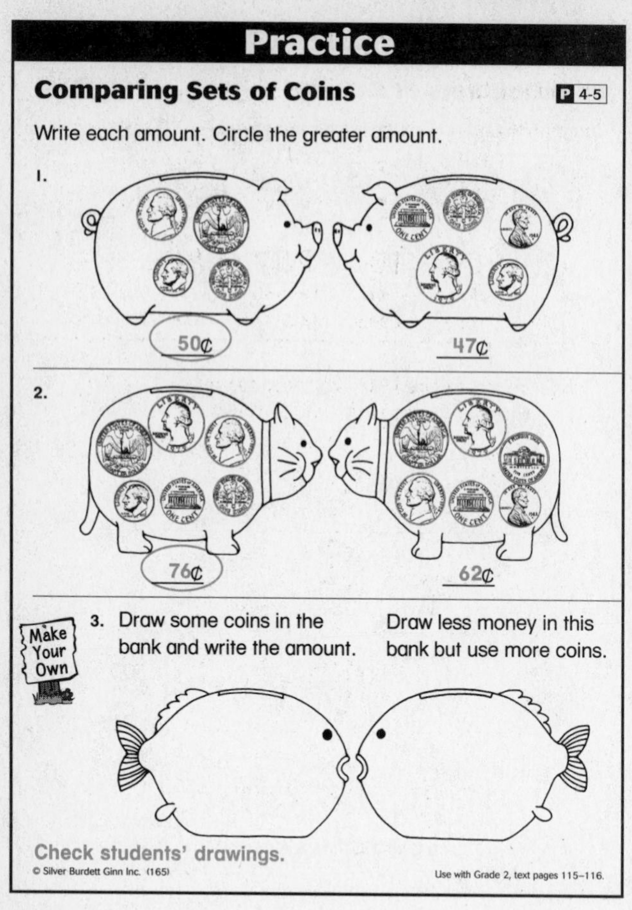

Practice
Comparing Sets of Coins
P 4-5
Write each amount. Circle the greater amount.
1.
50¢
47¢
2.
76¢
62¢
Make Your Own
3. Draw some coins in the bank and write the amount.
Draw less money in this bank but use more coins.
Check students' drawings.
© Silver Burdett Ginn Inc. (165)
Use with Grade 2, text pages 115–116.

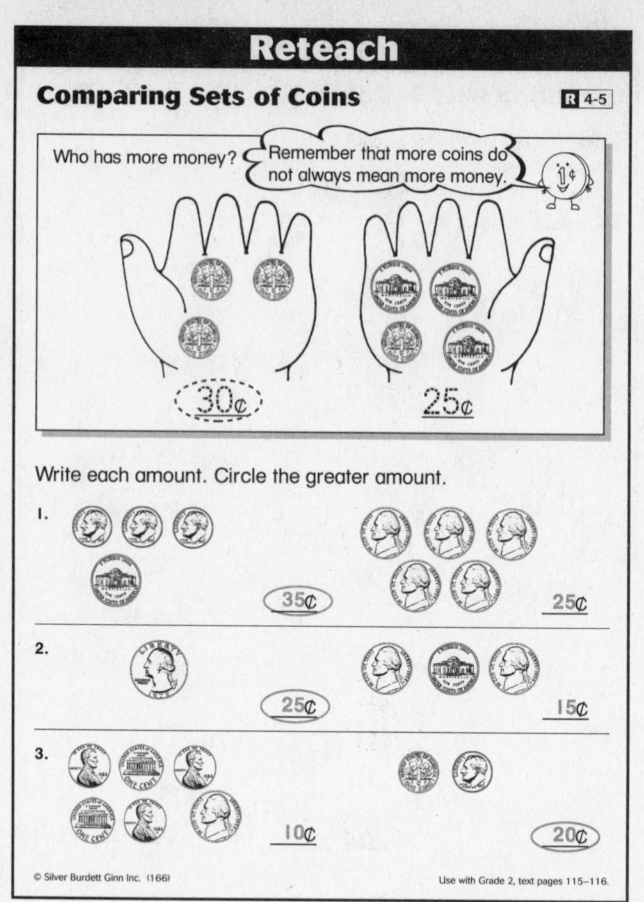

Reteach
Comparing Sets of Coins
R 4-5
Who has more money?
Remember that more coins do not always mean more money.
30¢
25¢
Write each amount. Circle the greater amount.
1.
35¢
25¢
2.
25¢
15¢
3.
10¢
20¢
© Silver Burdett Ginn Inc. (166)
Use with Grade 2, text pages 115–116.

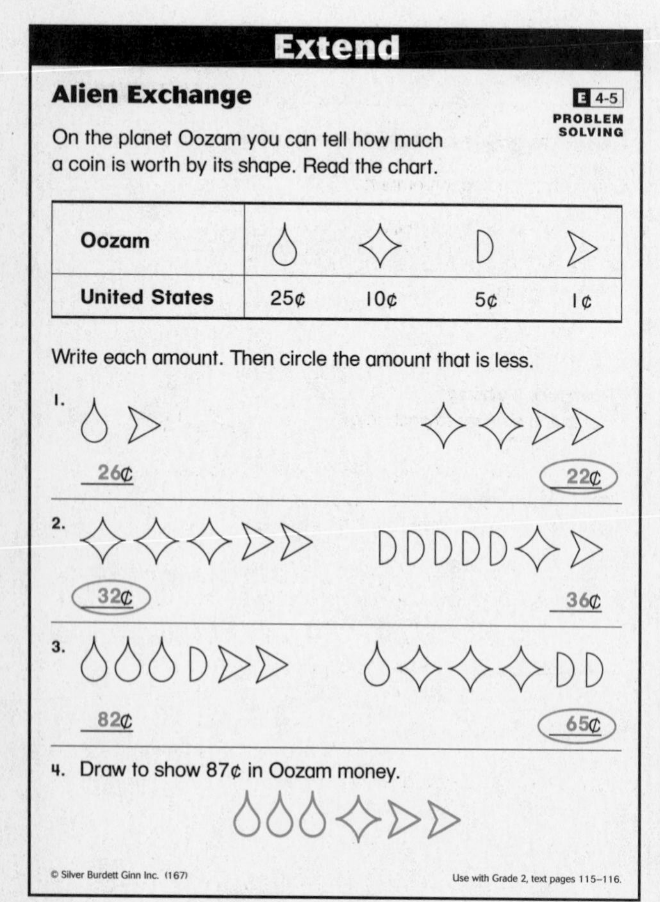

Extend
Alien Exchange
E 4-5
PROBLEM SOLVING
On the planet Oozam you can tell how much a coin is worth by its shape. Read the chart.
Oozam
United States
25¢
10¢
5¢
1¢
Write each amount. Then circle the amount that is less.
1.
26¢
22¢
2.
32¢
36¢
3.
82¢
65¢
4. Draw to show 87¢ in Oozam money.
© Silver Burdett Ginn Inc. (167)
Use with Grade 2, text pages 115–116.

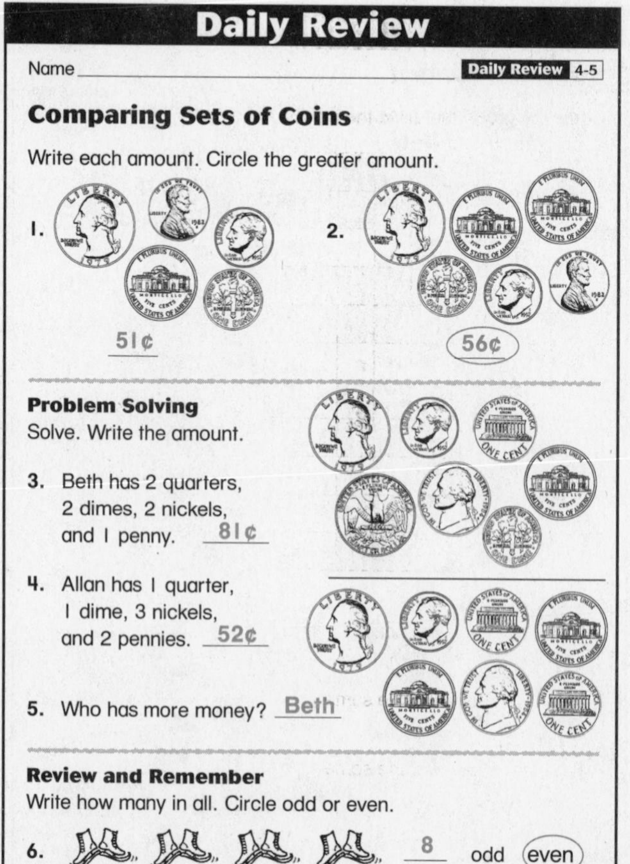

Daily Review
Name
Daily Review 4-5
Comparing Sets of Coins
Write each amount. Circle the greater amount.
1.
51¢
2.
56¢
Problem Solving
Solve. Write the amount.
3. Beth has 2 quarters, 2 dimes, 2 nickels, and 1 penny. 81¢
4. Allan has 1 quarter, 1 dime, 3 nickels, and 2 pennies. 52¢
5. Who has more money? Beth
Review and Remember
Write how many in all. Circle odd or even.
6.
8
odd
even

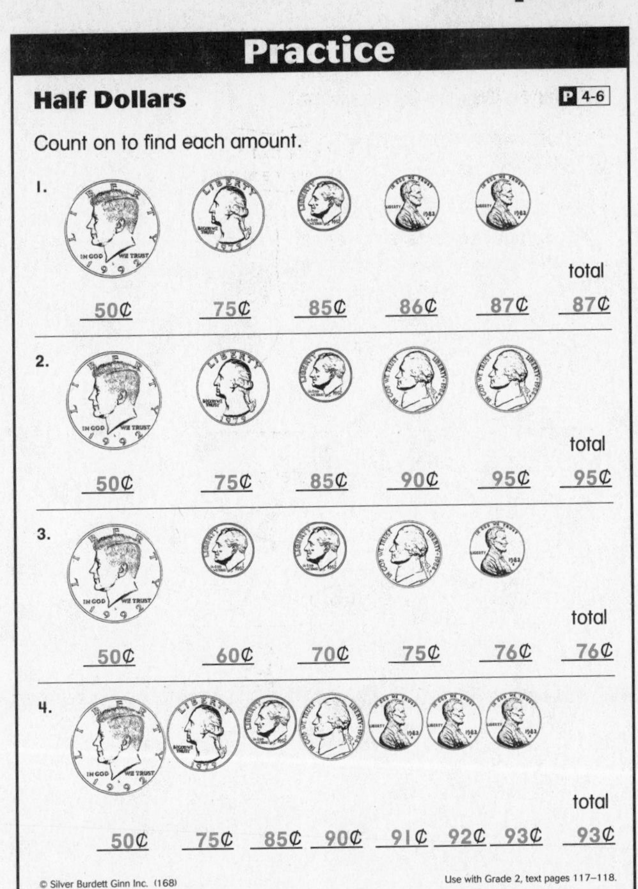

Practice

Half Dollars

P 4-6

Count on to find each amount.

1. 50¢ 75¢ 85¢ 86¢ 87¢ total 87¢

2. 50¢ 75¢ 85¢ 90¢ 95¢ total 95¢

3. 50¢ 60¢ 70¢ 75¢ 76¢ total 76¢

4. 50¢ 75¢ 85¢ 90¢ 91¢ 92¢ 93¢ total 93¢

Use with Grade 2, text pages 117–118.

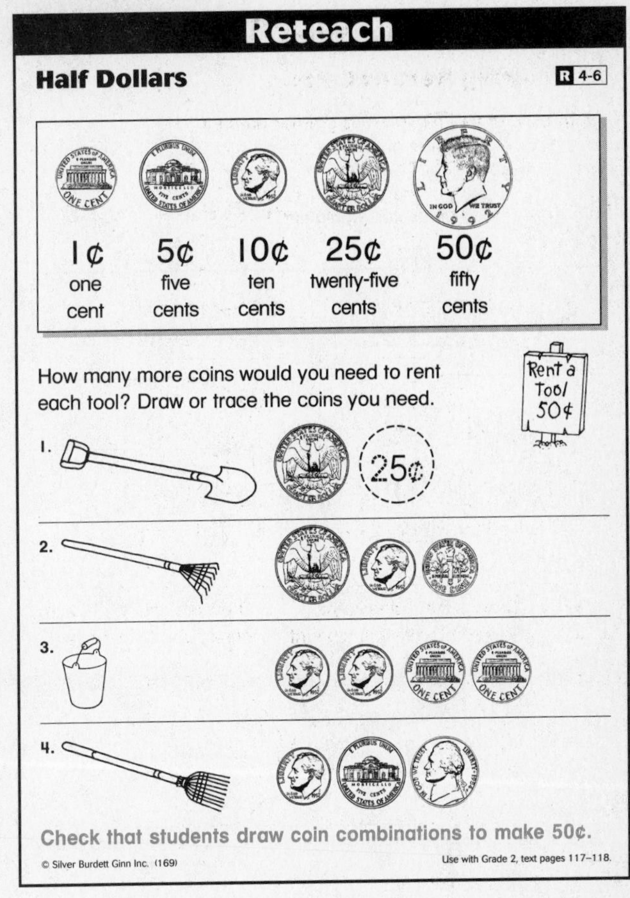

Reteach

Half Dollars

R 4-6

1¢	5¢	10¢	25¢	50¢
one cent	five cents	ten cents	twenty-five cents	fifty cents

How many more coins would you need to rent each tool? Draw or trace the coins you need.

1. 25¢

2.

3.

4.

Check that students draw coin combinations to make 50¢.

Use with Grade 2, text pages 117–118.

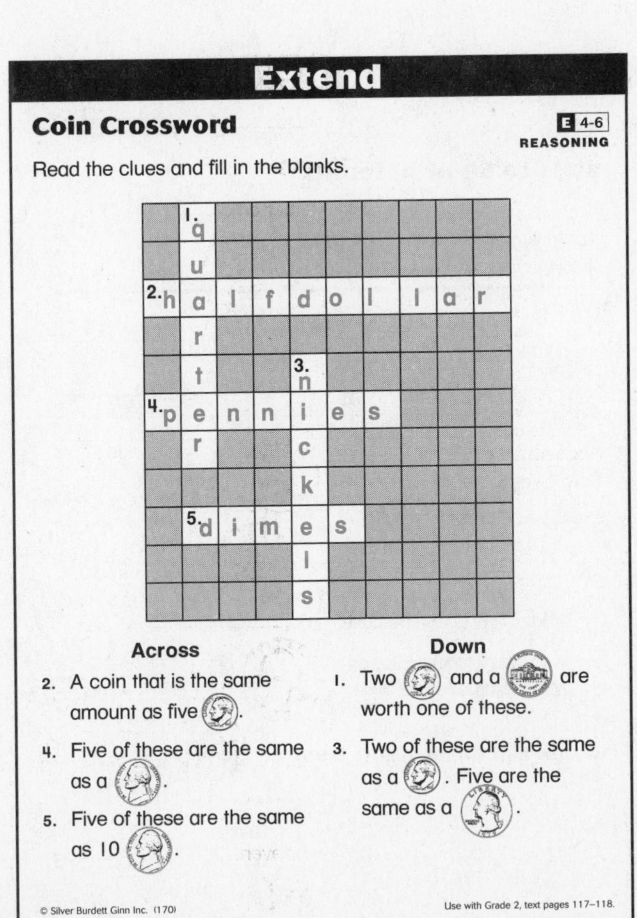

Extend

Coin Crossword

E 4-6 REASONING

Read the clues and fill in the blanks.

Across

2. A coin that is the same amount as five (quarter).
4. Five of these are the same as a (nickel).
5. Five of these are the same as 10 (nickel).

Down

1. Two (dime) and a (nickel) are worth one of these.
3. Two of these are the same as a (dime). Five are the same as a (quarter).

Use with Grade 2, text pages 117–118.

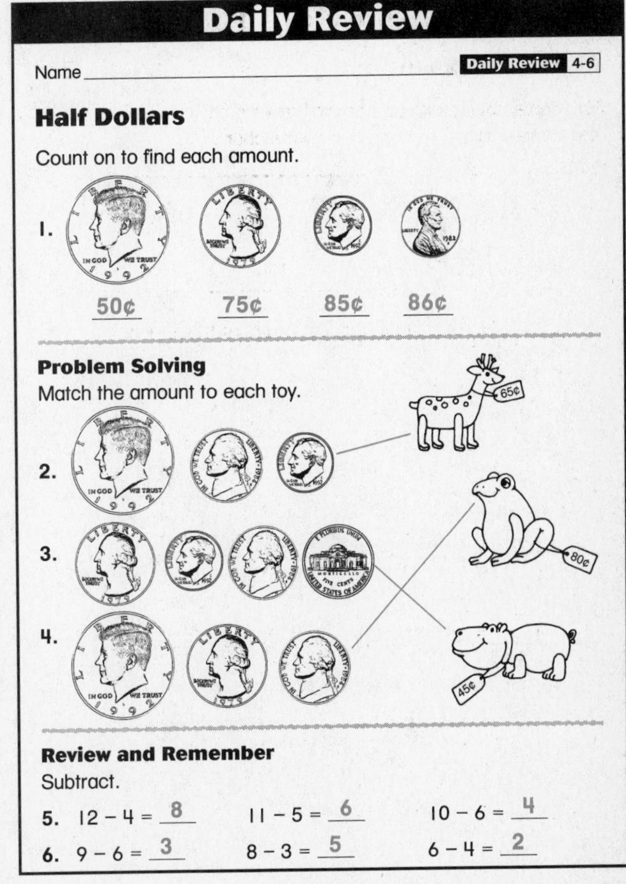

Daily Review

Name ____________________

Daily Review 4-6

Half Dollars

Count on to find each amount.

1. 50¢ 75¢ 85¢ 86¢

Problem Solving

Match the amount to each toy.

2.

3.

4.

Review and Remember

Subtract.

5. 12 − 4 = 8 11 − 5 = 6 10 − 6 = 4

6. 9 − 6 = 3 8 − 3 = 5 6 − 4 = 2

Chapter 4 • Lesson 7

Practice

Ways to Show Amounts

P 4-7

Choose 4 items from the menu at the bottom of the page. Cut them out. Paste them on the chart in the Food column.

Write how many coins you would use to pay for each item.

25¢	90¢	98¢	84¢	38¢
72¢	79¢	43¢	67¢	27¢

Check that students' coin combinations equal the food prices.

Use with Grade 2, text pages 119–120.

Reteach

Ways to Show Amounts

R 4-7

Find two sets of coins for the amount of money in each bag.

Color each bag. Then use the same color to mark two sets of coins that have the amount shown on the bag.

Check that students color red: a, f; color blue: b, d; color green: c, e.

a.    

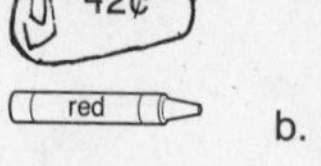

b.   

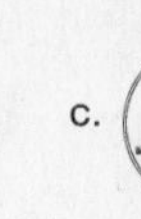

c.   

d.   

76¢

e. 

green

f.   

Use with Grade 2, text pages 119–120.

Extend

Money Tricks

E 4-7

PROBLEM SOLVING

You can combine different coins to make the same amount.

1. Make 52¢ with 4 coins. Write how many of each coin.

___ 2 ___ ___ 2

2. Make 52¢ with 3 coins. Write how many of each coin.

1 ___ ___ ___ 2

3. Make 46¢ with 4 coins. Write how many of each coin.

___ 1 2 ___ 1

4. Make 66¢ with 4 coins. Write how many of each coin.

1 ___ 1 1 1

Use with Grade 2, text pages 119–120.

Daily Review

Name ______________________

Daily Review 4-7

Ways to Show Amounts

Use coins to show the amount in different ways.
Use tally marks to show the coins you use.
Answers will vary.

1.

Ways to show 66¢				
half dollars	quarters	dimes	nickels	pennies
I		I	I	I
	II		III	I
	I	IIII		I
I			III	I

Problem Solving

Solve. Draw or trace coins.

2. Karen has 2 coins. She has 50¢.
What coins does she have? 2 quarters

3. Toby has 4 coins. He has 30¢.
What coins does he have? 2 dimes, 2 nickels

Review and Remember

Subtract.

4. $7 - 2 = 5$ $6 - 1 = 5$ $9 - 3 = 6$ $10 - 2 = 8$ $9 - 1 = 8$ $4 - 3 = 1$

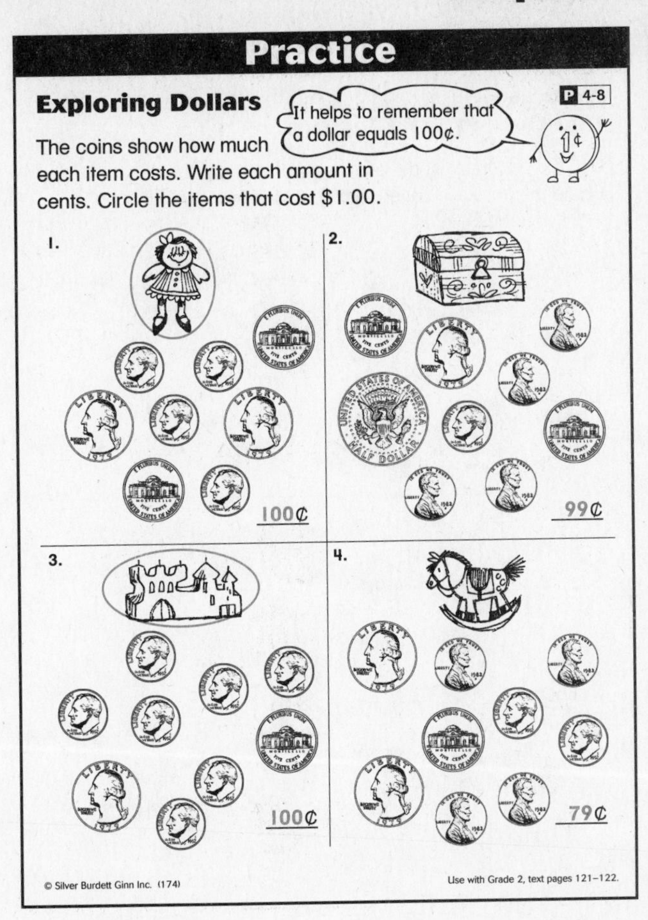

Practice

Exploring Dollars

P 4-8

It helps to remember that a dollar equals 100¢.

The coins show how much each item costs. Write each amount in cents. Circle the items that cost $1.00.

1. 100¢
2. 99¢
3. 100¢
4. 79¢

 Use with Grade 2, text pages 121–122.

Reteach

Exploring Dollars

R 4-8

100¢
one dollar
$1.00

Draw the number of each coin you need to make a dollar. Write each amount in cents.

50¢ 50¢	25¢ 25¢ 25¢ 25¢	10¢ 10¢ 10¢ 10¢ 10¢ 10¢ 10¢ 10¢ 10¢ 10¢
100¢	100¢	100¢

 Use with Grade 2, text pages 121–122.

Extend

Money Mystery

E 4-8
REASONING

Complete the table. Use the clues.

Clark has two coins.

Clark has more than 26¢ and less than 31¢.

Mia has one quarter.

Marc has one coin.

Marc has more money than Mia.

Cathy has three coins.

Cathy has 3¢ less than Clark.

Coins Each Child Has

Child						Total value
Clark		1		1		30¢
Mia		1				25¢
Marc	1					50¢
Cathy		1			2	27¢

 Use with Grade 2, text pages 121–122.

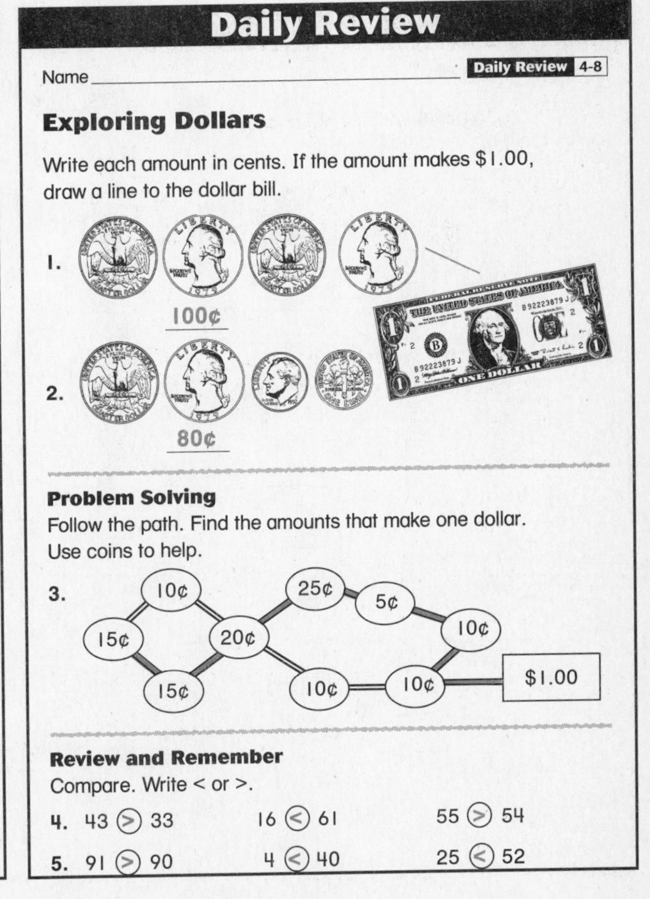

Daily Review

Name ____________________ Daily Review 4-8

Exploring Dollars

Write each amount in cents. If the amount makes $1.00, draw a line to the dollar bill.

1. 100¢
2. 80¢

Problem Solving

Follow the path. Find the amounts that make one dollar. Use coins to help.

3. 10¢ 15¢ 15¢ 20¢ 25¢ 5¢ 10¢ 10¢ 10¢ $1.00

Review and Remember

Compare. Write < or >.

4. 43 > 33 16 < 61 55 > 54
5. 91 > 90 4 < 40 25 < 52

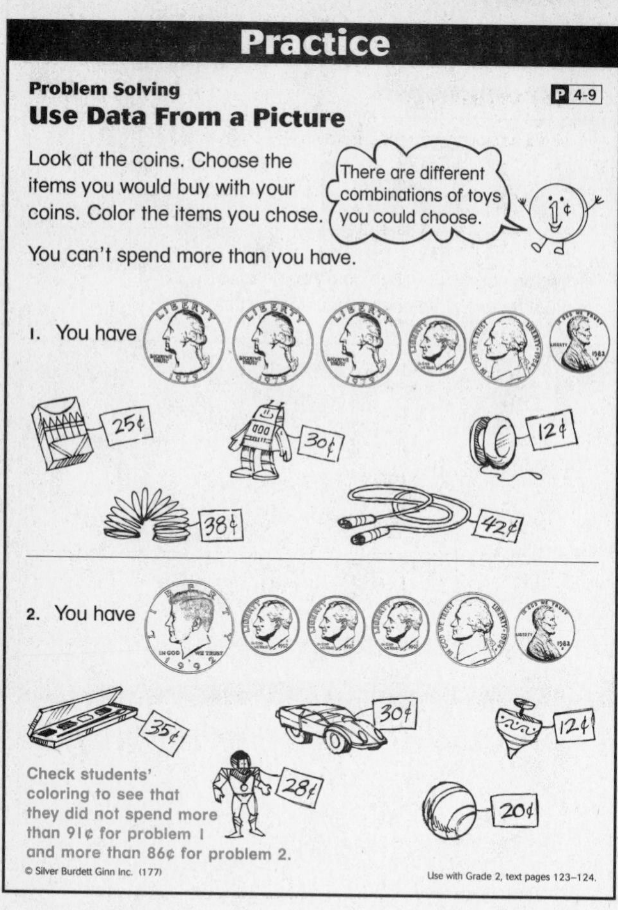

Practice

Problem Solving P 4-9

Use Data From a Picture

Look at the coins. Choose the items you would buy with your coins. Color the items you chose.

There are different combinations of toys you could choose.

You can't spend more than you have.

1. You have

25¢ 30¢ 12¢ 38¢ 42¢

2. You have

35¢ 30¢ 12¢ 28¢ 20¢

Check students' coloring to see that they did not spend more than 91¢ for problem 1 and more than 86¢ for problem 2.

 Use with Grade 2, text pages 123–124.

Reteach

Problem Solving R 4-9

Use Data From a Picture

Use the picture to find the price.
Circle the coins you need to buy each item.
Write how much in all.

46¢ 71¢ 85¢ 90¢

1. 46¢
2. 71¢
3. 85¢
4. 90¢

 Use with Grade 2, text pages 123–124.

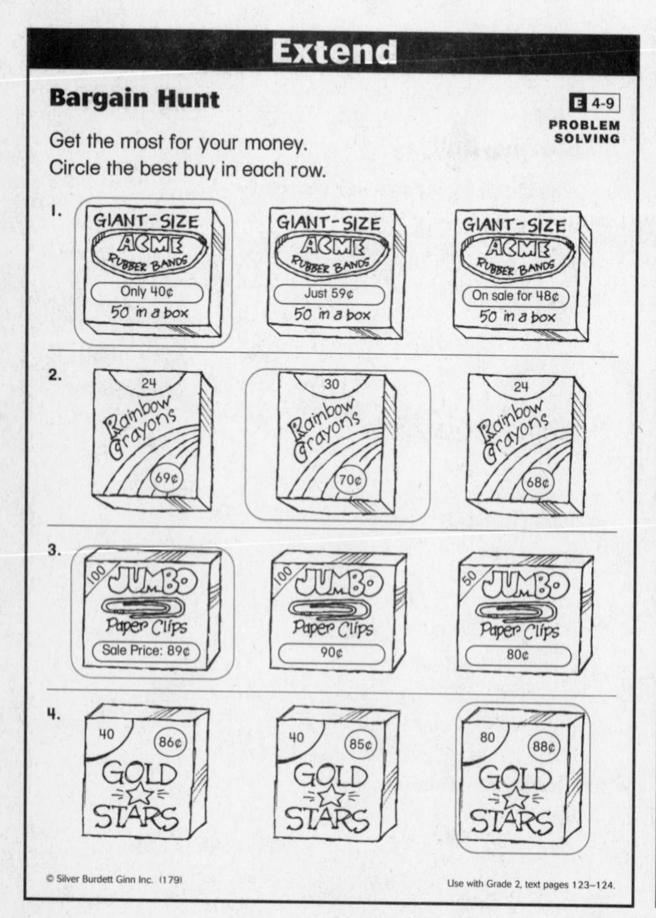

Extend

Bargain Hunt

E 4-9 PROBLEM SOLVING

Get the most for your money.
Circle the best buy in each row.

1. GIANT-SIZE ACME RUBBER BANDS Only 40¢ 50 in a box | GIANT-SIZE ACME RUBBER BANDS Just 59¢ 50 in a box | GIANT-SIZE ACME RUBBER BANDS On sale for 48¢ 50 in a box
2. 24 Rainbow Crayons 69¢ | 30 Rainbow Crayons 70¢ | 24 Rainbow Crayons 68¢
3. 100 JUMBO Paper Clips Sale Price: 89¢ | 100 JUMBO Paper Clips 90¢ | 50 JUMBO Paper Clips 80¢
4. 40 86¢ GOLD STARS | 40 85¢ GOLD STARS | 80 88¢ GOLD STARS

 Use with Grade 2, text pages 123–124.

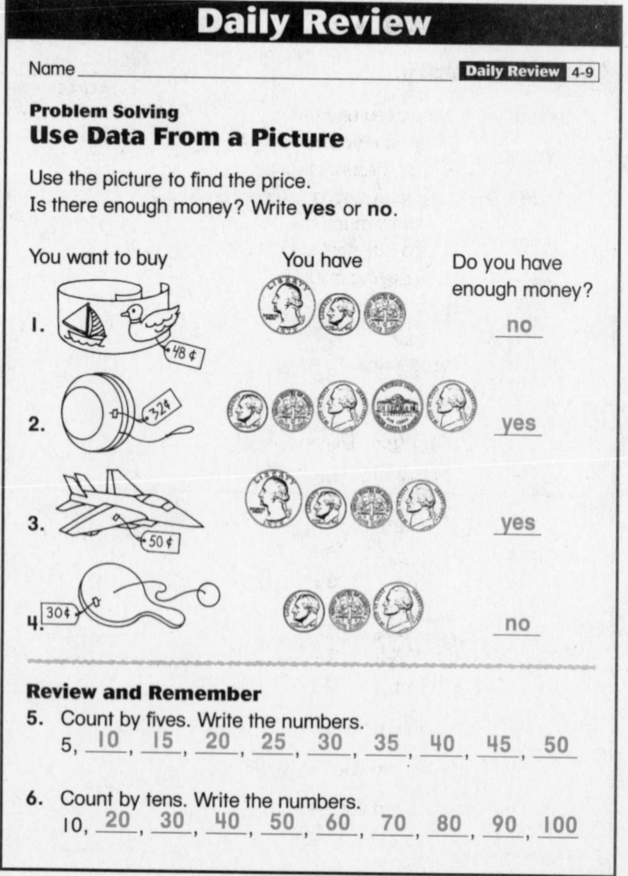

Daily Review

Name ______ Daily Review 4-9

Problem Solving

Use Data From a Picture

Use the picture to find the price.
Is there enough money? Write **yes** or **no**.

You want to buy	You have	Do you have enough money?
1. 48¢		no
2. 32¢		yes
3. 50¢		yes
4. 30¢		no

Review and Remember

5. Count by fives. Write the numbers.
5, 10, 15, 20, 25, 30, 35, 40, 45, 50

6. Count by tens. Write the numbers.
10, 20, 30, 40, 50, 60, 70, 80, 90, 100

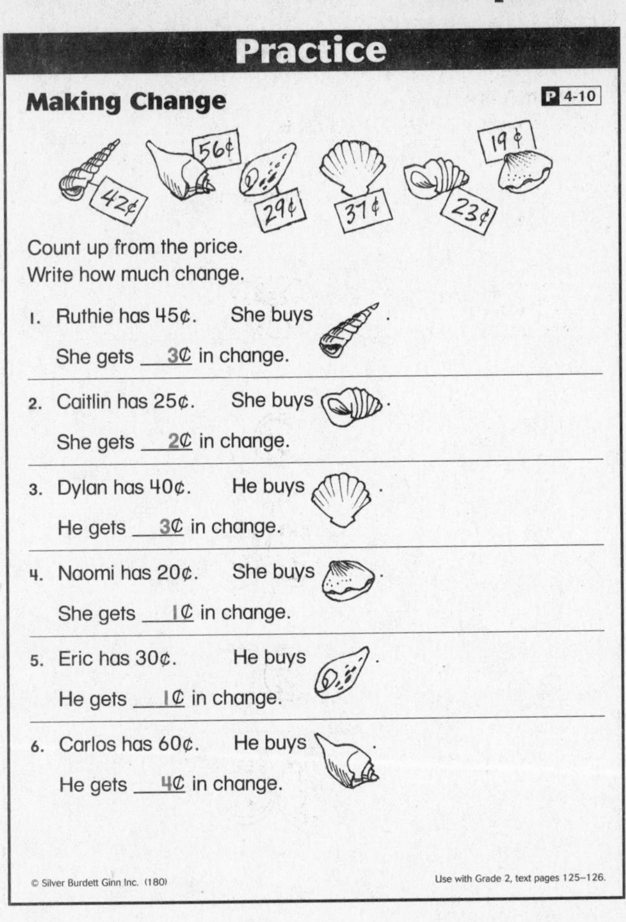

Practice

Making Change

P 4-10

Count up from the price.
Write how much change.

1. Ruthie has 45¢. She buys [shell]. She gets 3¢ in change.
2. Caitlin has 25¢. She buys [shell]. She gets 2¢ in change.
3. Dylan has 40¢. He buys [shell]. He gets 3¢ in change.
4. Naomi has 20¢. She buys [shell]. She gets 1¢ in change.
5. Eric has 30¢. He buys [shell]. He gets 1¢ in change.
6. Carlos has 60¢. He buys [shell]. He gets 4¢ in change.

Use with Grade 2, text pages 125–126.

Reteach

Making Change

R 4-10

Write the amount you pay. Draw pennies as you count up from the price. Write how much change.

Price	You pay	Count up from price	Your change
1. 23¢	25¢	1¢ 1¢	2¢
2. 46¢	50¢	1¢ 1¢ 1¢ 1¢	4¢
3. 41¢	45¢	1¢ 1¢ 1¢ 1¢	4¢
4. 37¢	40¢	1¢ 1¢ 1¢	3¢

Use with Grade 2, text pages 125–126.

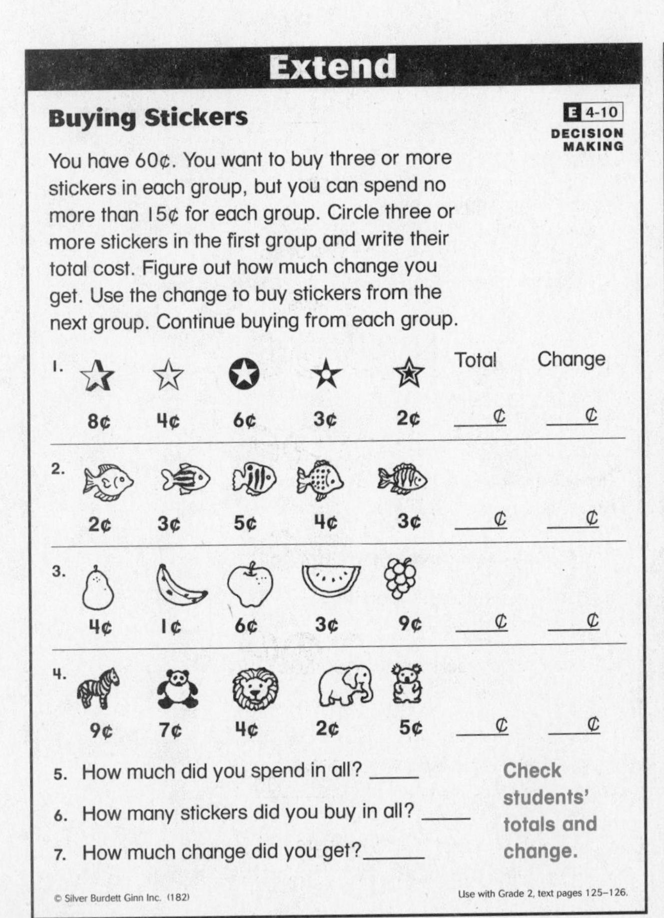

Extend

Buying Stickers

E 4-10
DECISION MAKING

You have 60¢. You want to buy three or more stickers in each group, but you can spend no more than 15¢ for each group. Circle three or more stickers in the first group and write their total cost. Figure out how much change you get. Use the change to buy stickers from the next group. Continue buying from each group.

						Total	Change
1.	8¢	4¢	6¢	3¢	2¢	___¢	___¢
2.	2¢	3¢	5¢	4¢	3¢	___¢	___¢
3.	4¢	1¢	6¢	3¢	9¢	___¢	___¢
4.	9¢	7¢	4¢	2¢	5¢	___¢	___¢

5. How much did you spend in all? ____
6. How many stickers did you buy in all? ____
7. How much change did you get? ____

Check students' totals and change.

Use with Grade 2, text pages 125–126.

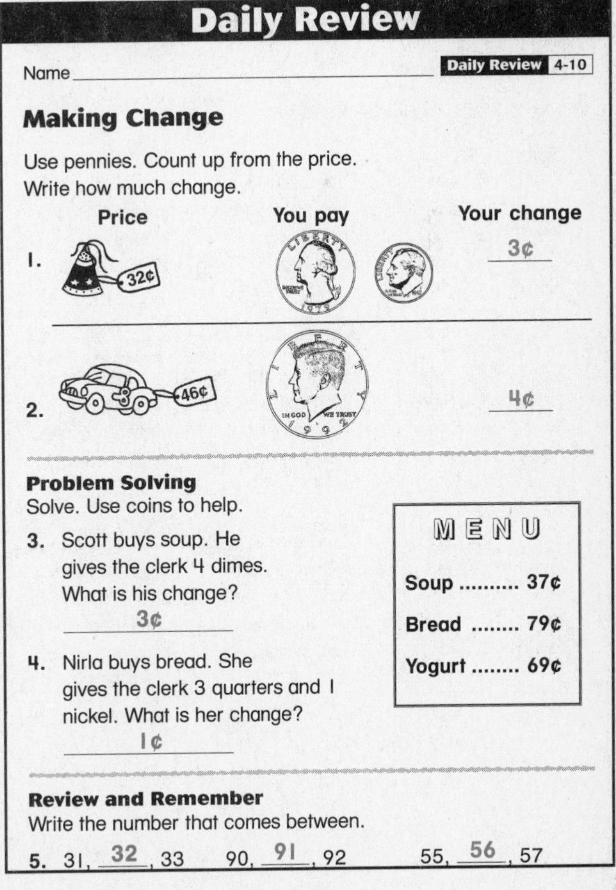

Daily Review

Name ____________________ Daily Review 4-10

Making Change

Use pennies. Count up from the price.
Write how much change.

	Price	You pay	Your change
1.	32¢		3¢
2.	46¢		4¢

Problem Solving
Solve. Use coins to help.

3. Scott buys soup. He gives the clerk 4 dimes. What is his change? 3¢
4. Nirla buys bread. She gives the clerk 3 quarters and 1 nickel. What is her change? 1¢

MENU
Soup .... 37¢
Bread .... 79¢
Yogurt .... 69¢

Review and Remember
Write the number that comes between.

5. 31, 32, 33   90, 91, 92   55, 56, 57

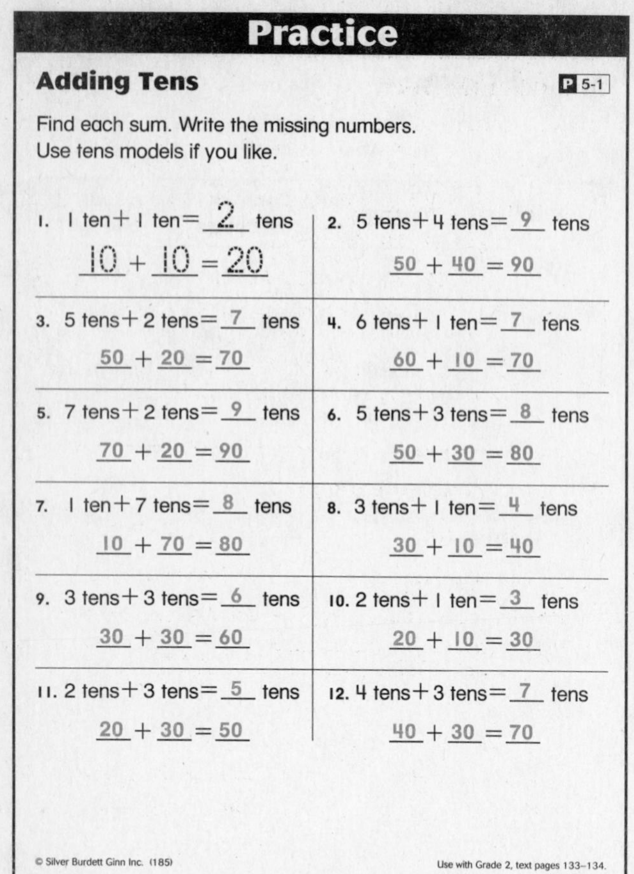

Practice

Adding Tens

P 5-1

Find each sum. Write the missing numbers.
Use tens models if you like.

1. 1 ten + 1 ten = 2 tens
   10 + 10 = 20
2. 5 tens + 4 tens = 9 tens
   50 + 40 = 90
3. 5 tens + 2 tens = 7 tens
   50 + 20 = 70
4. 6 tens + 1 ten = 7 tens
   60 + 10 = 70
5. 7 tens + 2 tens = 9 tens
   70 + 20 = 90
6. 5 tens + 3 tens = 8 tens
   50 + 30 = 80
7. 1 ten + 7 tens = 8 tens
   10 + 70 = 80
8. 3 tens + 1 ten = 4 tens
   30 + 10 = 40
9. 3 tens + 3 tens = 6 tens
   30 + 30 = 60
10. 2 tens + 1 ten = 3 tens
    20 + 10 = 30
11. 2 tens + 3 tens = 5 tens
    20 + 30 = 50
12. 4 tens + 3 tens = 7 tens
    40 + 30 = 70

Use with Grade 2, text pages 133–134.

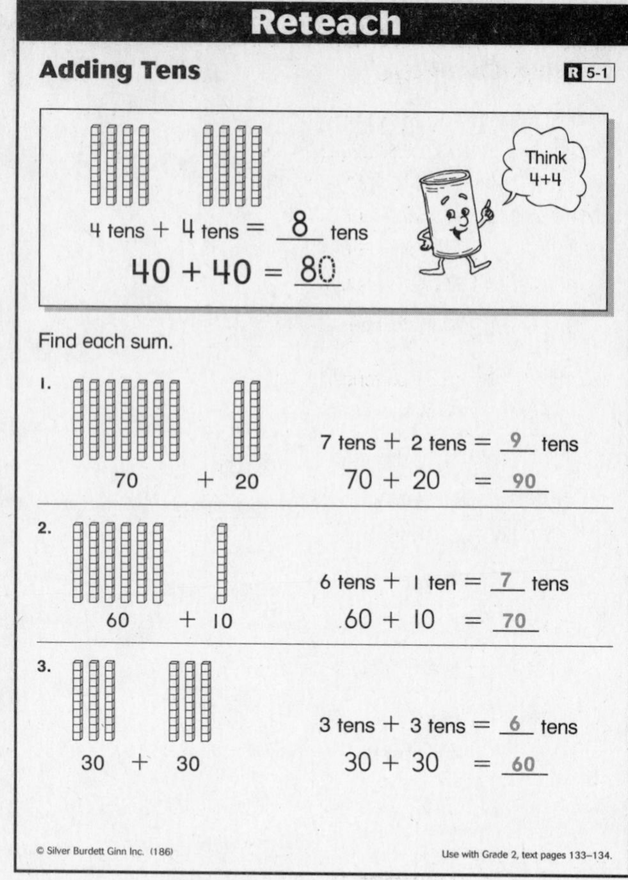

Reteach

Adding Tens

R 5-1

4 tens + 4 tens = 8 tens
40 + 40 = 80

Find each sum.

1. 70 + 20
   7 tens + 2 tens = 9 tens
   70 + 20 = 90
2. 60 + 10
   6 tens + 1 ten = 7 tens
   60 + 10 = 70
3. 30 + 30
   3 tens + 3 tens = 6 tens
   30 + 30 = 60

Use with Grade 2, text pages 133–134.

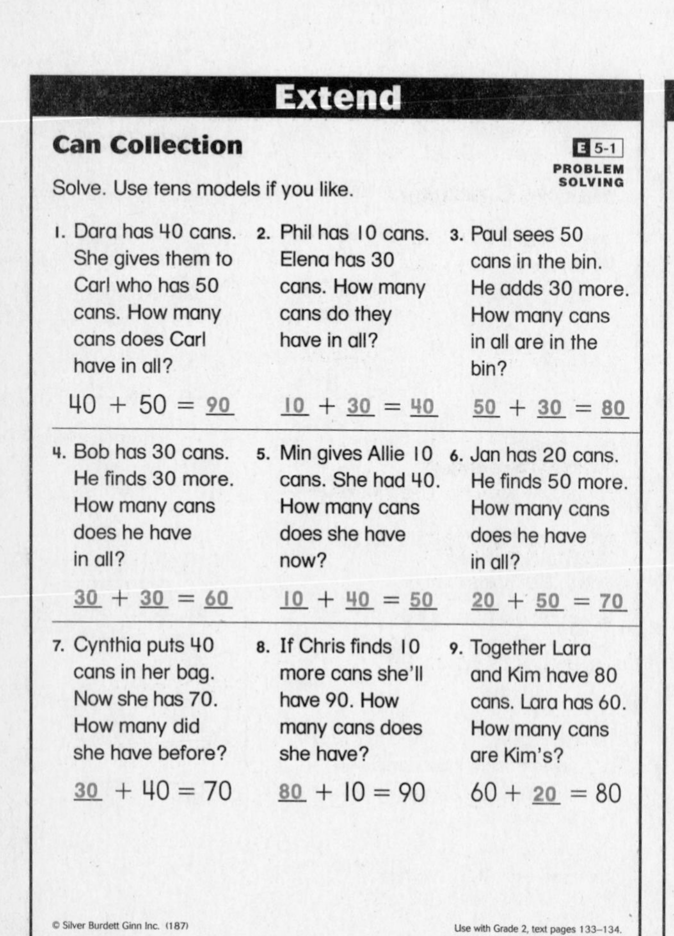

Extend

Can Collection

E 5-1
PROBLEM SOLVING

Solve. Use tens models if you like.

1. Dara has 40 cans. She gives them to Carl who has 50 cans. How many cans does Carl have in all?
   40 + 50 = 90
2. Phil has 10 cans. Elena has 30 cans. How many cans do they have in all?
   10 + 30 = 40
3. Paul sees 50 cans in the bin. He adds 30 more. How many cans in all are in the bin?
   50 + 30 = 80
4. Bob has 30 cans. He finds 30 more. How many cans does he have in all?
   30 + 30 = 60
5. Min gives Allie 10 cans. She had 40. How many cans does she have now?
   10 + 40 = 50
6. Jan has 20 cans. He finds 50 more. How many cans does he have in all?
   20 + 50 = 70
7. Cynthia puts 40 cans in her bag. Now she has 70. How many did she have before?
   30 + 40 = 70
8. If Chris finds 10 more cans she'll have 90. How many cans does she have?
   80 + 10 = 90
9. Together Lara and Kim have 80 cans. Lara has 60. How many cans are Kim's?
   60 + 20 = 80

Use with Grade 2, text pages 133–134.

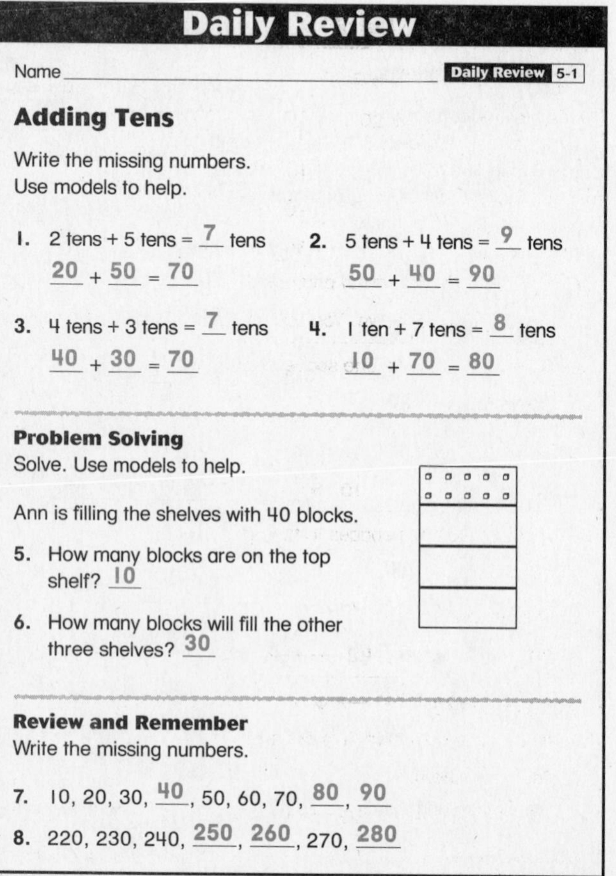

Daily Review

Name ______________________

Daily Review 5-1

Adding Tens

Write the missing numbers.
Use models to help.

1. 2 tens + 5 tens = 7 tens
   20 + 50 = 70
2. 5 tens + 4 tens = 9 tens
   50 + 40 = 90
3. 4 tens + 3 tens = 7 tens
   40 + 30 = 70
4. 1 ten + 7 tens = 8 tens
   10 + 70 = 80

Problem Solving

Solve. Use models to help.

Ann is filling the shelves with 40 blocks.

5. How many blocks are on the top shelf? 10
6. How many blocks will fill the other three shelves? 30

Review and Remember

Write the missing numbers.

7. 10, 20, 30, 40, 50, 60, 70, 80, 90
8. 220, 230, 240, 250, 260, 270, 280

Chapter 5 • Lesson 2

Practice

Counting On Tens

P 5-2

20	21	22	23	24	25	26	27	28	29
30	31	32	33	34	35	36	37	38	39
40	41	42	43	44	45	46	47	48	49
50	51	52	53	54	55	56	57	58	59
60	61	62	63	64	65	66	67	68	69
70	71	72	73	74	75	76	77	78	79

Use the chart to count on tens.

1.

Add 10	
27	37
38	48
56	66
61	71

2.

Add 20	
42	62
55	75
22	42
37	57

3.

Add 30	
20	50
25	55
34	64
49	79

4.

Add 10	
23	33
39	49
65	75
59	69

Use with Grade 2, text pages 135–136.

Reteach

Counting On Tens

R 5-2

0	1	2	3	4	5	6	7	8	9
10	11	12	13	14	15	16	17	18	19
20	21	22	23	24	25	26	27	28	29
30	31	32	33	34	35	36	37	38	39
40	41	42	43	44	45	46	47	48	49

14 + 30 = ?

Start at 14. Count on 3 tens ⇨ 24, 34, 44

14 + 30 = 44

Use the chart. Count on tens to add.

1. 36 + 10
Start at 36.
Count on 1 ten.
36 + 10 = 46

2. 23 + 20
Start at 23.
Count on 2 tens.
23 + 20 = 43

3. 29 + 20
Start at 29.
Count on 2 tens.
29 + 20 = 49

4. 18 + 30
Start at 18.
Count on 3 tens.
18 + 30 = 48

Use with Grade 2, text pages 135–136.

Extend

Follow the Arrows

E 5-2
PATTERNS

Use the chart. Start at 20.
Move one space down.
The number is 30.
20 + 10 = 30
You added 10!

0	10	20	30	40
10	20	30	40	50
20	30	40	50	60
30	40	50	60	70

1. Test the pattern. Start at any number and move one space down. You added 10.
2. Start with 10. Move one space down. The number is 20.
3. Test the pattern.
40 ↓ = 50 10 ↓ = 20 50 ↓ = 60
4. If you move three spaces to the right →→→ it is like adding 30.
5. Test the pattern.
30 →→→ = 60 40 →→→ = 70 10 →→→ = 40
6. If you move like this → ↓, one space to the right, then one space down, it is like adding 20.
7. Test the pattern.

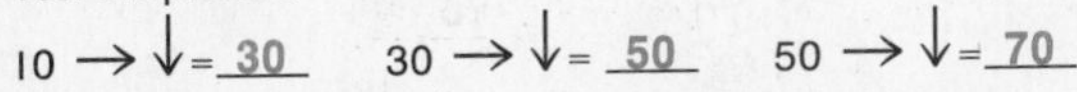
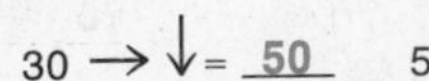

10 → ↓ = 30 30 → ↓ = 50 50 → ↓ = 70

Use with Grade 2, text pages 135–136.

Daily Review

Name ____________________

Daily Review 5-2

Counting On Tens

Count on by tens to add.
Use Workmat 5 if you like.

1. 28 + 30 = 58 34 + 20 = 54 63 + 10 = 73
2. 13 + 20 = 33 42 + 20 = 62 55 + 30 = 85
3. 24 + 10 = 34 41 + 30 = 71 20 + 39 = 59

Problem Solving

Solve. Use the table. Use models to help.

Book Club Sales	
Month	Books
January	24
February	10
March	41
April	20

4. How many books were sold in January and February?
34 books
5. How many books were sold in March and April?
61 books

Review and Remember

Add.

6. 7 + 3 = 10 9 + 2 = 11 8 + 0 = 8 4 + 3 = 7 5 + 4 = 9 2 + 5 = 7

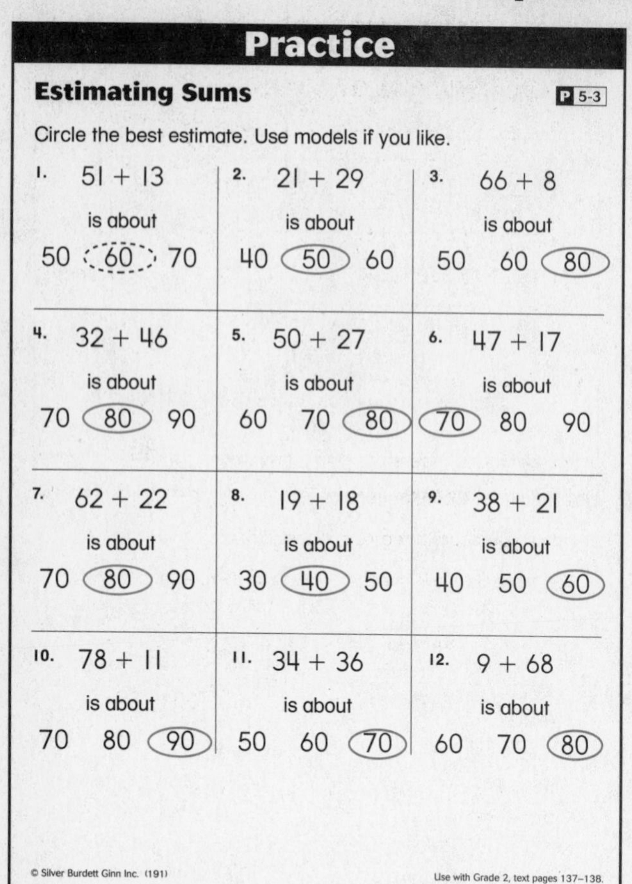

Practice

Estimating Sums

P 5-3

Circle the best estimate. Use models if you like.

1. 51 + 13 is about: 50 (60) 70
2. 21 + 29 is about: 40 (50) 60
3. 66 + 8 is about: 50 60 (80)
4. 32 + 46 is about: 70 (80) 90
5. 50 + 27 is about: 60 70 (80)
6. 47 + 17 is about: (70) 80 90
7. 62 + 22 is about: 70 (80) 90
8. 19 + 18 is about: 30 (40) 50
9. 38 + 21 is about: 40 50 (60)
10. 78 + 11 is about: 70 80 (90)
11. 34 + 36 is about: 50 60 (70)
12. 9 + 68 is about: 60 70 (80)

Use with Grade 2, text pages 137–138.

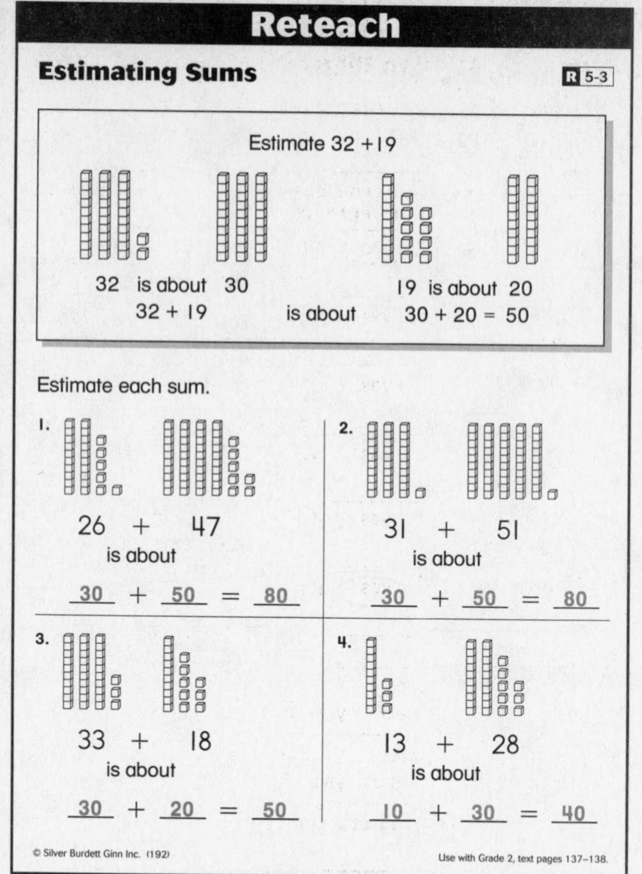

Reteach

Estimating Sums

R 5-3

Estimate 32 + 19

32 is about 30

19 is about 20

32 + 19 is about 30 + 20 = 50

Estimate each sum.

1. 26 + 47 is about 30 + 50 = 80
2. 31 + 51 is about 30 + 50 = 80
3. 33 + 18 is about 30 + 20 = 50
4. 13 + 28 is about 10 + 30 = 40

Use with Grade 2, text pages 137–138.

Extend

Can Count

E 5-3

NUMBER SENSE

Use the chart to estimate how many cans are collected in two weeks at each place.

Circle the best estimate. Use models if you like.

Place	Week 1	Week 2	Estimated number of cans
1. school	39	41	70 (80) 90
2. store	70	22	(90) 80 70
3. factory	21	52	60 (70) 80
4. office	29	16	40 (50) 60
5. park	24	46	60 (70) 80
6. museum	11	57	60 (70) 80

Use with Grade 2, text pages 137–138.

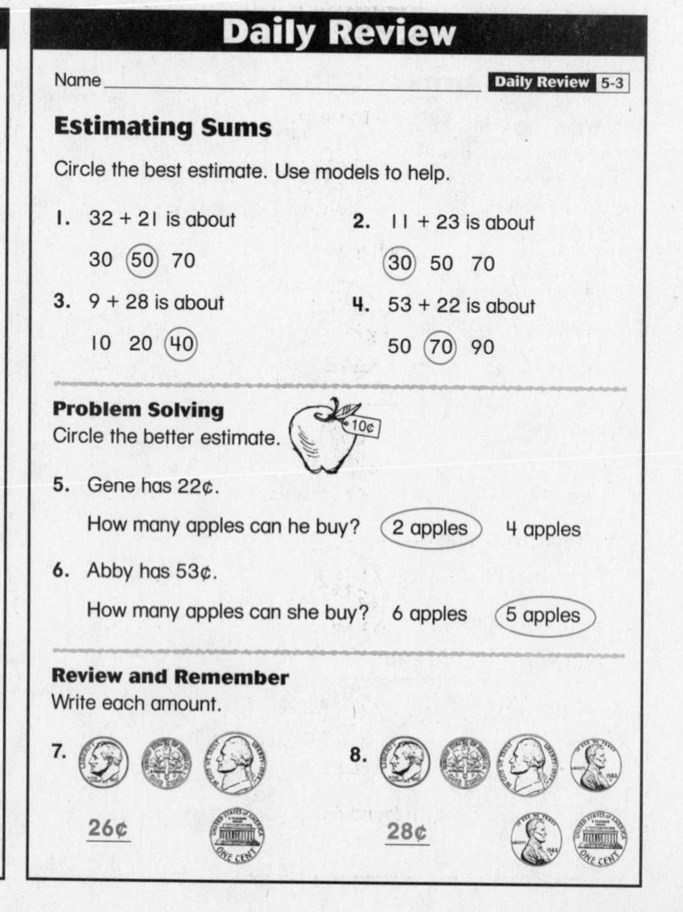

Daily Review

Name ____________________

Daily Review 5-3

Estimating Sums

Circle the best estimate. Use models to help.

1. 32 + 21 is about: 30 (50) 70
2. 11 + 23 is about: (30) 50 70
3. 9 + 28 is about: 10 20 (40)
4. 53 + 22 is about: 50 (70) 90

Problem Solving

Circle the better estimate.

5. Gene has 22¢. How many apples can he buy? (2 apples) 4 apples
6. Abby has 53¢. How many apples can she buy? 6 apples (5 apples)

Review and Remember

Write each amount.

7. 26¢
8. 28¢

Practice

Deciding When to Regroup

P 5-4

Complete the chart. Use tens and ones models if you like.

	Do you need to regroup?	How many in all?
1. I ten 3 ones Add 9 ones.	(yes) no	2 tens 2 ones
2. 3 tens 8 ones Add 5 ones.	(yes) no	4 tens 3 ones
3. 4 tens 2 ones Add 7 ones.	yes (no)	4 tens 9 ones
4. 4 tens 9 ones Add 8 ones.	(yes) no	5 tens 7 ones
5. 5 tens 5 ones Add 2 ones.	yes (no)	5 tens 7 ones
6. 6 tens 8 ones Add 6 ones.	(yes) no	7 tens 4 ones

7. 2 tens 4 ones Add ___ ones.	yes no	___ tens ___ ones
8. 2 tens 4 ones Add ___ ones.	yes no	___ tens ___ ones

Check that students regroup and add correctly.

Use with Grade 2, text pages 139–140.

Reteach

Deciding When to Regroup

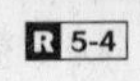

R 5-4

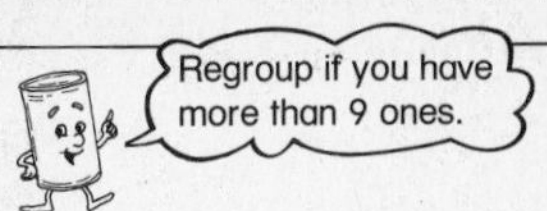

You have 2 tens and 6 ones. How do you add 7 ones?

① Show 2 tens 6 ones. ② Add 7 ones. ③ Regroup 10 ones as I ten.

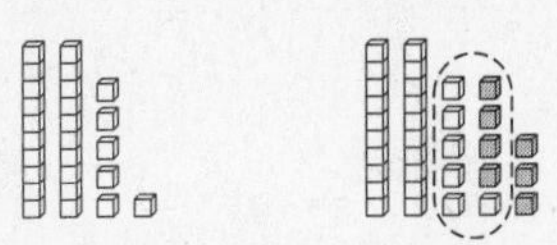

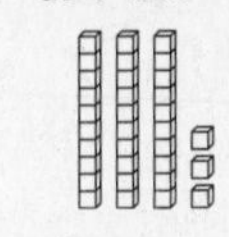

3 tens + 3 ones = 33

Decide if you need to regroup. Then add.

1. You have 3 tens 4 ones. Add 9 ones.

Regroup? (yes) no

4 tens 3 ones

2. You have 4 tens 3 ones. Add 8 ones.

Regroup? (yes) no

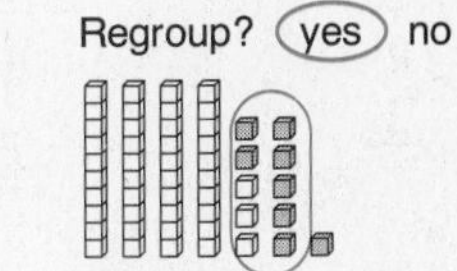

5 tens I one

Use with Grade 2, text pages 139–140.

Extend

Shoomoos

E 5-4 REASONING

These are Shoomoos.

These are not Shoomoos.

Circle the Shoomoos in each group.

1.

2.

3.

4.

Tell a classmate how you found the Shoomoos.

Use with Grade 2, text pages 139–140.

Daily Review

Name ______________________

Daily Review 5-4

Deciding When to Regroup

Use tens and ones models. Complete the chart.

	Do you need to regroup?	How many in all?
1. Show 1 ten 9 ones. Add 2 ones.	(yes) no	2 tens 1 one
2. Show 4 tens 4 ones. Add 5 ones.	yes (no)	4 tens 9 ones
3. Show 3 tens 4 ones. Add 6 ones.	(yes) no	4 tens 0 ones

Problem Solving

Solve. Use models to help.

4. Becky puts 10 stickers on a page. She has 42 stickers.
   How many pages can she fill? 4 pages
   How many stickers will be left over? 2 stickers

5. Max puts 10 stickers on a page. He has 26 stickers.
   How many pages can he fill? 2 pages
   How many stickers will be left over? 6 stickers

Review and Remember

Add.

6. $3+4+1=$ 8 $\quad 5+1+2=$ 8 $\quad 3+3+2=$ 8

7. $4+4+2=$ 10 $\quad 5+1+4=$ 10 $\quad 2+1+7=$ 10

8. $1+2+4=$ 7 $\quad 4+2+2=$ 8 $\quad 5+3+1=$ 9

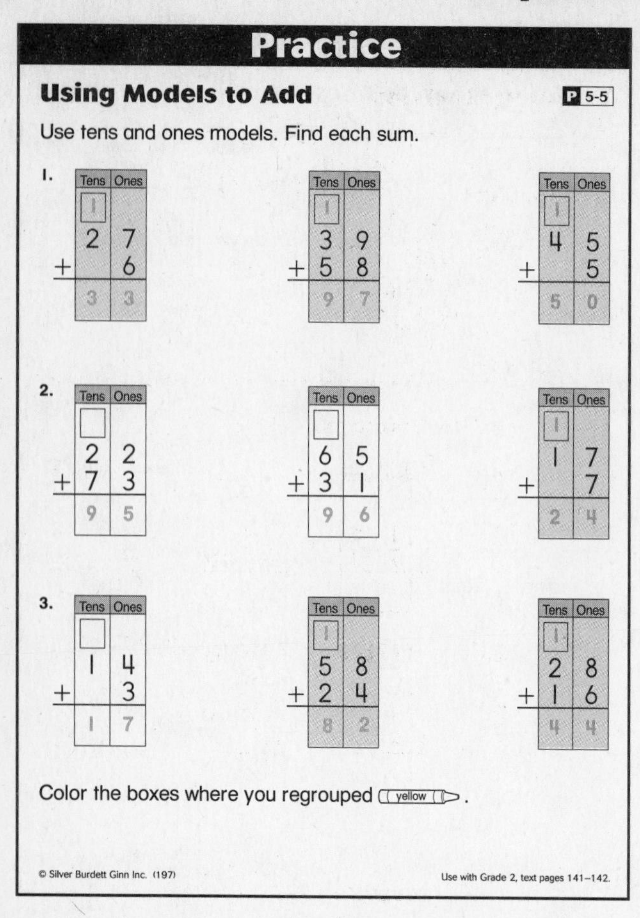

Practice

Using Models to Add

P 5-5

Use tens and ones models. Find each sum.

1. 27 + 6 = 33; 39 + 58 = 97; 45 + 5 = 50

2. 22 + 73 = 95; 65 + 31 = 96; 17 + 7 = 24

3. 14 + 3 = 17; 58 + 24 = 82; 28 + 16 = 44

Color the boxes where you regrouped yellow.

 Use with Grade 2, text pages 141–142.

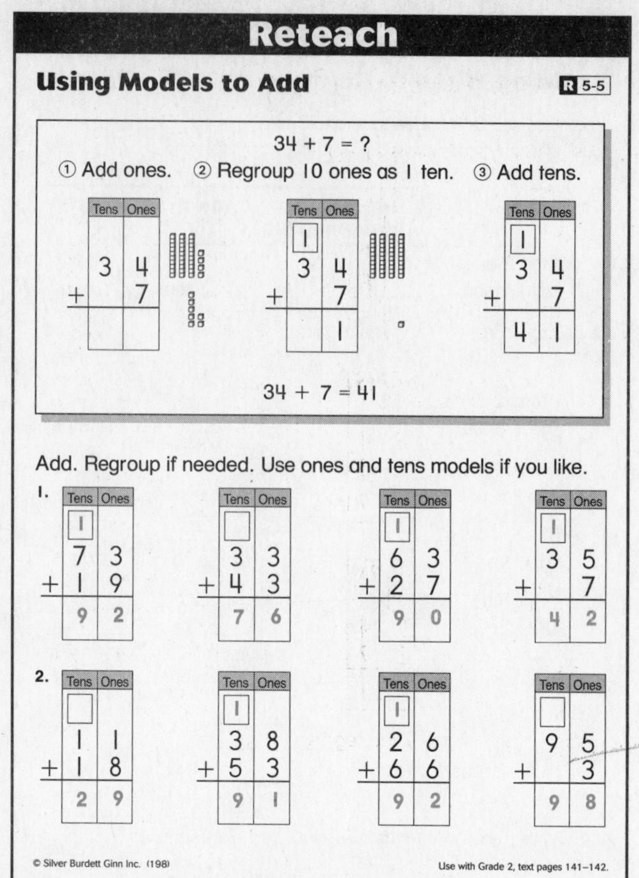

Reteach

Using Models to Add

R 5-5

34 + 7 = ?

① Add ones. ② Regroup 10 ones as 1 ten. ③ Add tens.

34 + 7 = 41

Add. Regroup if needed. Use ones and tens models if you like.

1. 73 + 19 = 92; 33 + 43 = 76; 63 + 27 = 90; 35 + 7 = 42

2. 11 + 18 = 29; 38 + 53 = 91; 26 + 66 = 92; 95 + 3 = 98

 Use with Grade 2, text pages 141–142.

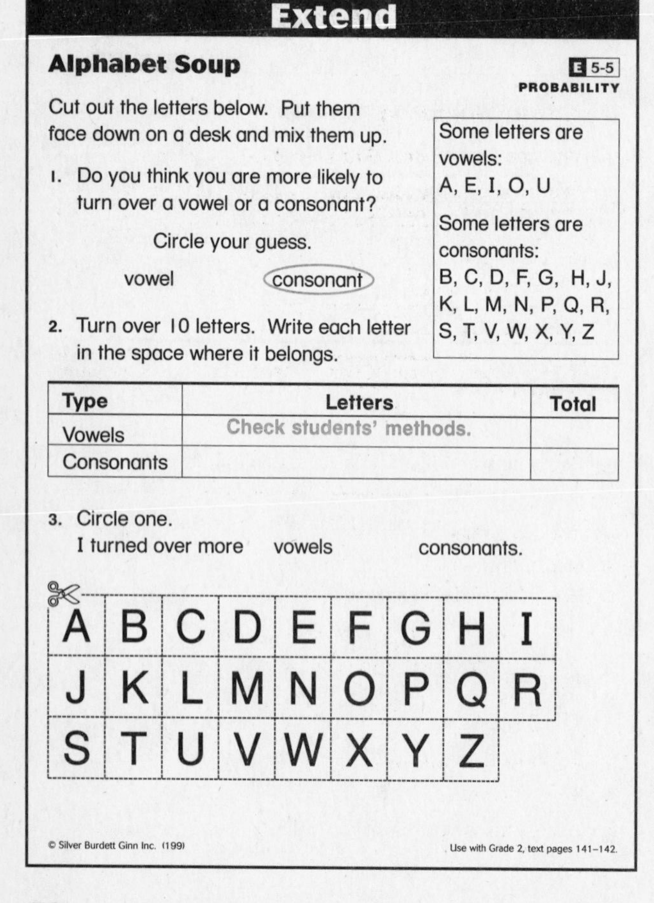

Extend

Alphabet Soup

E 5-5
PROBABILITY

Cut out the letters below. Put them face down on a desk and mix them up.

Some letters are vowels:
A, E, I, O, U

Some letters are consonants:
B, C, D, F, G, H, J, K, L, M, N, P, Q, R, S, T, V, W, X, Y, Z

1. Do you think you are more likely to turn over a vowel or a consonant?

   Circle your guess.

   vowel consonant

2. Turn over 10 letters. Write each letter in the space where it belongs.

Type	Letters	Total
Vowels	Check students' methods.	
Consonants		

3. Circle one.
   I turned over more vowels consonants.

A	B	C	D	E	F	G	H	I
J	K	L	M	N	O	P	Q	R
S	T	U	V	W	X	Y	Z	

 Use with Grade 2, text pages 141–142.

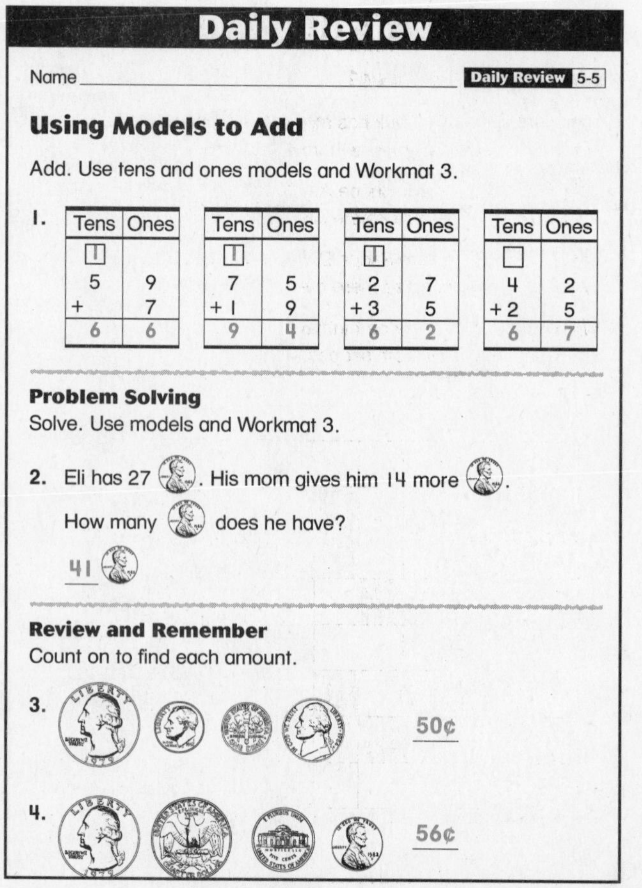

Daily Review

Name ____________ Daily Review 5-5

Using Models to Add

Add. Use tens and ones models and Workmat 3.

1. 59 + 7 = 66; 75 + 19 = 94; 27 + 35 = 62; 42 + 25 = 67

Problem Solving

Solve. Use models and Workmat 3.

2. Eli has 27 ¢. His mom gives him 14 more ¢.
   How many ¢ does he have?
   41 ¢

Review and Remember

Count on to find each amount.

3. 50¢

4. 56¢

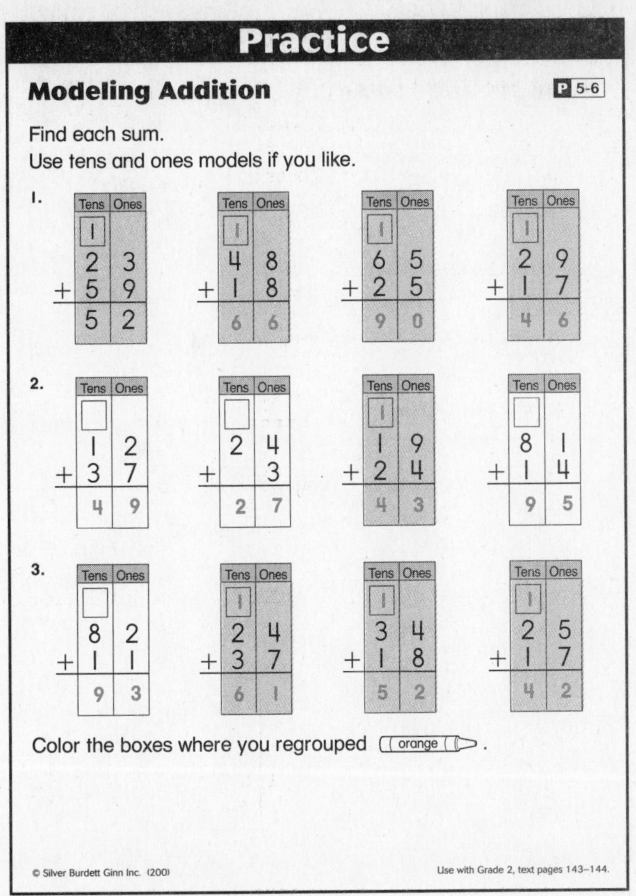

Practice

Modeling Addition

P 5-6

Find each sum.
Use tens and ones models if you like.

1.

	a	b	c	d
Regroup	1	1	1	1
	2 3	4 8	6 5	2 9
+	5 9	1 8	2 5	1 7
Sum	5 2	6 6	9 0	4 6

2.

	a	b	c	d
Regroup	☐	☐	1	☐
	1 2	2 4	1 9	8 1
+	3 7	3	2 4	1 4
Sum	4 9	2 7	4 3	9 5

3.

	a	b	c	d
Regroup	☐	1	1	1
	8 2	2 4	3 4	2 5
+	1 1	3 7	1 8	1 7
Sum	9 3	6 1	5 2	4 2

Color the boxes where you regrouped (orange).

 Use with Grade 2, text pages 143–144.

Reteach

Modeling Addition

R 5-6

① Add ones. Regroup.

Tens	Ones
1	
7	3
+ 1	8
	1

If you regroup, remember to write the 1 in the tens place.

② Add tens.

Tens	Ones
1	
7	3
+ 1	8
9	1

Find each sum. Use tens and ones models.

1.

	a	b	c	d
Regroup	☐	1	1	1
	4 0	1 6	4 7	3 4
+	2 7	7 4	4 6	9
Sum	6 7	9 0	9 3	4 3

2.

	a	b	c	d
Regroup	1	1	☐	1
	5 5	1 8	2 1	7 1
+	7	4 7	8	1 9
Sum	6 2	6 5	2 9	9 0

 Use with Grade 2, text pages 143–144.

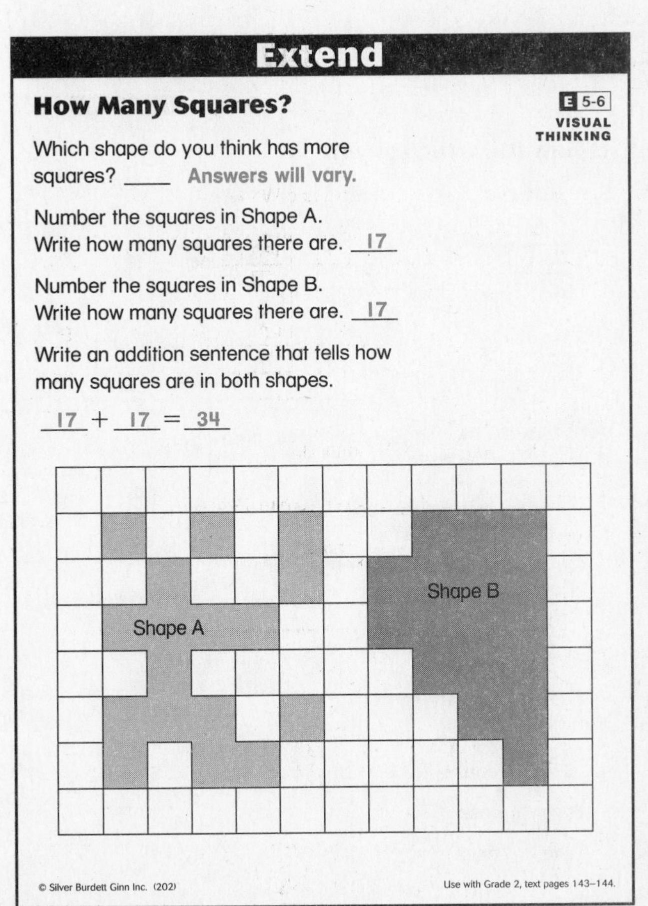

Extend

How Many Squares?

E 5-6 VISUAL THINKING

Which shape do you think has more squares? ____ Answers will vary.

Number the squares in Shape A.
Write how many squares there are. 17

Number the squares in Shape B.
Write how many squares there are. 17

Write an addition sentence that tells how many squares are in both shapes.

17 + 17 = 34

Shape A
Shape B

 Use with Grade 2, text pages 143–144.

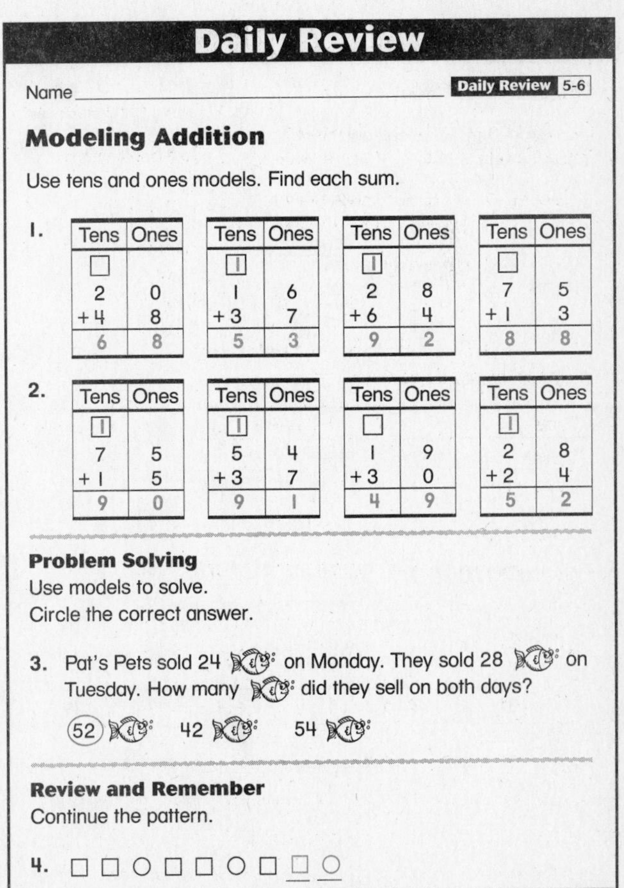

Daily Review

Name ____________________

Daily Review 5-6

Modeling Addition

Use tens and ones models. Find each sum.

1.

	a	b	c	d
Regroup	☐	1	1	☐
	2 0	1 6	2 8	7 5
+	4 8	3 7	6 4	1 3
Sum	6 8	5 3	9 2	8 8

2.

	a	b	c	d
Regroup	1	1	☐	1
	7 5	5 4	1 9	2 8
+	1 5	3 7	3 0	2 4
Sum	9 0	9 1	4 9	5 2

Problem Solving

Use models to solve.
Circle the correct answer.

3. Pat's Pets sold 24 fish on Monday. They sold 28 fish on Tuesday. How many fish did they sell on both days?

(52) fish 42 fish 54 fish

Review and Remember

Continue the pattern.

4. □ □ ○ □ □ ○ □ □ ○

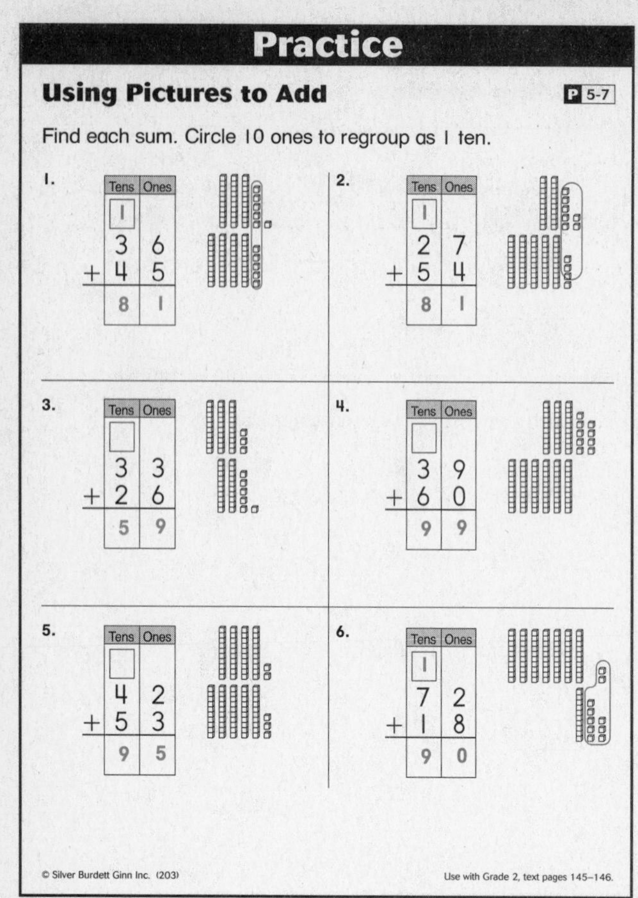

Practice

Using Pictures to Add

P 5-7

Find each sum. Circle 10 ones to regroup as 1 ten.

1.

Tens	Ones
1	
3	6
+ 4	5
8	1

2.

Tens	Ones
1	
2	7
+ 5	4
8	1

3.

Tens	Ones
3	3
+ 2	6
5	9

4.

Tens	Ones
3	9
+ 6	0
9	9

5.

Tens	Ones
4	2
+ 5	3
9	5

6.

Tens	Ones
1	
7	2
+ 1	8
9	0

Use with Grade 2, text pages 145–146.

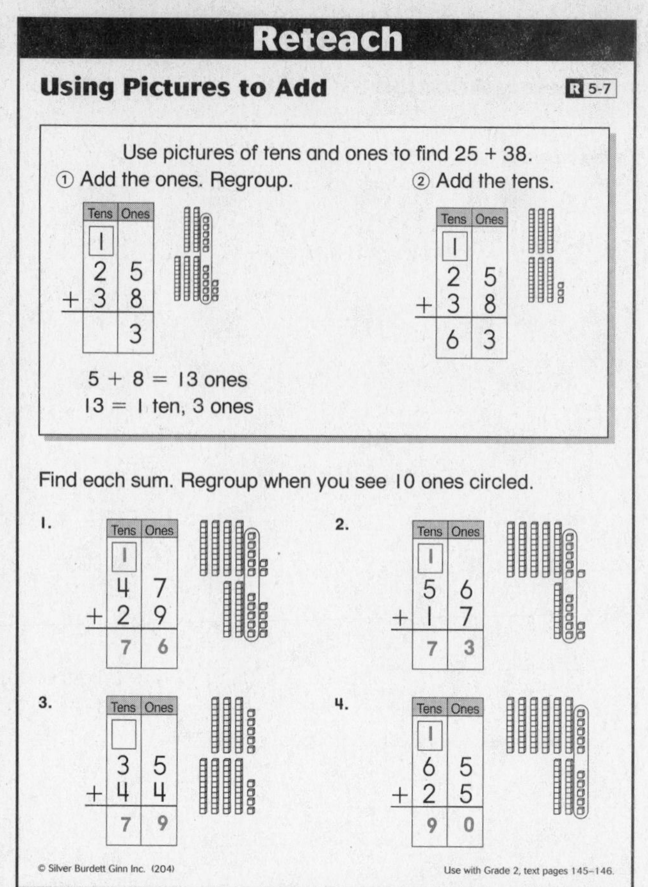

Reteach

Using Pictures to Add

R 5-7

Use pictures of tens and ones to find 25 + 38.

① Add the ones. Regroup.

Tens	Ones
1	
2	5
+ 3	8
	3

5 + 8 = 13 ones
13 = 1 ten, 3 ones

② Add the tens.

Tens	Ones
1	
2	5
+ 3	8
6	3

Find each sum. Regroup when you see 10 ones circled.

1.

Tens	Ones
1	
4	7
+ 2	9
7	6

2.

Tens	Ones
1	
5	6
+ 1	7
7	3

3.

Tens	Ones
3	5
+ 4	4
7	9

4.

Tens	Ones
1	
6	5
+ 2	5
9	0

Use with Grade 2, text pages 145–146.

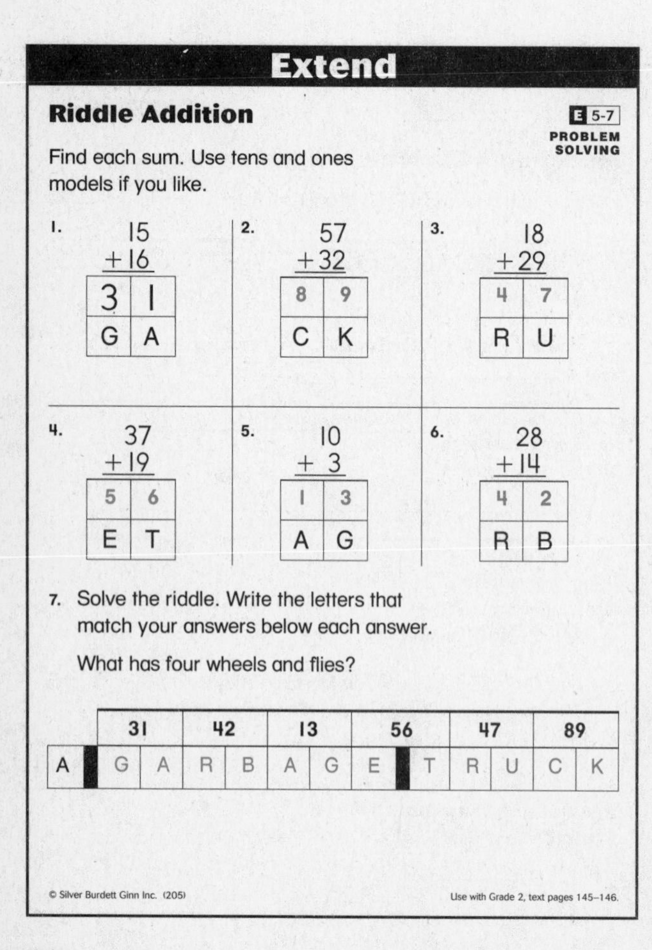

Extend

Riddle Addition

E 5-7
PROBLEM SOLVING

Find each sum. Use tens and ones models if you like.

1. 15 + 16 = 31 (G A)
2. 57 + 32 = 89 (C K)
3. 18 + 29 = 47 (R U)
4. 37 + 19 = 56 (E T)
5. 10 + 3 = 13 (A G)
6. 28 + 14 = 42 (R B)

7. Solve the riddle. Write the letters that match your answers below each answer.

What has four wheels and flies?

	31		42		13		56		47		89	
A	G	A	R	B	A	G	E	T	R	U	C	K

Use with Grade 2, text pages 145–146.

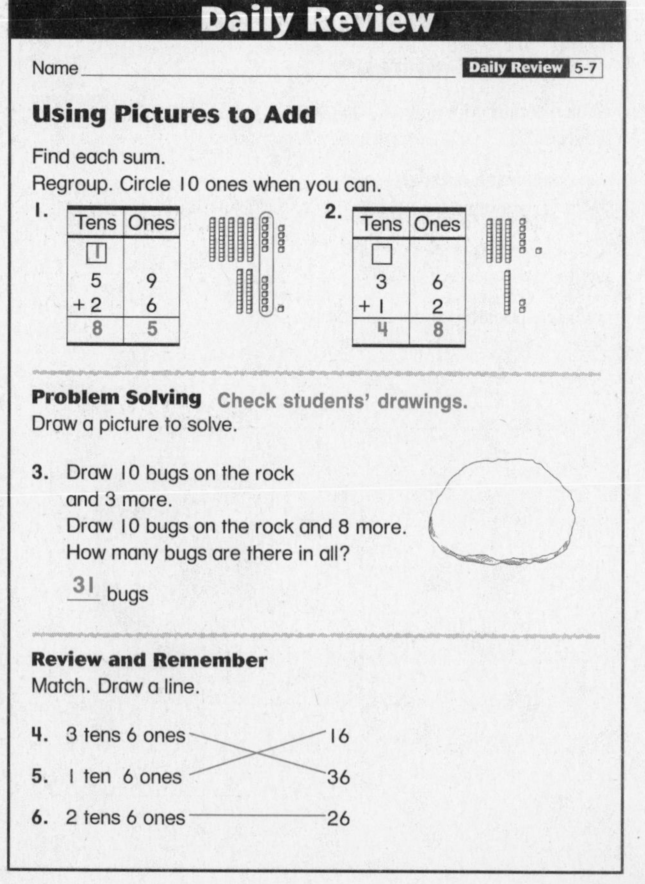

Daily Review

Name ____________________ Daily Review 5-7

Using Pictures to Add

Find each sum.
Regroup. Circle 10 ones when you can.

1.

Tens	Ones
1	
5	9
+ 2	6
8	5

2.

Tens	Ones
3	6
+ 1	2
4	8

Problem Solving Check students' drawings.
Draw a picture to solve.

3. Draw 10 bugs on the rock and 3 more.
Draw 10 bugs on the rock and 8 more.
How many bugs are there in all?
31 bugs

Review and Remember
Match. Draw a line.

4. 3 tens 6 ones — 36
5. 1 ten 6 ones — 16
6. 2 tens 6 ones — 26

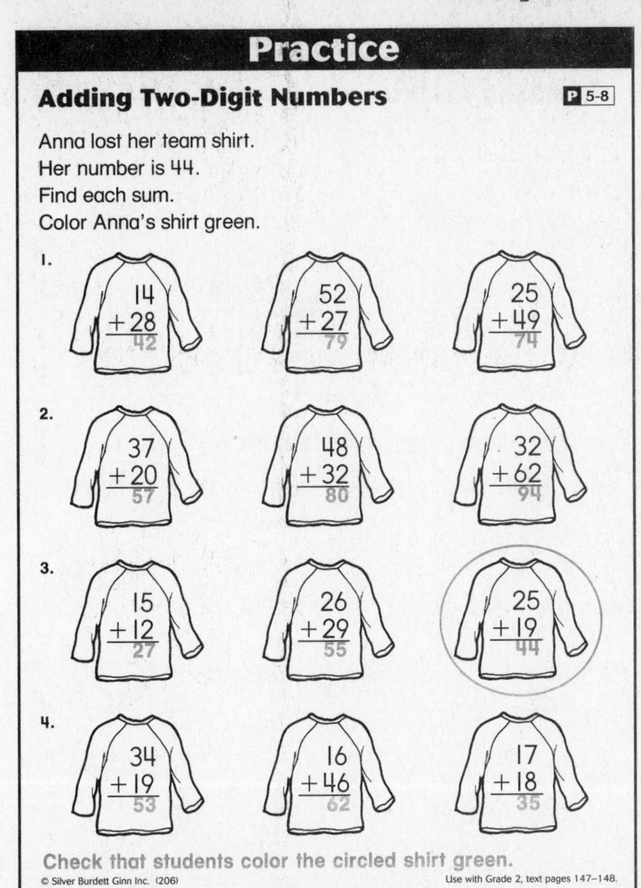

Practice

Adding Two-Digit Numbers

P 5-8

Anna lost her team shirt.
Her number is 44.
Find each sum.
Color Anna's shirt green.

1. 14 + 28 = 42 52 + 27 = 79 25 + 49 = 74

2. 37 + 20 = 57 48 + 32 = 80 32 + 62 = 94

3. 15 + 12 = 27 26 + 29 = 55 25 + 19 = 44

4. 34 + 19 = 53 16 + 46 = 62 17 + 18 = 35

Check that students color the circled shirt green.

 Use with Grade 2, text pages 147–148.

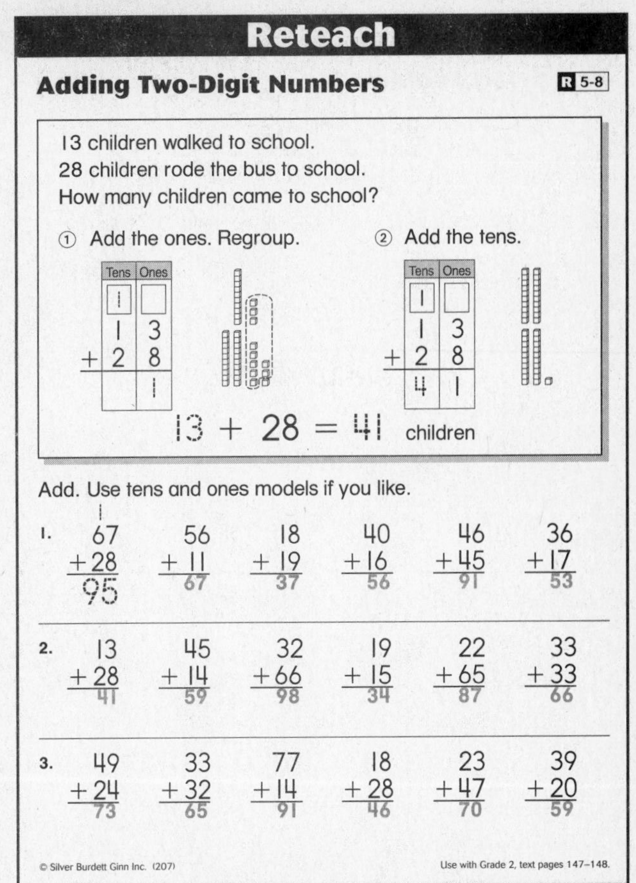

Reteach

Adding Two-Digit Numbers

R 5-8

13 children walked to school.
28 children rode the bus to school.
How many children came to school?

① Add the ones. Regroup. ② Add the tens.

Tens	Ones
1	
1	3
+ 2	8
	1

Tens	Ones
1	
1	3
+ 2	8
4	1

13 + 28 = 41 children

Add. Use tens and ones models if you like.

1. 67 + 28 = 95 56 + 11 = 67 18 + 19 = 37 40 + 16 = 56 46 + 45 = 91 36 + 17 = 53

2. 13 + 28 = 41 45 + 14 = 59 32 + 66 = 98 19 + 15 = 34 22 + 65 = 87 33 + 33 = 66

3. 49 + 24 = 73 33 + 32 = 65 77 + 14 = 91 18 + 28 = 46 23 + 47 = 70 39 + 20 = 59

 Use with Grade 2, text pages 147–148.

Extend

Change a Digit

E 5-8 NUMBER SENSE

Add. Write the sums.
Use tens and ones models if you like.

1. 26 + 17 = 43
Change the **1 ten** to **3 tens.**
What is the new sum? 63

2. 43 + 24 = 67
Change the **3 ones** to **5 ones.**
What is the new sum? 69

3. 56 + 17 = 73
Change the **5 tens** to **4 tens.**
What is the new sum? 63

4. 68 + 4 = 72
Change the **8 ones** to **7 ones.**
What is the new sum? 71

5. 35 + 14 = 49
Change a digit to make the sum 48. Change the 5 ones to 4 ones
(or change 4 ones to 3 ones)

6. 43 + 24 = 67
Change a digit to make the sum 68. Change the 3 ones to 4 ones
(or change 4 ones to 5 ones)

 Use with Grade 2, text pages 147–148.

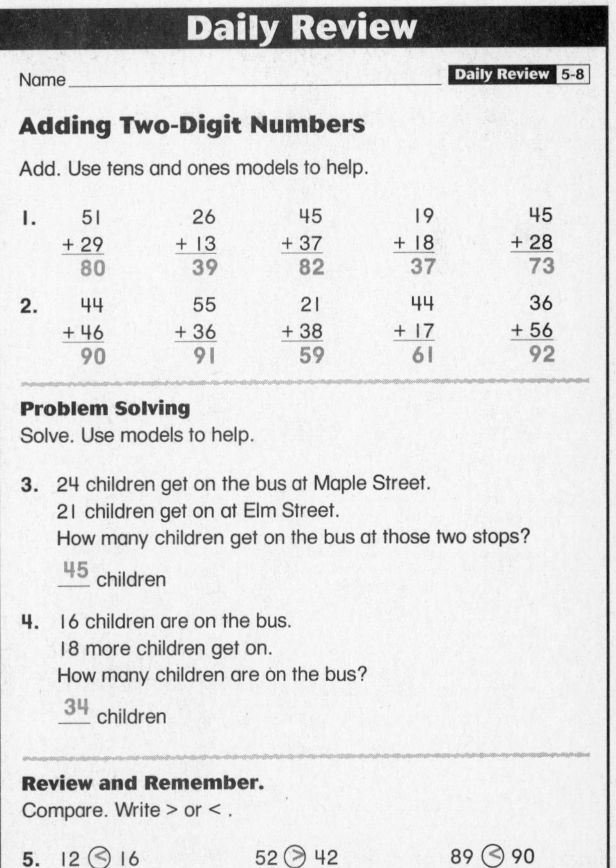

Daily Review

Name ______________________ Daily Review 5-8

Adding Two-Digit Numbers

Add. Use tens and ones models to help.

1. 51 + 29 = 80 26 + 13 = 39 45 + 37 = 82 19 + 18 = 37 45 + 28 = 73

2. 44 + 46 = 90 55 + 36 = 91 21 + 38 = 59 44 + 17 = 61 36 + 56 = 92

Problem Solving
Solve. Use models to help.

3. 24 children get on the bus at Maple Street.
21 children get on at Elm Street.
How many children get on the bus at those two stops?
45 children

4. 16 children are on the bus.
18 more children get on.
How many children are on the bus?
34 children

Review and Remember.
Compare. Write > or < .

5. 12 < 16 52 > 42 89 < 90

Practice

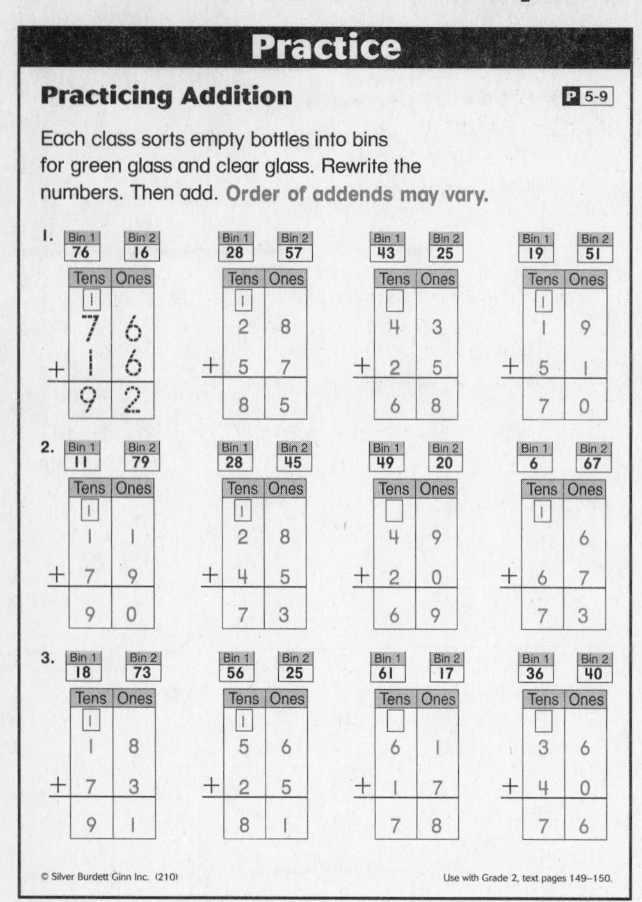

Practicing Addition

P 5-9

Each class sorts empty bottles into bins for green glass and clear glass. Rewrite the numbers. Then add. **Order of addends may vary.**

1.

Bin 1	Bin 2		Bin 1	Bin 2		Bin 1	Bin 2		Bin 1	Bin 2
76	16		28	57		43	25		19	51

Tens	Ones
1	
7	6
+ 1	6
9	2

Tens	Ones
1	
2	8
+ 5	7
8	5

Tens	Ones
4	3
+ 2	5
6	8

Tens	Ones
1	9
+ 5	1
7	0

2.

Bin 1	Bin 2		Bin 1	Bin 2		Bin 1	Bin 2		Bin 1	Bin 2
11	79		28	45		49	20		6	67

Tens	Ones
1	
1	1
+ 7	9
9	0

Tens	Ones
1	
2	8
+ 4	5
7	3

Tens	Ones
4	9
+ 2	0
6	9

Tens	Ones
1	
	6
+ 6	7
7	3

3.

Bin 1	Bin 2		Bin 1	Bin 2		Bin 1	Bin 2		Bin 1	Bin 2
18	73		56	25		61	17		36	40

Tens	Ones
1	
1	8
+ 7	3
9	1

Tens	Ones
1	
5	6
+ 2	5
8	1

Tens	Ones
6	1
+ 1	7
7	8

Tens	Ones
3	6
+ 4	0
7	6

Use with Grade 2, text pages 149–150.

Reteach

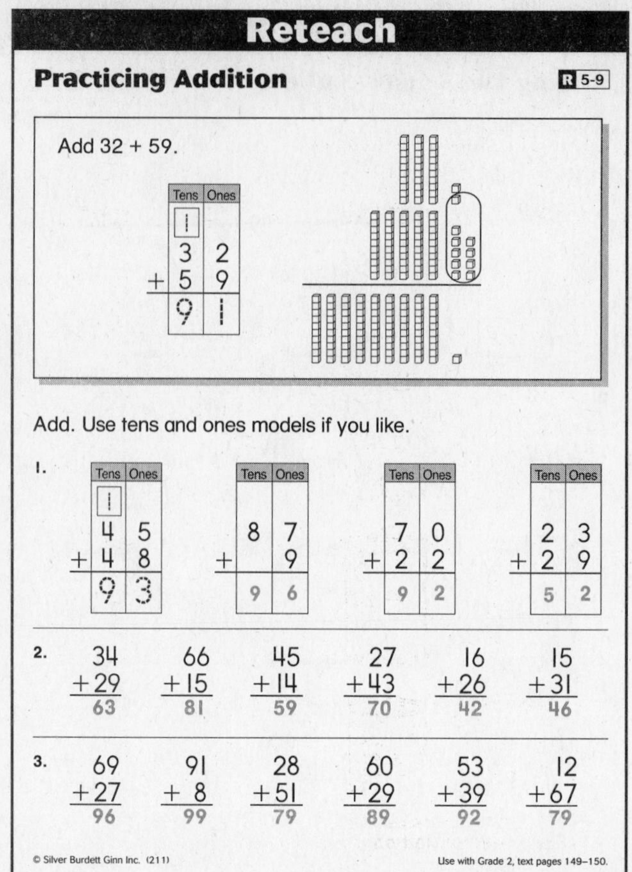

Practicing Addition

R 5-9

Add 32 + 59.

Tens	Ones
1	
3	2
+ 5	9
9	1

Add. Use tens and ones models if you like.

1.

Tens	Ones
1	
4	5
+ 4	8
9	3

Tens	Ones
8	7
+	9
9	6

Tens	Ones
7	0
+ 2	2
9	2

Tens	Ones
2	3
+ 2	9
5	2

2.

34	66	45	27	16	15
+29	+15	+14	+43	+26	+31
63	81	59	70	42	46

3.

69	91	28	60	53	12
+27	+ 8	+51	+29	+39	+67
96	99	79	89	92	79

Use with Grade 2, text pages 149–150.

Extend

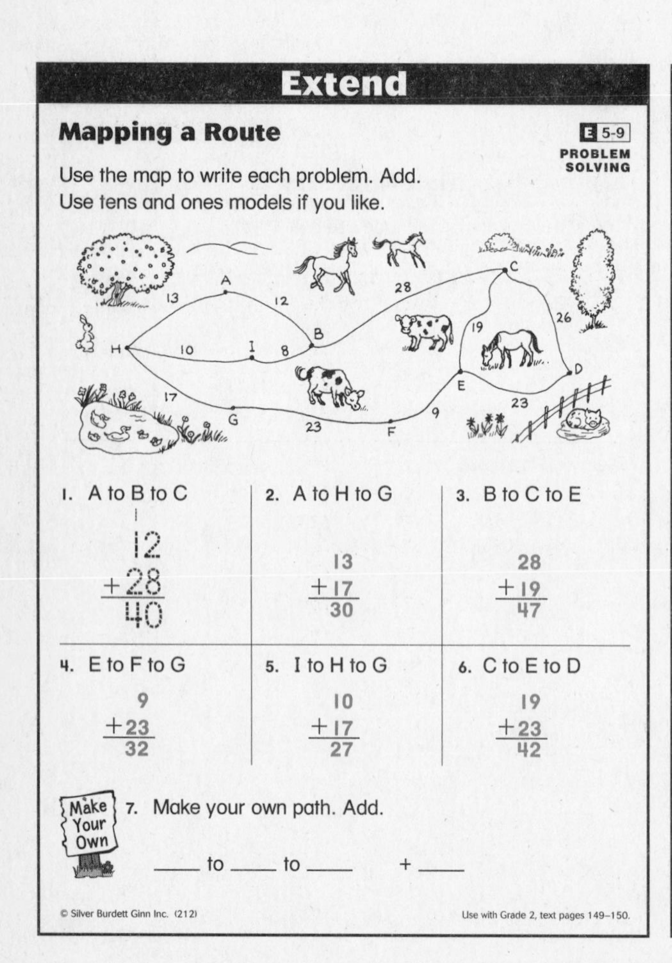

Mapping a Route

E 5-9
PROBLEM SOLVING

Use the map to write each problem. Add.
Use tens and ones models if you like.

1. A to B to C

12
+28
40

2. A to H to G

13
+17
30

3. B to C to E

28
+19
47

4. E to F to G

9
+23
32

5. I to H to G

10
+17
27

6. C to E to D

19
+23
42

7. Make your own path. Add.

_____ to _____ to _____ _____ + _____

Use with Grade 2, text pages 149–150.

Daily Review

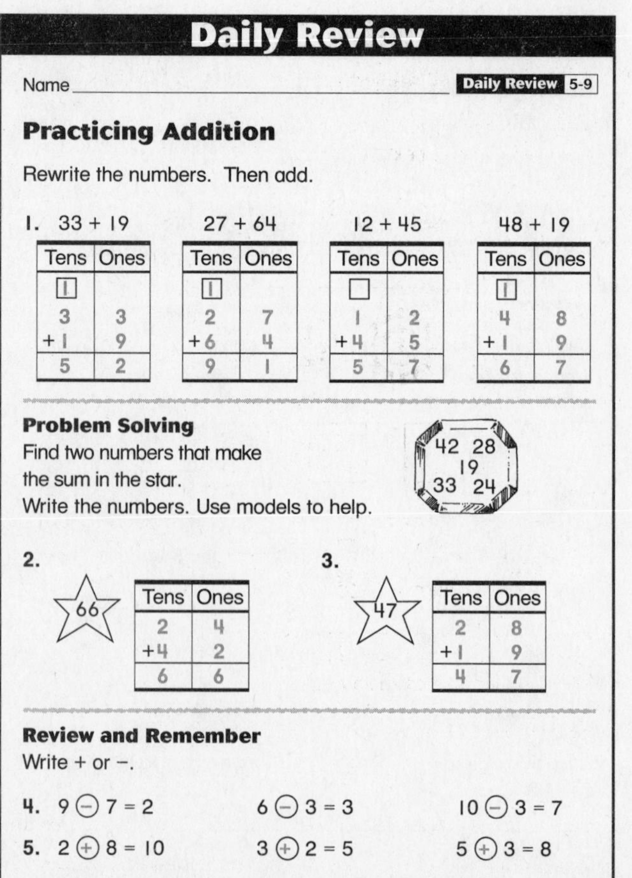

Name _____

Daily Review 5-9

Practicing Addition

Rewrite the numbers. Then add.

1. 33 + 19 27 + 64 12 + 45 48 + 19

Tens	Ones
1	
3	3
+ 1	9
5	2

Tens	Ones
1	
2	7
+ 6	4
9	1

Tens	Ones
1	2
+ 4	5
5	7

Tens	Ones
1	
4	8
+ 1	9
6	7

Problem Solving

Find two numbers that make the sum in the star. Write the numbers. Use models to help.

42 28
19
33 24

2. ⭐66

Tens	Ones
2	4
+4	2
6	6

3. ⭐47

Tens	Ones
2	8
+1	9
4	7

Review and Remember

Write + or −.

4. 9 ⊖ 7 = 2 6 ⊖ 3 = 3 10 ⊖ 3 = 7

5. 2 ⊕ 8 = 10 3 ⊕ 2 = 5 5 ⊕ 3 = 8

Practice

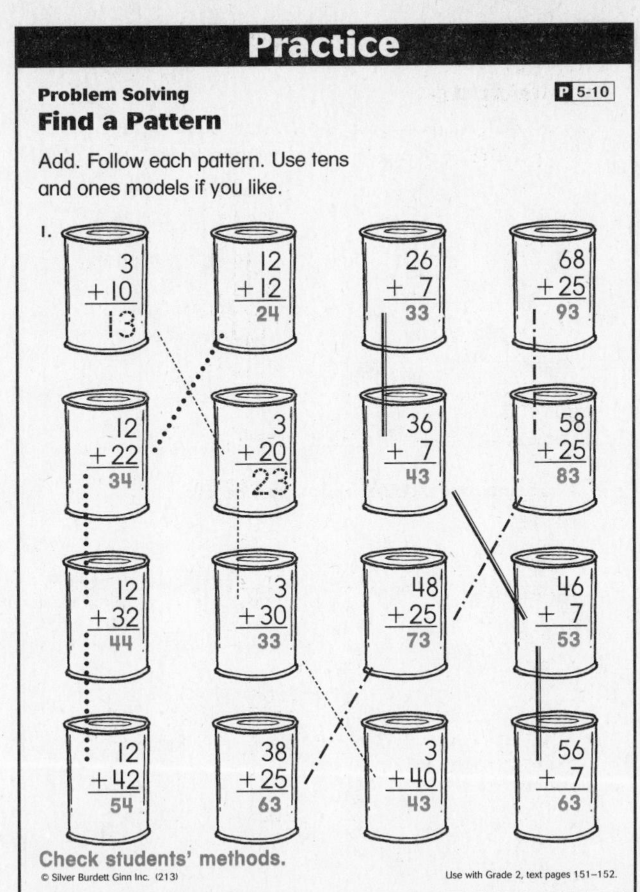

Problem Solving
Find a Pattern

P 5-10

Add. Follow each pattern. Use tens and ones models if you like.

1.

3 + 10 = 13	12 + 12 = 24	26 + 7 = 33	68 + 25 = 93
12 + 22 = 34	3 + 20 = 23	36 + 7 = 43	58 + 25 = 83
12 + 32 = 44	3 + 30 = 33	48 + 25 = 73	46 + 7 = 53
12 + 42 = 54	38 + 25 = 63	3 + 40 = 43	56 + 7 = 63

Check students' methods.

Use with Grade 2, text pages 151–152.

Reteach

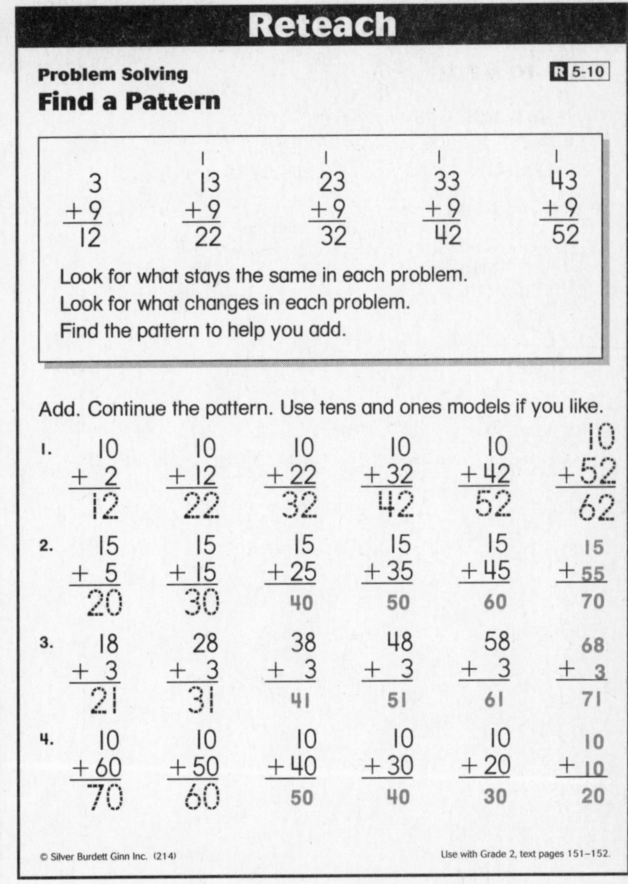

Problem Solving
Find a Pattern

R 5-10

3	13	23	33	43
+9	+9	+9	+9	+9
12	22	32	42	52

Look for what stays the same in each problem.
Look for what changes in each problem.
Find the pattern to help you add.

Add. Continue the pattern. Use tens and ones models if you like.

1.	10 + 2 = 12	10 + 12 = 22	10 + 22 = 32	10 + 32 = 42	10 + 42 = 52	10 + 52 = 62
2.	15 + 5 = 20	15 + 15 = 30	15 + 25 = 40	15 + 35 = 50	15 + 45 = 60	15 + 55 = 70
3.	18 + 3 = 21	28 + 3 = 31	38 + 3 = 41	48 + 3 = 51	58 + 3 = 61	68 + 3 = 71
4.	10 + 60 = 70	10 + 50 = 60	10 + 40 = 50	10 + 30 = 40	10 + 20 = 30	10 + 10 = 20

Use with Grade 2, text pages 151–152.

Extend

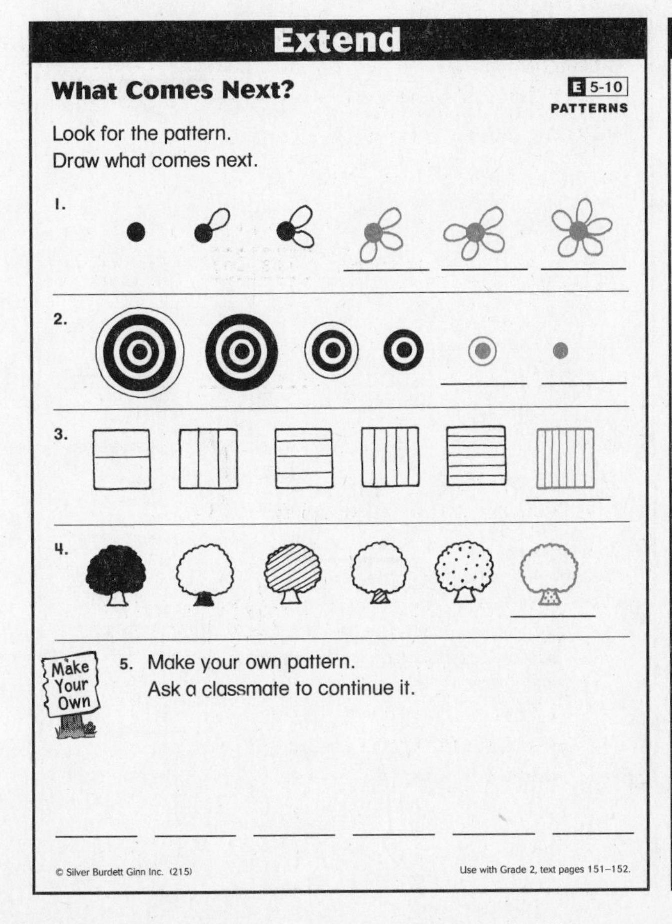

What Comes Next?

E 5-10
PATTERNS

Look for the pattern.
Draw what comes next.

1.

2.

3.

4.

Make Your Own

5. Make your own pattern.
Ask a classmate to continue it.

Use with Grade 2, text pages 151–152.

Daily Review

Name ____________________

Daily Review 5-10

Problem Solving
Find a Pattern

Add. Continue the pattern.
Write the next two addition facts.
Use tens and ones models if you like.

1.	4 + 7 = 11	4 + 17 = 21	4 + 27 = 31	4 + 37 = 41	4 + 47 = 51	4 + 57 = 61
2.	37 + 60 = 97	37 + 50 = 87	37 + 40 = 77	37 + 30 = 67	37 + 20 = 57	37 + 10 = 47
3.	23 + 52 = 75	23 + 42 = 65	23 + 32 = 55	23 + 22 = 45	23 + 12 = 35	23 + 2 = 25

Review and Remember

Look at the picture.
Complete the fact family.

4.

6 + 5 = 11   11 − 5 = 6
5 + 6 = 11   11 − 6 = 5

5.

8 + 4 = 12   12 − 8 = 4
4 + 8 = 12   12 − 4 = 8

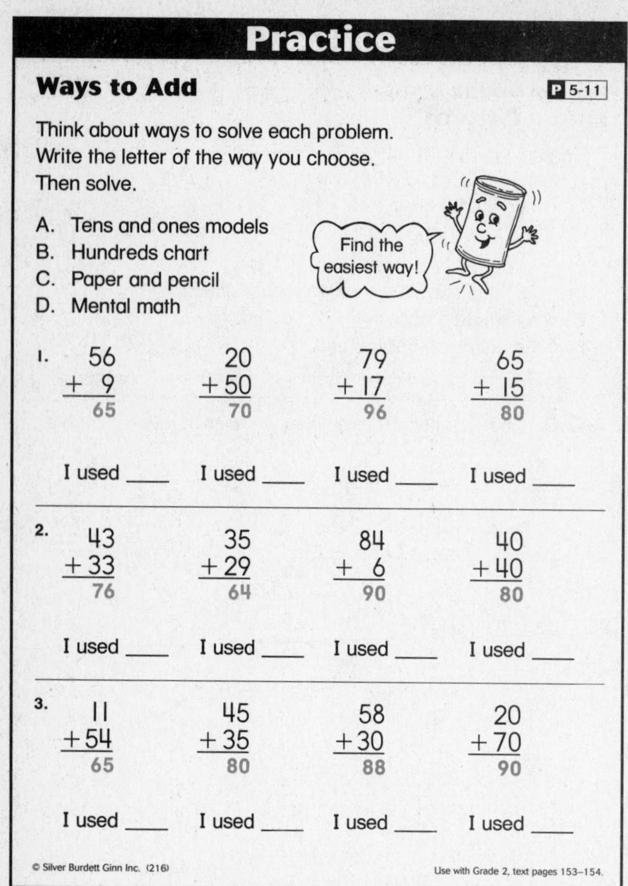

Practice

Ways to Add P 5-11

Think about ways to solve each problem.
Write the letter of the way you choose.
Then solve.

A. Tens and ones models
B. Hundreds chart
C. Paper and pencil
D. Mental math

1. 56 + 9 = 65 I used ___ | 20 + 50 = 70 I used ___ | 79 + 17 = 96 I used ___ | 65 + 15 = 80 I used ___

2. 43 + 33 = 76 I used ___ | 35 + 29 = 64 I used ___ | 84 + 6 = 90 I used ___ | 40 + 40 = 80 I used ___

3. 11 + 54 = 65 I used ___ | 45 + 35 = 80 I used ___ | 58 + 30 = 88 I used ___ | 20 + 70 = 90 I used ___

 Use with Grade 2, text pages 153–154.

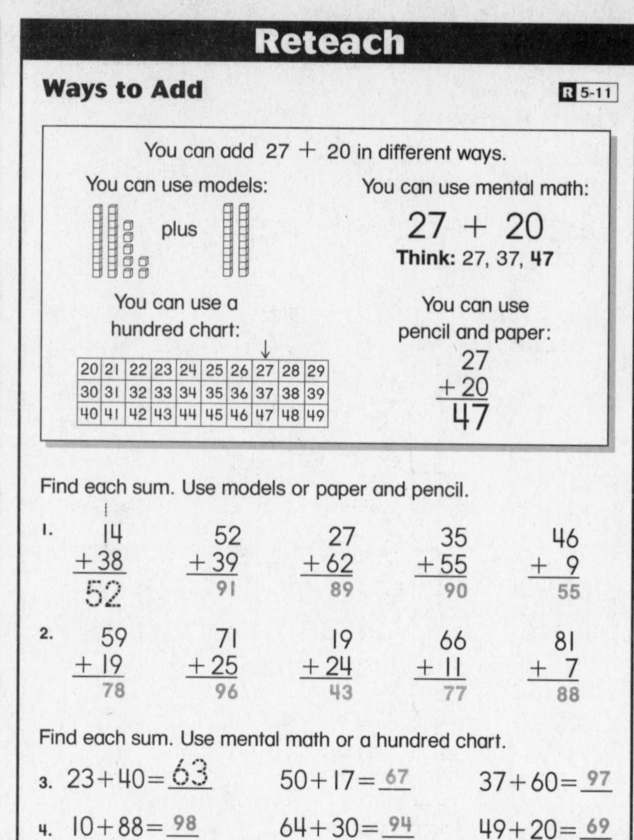

Reteach

Ways to Add R 5-11

You can add 27 + 20 in different ways.

You can use models: plus

You can use mental math: 27 + 20 **Think:** 27, 37, **47**

You can use a hundred chart:

20	21	22	23	24	25	26	27	28	29
30	31	32	33	34	35	36	37	38	39
40	41	42	43	44	45	46	47	48	49

You can use pencil and paper: 27 + 20 = 47

Find each sum. Use models or paper and pencil.

1. 14 + 38 = 52 | 52 + 39 = 91 | 27 + 62 = 89 | 35 + 55 = 90 | 46 + 9 = 55

2. 59 + 19 = 78 | 71 + 25 = 96 | 19 + 24 = 43 | 66 + 11 = 77 | 81 + 7 = 88

Find each sum. Use mental math or a hundred chart.

3. 23 + 40 = 63 | 50 + 17 = 67 | 37 + 60 = 97

4. 10 + 88 = 98 | 64 + 30 = 94 | 49 + 20 = 69

 Use with Grade 2, text pages 153–154.

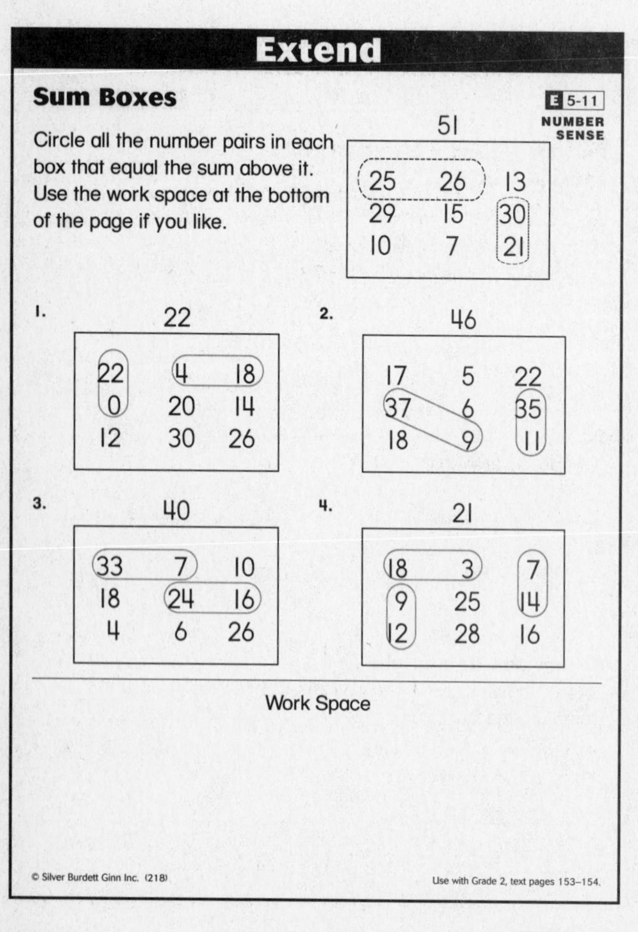

Extend

Sum Boxes E 5-11 NUMBER SENSE

Circle all the number pairs in each box that equal the sum above it. Use the work space at the bottom of the page if you like.

51

25	26	13
29	15	30
10	7	21

1. 22

22	4	18
0	20	14
12	30	26

2. 46

17	5	22
37	6	35
18	9	11

3. 40

33	7	10
18	24	16
4	6	26

4. 21

18	3	7
9	25	14
12	28	16

Work Space

 Use with Grade 2, text pages 153–154.

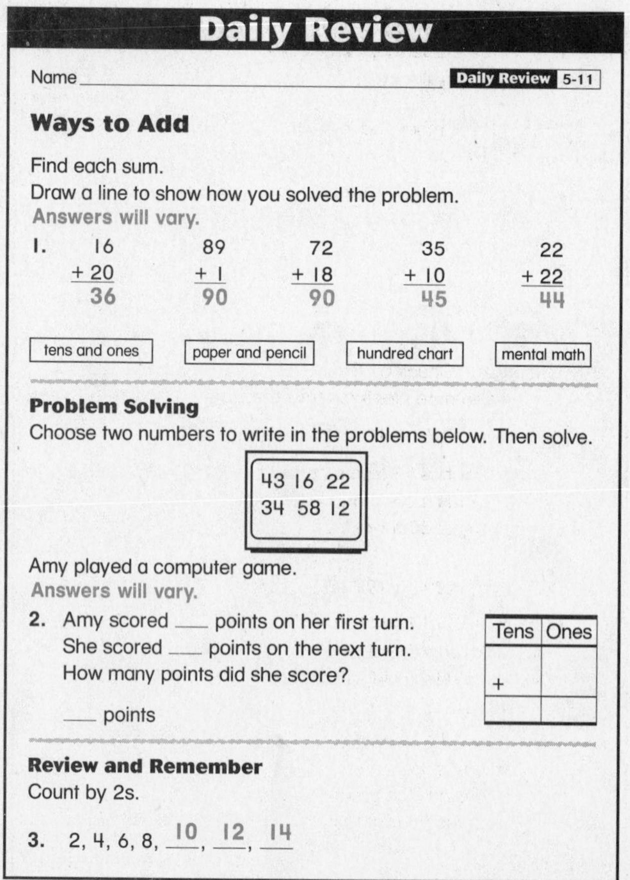

Daily Review

Name ______________________ Daily Review 5-11

Ways to Add

Find each sum.
Draw a line to show how you solved the problem.
Answers will vary.

1. 16 + 20 = 36 | 89 + 1 = 90 | 72 + 18 = 90 | 35 + 10 = 45 | 22 + 22 = 44

tens and ones | paper and pencil | hundred chart | mental math

Problem Solving

Choose two numbers to write in the problems below. Then solve.

43	16	22
34	58	12

Amy played a computer game.
Answers will vary.

2. Amy scored ___ points on her first turn.
She scored ___ points on the next turn.
How many points did she score?

___ points

Tens	Ones
+	

Review and Remember

Count by 2s.

3. 2, 4, 6, 8, 10, 12, 14

Practice

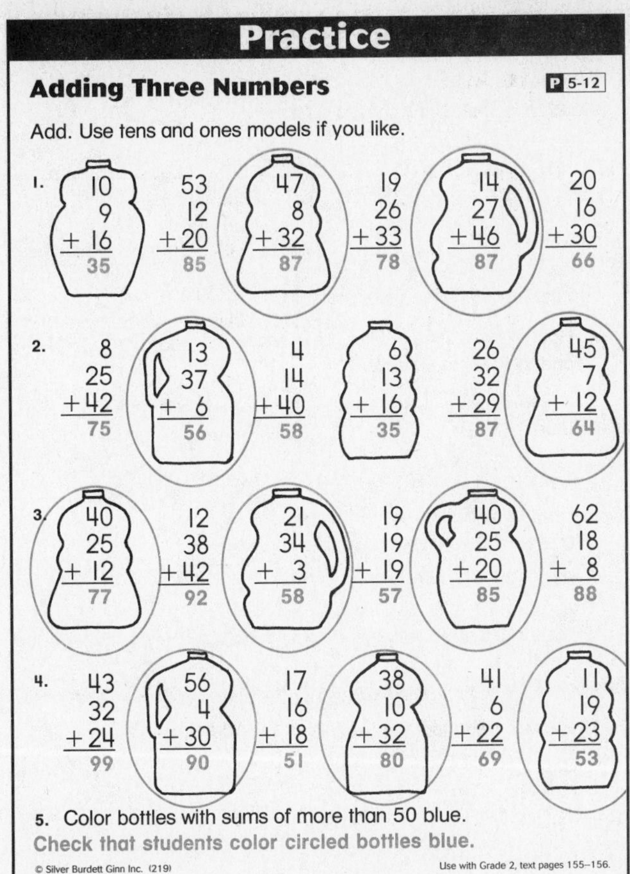

Adding Three Numbers

P 5-12

Add. Use tens and ones models if you like.

1.	10	53	47	19	14	20
	9	12	8	26	27	16
	+ 16	+ 20	+ 32	+ 33	+ 46	+ 30
	35	85	87	78	87	66
2.	8	13	4	6	26	45
	25	37	14	13	32	7
	+ 42	+ 6	+ 40	+ 16	+ 29	+ 12
	75	56	58	35	87	64
3.	40	12	21	19	40	62
	25	38	34	19	25	18
	+ 12	+ 42	+ 3	+ 19	+ 20	+ 8
	77	92	58	57	85	88
4.	43	56	17	38	41	11
	32	4	16	10	6	19
	+ 24	+ 30	+ 18	+ 32	+ 22	+ 23
	99	90	51	80	69	53

5. Color bottles with sums of more than 50 blue.

Check that students color circled bottles blue.

Use with Grade 2, text pages 155–156.

Reteach

Adding Three Numbers

R 5-12

Una's class found 13 green bottles, 32 clear bottles, and 27 brown bottles. How many bottles in all?

① Add the ones. Regroup.

13
32
+ 27
2

3 + 2 = 5
5 + 7 = 12

12 ones

② Add the tens.

1 + 1 = 2
2 + 3 = 5
5 + 2 = 7

7 tens

13
32
+ 27
72

Add. Use tens and ones models if you like.

1.	10	51	26	12	13
	9	23	18	12	21
	+ 5	+ 21	+ 24	+ 15	+ 35
	24	95	68	39	69
2.	63	44	27	58	24
	11	36	9	31	45
	+ 19	+ 4	+ 13	+ 3	+ 20
	93	84	49	92	89
3.	38	23	8	53	32
	14	25	42	33	30
	+ 26	+ 27	+ 37	+ 13	+ 17
	78	75	87	99	79

Use with Grade 2, text pages 155–156.

Extend

Use the Clues

E 5-12
REASONING

Three of these numbers added together make 83.

Sum 83 5 2 44 12 19 10 20

44
19
+ 20
83

Read the clues. Check by finding the sum. Circle the three numbers that make the sum.

1. **Sum 72** 36 12 (25) 7 (33) (14)

One number has the same number in both digits.
One number is more than 12 and less than 25.
One number is 20 more than 5.

2. **Sum 80** 29 (19) (49) (12) 20 11

One number is 10 more than 9.
One number is the sum of 27 + 22.
One number is the sum of 9 + 3.

3. **Sum 88** 24 31 (17) (43) (28) 35

One number is the sum of 17 + 11.
One number has the greatest value.
One number is 9 more than 8.

Use with Grade 2, text pages 155–156.

Daily Review

Name ____________________

Daily Review 5-12

Adding Three Numbers

Add. Use tens and ones models to help.

1.	36	17	2	44	80
	8	24	15	21	5
	+ 20	+ 5	+ 74	+ 9	+ 10
	64	46	91	74	95
2.	55	43	7	5	22
	14	28	77	40	38
	+ 7	+ 25	+ 1	+ 33	+ 15
	76	96	85	78	75

Problem Solving

Solve.
Use models to help.

Tigers	Bobcats
14	8
16	22
7	12

3. Which team scored 37 points? Tigers

4. Which team scored more points? Bobcats

Review and Remember

Write the amount in cents.

5. 100¢

Practice

Problem Solving P 5-13

Getting Data From a Table

The table shows how many cans the class collected every day for a week.

Cans Collected

Day	Mon.	Tues.	Wed.	Thurs.	Fri.
Number of cans	12	6	23	19	8

Use the table to solve the problems. Show your work.

1. Write the two days when the least number of cans were collected.
   Tuesday ______ Friday ______
2. How many cans were collected on Thursday and Friday together? 27
3. Write the two days when the most cans were collected.
   Wednesday ______ Thursday ______
4. How many cans were collected on Monday and Wednesday together? 35
5. How many cans were collected in all on the day that the least cans were collected and the day that the most cans were collected? 29

 Use with Grade 2, text pages 157–158.

Reteach

Problem Solving R 5-13

Getting Data From a Table

Bottles Collected

Team	Green	Red	Blue
Number of bottles	38	27	13

Use the table to solve each problem.

1. How many bottles did the green team and the blue team collect?
   Green 38
   Blue +13
   51

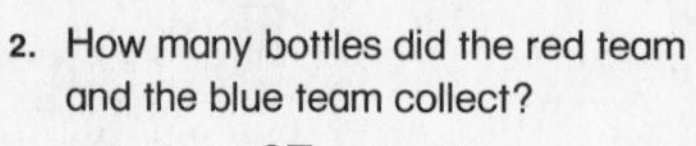

2. How many bottles did the red team and the blue team collect?
   Red 27
   Blue +13
   40

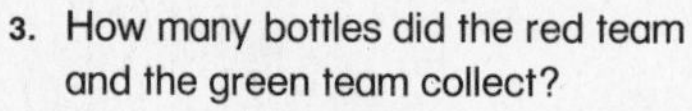

3. How many bottles did the red team and the green team collect?
   Red 27
   Green + 38
   65

 Use with Grade 2, text pages 157–158.

Extend

Pounds of Paper

E 5-13 DATA

The table shows how many pounds of paper two classes collected every day for a week.

Pounds of Paper Collected

Class	Mon.	Tues.	Wed.	Thurs.	Fri.
2-E	23	15	18	14	9
2-W	19	8	7	26	21

Use the table to solve each problem.

1. Write the total number of pounds collected by both classes on each day.
   Monday 42 Tuesday 23 Wednesday 25 Thursday 40 Friday 30
2. Circle in blue the day the most pounds were collected.
3. Circle in red the day the fewest pounds were collected.
   Check that students circle Monday in blue and Tuesday in red.
4. Circle one. Estimate the total number of pounds collected by both classes during the week.
   (more than **100**) less than **100**
5. Write the total number of pounds collected by each class. 79 2-E 81 2-W
6. How many pounds of paper were collected in all during the week? 160 pounds

 Use with Grade 2, text pages 157–158.

Daily Review

Name ______________________ **Daily Review 5-13**

Problem Solving

Getting Data From a Table

Every month for six months, second graders collected books for a book fair. The table shows how many books they collected.

Books Collected

Month	Number of Books
October	12
November	17
December	23
January	9
February	11
March	18

1. How many more books did they collect during December than January? 14 books
   23
   − 9
   14
2. During which two months did they collect the most books?
   December and March
3. How many books did they collect those months? 41 books
   23
   +18
   41

Review and Remember

Circle the set of coins needed to buy the item.

4. 

5. 

Chapter 6 • Lesson 1

Practice

Subtracting Tens

P 6-1

Find each difference. Write the missing numbers.
Use tens models if you like.

1. 2 tens − 1 ten = 1 ten
   20 − 10 = 10
2. 4 tens − 1 ten = 3 tens
   40 − 10 = 30
3. 5 tens − 2 tens = 3 tens
   50 − 20 = 30
4. 6 tens − 3 tens = 3 tens
   60 − 30 = 30
5. 7 tens − 5 tens = 2 tens
   70 − 50 = 20
6. 8 tens − 6 tens = 2 tens
   80 − 60 = 20
7. 9 tens − 4 tens = 5 tens
   90 − 40 = 50
8. 3 tens − 1 ten = 2 tens
   30 − 10 = 20

Use with Grade 2, text pages 165–166.

Reteach

Subtracting Tens

R 6-1

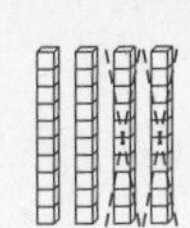
4 tens − 2 tens = 2 tens
40 − 20 = 20

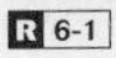
Think
4 − 2 = 2.

Cross out to find each difference.

1. 80 − 30 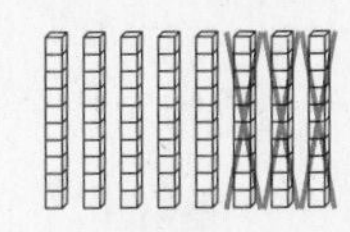 8 tens − 3 tens = 5 tens
   80 − 30 = 50
2. 60 − 20 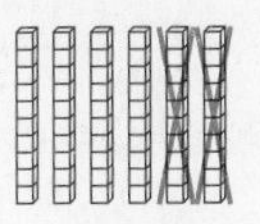 6 tens − 2 tens = 4 tens
   60 − 20 = 40
3. 30 − 10 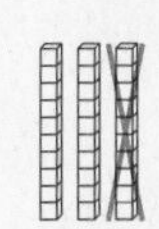 3 tens − 1 ten = 2 tens
   30 − 10 = 20
4. 70 − 40 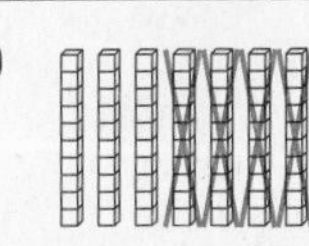 7 tens − 4 tens = 3 tens
   70 − 40 = 30

Use with Grade 2, text pages 165–166.

Extend

Look-Alikes

E 6-1
REASONING

Look at the numbers in each sea star. Decide how they are alike. Write another number that belongs to the group.

1. 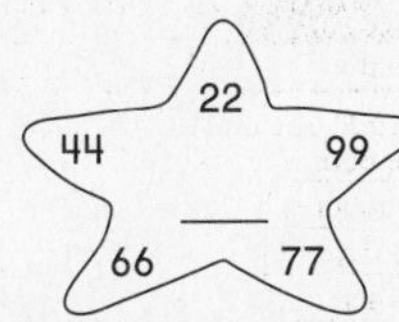

Check that number has identical digits.

2. 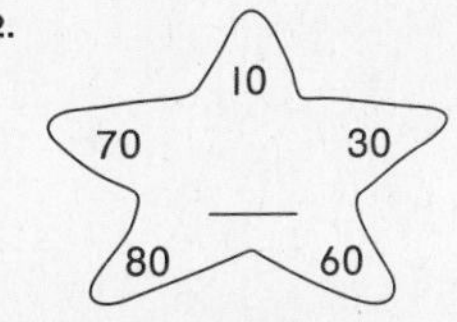

Check that number is a multiple of 10.

3. Make two groups of your own with these numbers. Add another number to each group.
Check that one group has multiples of 2 and the other has numbers with 5 in the ones place.

12 35 45 18 16 65 14 85

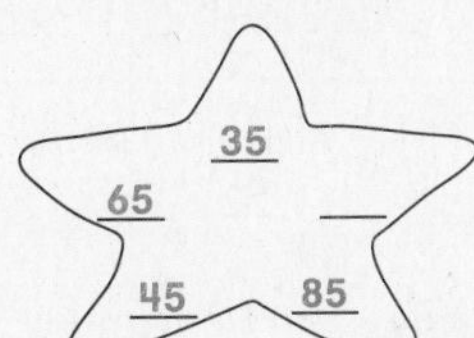

4. Write how the numbers you chose are alike.

Check students' descriptions.

Use with Grade 2, text pages 165–166.

Daily Review

Name ________________

Daily Review 6-1

Subtracting Tens

Find each difference. Write the missing numbers.
Use models if you like.

1. 6 tens − 3 tens = 3 tens
   60 − 30 = 30
2. 8 tens − 5 tens = 3 tens
   80 − 50 = 30
3. 4 tens − 2 tens = 2 tens
   40 − 20 = 20
4. 9 tens − 4 tens = 5 tens
   90 − 40 = 50

Problem Solving
Solve. Use models to help.

5. There are 10 stamps in each book.
   Jean buys 5 books.
   She uses 20 stamps.
   How many stamps does she have left? 30 stamps
6. There are 10 rolls in a pack.
   Matt buys 7 packs.
   He and his friends eat 10 rolls.
   How many rolls are left? 60 rolls

Review and Remember
Circle the amounts that equal 25¢.

7.     

Practice

Counting Back by Tens

P 6-2

Count back by tens to subtract.
Use Workmat 5 if you like.

1.

Subtract 10	
47	37
97	87
57	47
37	27
67	57

2.

Subtract 20	
42	22
92	72
22	2
52	32
72	52

3.

Subtract 30	
45	15
75	45
55	25
35	5
65	35

4.

Subtract 10	
13	3
93	83
53	43
83	73
23	13

5.

Subtract 20	
94	74
24	4
54	34
34	14
84	64

6.

Subtract 30	
39	9
49	19
69	39
99	69
59	29

 Use with Grade 2, text pages 167–168.

Reteach

Counting Back by Tens

R 6-2

0	1	2	3	4	5	6	7	8	9
10	11	12	13	14	15	16	17	18	19
20	21	22	23	24	25	26	27	28	29
30	31	32	33	34	35	36	37	38	39
40	41	42	43	44	45	46	47	48	49

24 − 20 = ?

Start at 24. Count back 2 tens. → 14, 4

24 − 20 = 4

Use the chart. Count back by tens to subtract.

1. 36 − 10
   Start at 36.
   Count back 1 ten.
   36 − 10 = 26

2. 44 − 30
   Start at 44.
   Count back 3 tens.
   44 − 30 = 14

3. 29 − 20
   Start at 29.
   Count back 2 tens.
   29 − 20 = 9

4. 38 − 30
   Start at 38.
   Count back 3 tens.
   38 − 30 = 8

 Use with Grade 2, text pages 167–168.

Extend

Moving Backward

E 6-2

PROBABILITY

What You Need
pencil
paper clip

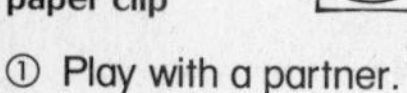

① Play with a partner.
② Start with a playing piece at 55. Take turns spinning.
③ Follow the directions to add or subtract. Then move your piece.
④ The first player to reach the top or bottom wins.

−30 +10 −20 −20 +20 −10

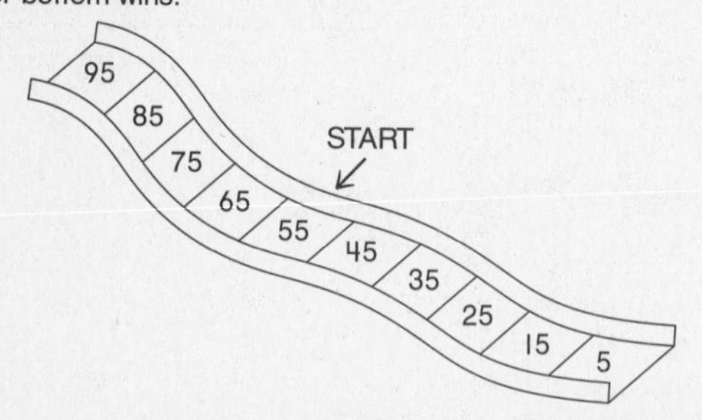

1. Did you move up or down most often? Most likely down
2. Write why you think that happened.
   Check that students realize there are more subtraction directions than addition directions on the spinner.

 Use with Grade 2, text pages 167–168.

Daily Review

Name ____________

Daily Review 6-2

Counting Back by Tens

Count back by tens to subtract.
Use Workmat 5 if you like.

1. 45 − 20 = 25 32 − 10 = 22 61 − 30 = 31
2. 46 − 10 = 36 57 − 30 = 27 28 − 10 = 18
3. 84 − 20 = 64 93 − 30 = 63 76 − 20 = 56

Problem Solving
Solve. Use the table. Use models to help.

Ticket Sales for the Play	
Thursday	52
Friday	40
Saturday	65
Sunday	50

4. Did more people come to the play on Friday or Saturday? Saturday

5. How many more people came on Saturday than on Sunday? 15 people

Review and Remember
Use doubles to add.

6. 4 + 4 = 8 3 + 3 = 6 5 + 5 = 10
   4 + 5 = 9 3 + 4 = 7 5 + 6 = 11

Practice

Deciding When to Regroup

P 6-3

Complete the chart. Use tens and ones models if you like.

Start with	Take away	Regroup?	How many are left?
1. 2 tens 5 ones	6 ones	(yes) no	1 ten 9 ones
2. 3 tens 6 ones	5 ones	yes (no)	3 tens 1 one
3. 4 tens 1 one	3 ones	(yes) no	3 tens 8 ones
4. 5 tens 4 ones	8 ones	(yes) no	4 tens 6 ones
5. 6 tens 3 ones	5 ones	(yes) no	5 tens 8 ones
6. 7 tens 7 ones	6 ones	yes (no)	7 tens 1 one
7. 8 tens 0 ones	2 ones	(yes) no	7 tens 8 ones
8. 9 tens 8 ones	9 ones	(yes) no	8 tens 9 ones

 Use with Grade 2, text pages 169–170.

Reteach

Deciding When to Regroup

R 6-3

You have 2 tens and 6 ones.
Take away 7 ones.

Regroup if you don't have enough ones.

Decide if you need to regroup.	Regroup 1 ten.	Take away 7 ones.
Tens / Ones	Tens / Ones	Tens / Ones
Not enough ones. You need to regroup.	1 ten 16 ones	1 ten 9 ones left

Circle to show if you need to regroup.
Use tens and ones models.

1. You have 2 tens and 2 ones. Take away 5 ones.
   (regroup) don't regroup
2. You have 4 tens and 9 ones. Take away 3 ones.
   regroup (don't regroup)

Draw to regroup. Then subtract.

3. You have 3 tens and 3 ones. Take away 9 ones.
   2 tens 4 ones

Tens	Ones

 Use with Grade 2, text pages 169–170.

Extend

Check It Out

E 6-3
REASONING

1. Subtract 5. Write how many are left. Write that amount in the box on the left on the next line. Then start again and subtract 5. The first one has been done for you.

Start with	Take away	How many are left?
5 tens 2 ones	5 ones	4 tens 7 ones
4 tens 7 ones	5 ones	4 tens 2 ones
4 tens 2 ones	5 ones	3 tens 7 ones
3 tens 7 ones	5 ones	3 tens 2 ones
3 tens 2 ones	5 ones	2 tens 7 ones
2 tens 7 ones	5 ones	2 tens 2 ones

2. What do you notice about the amounts left? Students should notice the alternating 7 and 2 in the ones place.

 Use with Grade 2, text pages 169–170.

Daily Review

Name ____________

Daily Review 6-3

Deciding When to Regroup

Use tens and ones models and Workmat 3.
Complete the chart.

	Do you need to regroup?	How many are left?
1. Show 4 tens 5 ones. Subtract 7 ones.	(yes) no	3 tens 8 ones
2. Show 5 tens 9 ones. Subtract 6 ones.	yes (no)	5 tens 3 ones
3. Show 3 tens 6 ones. Subtract 8 ones.	(yes) no	2 tens 8 ones

Problem Solving

Solve. Use models to help.

4. There are 10 fruit bars in a pack. Ellen has 3 packs and 4 bars.
   She gives away 6 fruit bars. How many packs and bars does she have left?
   2 packs 8 fruit bars

Review and Remember

Write the missing numbers.

5. 10 + 5 = 15 10 + 3 = 13 10 + 6 = 16
6. 10 + 1 = 11 10 + 4 = 14 10 + 8 = 18

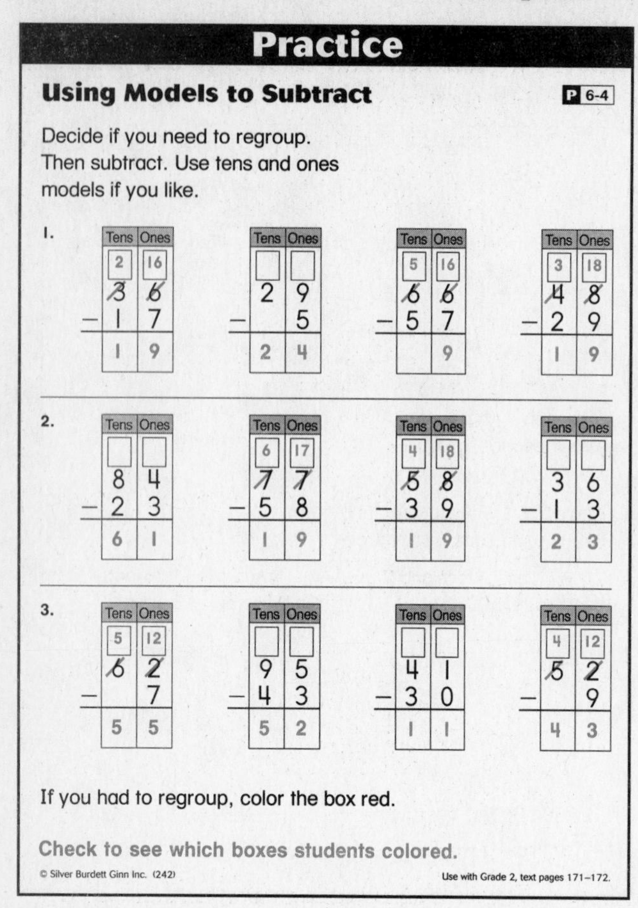

Practice

Using Models to Subtract

P 6-4

Decide if you need to regroup.
Then subtract. Use tens and ones models if you like.

1.

Tens	Ones
2	16
3	6
− 1	7
1	9

Tens	Ones
2	9
−	5
2	4

Tens	Ones
5	16
6	6
− 5	7
	9

Tens	Ones
3	18
4	8
− 2	9
1	9

2.

Tens	Ones
8	4
− 2	3
6	1

Tens	Ones
6	17
7	7
− 5	8
1	9

Tens	Ones
4	18
5	8
− 3	9
1	9

Tens	Ones
3	6
− 1	3
2	3

3.

Tens	Ones
5	12
6	2
−	7
5	5

Tens	Ones
9	5
− 4	3
5	2

Tens	Ones
4	1
− 3	0
1	1

Tens	Ones
4	12
5	2
−	9
4	3

If you had to regroup, color the box red.

Check to see which boxes students colored.

 Use with Grade 2, text pages 171–172.

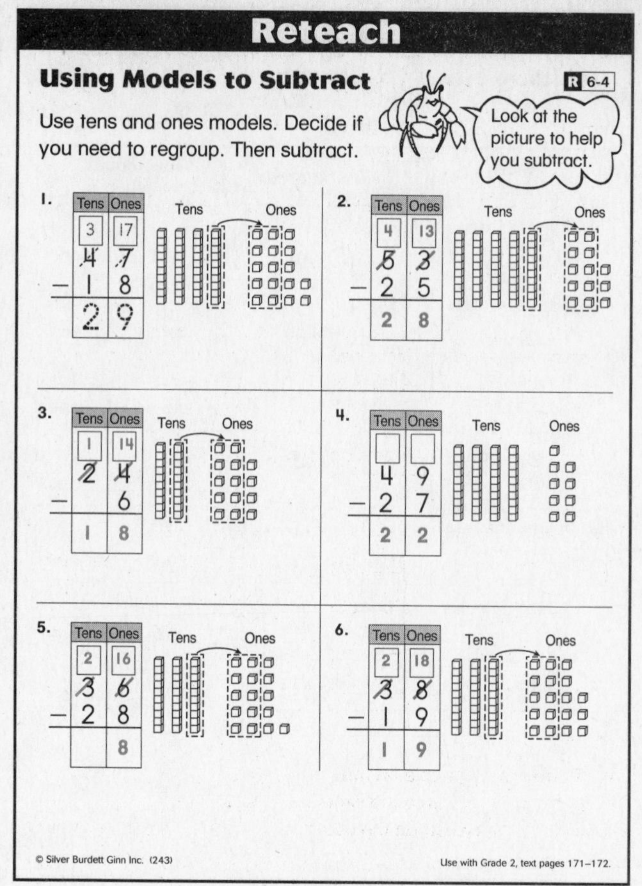

Reteach

Using Models to Subtract

R 6-4

Use tens and ones models. Decide if you need to regroup. Then subtract.

Look at the picture to help you subtract.

1.

Tens	Ones
3	17
4	7
− 1	8
2	9

2.

Tens	Ones
4	13
5	3
− 2	5
2	8

3.

Tens	Ones
1	14
2	4
−	6
1	8

4.

Tens	Ones
4	9
− 2	7
2	2

5.

Tens	Ones
2	16
3	6
− 2	8
	8

6.

Tens	Ones
2	18
3	8
− 1	9
1	9

 Use with Grade 2, text pages 171–172.

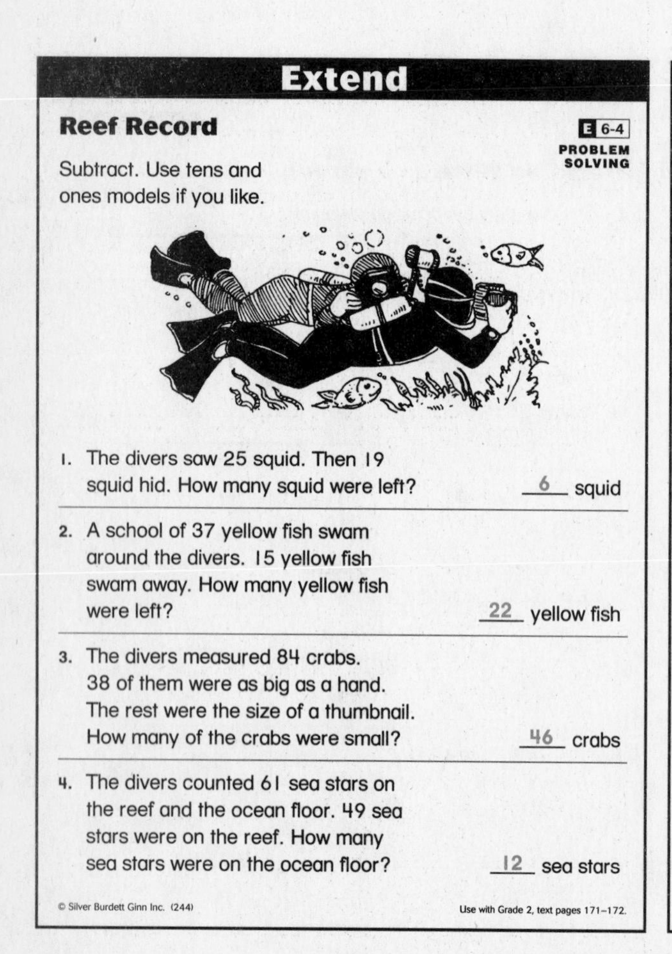

Extend

Reef Record

E 6-4
PROBLEM SOLVING

Subtract. Use tens and ones models if you like.

1. The divers saw 25 squid. Then 19 squid hid. How many squid were left? 6 squid
2. A school of 37 yellow fish swam around the divers. 15 yellow fish swam away. How many yellow fish were left? 22 yellow fish
3. The divers measured 84 crabs. 38 of them were as big as a hand. The rest were the size of a thumbnail. How many of the crabs were small? 46 crabs
4. The divers counted 61 sea stars on the reef and the ocean floor. 49 sea stars were on the reef. How many sea stars were on the ocean floor? 12 sea stars

 Use with Grade 2, text pages 171–172.

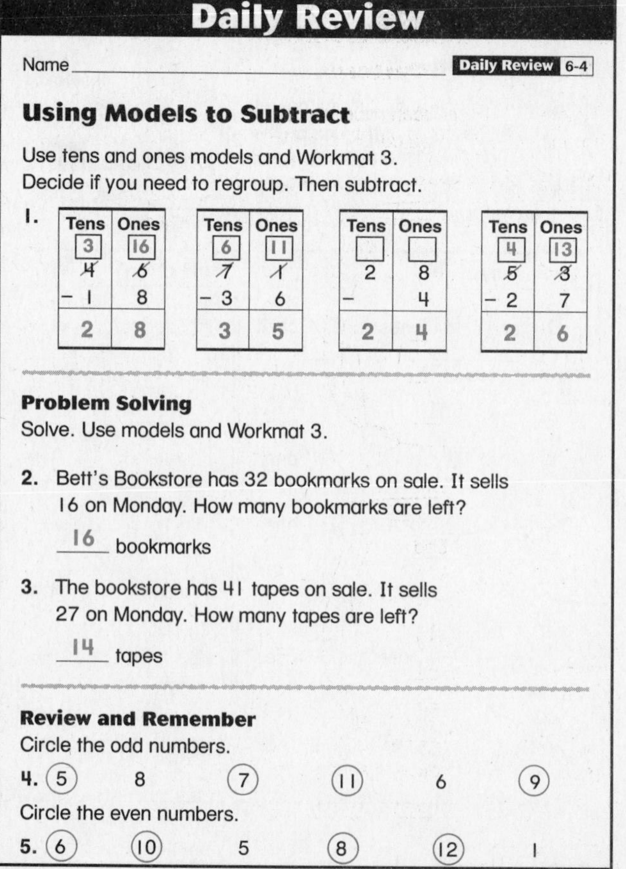

Daily Review

Name ______________ Daily Review 6-4

Using Models to Subtract

Use tens and ones models and Workmat 3.
Decide if you need to regroup. Then subtract.

1.

Tens	Ones
3	16
4	6
− 1	8
2	8

Tens	Ones
6	11
7	1
− 3	6
3	5

Tens	Ones
2	8
−	4
2	4

Tens	Ones
4	13
5	3
− 2	7
2	6

Problem Solving

Solve. Use models and Workmat 3.

2. Bett's Bookstore has 32 bookmarks on sale. It sells 16 on Monday. How many bookmarks are left?
   16 bookmarks
3. The bookstore has 41 tapes on sale. It sells 27 on Monday. How many tapes are left?
   14 tapes

Review and Remember

Circle the odd numbers.

4. (5) 8 (7) (11) 6 (9)

Circle the even numbers.

5. (6) (10) 5 (8) (12) 1

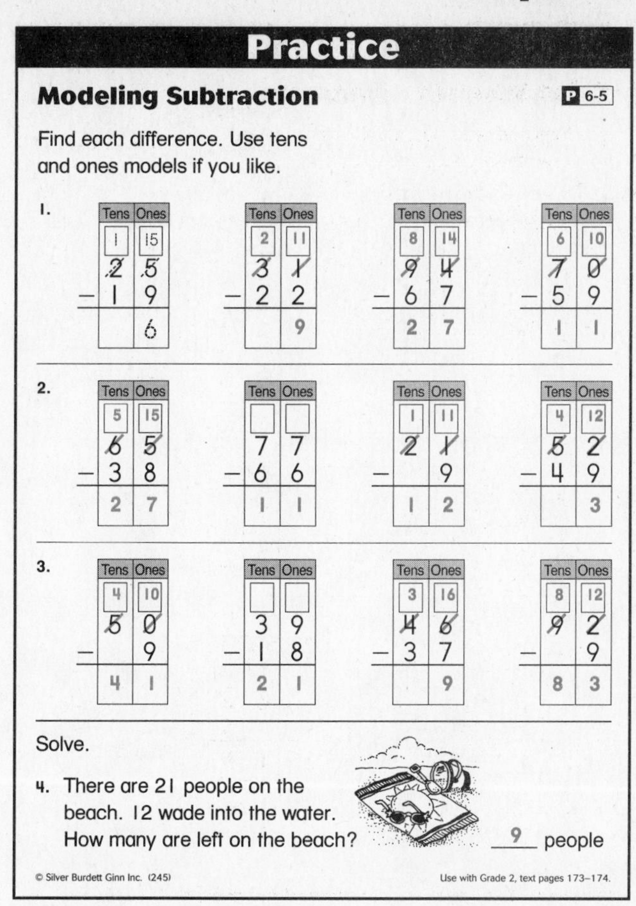

Practice

Modeling Subtraction

P 6-5

Find each difference. Use tens and ones models if you like.

	Tens Ones	Tens Ones	Tens Ones	Tens Ones
1.	[1] [15] 2 5 − 1 9 6	[2] [11] 3 1 − 2 2 9	[8] [14] 9 4 − 6 7 2 7	[6] [10] 7 0 − 5 9 1 1
2.	[5] [15] 6 5 − 3 8 2 7	[ ] [ ] 7 7 − 6 6 1 1	[1] [11] 2 1 − 9 1 2	[4] [12] 5 2 − 4 9 3
3.	[4] [10] 5 0 − 9 4 1	[ ] [ ] 3 9 − 1 8 2 1	[3] [16] 4 6 − 3 7 9	[8] [12] 9 2 − 9 8 3

Solve.

4. There are 21 people on the beach. 12 wade into the water. How many are left on the beach? 9 people

Use with Grade 2, text pages 173–174.

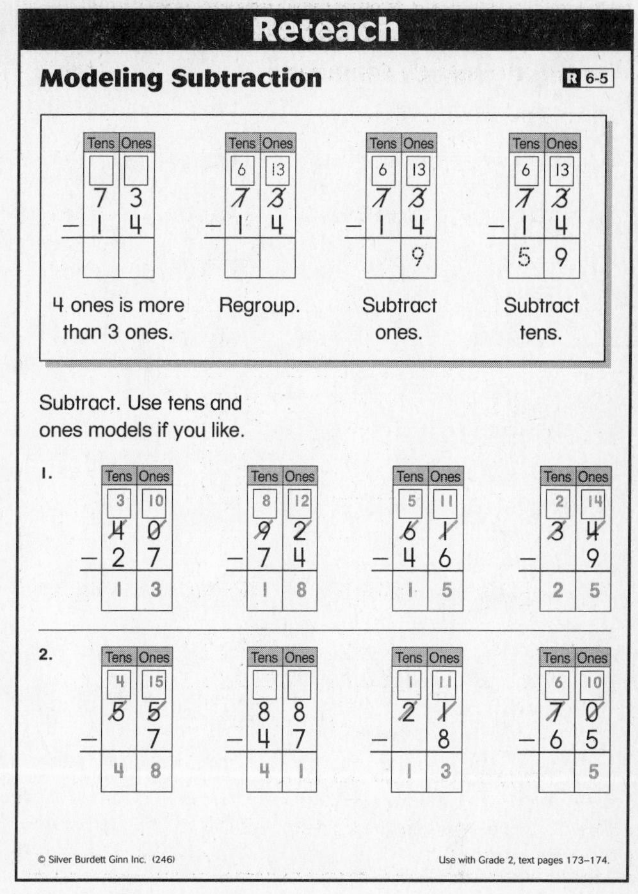

Reteach

Modeling Subtraction

R 6-5

Tens Ones	Tens Ones	Tens Ones	Tens Ones
[ ] [ ] 7 3 − 1 4	[6] [13] 7 3 − 1 4	[6] [13] 7 3 − 1 4 9	[6] [13] 7 3 − 1 4 5 9
4 ones is more than 3 ones.	Regroup.	Subtract ones.	Subtract tens.

Subtract. Use tens and ones models if you like.

	Tens Ones	Tens Ones	Tens Ones	Tens Ones
1.	[3] [10] 4 0 − 2 7 1 3	[8] [12] 9 2 − 7 4 1 8	[5] [11] 6 1 − 4 6 1 5	[2] [14] 3 4 − 9 2 5
2.	[4] [15] 5 5 − 7 4 8	[ ] [ ] 8 8 − 4 7 4 1	[1] [11] 2 1 − 8 1 3	[6] [10] 7 0 − 6 5 5

Use with Grade 2, text pages 173–174.

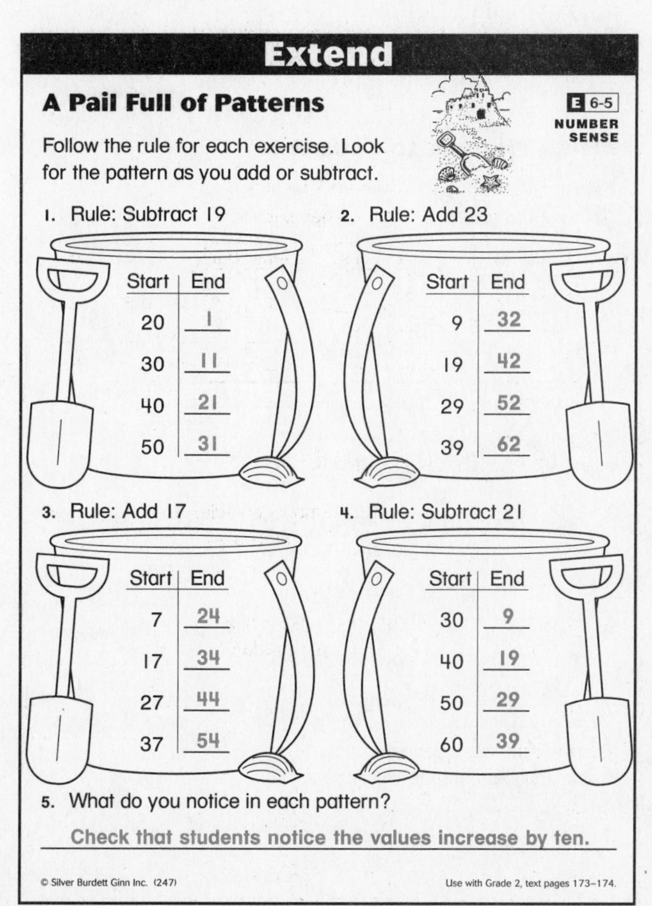

Extend

A Pail Full of Patterns

E 6-5 NUMBER SENSE

Follow the rule for each exercise. Look for the pattern as you add or subtract.

1. Rule: Subtract 19

Start	End
20	1
30	11
40	21
50	31

2. Rule: Add 23

Start	End
9	32
19	42
29	52
39	62

3. Rule: Add 17

Start	End
7	24
17	34
27	44
37	54

4. Rule: Subtract 21

Start	End
30	9
40	19
50	29
60	39

5. What do you notice in each pattern?

Check that students notice the values increase by ten.

Use with Grade 2, text pages 173–174.

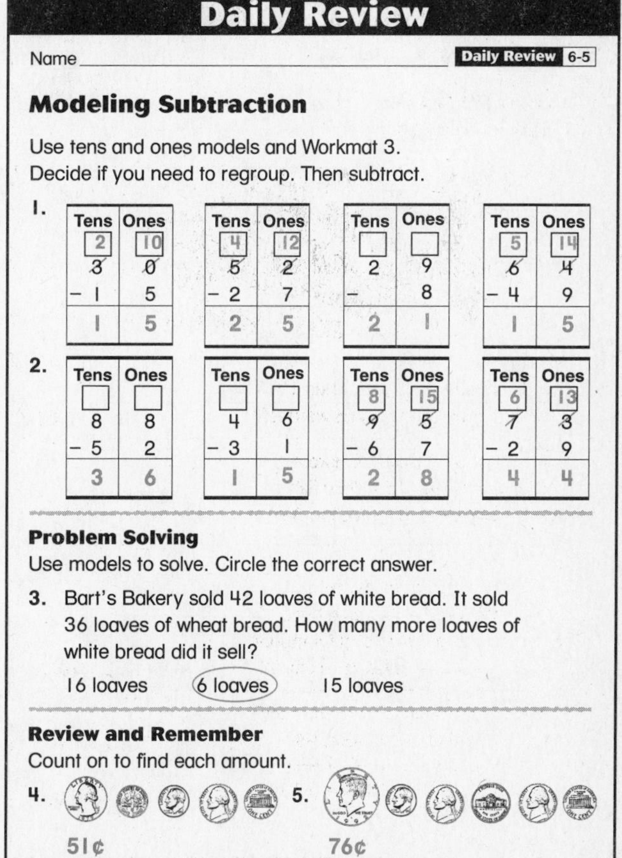

Daily Review

Name ______________________

Daily Review 6-5

Modeling Subtraction

Use tens and ones models and Workmat 3. Decide if you need to regroup. Then subtract.

	Tens Ones	Tens Ones	Tens Ones	Tens Ones
1.	[2] [10] 3 0 − 1 5 1 5	[4] [12] 5 2 − 2 7 2 5	[ ] [ ] 2 9 − 8 2 1	[5] [14] 6 4 − 4 9 1 5
2.	[ ] [ ] 8 8 − 5 2 3 6	[ ] [ ] 4 6 − 3 1 1 5	[8] [15] 9 5 − 6 7 2 8	[6] [13] 7 3 − 2 9 4 4

Problem Solving

Use models to solve. Circle the correct answer.

3. Bart's Bakery sold 42 loaves of white bread. It sold 36 loaves of wheat bread. How many more loaves of white bread did it sell?

16 loaves (6 loaves) 15 loaves

Review and Remember

Count on to find each amount.

4. 51¢

5. 76¢

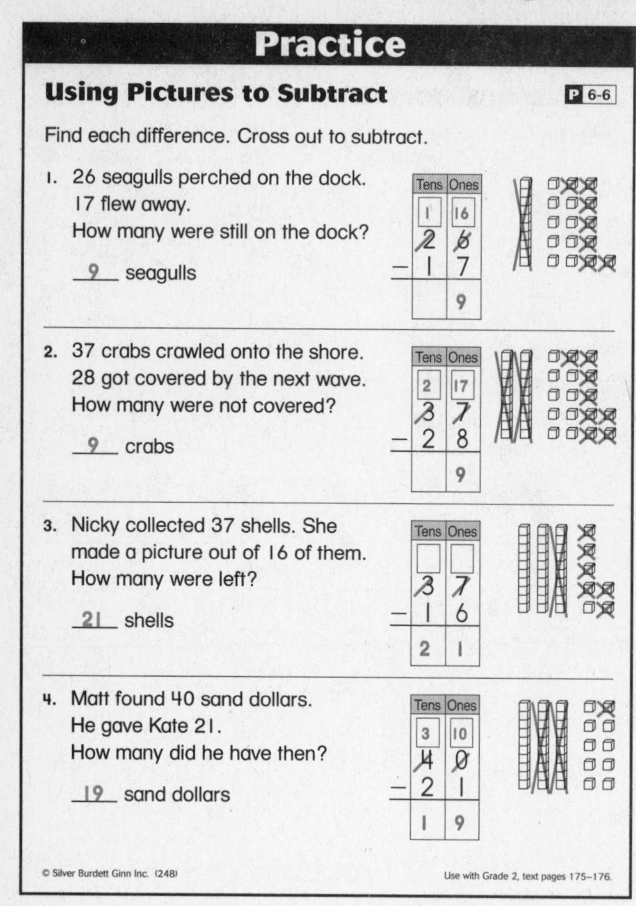

Practice

Using Pictures to Subtract

P 6-6

Find each difference. Cross out to subtract.

1. 26 seagulls perched on the dock. 17 flew away. How many were still on the dock?
   9 seagulls

Tens	Ones
1	16
2	6
− 1	7
	9

2. 37 crabs crawled onto the shore. 28 got covered by the next wave. How many were not covered?
   9 crabs

Tens	Ones
2	17
3	7
− 2	8
	9

3. Nicky collected 37 shells. She made a picture out of 16 of them. How many were left?
   21 shells

Tens	Ones
3	7
− 1	6
2	1

4. Matt found 40 sand dollars. He gave Kate 21. How many did he have then?
   19 sand dollars

Tens	Ones
3	10
4	0
− 2	1
1	9

 Use with Grade 2, text pages 175–176.

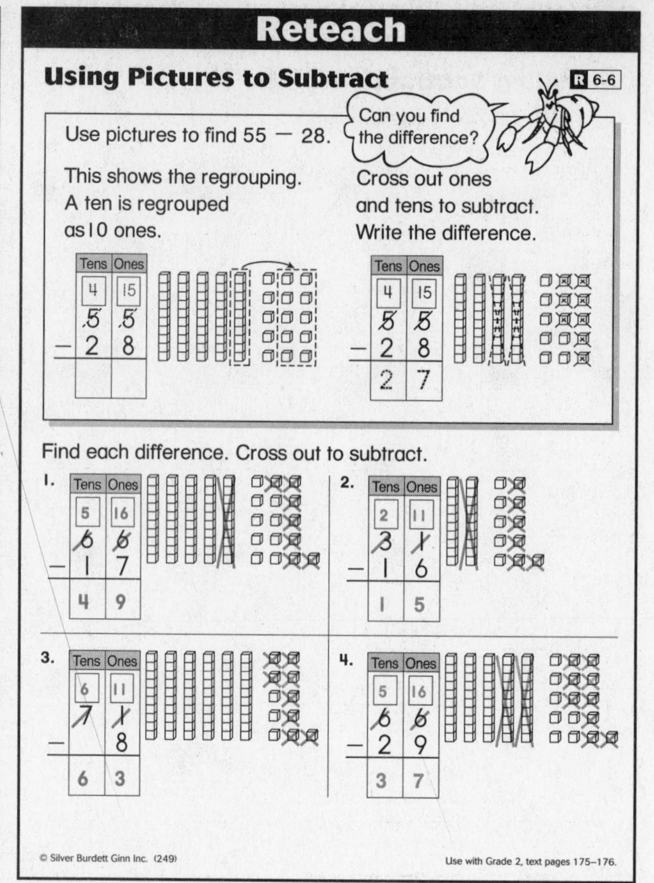

Reteach

Using Pictures to Subtract

R 6-6

Can you find the difference?

Use pictures to find 55 − 28.

This shows the regrouping. A ten is regrouped as 10 ones.

Tens	Ones
4	15
5	5
− 2	8

Cross out ones and tens to subtract. Write the difference.

Tens	Ones
4	15
5	5
− 2	8
2	7

Find each difference. Cross out to subtract.

1.

Tens	Ones
5	16
6	6
− 1	7
4	9

2.

Tens	Ones
2	11
3	1
− 1	6
1	5

3.

Tens	Ones
6	11
7	1
−	8
6	3

4.

Tens	Ones
5	16
6	6
− 2	9
3	7

 Use with Grade 2, text pages 175–176.

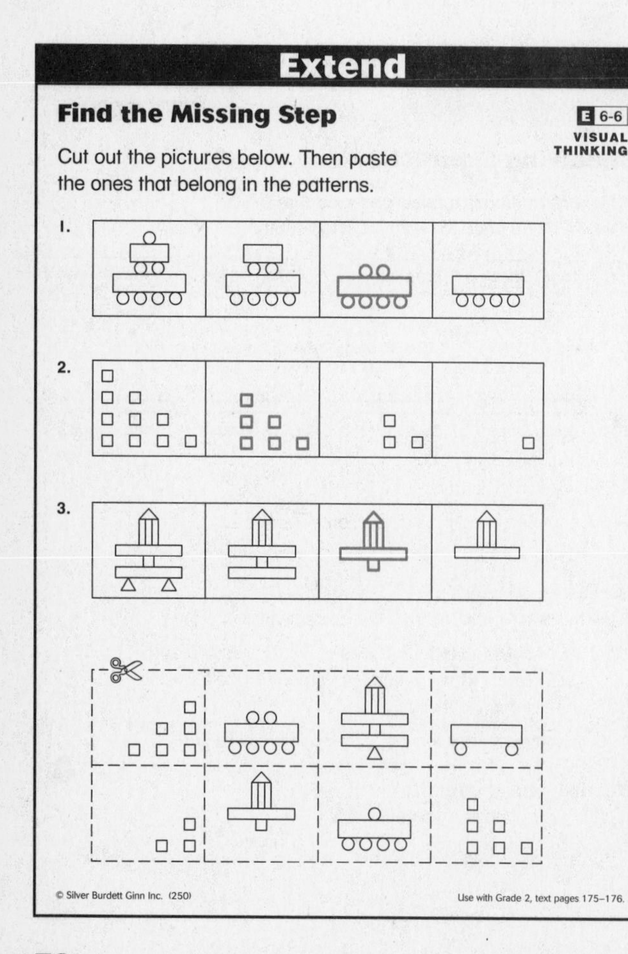

Extend

Find the Missing Step

E 6-6 VISUAL THINKING

Cut out the pictures below. Then paste the ones that belong in the patterns.

1.

2.

3.

 Use with Grade 2, text pages 175–176.

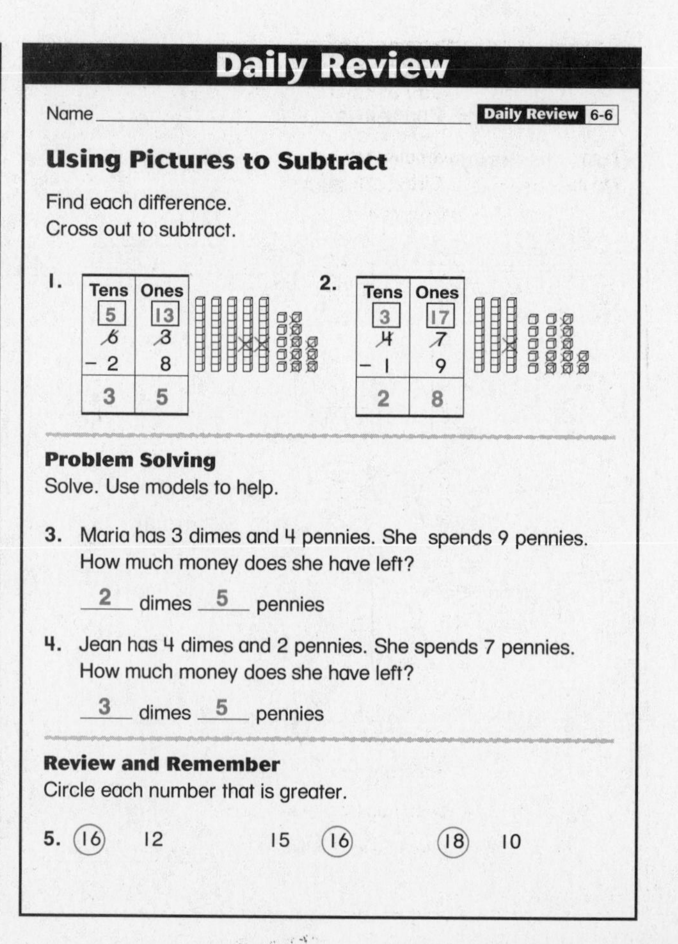

Daily Review

Name ____________________ Daily Review 6-6

Using Pictures to Subtract

Find each difference.
Cross out to subtract.

1.

Tens	Ones
5	13
6	3
− 2	8
3	5

2.

Tens	Ones
3	17
4	7
− 1	9
2	8

Problem Solving
Solve. Use models to help.

3. Maria has 3 dimes and 4 pennies. She spends 9 pennies. How much money does she have left?
   2 dimes 5 pennies

4. Jean has 4 dimes and 2 pennies. She spends 7 pennies. How much money does she have left?
   3 dimes 5 pennies

Review and Remember
Circle each number that is greater.

5. (16) 12   15 (16)   (18) 10

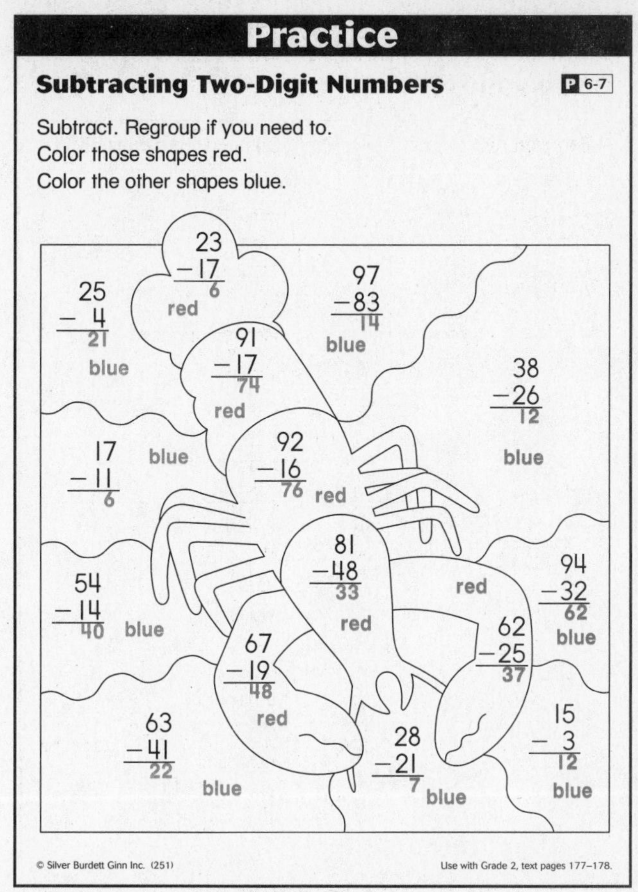

Practice

Subtracting Two-Digit Numbers P 6-7

Subtract. Regroup if you need to.
Color those shapes red.
Color the other shapes blue.

- 23 − 17 = 6 red
- 25 − 4 = 21 blue
- 97 − 83 = 14 blue
- 91 − 17 = 74 red
- 38 − 26 = 12 blue
- 17 − 11 = 6 blue
- 92 − 16 = 76 red
- 81 − 48 = 33 red
- 94 − 32 = 62 blue
- 54 − 14 = 40 blue
- 67 − 19 = 48 red
- 62 − 25 = 37 red
- 63 − 41 = 22 blue
- 28 − 21 = 7 blue
- 15 − 3 = 12 blue

 Use with Grade 2, text pages 177–178.

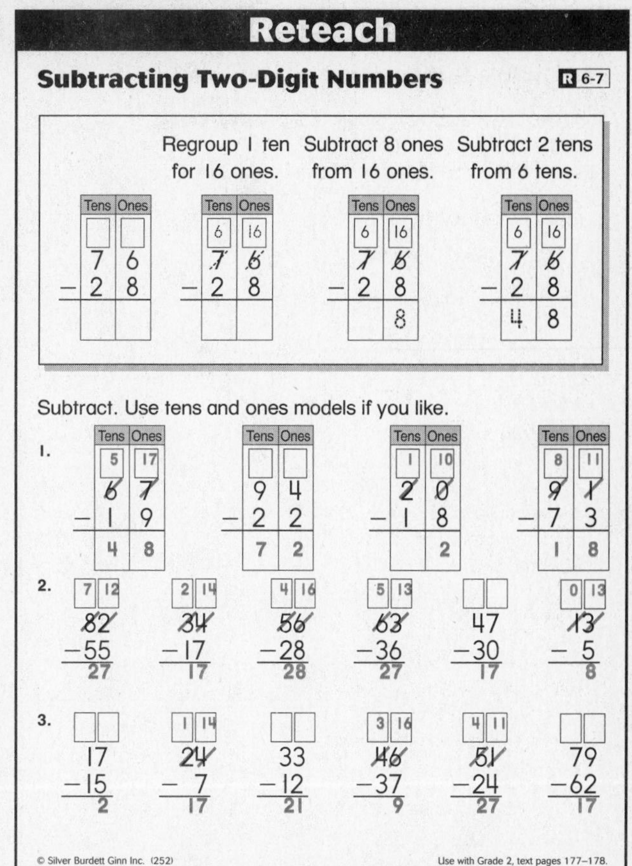

Reteach

Subtracting Two-Digit Numbers R 6-7

	Regroup 1 ten for 16 ones.	Subtract 8 ones from 16 ones.	Subtract 2 tens from 6 tens.
76 − 28	6 16 / 7̸ 6̸ − 2 8	6 16 / 7̸ 6̸ − 2 8 = 8	6 16 / 7̸ 6̸ − 2 8 = 48

Subtract. Use tens and ones models if you like.

1. 67 − 19 = 48 (5 17) 94 − 22 = 72 20 − 18 = 2 (1 10) 91 − 73 = 18 (8 11)
2. 82 − 55 = 27 (7 12) 34 − 17 = 17 (2 14) 56 − 28 = 28 (4 16) 63 − 36 = 27 (5 13) 47 − 30 = 17 13 − 5 = 8 (0 13)
3. 17 − 15 = 2 24 − 7 = 17 (1 14) 33 − 12 = 21 46 − 37 = 9 (3 16) 51 − 24 = 27 (4 11) 79 − 62 = 17

 Use with Grade 2, text pages 177–178.

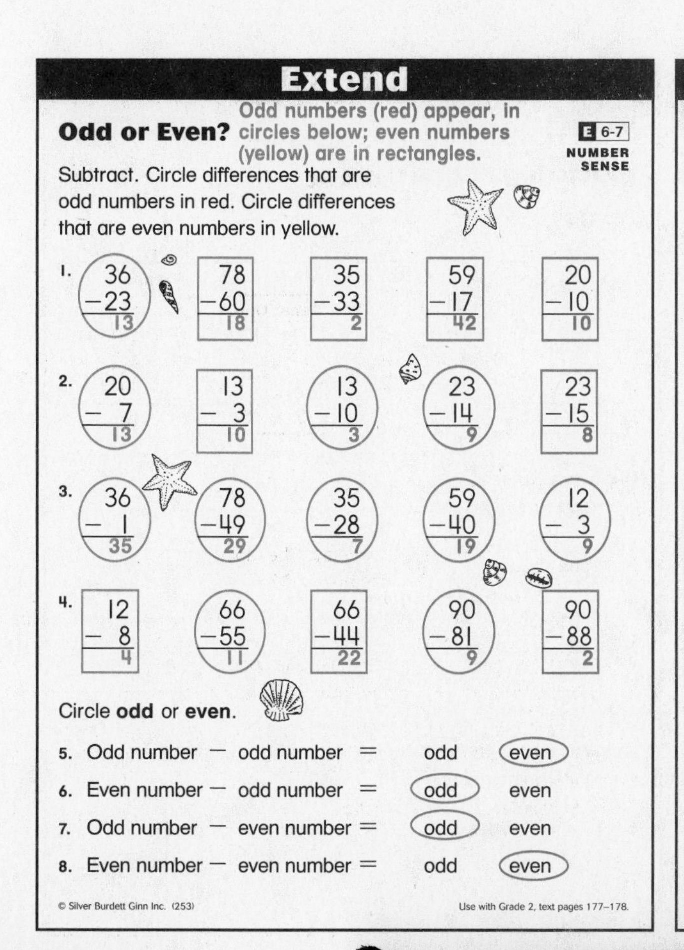

Extend

Odd or Even? E 6-7 NUMBER SENSE

Odd numbers (red) appear, in circles below; even numbers (yellow) are in rectangles.

Subtract. Circle differences that are odd numbers in red. Circle differences that are even numbers in yellow.

1. 36 − 23 = 13 78 − 60 = 18 35 − 33 = 2 59 − 17 = 42 20 − 10 = 10
2. 20 − 7 = 13 13 − 3 = 10 13 − 10 = 3 23 − 14 = 9 23 − 15 = 8
3. 36 − 1 = 35 78 − 49 = 29 35 − 28 = 7 59 − 40 = 19 12 − 3 = 9
4. 12 − 8 = 4 66 − 55 = 11 66 − 44 = 22 90 − 81 = 9 90 − 88 = 2

Circle **odd** or **even**.

5. Odd number − odd number = odd (even)
6. Even number − odd number = (odd) even
7. Odd number − even number = (odd) even
8. Even number − even number = odd (even)

 Use with Grade 2, text pages 177–178.

Daily Review

Name ______________________ Daily Review 6-7

Subtracting Two-Digit Numbers

Subtract. Use tens and ones models if you like.

1. 38 − 17 = 21 54 − 25 = 29 26 − 3 = 23 72 − 56 = 16 90 − 50 = 40
2. 47 − 9 = 38 61 − 43 = 18 85 − 31 = 54 49 − 19 = 30 64 − 56 = 8

Problem Solving

Solve. Use models to help.

Cindy and Jeff are playing a computer game.

3. On the first turn, Cindy scores 54 points. Jeff scores 38 points. How many more points did Cindy score?
   16 more points
4. On the second turn, Cindy scores 42 points. How many more points did she score on her first turn than on her second turn? 12 more points

Review and Remember

Add.

5. $4 + 6 + 4 =$ 14 $2 + 9 + 1 =$ 12 $8 + 0 + 8 =$ 16
6. $5 + 6 + 5 =$ 16 $3 + 9 + 5 =$ 17 $9 + 5 + 0 =$ 14

Chapter 6 • Lesson 8

Practice

Practicing Subtraction

P 6-8

Subtract. If you had to regroup, color the box yellow. Write the letters in the yellow boxes in order below.

1.	2.	3.	4.	5.	6.
85 − 14 = 71	5 13 63 − 44 = 19	79 − 66 = 13	7 10 80 − 48 = 32	27 − 6 = 21	7 10 80 − 36 = 44
D	B	P	E	N	L
7. 7 10 80 − 75 = 5	**8.** 54 − 21 = 33	**9.** 2 17 37 − 19 = 18	**10.** 8 14 94 − 17 = 77	**11.** 49 − 24 = 25	**12.** 5 18 68 − 29 = 39
U	D	G	A	H	W
13. 4 14 54 − 26 = 28	**14.** 98 − 56 = 42	**15.** 5 13 63 − 29 = 34	**16.** 6 11 71 − 52 = 19	**17.** 79 − 38 = 41	**18.** 3 12 42 − 18 = 24
H	O	A	L	N	E

Answer: B E L U G A W H A L E

 Use with Grade 2, text pages 179–80.

Reteach

Practicing Subtraction

R 6-8

Remember to regroup a ten when you need more ones.

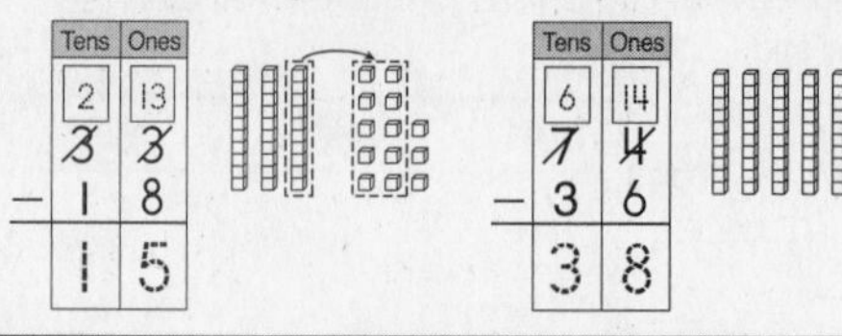

Tens	Ones
2	13
3	3
− 1	8
1	5

Tens	Ones
6	14
7	4
− 3	6
3	8

Subtract. Use tens and ones models if you like.

1.
- Tens/Ones: regroup 0 11; 11 − 8 = 3
- 55 − 34 = 21
- regroup 7 18; 88 − 29 = 59
- regroup 4 14; 54 − 45 = 9

2.
- regroup 1 12; 22 − 17 = 5
- regroup 5 16; 66 − 19 = 47
- 99 − 86 = 13
- regroup 2 10; 30 − 23 = 7

3.
- 3 14: 44 − 36 = 8
- 77 − 63 = 14
- 19 − 14 = 5
- 1 10: 20 − 7 = 13
- 2 13: 33 − 19 = 14
- 8 12: 92 − 47 = 45

 Use with Grade 2, text pages 179–80.

Extend

Number, Please!

E 6-8 PROBLEM SOLVING

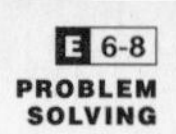

Use the numbers in the box to replace each shape. Use each number only once. Then write the answer. The answers are not in the box. Answers will vary. Sample answers are given.

12	14	35
	17	8
28	7	46

1. Becca has ⊡ model cars. Her sister has ⊙ cars. How many more cars does Becca have than her sister?
   ⊡ = 8
   ⊙ = 7
   Answer: 1 cars

2. Abby has ◺ marbles. Leah gives her ◢ marbles. How many marbles does Abby have now?
   ◺ = 14
   ◢ = 12
   Answer: 26 marbles

3. Tim has ➤ baseball cards. Ali has ▲ baseball cards. How many more baseball cards does Tim have than Ali?
   ➤ = 46
   ▲ = 35
   Answer: 11 cards

4. Joel picks up ☆ jacks. Eric picks up 🪐 jacks. How many jacks do Joel and Eric pick up?
   ☆ = 28
   🪐 = 17
   Answer: 45 jacks

 Use with Grade 2, text pages 179–80.

Daily Review

Name ____________ Daily Review 6-8

Practicing Subtraction

Rewrite the numbers. Then subtract.

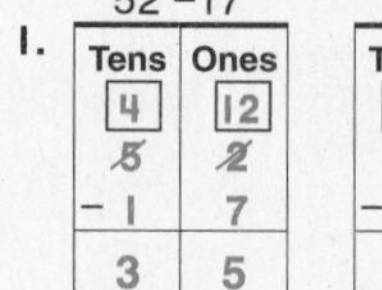

1.
- 52 − 17: Tens/Ones regroup 4 12; 5 2 − 1 7 = 3 5
- 73 − 41: 7 3 − 4 1 = 3 2
- 60 − 39: regroup 5 10; 6 0 − 3 9 = 2 1
- 47 − 27: 4 7 − 2 7 = 2 0

Problem Solving

Find the missing numbers. Use models to help.

13, 41, 25, 37

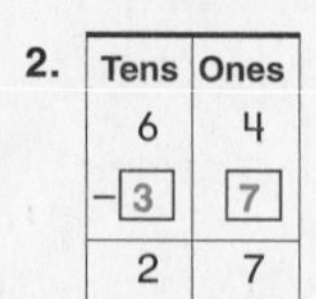

2. 64 − 37 = 27
3. 51 − 25 = 26
4. 40 − 13 = 27

Review and Remember

Circle the numbers.

5. 3 tens 4 ones: (34) 43
6. 1 ten 6 ones: (16) 61
7. 5 tens 0 ones: 55 (50)

Practice

Problem Solving P 6-9

Find a Pattern

Subtract. Continue the pattern. Use tens and ones models.

1.

93 − 5	88
93 − 15	78
93 − 25	68
93 − 35	58
93 − 45	48

52 − 1	51
52 − 11	41
52 − 21	31
52 − 31	21
52 − 41	11

47 − 3	44
47 − 13	34
47 − 23	24
47 − 33	14
47 − 43	4

2.

83 − 4	79
83 − 14	69
83 − 24	59
83 − 34	49
83 − 44	39

69 − 8	61
69 − 18	51
69 − 28	41
69 − 38	31
69 − 48	21

75 − 6	69
75 − 16	59
75 − 26	49
75 − 36	39
75 − 46	29

3.

57 − 10	47
57 − 20	37
57 − 30	27
57 − 40	17
57 − 50	7

90 − 9	81
90 − 19	71
90 − 29	61
90 − 39	51
90 − 49	41

88 − 7	81
88 − 17	71
88 − 27	61
88 − 37	51
88 − 47	41

 Use with Grade 2, text pages 181–82.

Reteach

Problem Solving R 6-9

Find a Pattern

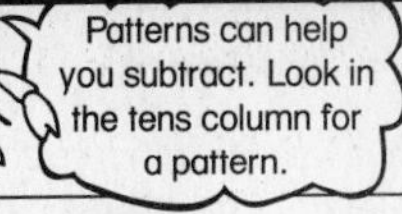

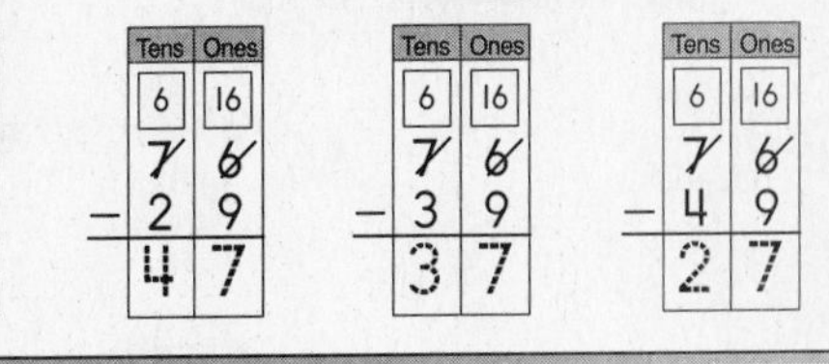

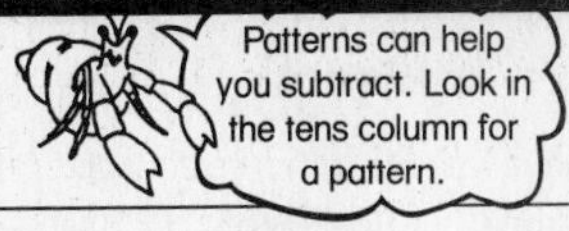

Tens	Ones
6	16
7	6
− 1	9
5	7

Tens	Ones
6	16
7	6
− 2	9
4	7

Tens	Ones
6	16
7	6
− 3	9
3	7

Tens	Ones
6	16
7	6
− 4	9
2	7

Patterns can help you subtract. Look in the tens column for a pattern.

Subtract. Continue the pattern.
Use tens and ones models if you like.

1.

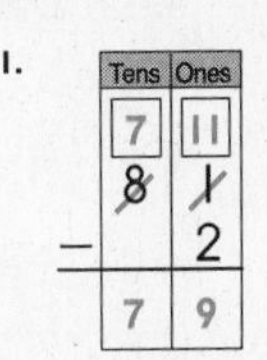
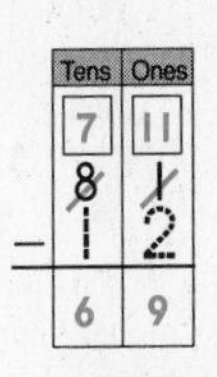
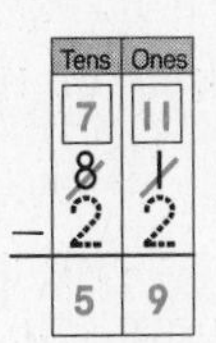

Tens	Ones
7	11
8	1
−	2
7	9

Tens	Ones
7	11
8	1
− 1	2
6	9

Tens	Ones
7	11
8	1
− 2	2
5	9

Tens	Ones
7	11
8	1
− 3	2
4	9

2.

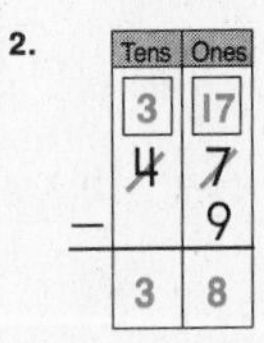

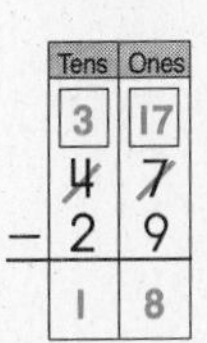
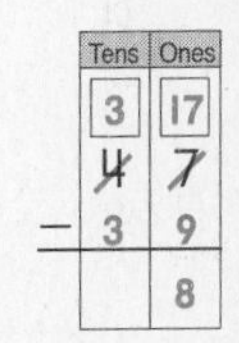

Tens	Ones
3	17
4	7
−	9
3	8

Tens	Ones
3	17
4	7
− 1	9
2	8

Tens	Ones
3	17
4	7
− 2	9
1	8

Tens	Ones
3	17
4	7
− 3	9
	8

3. For each set of problems, I subtracted 10 more each time.

 Use with Grade 2, text pages 181–82.

Extend

Follow Those Arrows

E 6-9 PATTERNS

1. Start at 75 and move one space down. Subtract the two numbers.
   The difference is 25.
2. Start at any number and move one space down. Subtract the two numbers.
   The difference is 25.

75	80	85	90	95
50	55	60	65	70
25	30	35	40	45
0	5	10	15	20

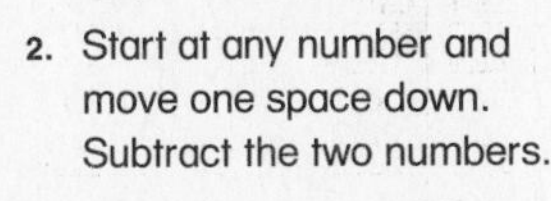

3. Test the pattern.

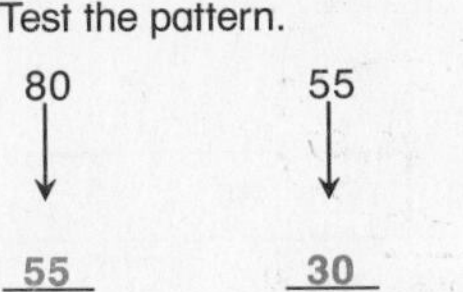

80 ↓ 55   55 ↓ 30   65 ↓ 40

4. If you move one space to the left, it is like subtracting 5.
5. Test the pattern.
   ← 5 = 0   ← 65 = 60   ← 90 = 85
6. If you move like this ↓ →, one space down and one space to the right, it is like subtracting 20.
7. Test the pattern.
   30 ↓ → = 10   85 ↓ → = 65   40 ↓ → = 20

 Use with Grade 2, text pages 181–82.

Daily Review

Name ____________________ Daily Review 6-9

Problem Solving

Find a Pattern

Subtract. Continue the pattern.
Use models if you like.

1. 74 − 5 = 69   74 − 15 = 59   74 − 25 = 49   74 − 35 = 39   74 − 45 = 29
2. 50 − 3 = 47   50 − 13 = 37   50 − 23 = 27   50 − 33 = 17   50 − 43 = 7
3. 96 − 10 = 86   96 − 20 = 76   96 − 30 = 66   96 − 40 = 56   96 − 50 = 46
4. 62 − 12 = 50   62 − 22 = 40   62 − 32 = 30   62 − 42 = 20   62 − 52 = 10

Review and Remember

Write the missing numbers.

5. 6 + [5] = 11   2 + [8] = 10   [4] + 9 = 13
6. [8] + 7 = 15   9 + [9] = 18   [7] + 2 = 9

Practice

Ways to Subtract

P 6-10

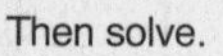

Use the easiest way!

Think about ways to solve each problem.
Write the letter of the way you choose.
Then solve.

A. tens and ones models
B. hundreds chart
C. paper and pencil
D. mental math

1. 56 − 9 = 47 I used ___. 80 − 50 = 30 I used ___. 79 − 47 = 32 I used ___. 85 − 15 = 70 I used ___.

2. 43 − 33 = 10 I used ___. 35 − 29 = 6 I used ___. 84 − 76 = 8 I used ___. 70 − 60 = 10 I used ___.

3. 61 − 54 = 7 I used ___. 45 − 35 = 10 I used ___. 58 − 30 = 28 I used ___. 90 − 70 = 20 I used ___.

Check that students' answers are reasonable.

 Use with Grade 2, text pages 183–84.

Reteach

Ways to Subtract

R 6-10

How would you find the difference?

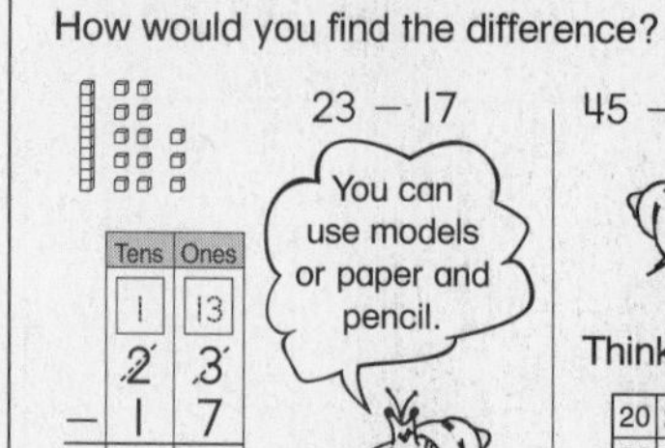
23 − 17
Tens Ones
1 13
2 3
− 1 7
6
You can use models or paper and pencil.
45 − 20
You can use mental math or a one-hundred chart.
Think: 45, 35, **25**

20	21	22	23	24	25	26	27	28	29
30	31	32	33	34	35	36	37	38	39
40	41	42	43	44	45	46	47	48	49

Find each difference. Use tens and ones models and Teaching Tool 5.

1.

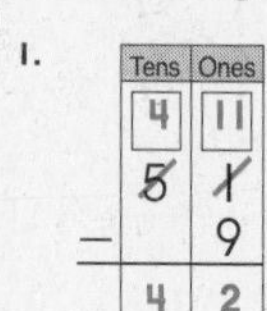
Tens Ones
4 11
5 1
− 9
4 2

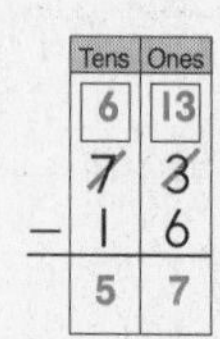
Tens Ones
6 13
7 3
− 1 6
5 7

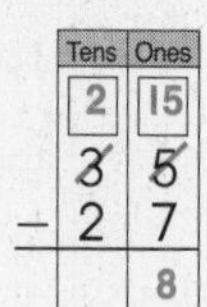
Tens Ones
2 15
3 5
− 2 7
8

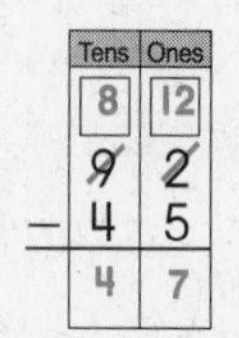
Tens Ones
8 12
9 2
− 4 5
4 7

Find each difference. Use mental math or a one-hundred chart.

2. 50 − 40 = 10 38 − 18 = 20 42 − 22 = 20 65 − 35 = 30 70 − 60 = 10 22 − 12 = 10

 Use with Grade 2, text pages 183–84.

Extend

Picture This

E 6-10 VISUAL THINKING

Look at the grid at the right.
Copy each shape in the correct box on the grid below.

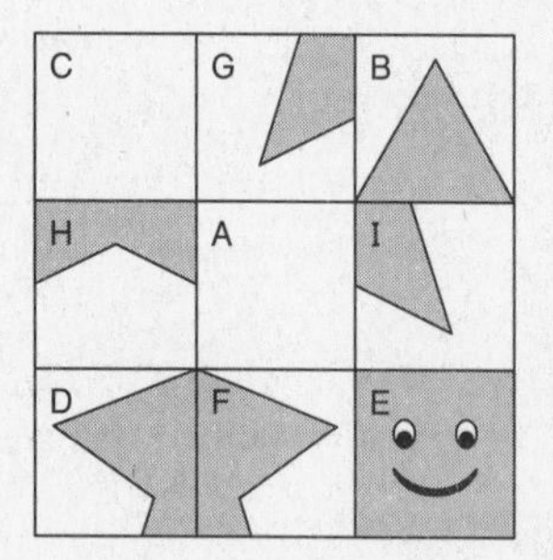
C
G
B
H
A
I
D
F
E

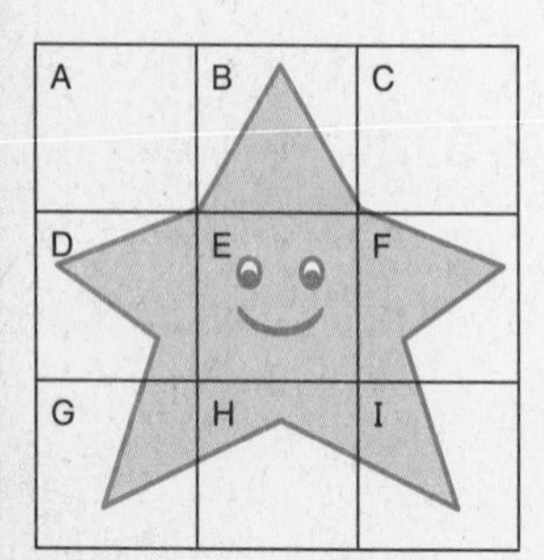
A
B
C
D
E
F
G
H
I

Write what you see.

I see a smiling star.

 Use with Grade 2, text pages 183–84.

Daily Review

Name ______________________

Daily Review 6-10

Ways to Subtract

Find each difference.
Draw a line to show how you solved the problem.
Answers will vary.

1. 54 − 37 = 17 72 − 48 = 24 69 − 37 = 32 80 − 29 = 51 46 − 6 = 40

tens and ones | hundreds chart | paper and pencil | mental math

Problem Solving

Choose a number to write in each problem.
Then solve. Answers will vary.

14 32 25 8

2. The School Store sold 45 pencils in March. It sold ___ in April. How many more pencils did it sell in March?
___ more pencils

3. The store sold 50 pens in March. It sold ___ in April. How many more pens did it sell in March?
___ more pens

Review and Remember

Circle the amounts that equal $1.00.

4.

Practice

Checking Subtraction With Addition

P 6-11

Subtract. Check by adding.
Use tens and ones models if you like.

	Subtract	Check
1.	59 − 6 = 53	53 + 6 = 59
2.	86 − 27 = 59	59 + 27 = 86
3.	75 − 63 = 12	12 + 63 = 75
4.	49 − 26 = 23	23 + 26 = 49
5.	36 − 18 = 18	18 + 18 = 36
6.	51 − 6 = 45	45 + 6 = 51
7.	60 − 34 = 26	26 + 34 = 60
8.	37 − 18 = 19	19 + 18 = 37
9.	89 − 18 = 71	71 + 18 = 89
10.	72 − 34 = 38	38 + 34 = 72

 Use with Grade 2, text pages 185–86.

Reteach

Checking Subtraction With Addition

R 6-11

Subtract 11 from 16. Then add 11 to check. You should have the 16 shells you started with.

16 − 11 = 5 → 5 + 11 = 16

Subtract. Check by adding.
Use tens and ones models if you like.

	Subtract	Check
1.	98 − 37 = 61	61 + 37 = 98
2.	34 − 24 = 10	10 + 24 = 34
3.	65 − 8 = 57	57 + 8 = 65
4.	40 − 31 = 9	9 + 31 = 40
5.	78 − 49 = 29	29 + 49 = 78
6.	51 − 17 = 34	34 + 17 = 51

 Use with Grade 2, text pages 185–86.

Extend

Jellyfish Jumble

E 6-11 NUMBER SENSE

Use the numbers in each jellyfish to make a subtraction problem.
Check by adding. Answers will vary.

1. Jellyfish: 51, 35, 16 — 51 − 35 = 16 → 16 + 35 = 51

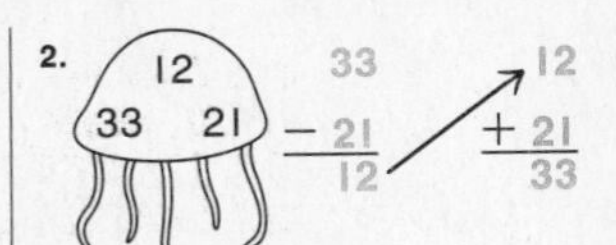

2. 33 − 21 = 12 → 12 + 21 = 33

3. 82 − 38 = 44 → 38 + 44 = 82

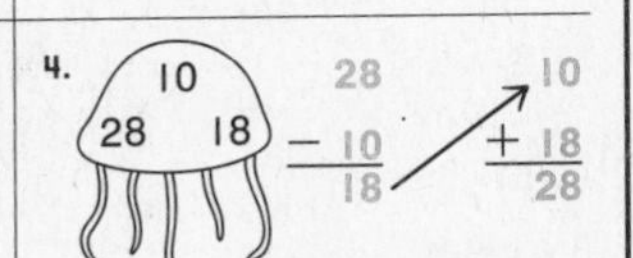

4. 28 − 10 = 18 → 10 + 18 = 28

5. 56 − 29 = 27 → 29 + 27 = 56

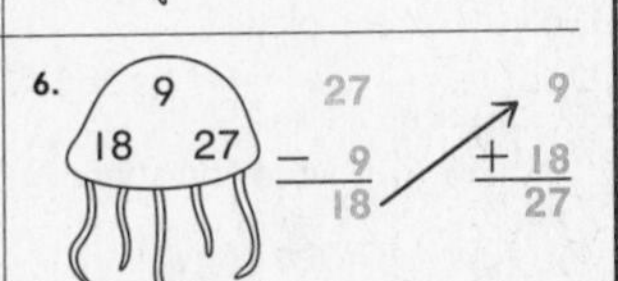

6. 27 − 9 = 18 → 9 + 18 = 27

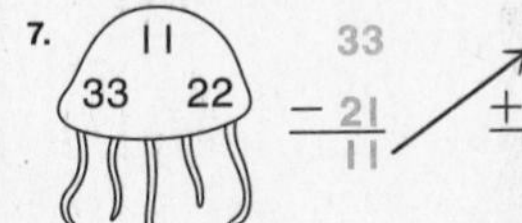

7. 33 − 21 = 11 → 22 + 11 = 33

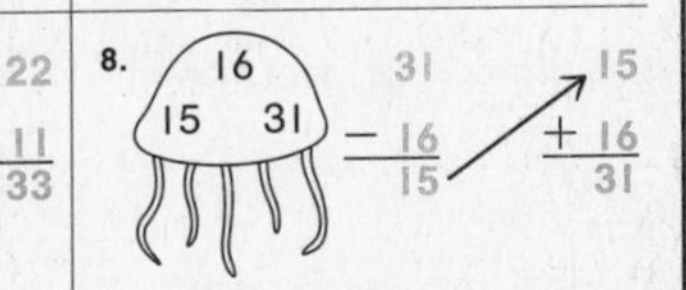

8. 31 − 16 = 15 → 15 + 16 = 31

 Use with Grade 2, text pages 185–86.

Daily Review

Name ____________________ Daily Review 6-11

Checking Subtraction With Addition

Subtract. Check by adding.
Use tens and ones models if you like.

	Subtract	Check
1.	82 − 35 = 47	47 + 35 = 82
2.	24 − 7 = 17	17 + 7 = 24
3.	65 − 47 = 18	18 + 47 = 65
4.	56 − 28 = 28	28 + 28 = 56

Problem Solving

Solve. Check by adding.

5. Susan makes 52 cards. She sells 27 cards. How many cards are left?
   25 cards are left.

6. Darrell makes 32 bracelets. He sells 24 bracelets. How many bracelets are left?
   8 are left.

Review and Remember

Draw a group with 10 more. Write how many.

7.  15

8.  13

Chapter 6 • Lesson 12

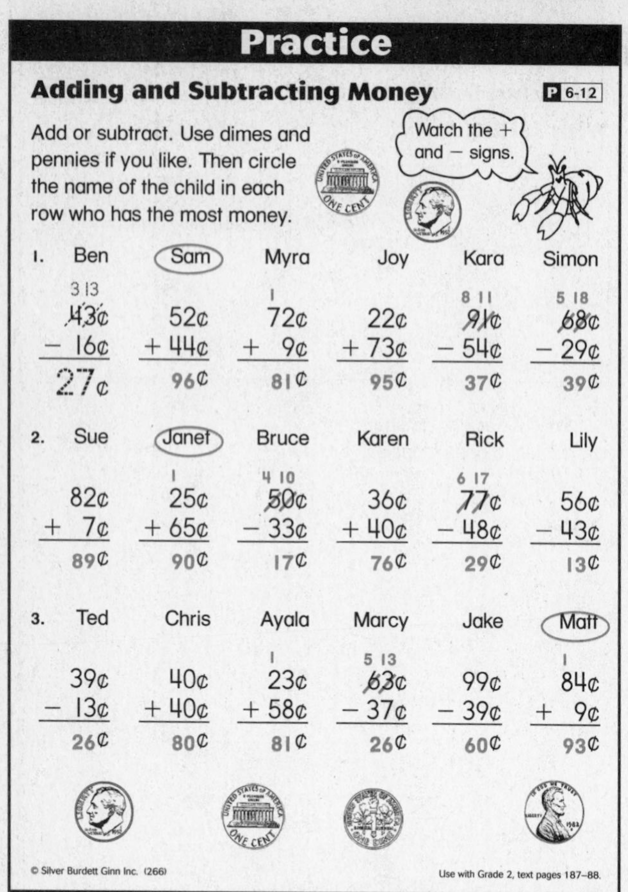

Practice

Adding and Subtracting Money

P 6-12

Add or subtract. Use dimes and pennies if you like. Then circle the name of the child in each row who has the most money.

	Ben	Sam (circled)	Myra	Joy	Kara	Simon
1.	43¢ − 16¢ = 27¢	52¢ + 44¢ = 96¢	72¢ + 9¢ = 81¢	22¢ + 73¢ = 95¢	91¢ − 54¢ = 37¢	68¢ − 29¢ = 39¢

	Sue	Janet (circled)	Bruce	Karen	Rick	Lily
2.	82¢ + 7¢ = 89¢	25¢ + 65¢ = 90¢	50¢ − 33¢ = 17¢	36¢ + 40¢ = 76¢	77¢ − 48¢ = 29¢	56¢ − 43¢ = 13¢

	Ted	Chris	Ayala	Marcy	Jake	Matt (circled)
3.	39¢ − 13¢ = 26¢	40¢ + 40¢ = 80¢	23¢ + 58¢ = 81¢	63¢ − 37¢ = 26¢	99¢ − 39¢ = 60¢	84¢ + 9¢ = 93¢

 Use with Grade 2, text pages 187–88.

Reteach

Adding and Subtracting Money

R 6-12

Add. 48¢ + 37¢ = 85¢

Adding and subtracting money is like adding and subtracting other numbers.

Subtract. 85¢ − 37¢ = 48¢

Add or subtract. Use dimes and pennies if you like. Look for the pattern. Write the next problem.

1.	91¢ − 2¢ = 89¢	91¢ − 12¢ = 79¢	91¢ − 22¢ = 69¢	91¢ − 32¢ = 59¢	91¢ − 42¢ = 49¢
2.	67¢ − 48¢ = 19¢	67¢ − 38¢ = 29¢	67¢ − 28¢ = 39¢	67¢ − 18¢ = 49¢	67¢ − 8¢ = 59¢
3.	48¢ + 35¢ = 83¢	48¢ + 36¢ = 84¢	48¢ + 37¢ = 85¢	48¢ + 38¢ = 86¢	48¢ + 39¢ = 87¢
4.	15¢ + 15¢ = 30¢	16¢ + 16¢ = 32¢	17¢ + 17¢ = 34¢	18¢ + 18¢ = 36¢	19¢ + 19¢ = 38¢

 Use with Grade 2, text pages 187–88.

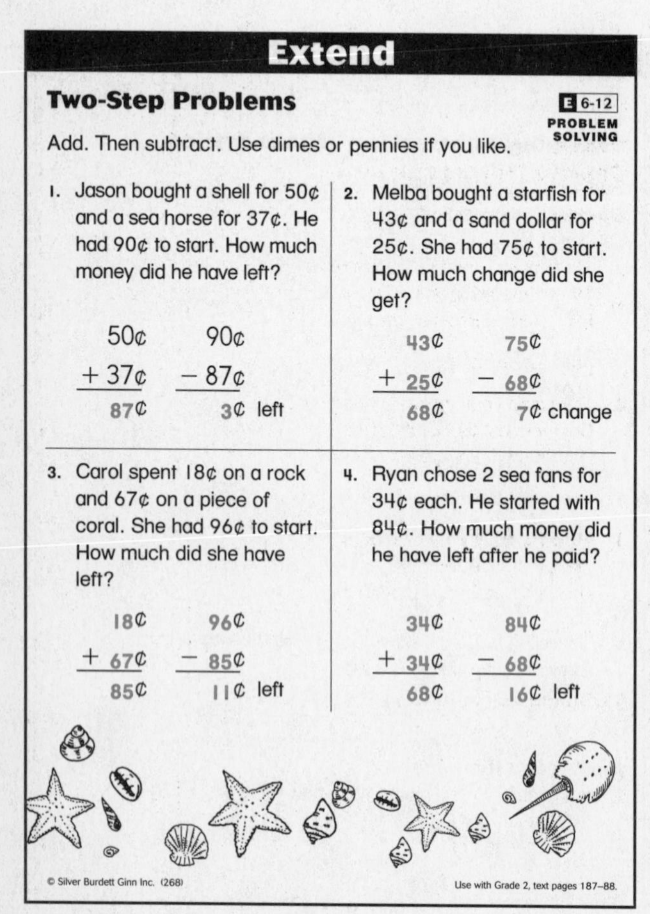

Extend

Two-Step Problems

E 6-12 PROBLEM SOLVING

Add. Then subtract. Use dimes or pennies if you like.

1. Jason bought a shell for 50¢ and a sea horse for 37¢. He had 90¢ to start. How much money did he have left?
   50¢ + 37¢ = 87¢; 90¢ − 87¢ = 3¢ left

2. Melba bought a starfish for 43¢ and a sand dollar for 25¢. She had 75¢ to start. How much change did she get?
   43¢ + 25¢ = 68¢; 75¢ − 68¢ = 7¢ change

3. Carol spent 18¢ on a rock and 67¢ on a piece of coral. She had 96¢ to start. How much did she have left?
   18¢ + 67¢ = 85¢; 96¢ − 85¢ = 11¢ left

4. Ryan chose 2 sea fans for 34¢ each. He started with 84¢. How much money did he have left after he paid?
   34¢ + 34¢ = 68¢; 84¢ − 68¢ = 16¢ left

 Use with Grade 2, text pages 187–88.

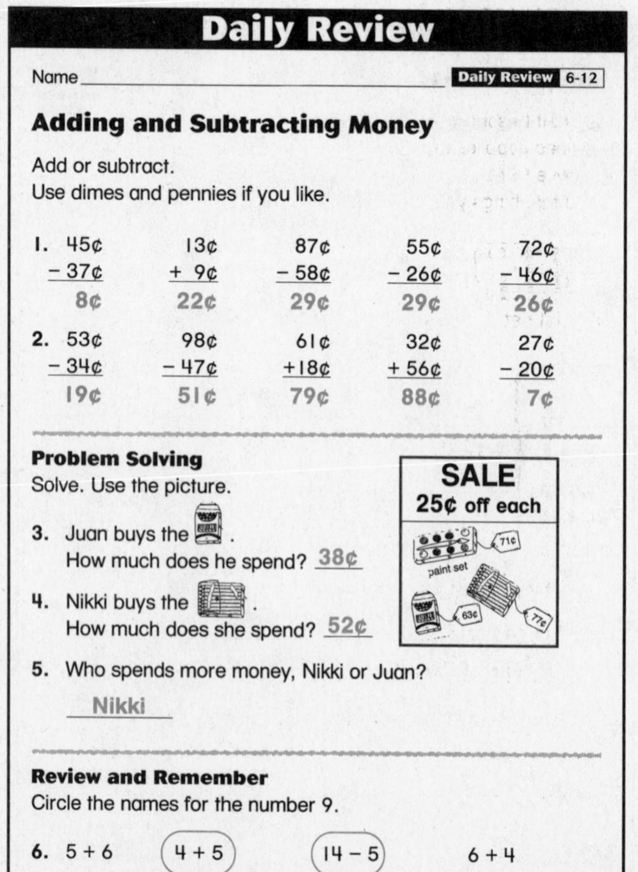

Daily Review

Name ______________________ Daily Review 6-12

Adding and Subtracting Money

Add or subtract.
Use dimes and pennies if you like.

1.	45¢ − 37¢ = 8¢	13¢ + 9¢ = 22¢	87¢ − 58¢ = 29¢	55¢ − 26¢ = 29¢	72¢ − 46¢ = 26¢
2.	53¢ − 34¢ = 19¢	98¢ − 47¢ = 51¢	61¢ + 18¢ = 79¢	32¢ + 56¢ = 88¢	27¢ − 20¢ = 7¢

Problem Solving

Solve. Use the picture.

3. Juan buys the [picture]. How much does he spend? 38¢
4. Nikki buys the [picture]. How much does she spend? 52¢
5. Who spends more money, Nikki or Juan? Nikki

Review and Remember

Circle the names for the number 9.

6. 5 + 6 (4 + 5) (14 − 5) 6 + 4

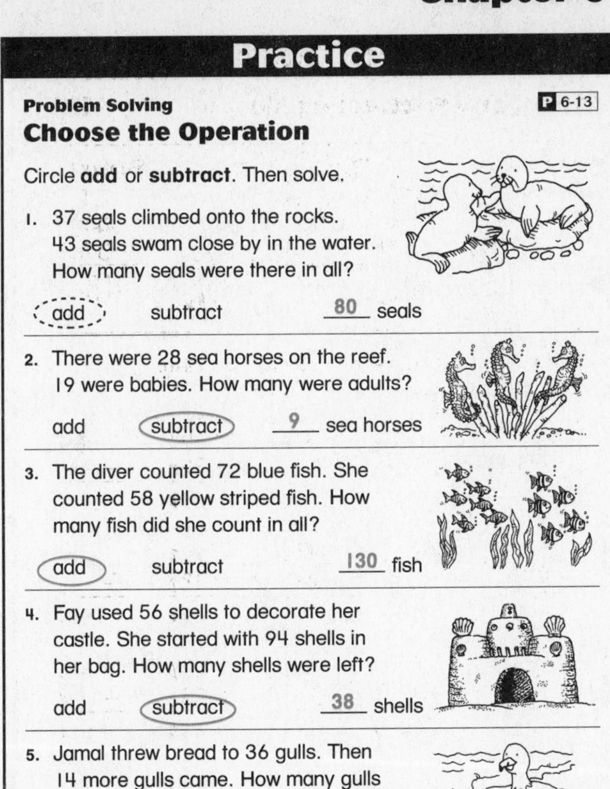

Practice

Problem Solving P 6-13

Choose the Operation

Circle **add** or **subtract**. Then solve.

1. 37 seals climbed onto the rocks. 43 seals swam close by in the water. How many seals were there in all?

   (add) subtract 80 seals

2. There were 28 sea horses on the reef. 19 were babies. How many were adults?

   add (subtract) 9 sea horses

3. The diver counted 72 blue fish. She counted 58 yellow striped fish. How many fish did she count in all?

   (add) subtract 130 fish

4. Fay used 56 shells to decorate her castle. She started with 94 shells in her bag. How many shells were left?

   add (subtract) 38 shells

5. Jamal threw bread to 36 gulls. Then 14 more gulls came. How many gulls did he feed in all?

   (add) subtract 50 gulls

 Use with Grade 2, text pages 189–90.

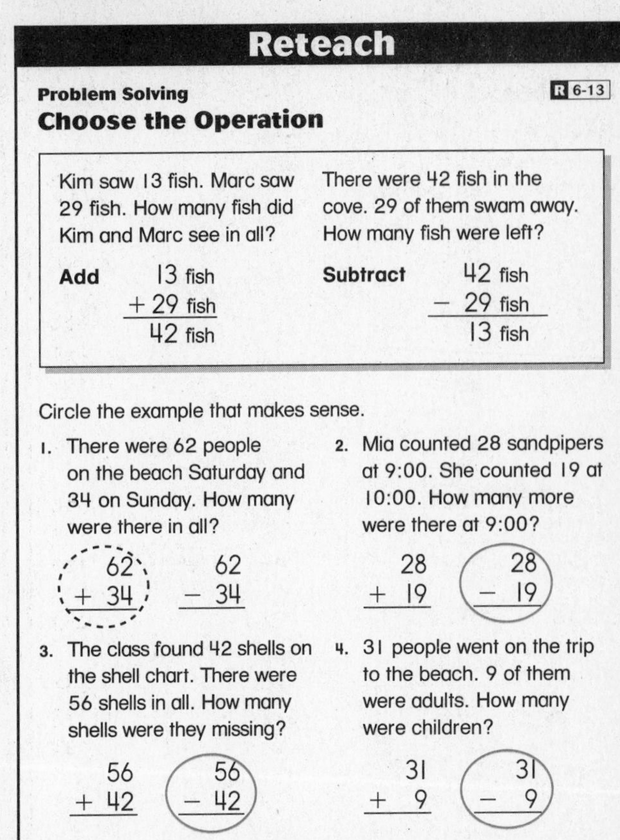

Reteach

Problem Solving R 6-13

Choose the Operation

Kim saw 13 fish. Marc saw 29 fish. How many fish did Kim and Marc see in all?

Add 13 fish + 29 fish = 42 fish

There were 42 fish in the cove. 29 of them swam away. How many fish were left?

Subtract 42 fish − 29 fish = 13 fish

Circle the example that makes sense.

1. There were 62 people on the beach Saturday and 34 on Sunday. How many were there in all?

   (62 + 34) 62 − 34

2. Mia counted 28 sandpipers at 9:00. She counted 19 at 10:00. How many more were there at 9:00?

   28 + 19 (28 − 19)

3. The class found 42 shells on the shell chart. There were 56 shells in all. How many shells were they missing?

   56 + 42 (56 − 42)

4. 31 people went on the trip to the beach. 9 of them were adults. How many were children?

   31 + 9 (31 − 9)

 Use with Grade 2, text pages 189–90.

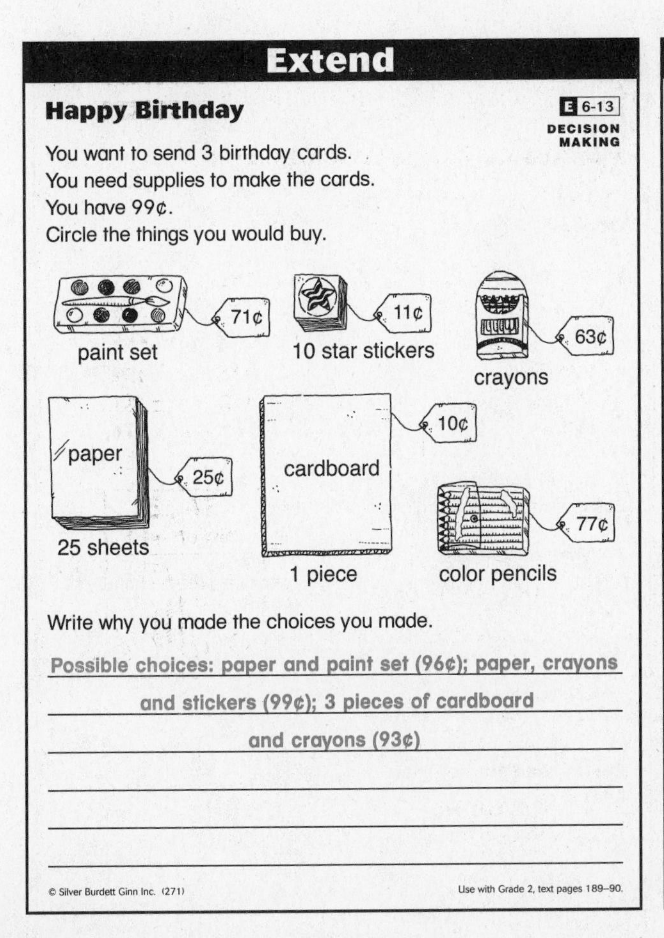

Extend

Happy Birthday

E 6-13 DECISION MAKING

You want to send 3 birthday cards.
You need supplies to make the cards.
You have 99¢.
Circle the things you would buy.

Write why you made the choices you made.

Possible choices: paper and paint set (96¢); paper, crayons and stickers (99¢); 3 pieces of cardboard and crayons (93¢)

 Use with Grade 2, text pages 189–90.

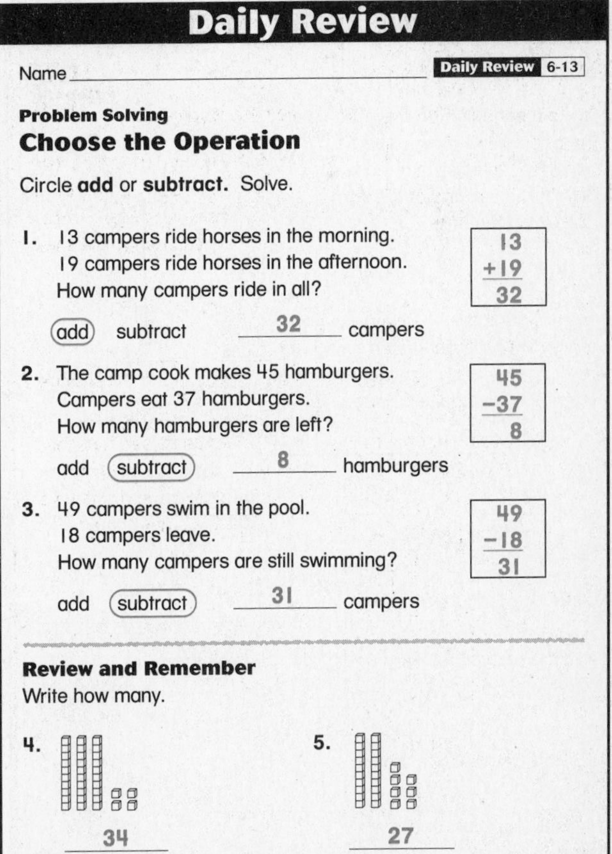

Daily Review

Name ______________________ Daily Review 6-13

Problem Solving

Choose the Operation

Circle **add** or **subtract.** Solve.

1. 13 campers ride horses in the morning. 19 campers ride horses in the afternoon. How many campers ride in all?

   (add) subtract 32 campers

   13 + 19 = 32

2. The camp cook makes 45 hamburgers. Campers eat 37 hamburgers. How many hamburgers are left?

   add (subtract) 8 hamburgers

   45 − 37 = 8

3. 49 campers swim in the pool. 18 campers leave. How many campers are still swimming?

   add (subtract) 31 campers

   49 − 18 = 31

Review and Remember

Write how many.

4. 34

5. 27

Chapter 7 • Lesson 1

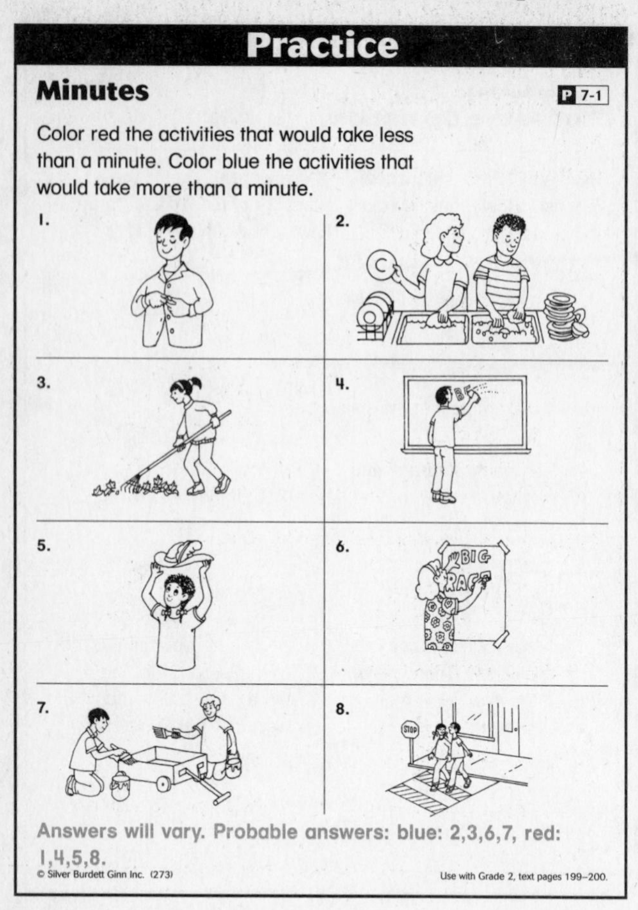

Practice

Minutes

P 7-1

Color red the activities that would take less than a minute. Color blue the activities that would take more than a minute.

1.
2.
3.
4.
5.
6.
7.
8.

Answers will vary. Probable answers: blue: 2,3,6,7, red: 1,4,5,8.

Use with Grade 2, text pages 199–200.

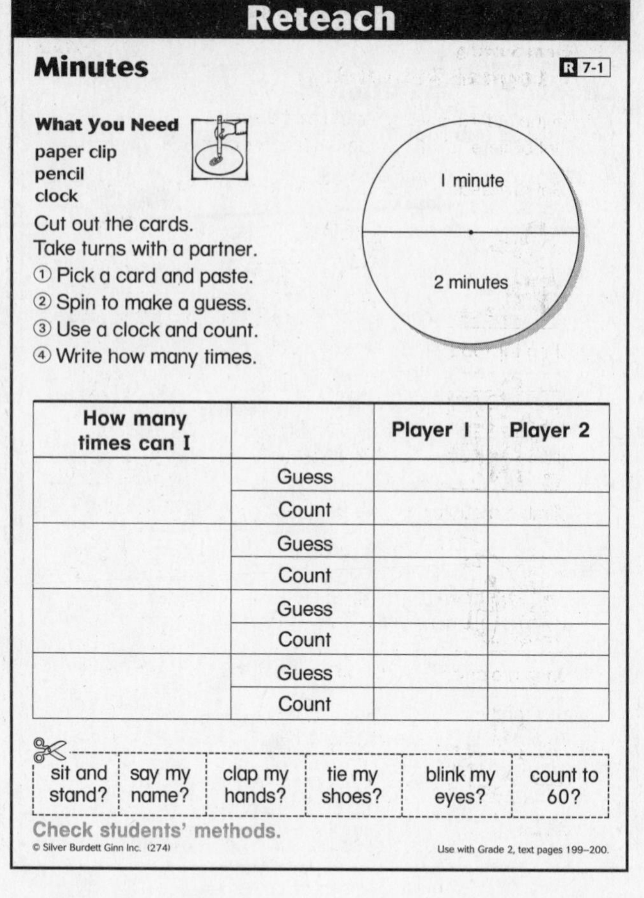

Reteach

Minutes

R 7-1

What You Need
paper clip
pencil
clock

Cut out the cards.
Take turns with a partner.
① Pick a card and paste.
② Spin to make a guess.
③ Use a clock and count.
④ Write how many times.

How many times can I		Player 1	Player 2
	Guess		
	Count		
	Guess		
	Count		
	Guess		
	Count		
	Guess		
	Count		

sit and stand?	say my name?	clap my hands?	tie my shoes?	blink my eyes?	count to 60?

Check students' methods.

Use with Grade 2, text pages 199–200.

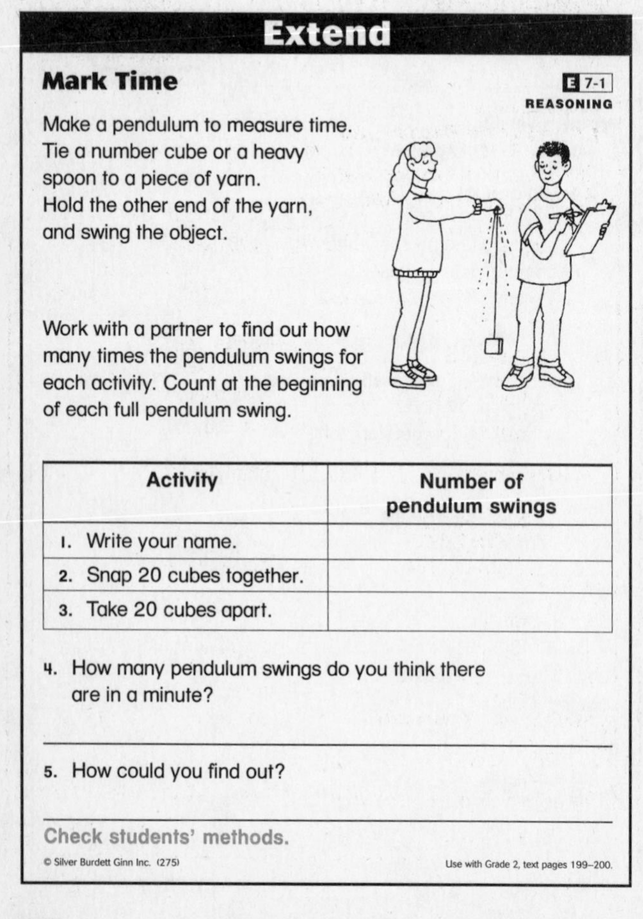

Extend

Mark Time

E 7-1
REASONING

Make a pendulum to measure time.
Tie a number cube or a heavy spoon to a piece of yarn.
Hold the other end of the yarn, and swing the object.

Work with a partner to find out how many times the pendulum swings for each activity. Count at the beginning of each full pendulum swing.

Activity	Number of pendulum swings
1. Write your name.	
2. Snap 20 cubes together.	
3. Take 20 cubes apart.	

4. How many pendulum swings do you think there are in a minute?

5. How could you find out?

Check students' methods.

Use with Grade 2, text pages 199–200.

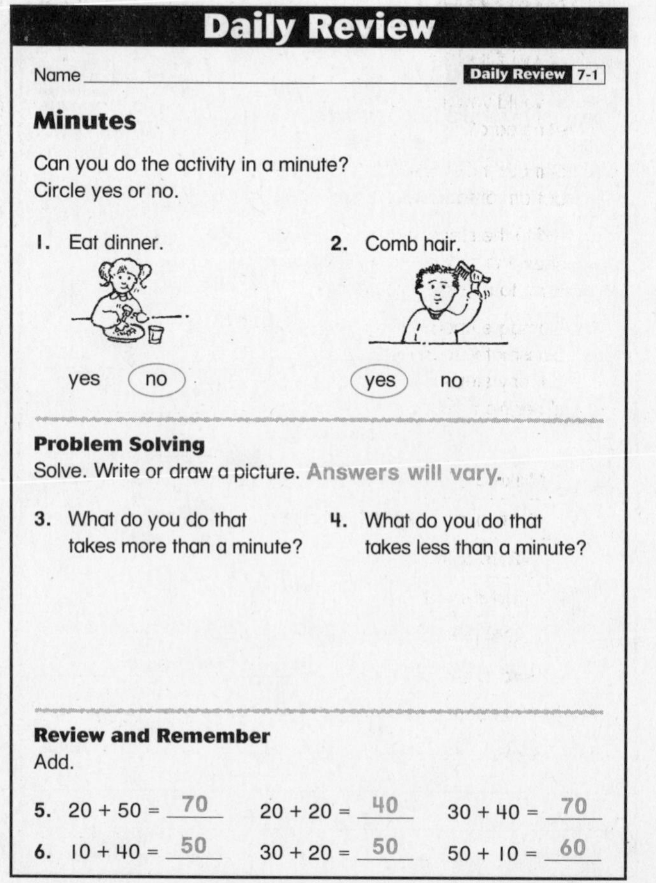

Daily Review

Name ____________ Daily Review 7-1

Minutes

Can you do the activity in a minute?
Circle yes or no.

1. Eat dinner. yes (no)

2. Comb hair. (yes) no

Problem Solving
Solve. Write or draw a picture. Answers will vary.

3. What do you do that takes more than a minute?

4. What do you do that takes less than a minute?

Review and Remember
Add.

5. 20 + 50 = 70　　20 + 20 = 40　　30 + 40 = 70

6. 10 + 40 = 50　　30 + 20 = 50　　50 + 10 = 60

Practice

Problem Solving **P 7-2**

Use Logical Reasoning

Circle the activities that take about the same amount of time. Think minutes, hours, or days.

1. Get dressed. | Build a model plane. | Wrap a present.
2. Shop for food. | Wash a car. | Write your name.
3. Climb a mountain. | Eat a bowl of cereal. | Take a bath.
4. Snap a picture. | Put on your boots. | Clap your hands.

© Silver Burdett Ginn Inc. (276) Use with Grade 2, text pages 201–202.

Reteach

Problem Solving **R 7-2**

Use Logical Reasoning

About how long does each take?
Circle the more reasonable answer.

1. Build a castle. — 20 minutes / 3 days
2. Make a sandwich. — 5 minutes / 3 hours
3. Feed a cat. — 4 minutes / 2 hours
4. Plant a tree. — 5 minutes / 1 hour

Circle the activities that take about an hour.

5. Play a game of soccer.
6. Blow up a balloon.
7. Open a present.
8. Put a puzzle together.

© Silver Burdett Ginn Inc. (277) Use with Grade 2, text pages 201–202.

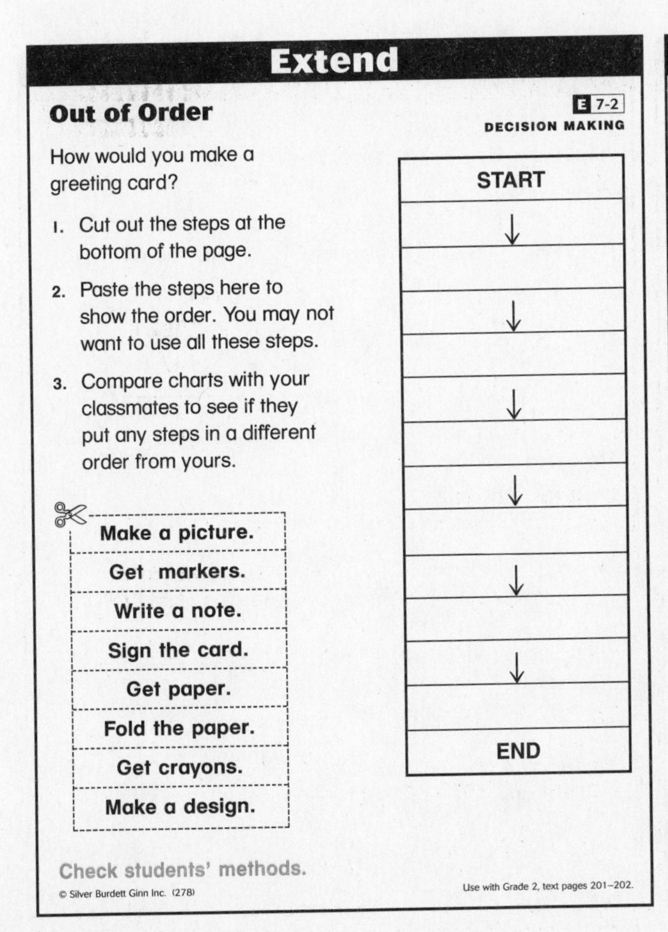

Extend

E 7-2 DECISION MAKING

Out of Order

How would you make a greeting card?

1. Cut out the steps at the bottom of the page.
2. Paste the steps here to show the order. You may not want to use all these steps.
3. Compare charts with your classmates to see if they put any steps in a different order from yours.

START → → → → → → END

- Make a picture.
- Get markers.
- Write a note.
- Sign the card.
- Get paper.
- Fold the paper.
- Get crayons.
- Make a design.

Check students' methods.

© Silver Burdett Ginn Inc. (278) Use with Grade 2, text pages 201–202.

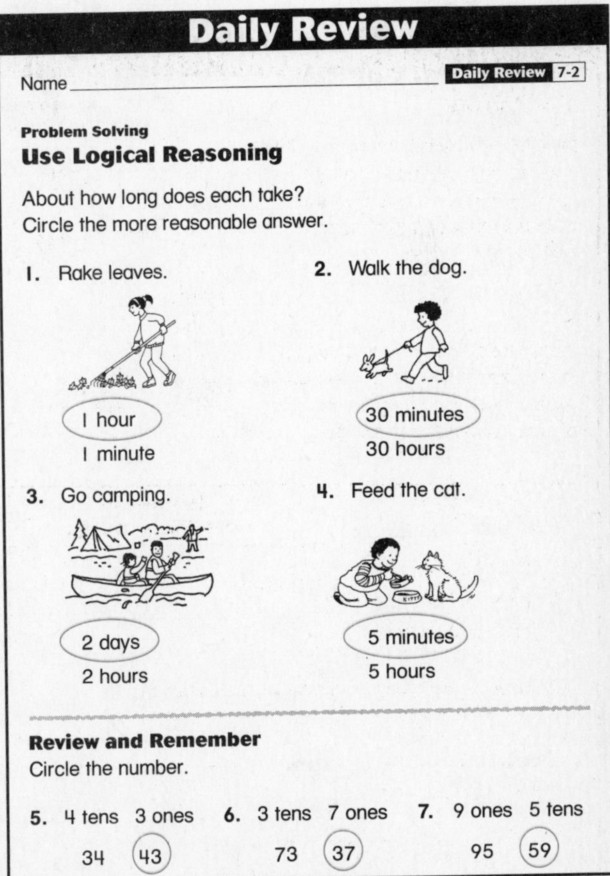

Daily Review

Daily Review 7-2

Name ____________________

Problem Solving

Use Logical Reasoning

About how long does each take?
Circle the more reasonable answer.

1. Rake leaves. — 1 hour / 1 minute
2. Walk the dog. — 30 minutes / 30 hours
3. Go camping. — 2 days / 2 hours
4. Feed the cat. — 5 minutes / 5 hours

Review and Remember

Circle the number.

5. 4 tens 3 ones — 34 / 43
6. 3 tens 7 ones — 73 / 37
7. 9 ones 5 tens — 95 / 59

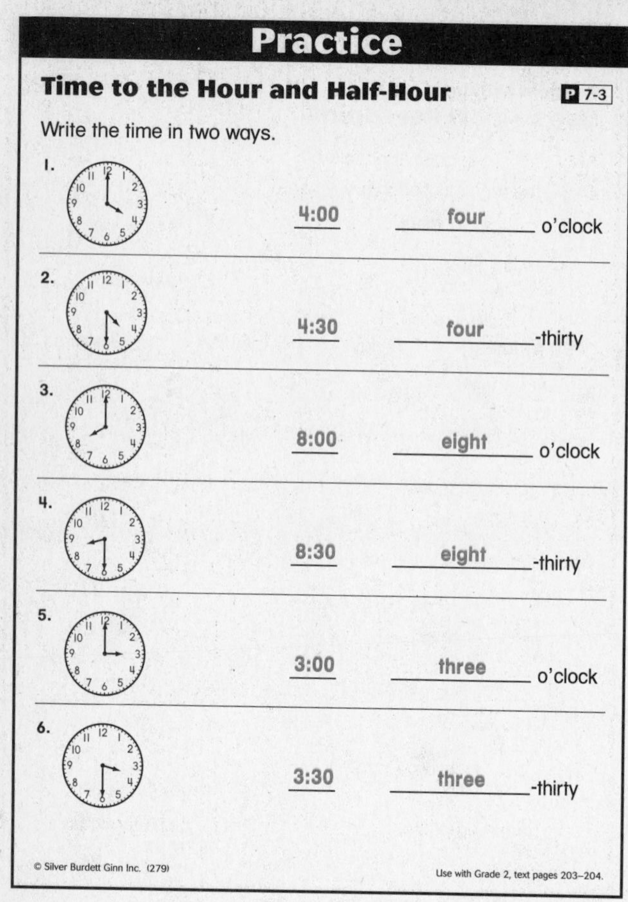

Practice

Time to the Hour and Half-Hour

P 7-3

Write the time in two ways.

1. 4:00 four o'clock
2. 4:30 four-thirty
3. 8:00 eight o'clock
4. 8:30 eight-thirty
5. 3:00 three o'clock
6. 3:30 three-thirty

Use with Grade 2, text pages 203–204.

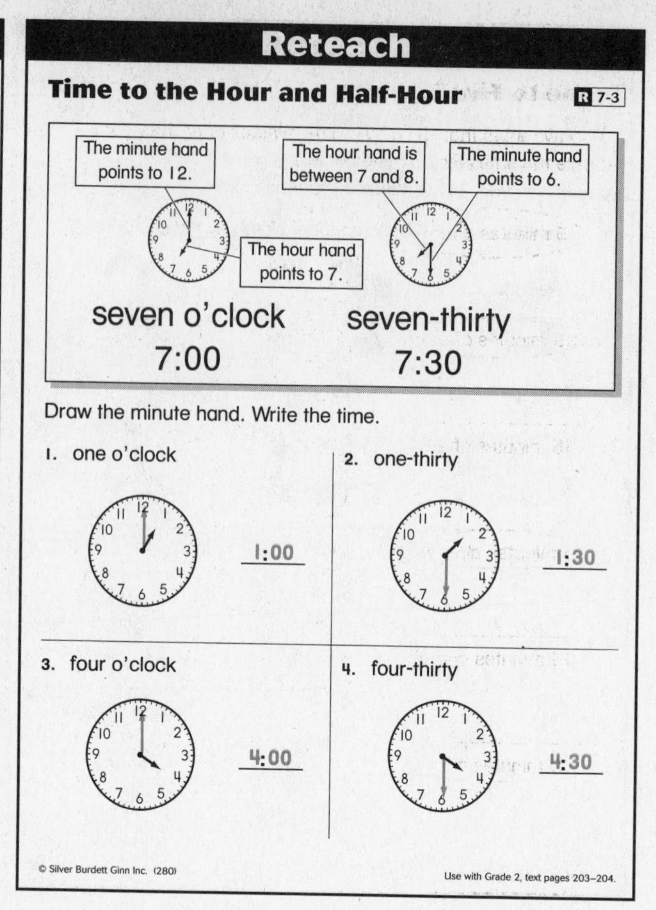

Reteach

Time to the Hour and Half-Hour

R 7-3

Draw the minute hand. Write the time.

1. one o'clock 1:00
2. one-thirty 1:30
3. four o'clock 4:00
4. four-thirty 4:30

Use with Grade 2, text pages 203–204.

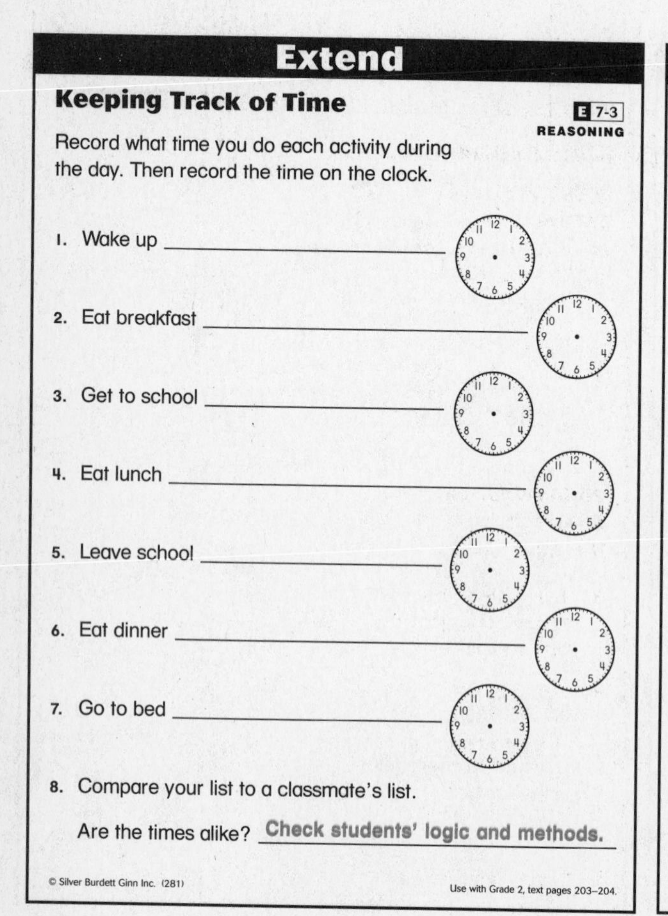

Extend

Keeping Track of Time

E 7-3
REASONING

Record what time you do each activity during the day. Then record the time on the clock.

1. Wake up ____
2. Eat breakfast ____
3. Get to school ____
4. Eat lunch ____
5. Leave school ____
6. Eat dinner ____
7. Go to bed ____
8. Compare your list to a classmate's list.

   Are the times alike? Check students' logic and methods.

Use with Grade 2, text pages 203–204.

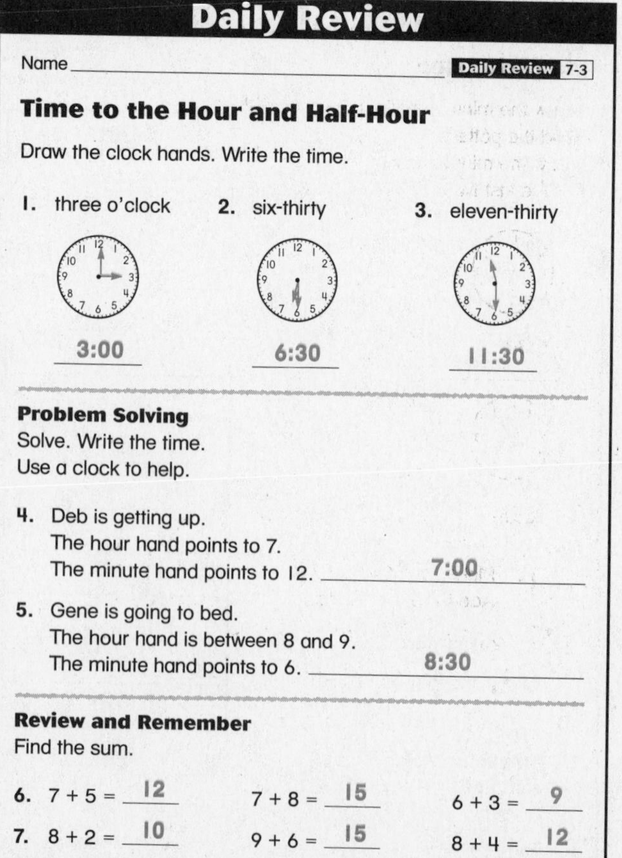

Daily Review

Name ____

Daily Review 7-3

Time to the Hour and Half-Hour

Draw the clock hands. Write the time.

1. three o'clock 3:00
2. six-thirty 6:30
3. eleven-thirty 11:30

Problem Solving

Solve. Write the time.
Use a clock to help.

4. Deb is getting up.
   The hour hand points to 7.
   The minute hand points to 12. 7:00
5. Gene is going to bed.
   The hour hand is between 8 and 9.
   The minute hand points to 6. 8:30

Review and Remember

Find the sum.

6. 7 + 5 = 12   7 + 8 = 15   6 + 3 = 9
7. 8 + 2 = 10   9 + 6 = 15   8 + 4 = 12

Chapter 7 • Lesson 4

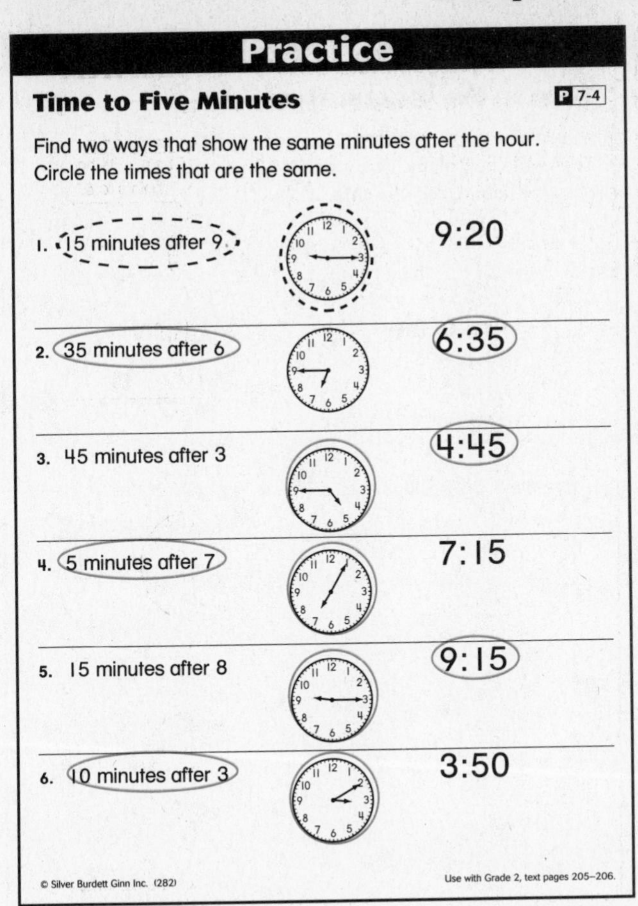

Practice

Time to Five Minutes P 7-4

Find two ways that show the same minutes after the hour.
Circle the times that are the same.

1. 15 minutes after 9 — 9:20
2. 35 minutes after 6 — 6:35
3. 45 minutes after 3 — 4:45
4. 5 minutes after 7 — 7:15
5. 15 minutes after 8 — 9:15
6. 10 minutes after 3 — 3:50

Use with Grade 2, text pages 205–206.

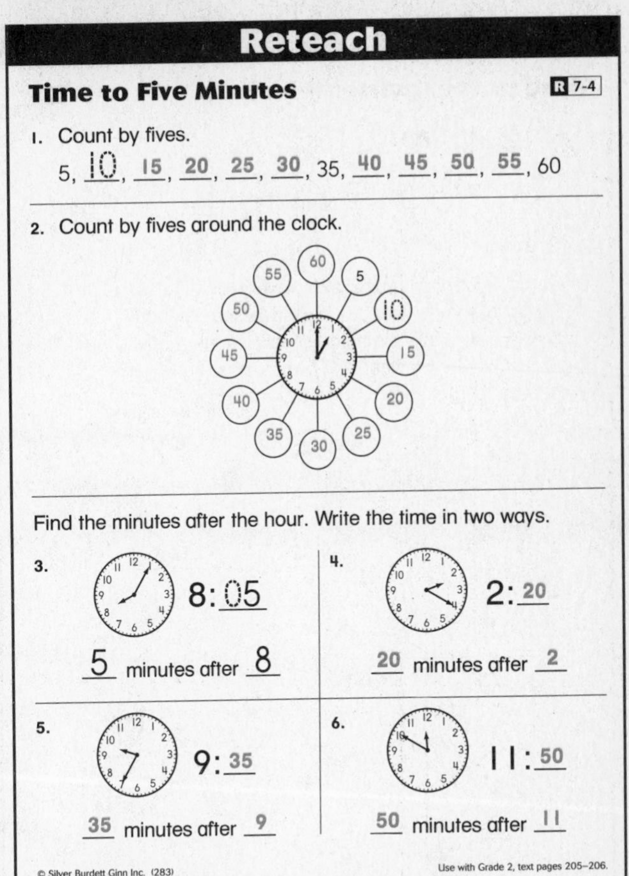

Reteach

Time to Five Minutes R 7-4

1. Count by fives.
5, 10, 15, 20, 25, 30, 35, 40, 45, 50, 55, 60

2. Count by fives around the clock.

Find the minutes after the hour. Write the time in two ways.

3. 8: 05
5 minutes after 8

4. 2: 20
20 minutes after 2

5. 9: 35
35 minutes after 9

6. 11: 50
50 minutes after 11

Use with Grade 2, text pages 205–206.

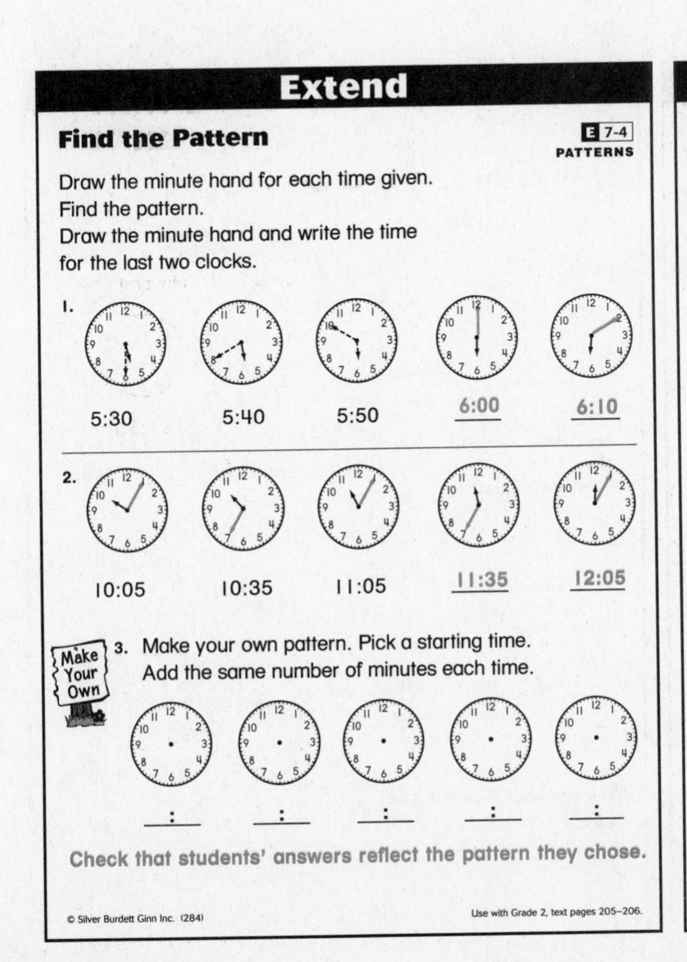

Extend

Find the Pattern E 7-4 PATTERNS

Draw the minute hand for each time given.
Find the pattern.
Draw the minute hand and write the time for the last two clocks.

1. 5:30 5:40 5:50 6:00 6:10

2. 10:05 10:35 11:05 11:35 12:05

Make Your Own 3. Make your own pattern. Pick a starting time.
Add the same number of minutes each time.

___:___ ___:___ ___:___ ___:___ ___:___

Check that students' answers reflect the pattern they chose.

Use with Grade 2, text pages 205–206.

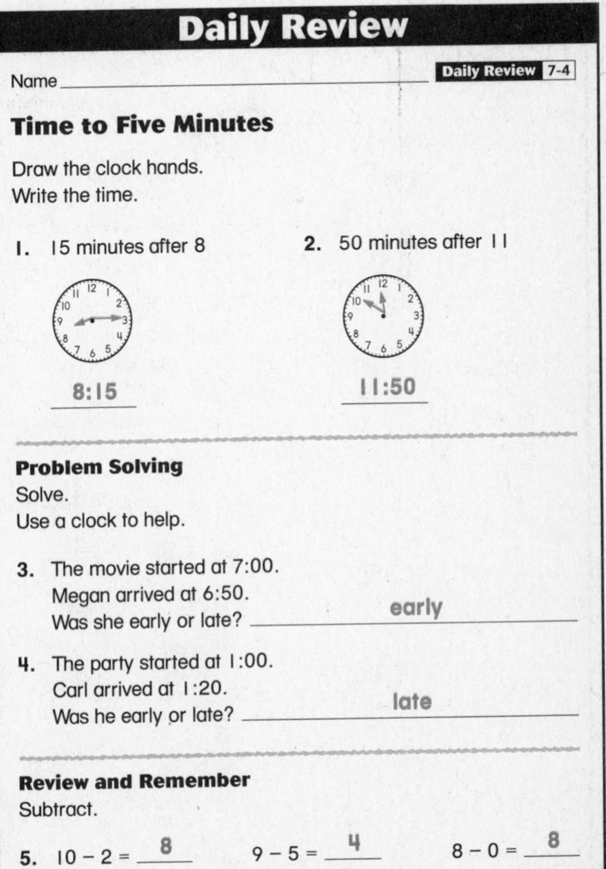

Daily Review

Name ____________ Daily Review 7-4

Time to Five Minutes

Draw the clock hands.
Write the time.

1. 15 minutes after 8
8:15

2. 50 minutes after 11
11:50

Problem Solving

Solve.
Use a clock to help.

3. The movie started at 7:00.
Megan arrived at 6:50.
Was she early or late? early

4. The party started at 1:00.
Carl arrived at 1:20.
Was he early or late? late

Review and Remember

Subtract.

5. 10 − 2 = 8 9 − 5 = 4 8 − 0 = 8

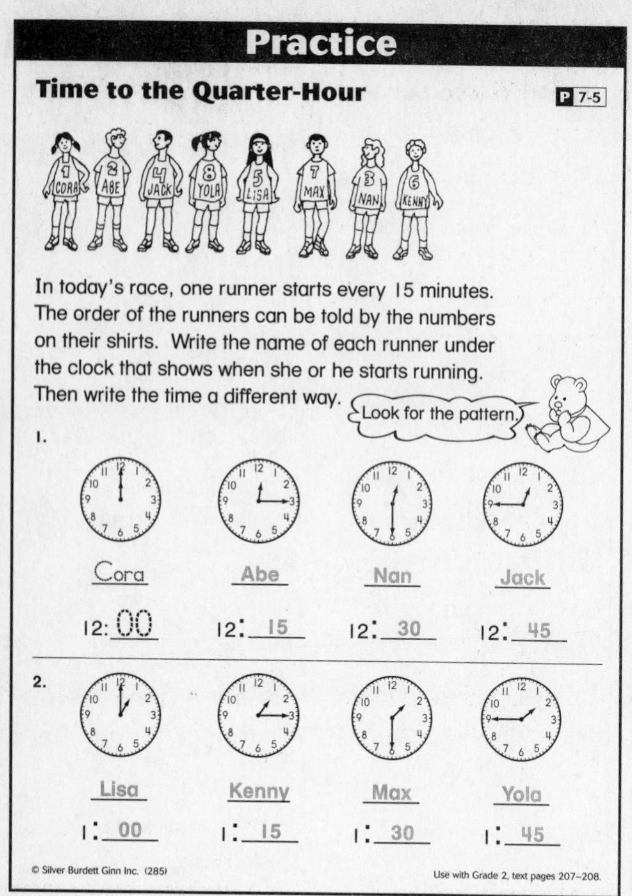

Practice

Time to the Quarter-Hour P 7-5

In today's race, one runner starts every 15 minutes. The order of the runners can be told by the numbers on their shirts. Write the name of each runner under the clock that shows when she or he starts running. Then write the time a different way.

Look for the pattern.

1. Cora 12:00 | Abe 12:15 | Nan 12:30 | Jack 12:45

2. Lisa 1:00 | Kenny 1:15 | Max 1:30 | Yola 1:45

 Use with Grade 2, text pages 207–208.

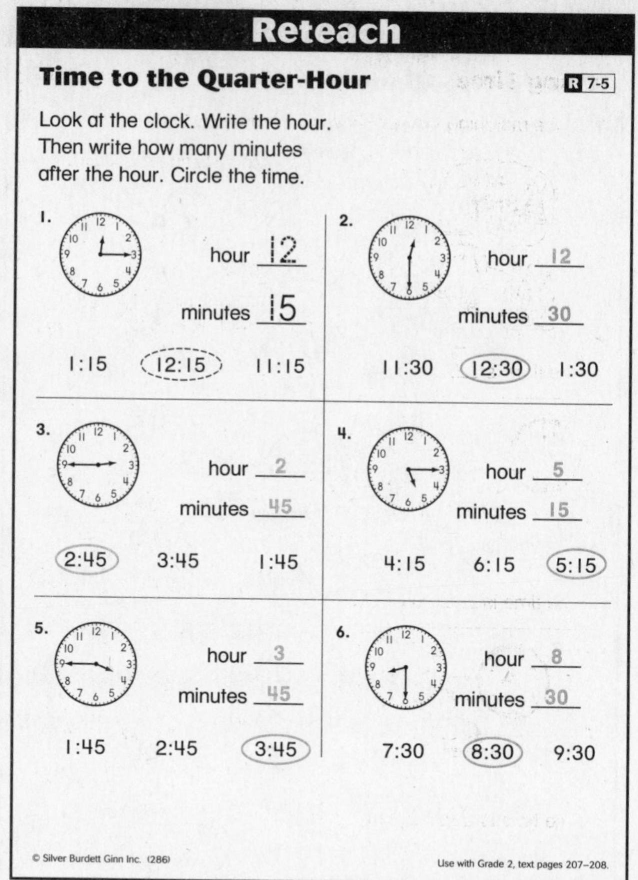

Reteach

Time to the Quarter-Hour R 7-5

Look at the clock. Write the hour. Then write how many minutes after the hour. Circle the time.

1. hour 12, minutes 15 — 1:15 (12:15) 11:15
2. hour 12, minutes 30 — 11:30 (12:30) 1:30
3. hour 2, minutes 45 — (2:45) 3:45 1:45
4. hour 5, minutes 15 — 4:15 6:15 (5:15)
5. hour 3, minutes 45 — 1:45 2:45 (3:45)
6. hour 8, minutes 30 — 7:30 (8:30) 9:30

 Use with Grade 2, text pages 207–208.

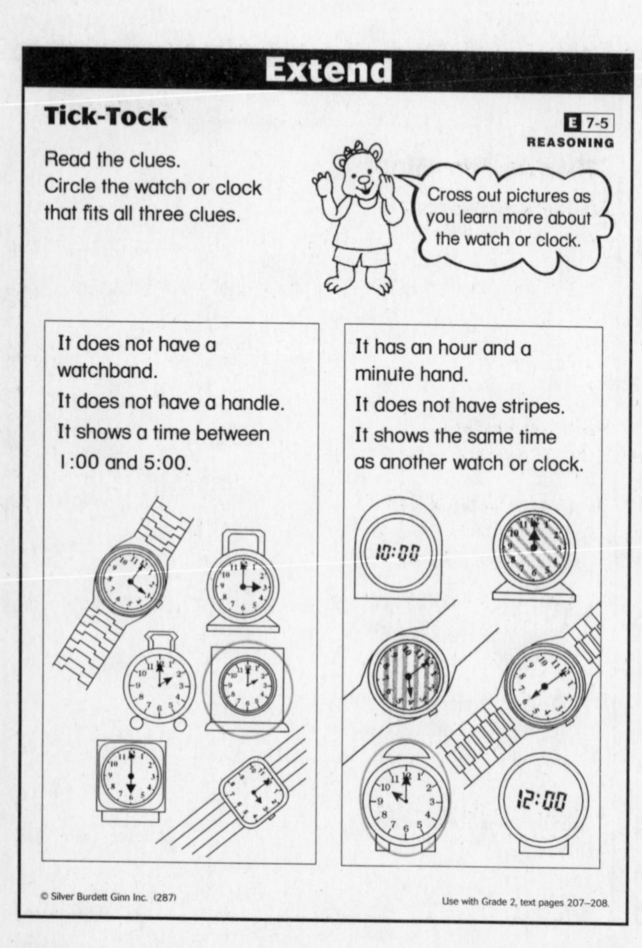

Extend

Tick-Tock E 7-5 REASONING

Read the clues.
Circle the watch or clock that fits all three clues.

Cross out pictures as you learn more about the watch or clock.

It does not have a watchband.
It does not have a handle.
It shows a time between 1:00 and 5:00.

It has an hour and a minute hand.
It does not have stripes.
It shows the same time as another watch or clock.

 Use with Grade 2, text pages 207–208.

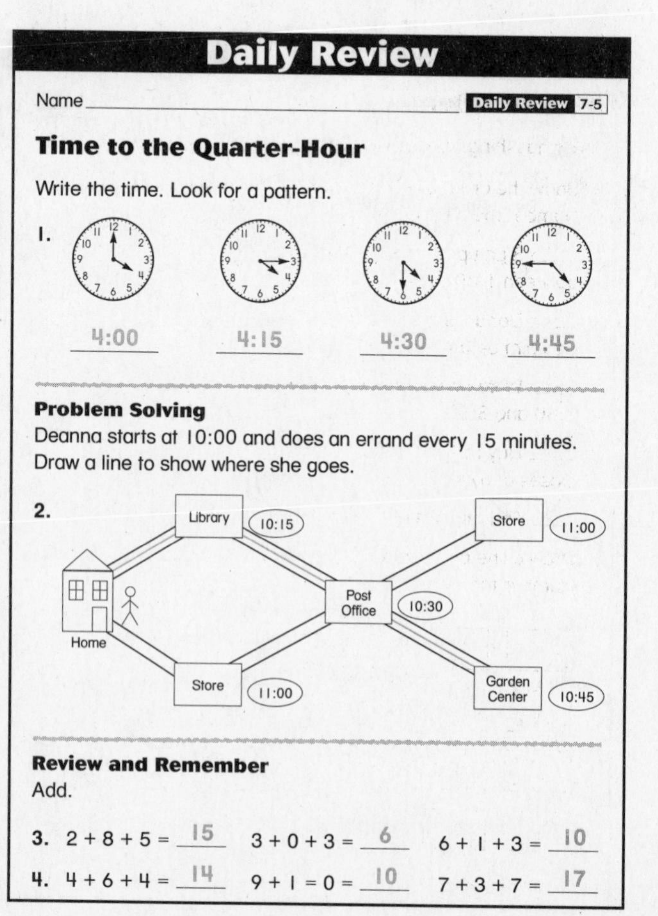

Daily Review

Name ____________ Daily Review 7-5

Time to the Quarter-Hour

Write the time. Look for a pattern.

1. 4:00 | 4:15 | 4:30 | 4:45

Problem Solving

Deanna starts at 10:00 and does an errand every 15 minutes. Draw a line to show where she goes.

2.

Review and Remember

Add.

3. 2 + 8 + 5 = 15   3 + 0 + 3 = 6   6 + 1 + 3 = 10

4. 4 + 6 + 4 = 14   9 + 1 = 0 = 10   7 + 3 + 7 = 17

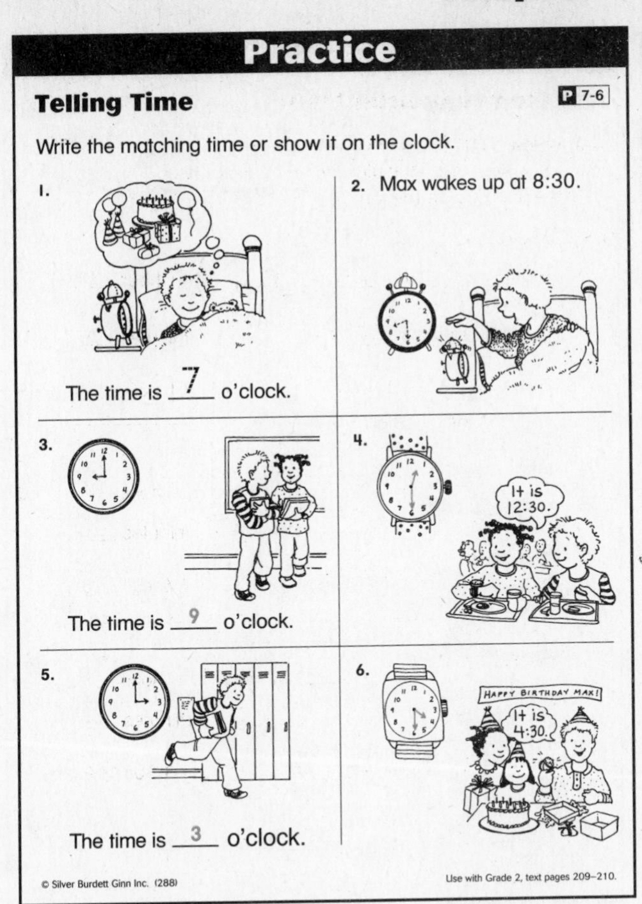

Practice

Telling Time

P 7-6

Write the matching time or show it on the clock.

1. The time is 7 o'clock.

2. Max wakes up at 8:30.

3. The time is 9 o'clock.

4.

5. The time is 3 o'clock.

6.

Use with Grade 2, text pages 209–210.

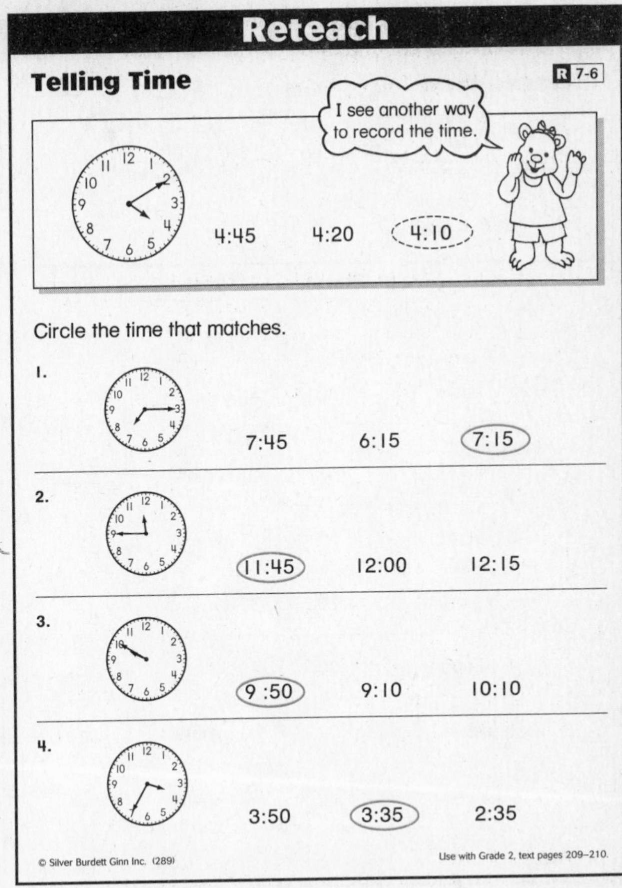

Reteach

Telling Time

R 7-6

4:45 4:20 (4:10)

Circle the time that matches.

1. 7:45 6:15 (7:15)
2. (11:45) 12:00 12:15
3. (9:50) 9:10 10:10
4. 3:50 (3:35) 2:35

Use with Grade 2, text pages 209–210.

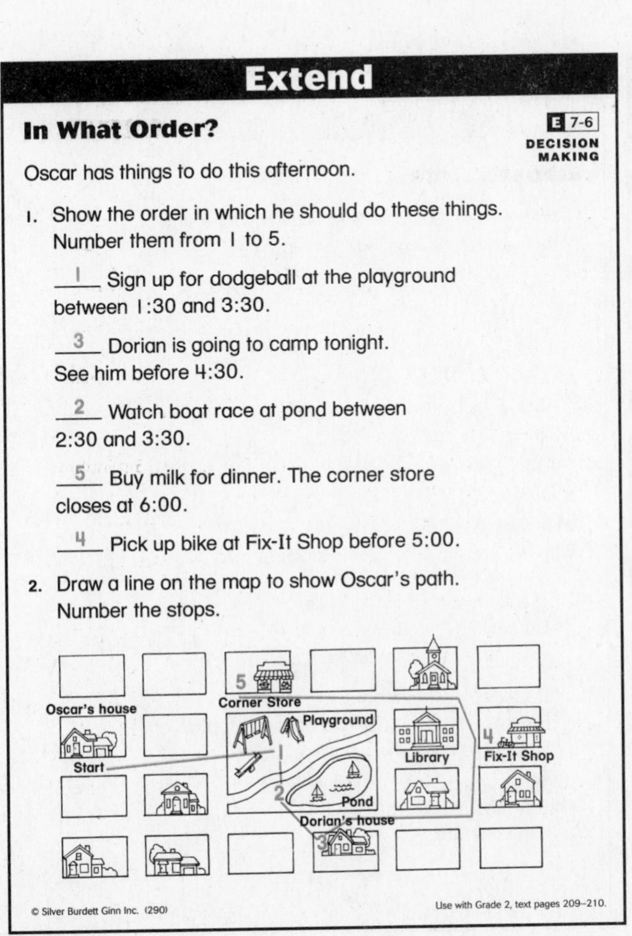

Extend

In What Order?

E 7-6
DECISION MAKING

Oscar has things to do this afternoon.

1. Show the order in which he should do these things. Number them from 1 to 5.

   1 Sign up for dodgeball at the playground between 1:30 and 3:30.

   3 Dorian is going to camp tonight. See him before 4:30.

   2 Watch boat race at pond between 2:30 and 3:30.

   5 Buy milk for dinner. The corner store closes at 6:00.

   4 Pick up bike at Fix-It Shop before 5:00.

2. Draw a line on the map to show Oscar's path. Number the stops.

Use with Grade 2, text pages 209–210.

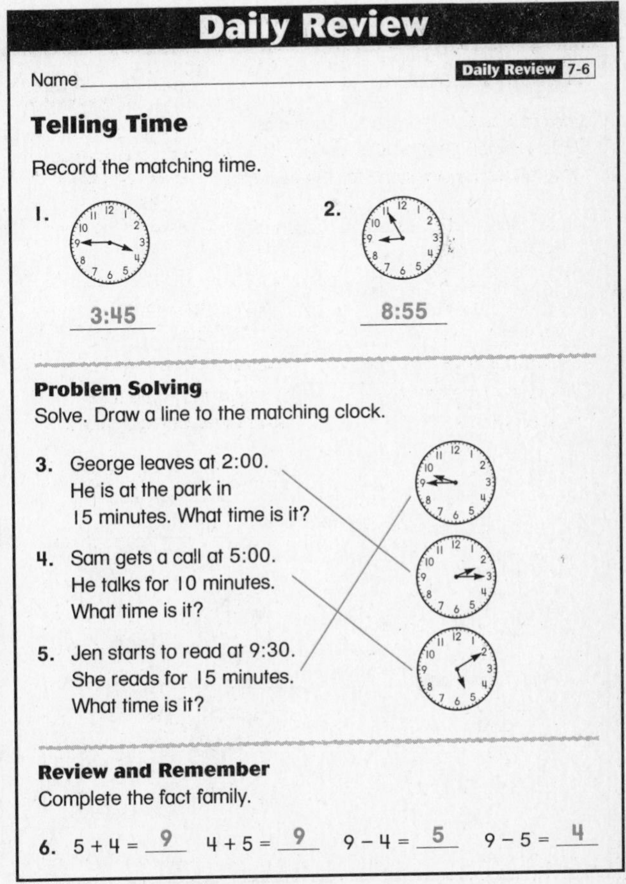

Daily Review

Name ______

Daily Review 7-6

Telling Time

Record the matching time.

1. 3:45
2. 8:55

Problem Solving

Solve. Draw a line to the matching clock.

3. George leaves at 2:00. He is at the park in 15 minutes. What time is it?
4. Sam gets a call at 5:00. He talks for 10 minutes. What time is it?
5. Jen starts to read at 9:30. She reads for 15 minutes. What time is it?

Review and Remember

Complete the fact family.

6. 5 + 4 = 9 4 + 5 = 9 9 − 4 = 5 9 − 5 = 4

Practice

Elapsed Time

P 7-7

Write each end time.

Activity	Starts	Lasts	Ends
1. Pick up toys.	4:30	1 hour	5:30
2. Write a letter.	2:30	30 minutes	3:00
3. Play soccer.	10:00	1 hour and 30 minutes	11:30
4. Feed a pet.	5:00	15 minutes	5:15
5. Read a story.	7:30	30 minutes	8:00
6. Go to the park.	1:00	2 hours	3:00
7. Wash dishes.	6:00	30 minutes	6:30
8. Play a game.	3:30	30 minutes	4:00

Use with Grade 2, text pages 211–212.

Reteach

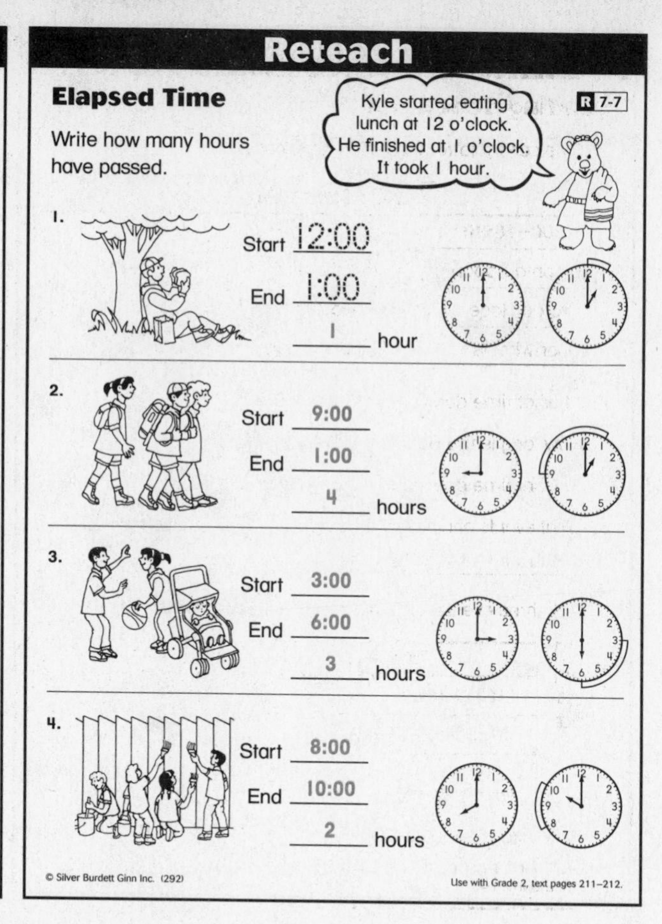

Elapsed Time

R 7-7

Write how many hours have passed.

Kyle started eating lunch at 12 o'clock.
He finished at 1 o'clock.
It took 1 hour.

1. Start 12:00
   End 1:00
   1 hour

2. Start 9:00
   End 1:00
   4 hours

3. Start 3:00
   End 6:00
   3 hours

4. Start 8:00
   End 10:00
   2 hours

Use with Grade 2, text pages 211–212.

Extend

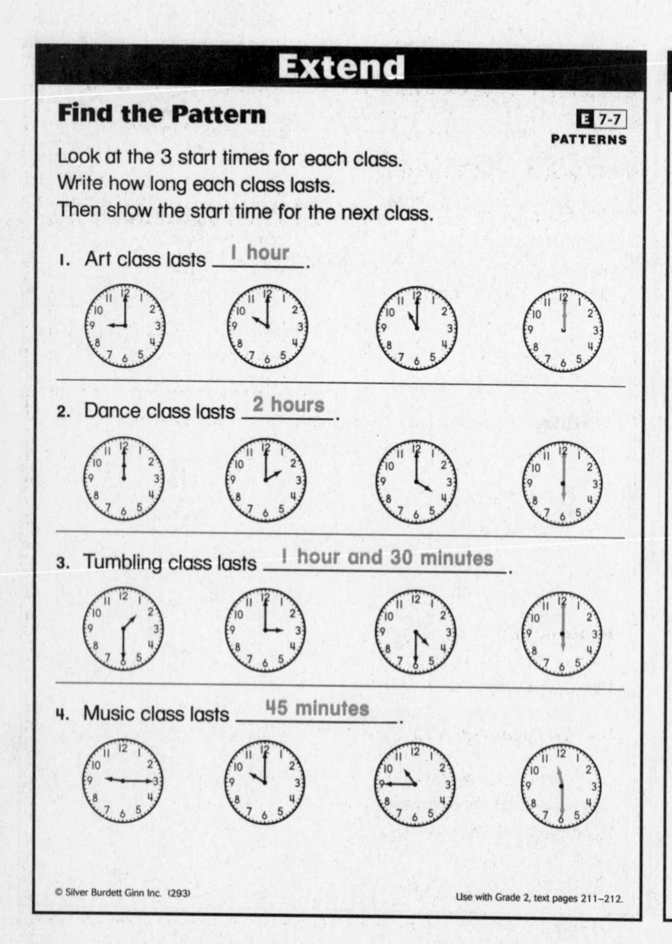

Find the Pattern

E 7-7
PATTERNS

Look at the 3 start times for each class.
Write how long each class lasts.
Then show the start time for the next class.

1. Art class lasts 1 hour.
2. Dance class lasts 2 hours.
3. Tumbling class lasts 1 hour and 30 minutes.
4. Music class lasts 45 minutes.

Use with Grade 2, text pages 211–212.

Daily Review

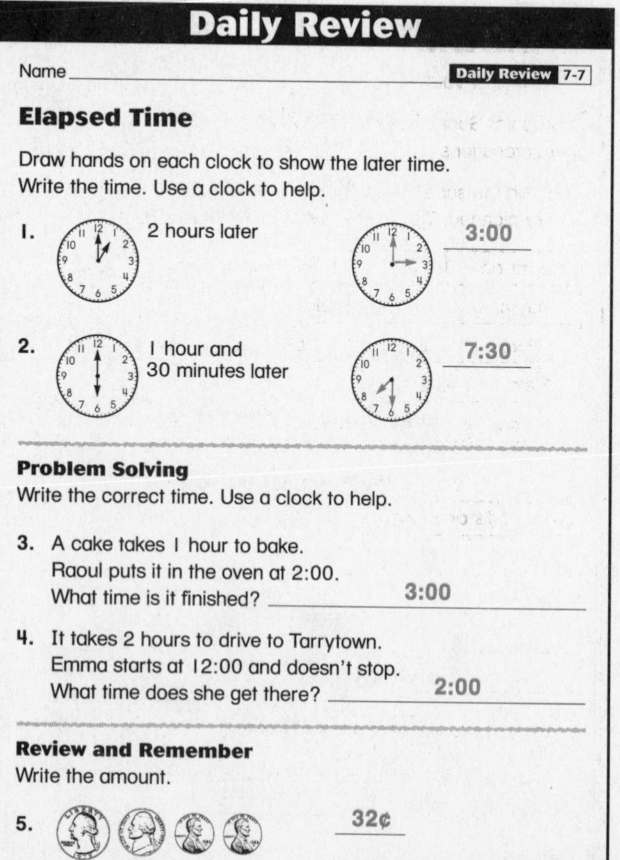

Name ____________________ Daily Review 7-7

Elapsed Time

Draw hands on each clock to show the later time.
Write the time. Use a clock to help.

1. 2 hours later — 3:00
2. 1 hour and 30 minutes later — 7:30

Problem Solving

Write the correct time. Use a clock to help.

3. A cake takes 1 hour to bake.
   Raoul puts it in the oven at 2:00.
   What time is it finished? 3:00

4. It takes 2 hours to drive to Tarrytown.
   Emma starts at 12:00 and doesn't stop.
   What time does she get there? 2:00

Review and Remember

Write the amount.

5. 32¢

Practice

Reading Schedules

P 7-8

Use the schedule to answer the questions.

Silly Sports Day

10:00–10:30	10:30–11:15	11:15–11:45
Egg on a Spoon	Ball Bounce	Hopping Race
Tiptoe Race	Headstands	Book Balance
Cartwheels	Bubble Catch	Water Balloons

1. At what time does Ball Bounce begin? 10:30
2. How long is the Book Balance? 30 minutes
3. At what time does the Tiptoe Race end? 10:30
4. What events end at 11:15? Ball Bounce, Headstands, and Bubble Catch
5. Pick three events and make a schedule for yourself.

Time	Event
10:00-10:30	
10:30-11:15	
11:15-11:45	

Check that students pick one event from each time.

 Use with Grade 2, text pages 213–214.

Reteach

Reading Schedules

R 7-8

Use the schedule to record the times. Complete the sentences.

1:00–1:30 means the parade is from 1:00 to 1:30.

Field Day

Time	Event
1:00 – 1:30	Parade
1:30 – 2:00	Relay Race
2:00 – 2:30	Cross-Country Race
2:30 – 3:00	100-Yard Dash

1. 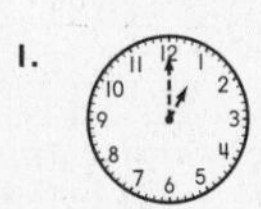 

The parade starts at 1:00. It ends at 1:30.

2.  

The relay race starts at 1:30. It ends at 2:00.

3.  

The cross-country race starts at 2:00. It ends at 2:30.

4. 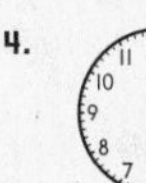  

The 100-yard dash starts at 2:30. It ends at 3:00.

 Use with Grade 2, text pages 213–214.

Extend

Make a Plan

E 7-8 DECISION MAKING

The Junior Sports events are being held in four locations. Check that students' decisions reflect an understanding of the schedule.

1. Read the schedule to find out what events are planned. Then make a schedule for yourself.

Location	8:00-8:30	8:30-9:00	9:00-9:30	9:30-10:00
Gym	volleyball		tumbling	trampoline
Pool	diving	swimming show		relay race
Field 1	exercises	softball game		
Field 2	running races		soccer game	

My Own Schedule

When? (start-end)	Where?	What?

2. What is the greatest number of events you could attend? 3 complete events or 4 partial events

 Use with Grade 2, text pages 213–214.

Daily Review

Name ____________ Daily Review 7-8

Reading Schedules

Use the schedule. Write the time each activity starts. Draw the clock hands.

Lazy Days Camp

Time	Activity
8:00	Swimming
9:15	Crafts
10:00	Boating
10:45	Horseback Riding
11:30	Lunch

1. Crafts  9:15
2. Swimming  8:00
3. Boating  10:00

Problem Solving

Use the schedule to solve. Use a clock to help.

4. Nina goes horseback riding until lunch. How long does she ride? 45 minutes

Review and Remember

Write the number that comes just after.

5. 47, 48 60, 61 18, 19

Practice

Problem Solving P 7-9

Using a Calendar

Use the calendar to answer the questions.

January

S	M	T	W	T	F	S
	1	2	3	4	5	6
7	8	9	10	11	12	13
14	15	16	17	18	19	20
21	22	23	24	25	26	27
28	29	30	31			

February

S	M	T	W	T	F	S
				1	2	3
4	5	6	7	8	9	10
11	12	13	14	15	16	17
18	19	20	21	22	23	24
25	26	27	28			

March

S	M	T	W	T	F	S
				1	2	3
4	5	6	7	8	9	10
11	12	13	14	15	16	17
18	19	20	21	22	23	24
25	26	27	28	29	30	31

April

S	M	T	W	T	F	S
1	2	3	4	5	6	7
8	9	10	11	12	13	14
15	16	17	18	19	20	21
22	23	24	25	26	27	28
29	30					

May

S	M	T	W	T	F	S
		1	2	3	4	5
6	7	8	9	10	11	12
13	14	15	16	17	18	19
20	21	22	23	24	25	26
27	28	29	30	31		

June

S	M	T	W	T	F	S
					1	2
3	4	5	6	7	8	9
10	11	12	13	14	15	16
17	18	19	20	21	22	23
24	25	26	27	28	29	30

July

S	M	T	W	T	F	S
1	2	3	4	5	6	7
8	9	10	11	12	13	14
15	16	17	18	19	20	21
22	23	24	25	26	27	28
29	30	31				

August

S	M	T	W	T	F	S
			1	2	3	4
5	6	7	8	9	10	11
12	13	14	15	16	17	18
19	20	21	22	23	24	25
26	27	28	29	30	31	

September

S	M	T	W	T	F	S
						1
2	3	4	5	6	7	8
9	10	11	12	13	14	15
16	17	18	19	20	21	22
23	24	25	26	27	28	29
30						

October

S	M	T	W	T	F	S
	1	2	3	4	5	6
7	8	9	10	11	12	13
14	15	16	17	18	19	20
21	22	23	24	25	26	27
28	29	30	31			

November

S	M	T	W	T	F	S
				1	2	3
4	5	6	7	8	9	10
11	12	13	14	15	16	17
18	19	20	21	22	23	24
25	26	27	28	29	30	

December

S	M	T	W	T	F	S
						1
2	3	4	5	6	7	8
9	10	11	12	13	14	15
16	17	18	19	20	21	22
23	24	25	26	27	28	29
30	31					

1. What is the first month of the year? January
2. How many months have 30 days? 4
3. What month comes after February? March
4. What is the eighth month? August
5. How many months have 31 days? 7

 Use with Grade 2, text pages 215–216.

Reteach

Problem Solving R 7-9

Using a Calendar

1. Complete the calendar.

November

Sunday	Monday	Tuesday	Wednesday	Thursday	Friday	Saturday
1	2	3	4	5	6	7
8	9	10	11	12	13	14
15	16	17	18	19	20	21
22	23	24	25	26	27	28
29	30					

Use the calendar to answer the questions.

2. There are 30 days in the month of November.
3. There are 4 Wednesdays in this month.
4. The ninth of November is a Monday.
5. The first day of this month is on Sunday.

 Use with Grade 2, text pages 215–216.

Extend

An Extra Day!

E 7-9 PROBLEM SOLVING

February usually has 28 days. Every fourth year, February has 29 days. This is called a leap year.

1. Complete the calendar for a leap year.

February

Sunday	Monday	Tuesday	Wednesday	Thursday	Friday	Saturday
						1
2	3	4	5	6	7	8
9	10	11	12	13	14	15
16	17	18	19	20	21	22
23	24	25	26	27	28	29

Use the calendar to answer the questions.

2. What day comes 3 days after February 23? February 26
3. What day comes 4 days before February 18? February 14
4. What day of the week is March 1? Sunday
5. What day of the week is January 31? Friday

 Use with Grade 2, text pages 215–216.

Daily Review

Name ____________________ Daily Review 7-9

Problem Solving

Using a Calendar

Complete the calendar.

Sunday	Monday	Tuesday	Wednesday	Thursday	Friday	Saturday
		1	2	3	4	5
6	7	8	9	10	11	12
13	14	15	16	17	18	19
20	21	22	23	24	25	26
27	28	29	30			

Problem Solving

Solve. Use the calendar above.

1. How many Saturdays are in this month? 4
2. Kate is having a party on the last Friday of this month. What date is the party? 25
3. Marcos leaves for a trip on the 17th. He is gone for 3 days. What day of the week does he come back? Sunday

Review and Remember

Write the missing number. Use counters to help.

4. 10 + 5 = 15   10 + 1 = 11   10 + 7 = 17

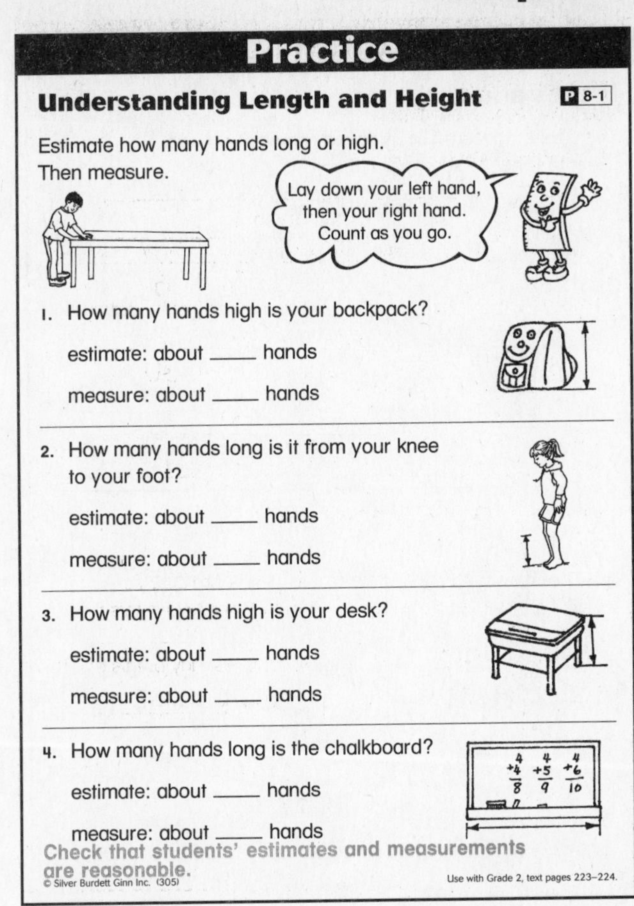

Practice

Understanding Length and Height

P 8-1

Estimate how many hands long or high.
Then measure.

Lay down your left hand, then your right hand. Count as you go.

1. How many hands high is your backpack?

   estimate: about ____ hands

   measure: about ____ hands

2. How many hands long is it from your knee to your foot?

   estimate: about ____ hands

   measure: about ____ hands

3. How many hands high is your desk?

   estimate: about ____ hands

   measure: about ____ hands

4. How many hands long is the chalkboard?

   estimate: about ____ hands

   measure: about ____ hands

Check that students' estimates and measurements are reasonable.

Use with Grade 2, text pages 223–224.

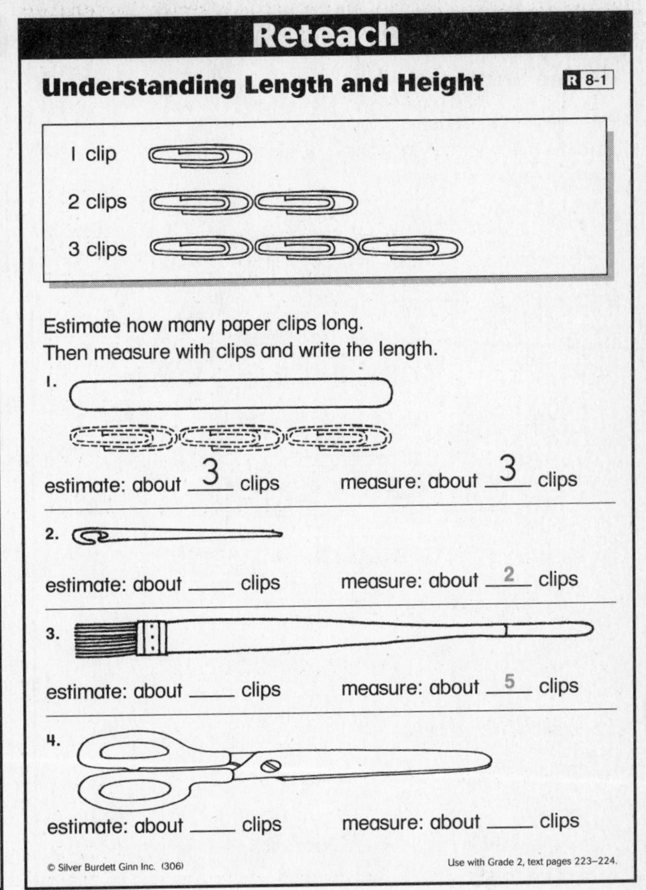

Reteach

Understanding Length and Height

R 8-1

1 clip

2 clips

3 clips

Estimate how many paper clips long.
Then measure with clips and write the length.

1. estimate: about 3 clips measure: about 3 clips

2. estimate: about ____ clips measure: about 2 clips

3. estimate: about ____ clips measure: about 5 clips

4. estimate: about ____ clips measure: about ____ clips

Use with Grade 2, text pages 223–224.

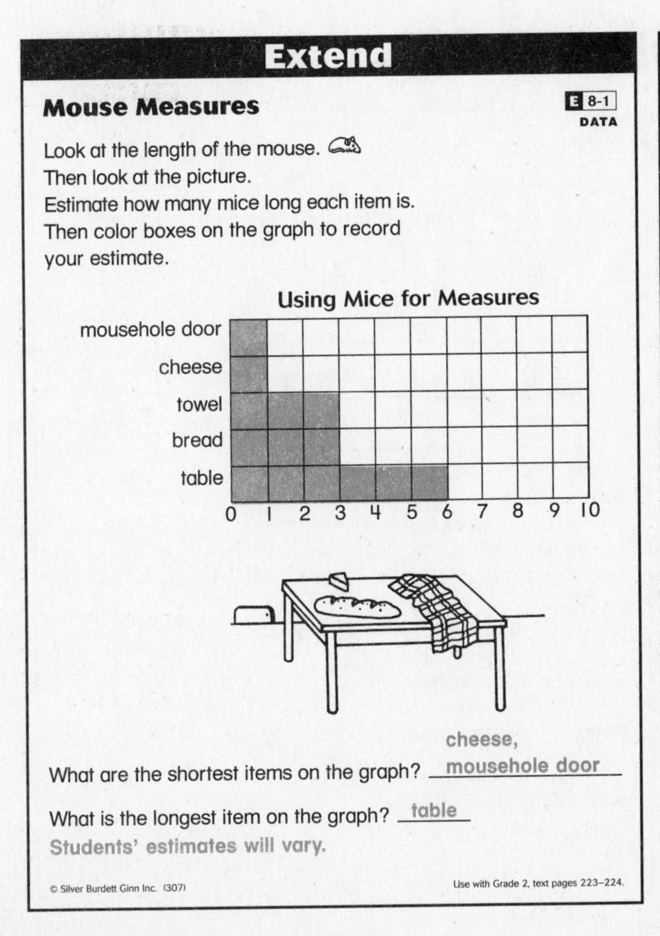

Extend

Mouse Measures

E 8-1
DATA

Look at the length of the mouse.
Then look at the picture.
Estimate how many mice long each item is.
Then color boxes on the graph to record your estimate.

What are the shortest items on the graph? cheese, mousehole door

What is the longest item on the graph? table

Students' estimates will vary.

Use with Grade 2, text pages 223–224.

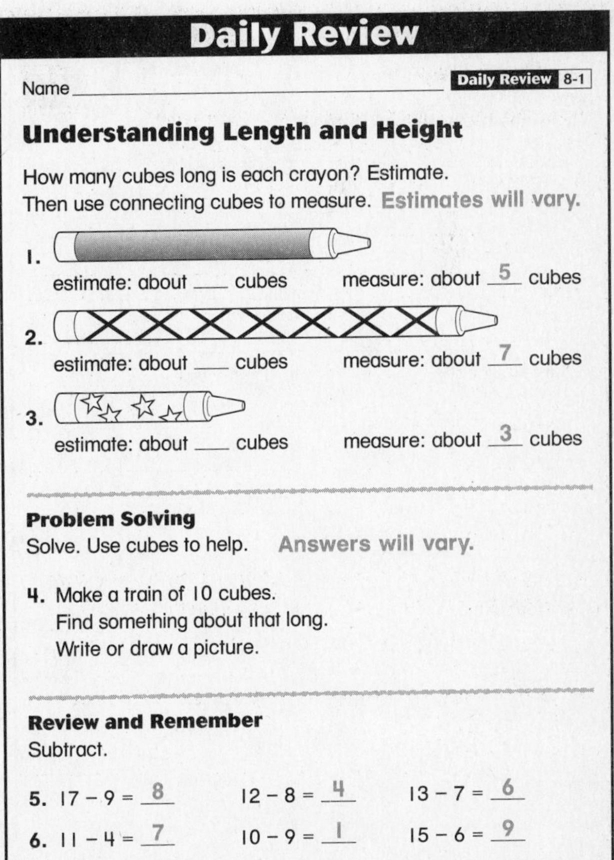

Daily Review

Name ________________________

Daily Review 8-1

Understanding Length and Height

How many cubes long is each crayon? Estimate.
Then use connecting cubes to measure. Estimates will vary.

1. estimate: about ____ cubes measure: about 5 cubes

2. estimate: about ____ cubes measure: about 7 cubes

3. estimate: about ____ cubes measure: about 3 cubes

Problem Solving

Solve. Use cubes to help. Answers will vary.

4. Make a train of 10 cubes.
   Find something about that long.
   Write or draw a picture.

Review and Remember

Subtract.

5. $17 - 9 = 8$ $12 - 8 = 4$ $13 - 7 = 6$

6. $11 - 4 = 7$ $10 - 9 = 1$ $15 - 6 = 9$

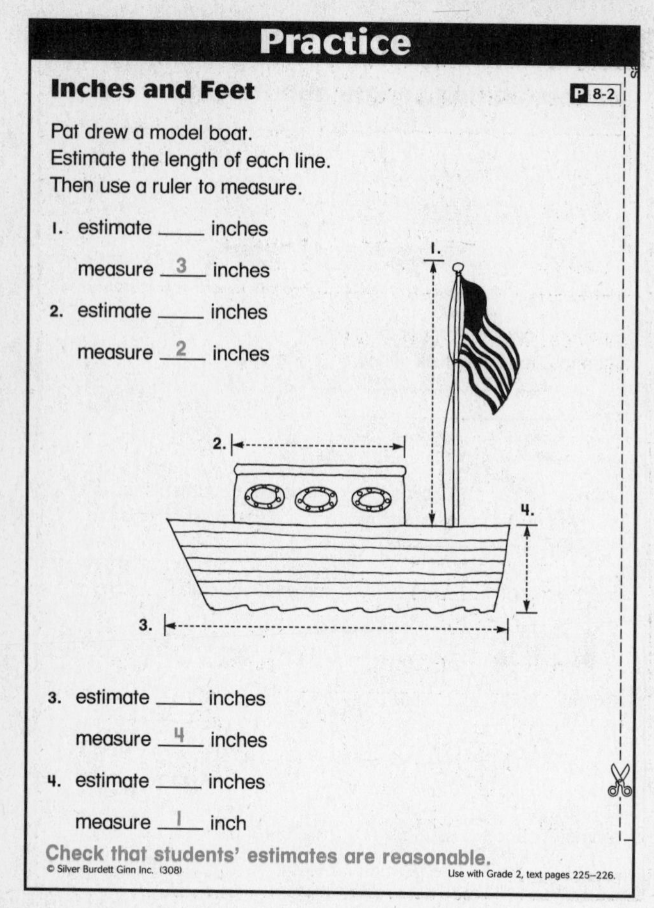

Practice

Inches and Feet P 8-2

Pat drew a model boat.
Estimate the length of each line.
Then use a ruler to measure.

1. estimate ___ inches
   measure 3 inches
2. estimate ___ inches
   measure 2 inches

3. estimate ___ inches
   measure 4 inches
4. estimate ___ inches
   measure 1 inch

Check that students' estimates are reasonable.

 Use with Grade 2, text pages 225–226.

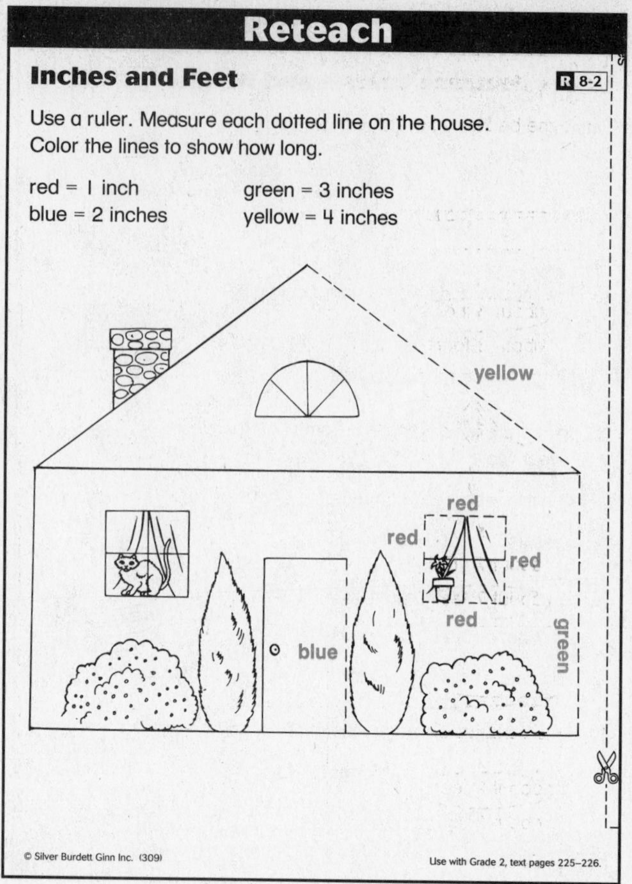

Reteach

Inches and Feet R 8-2

Use a ruler. Measure each dotted line on the house.
Color the lines to show how long.

red = 1 inch
blue = 2 inches
green = 3 inches
yellow = 4 inches

 Use with Grade 2, text pages 225–226.

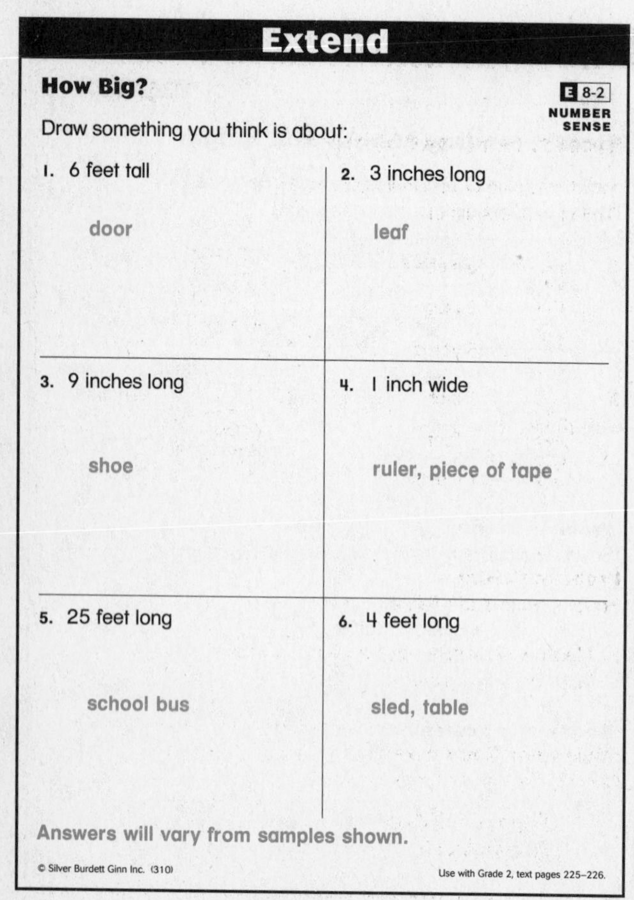

Extend

How Big? E 8-2 NUMBER SENSE

Draw something you think is about:

1. 6 feet tall door	2. 3 inches long leaf
3. 9 inches long shoe	4. 1 inch wide ruler, piece of tape
5. 25 feet long school bus	6. 4 feet long sled, table

Answers will vary from samples shown.

 Use with Grade 2, text pages 225–226.

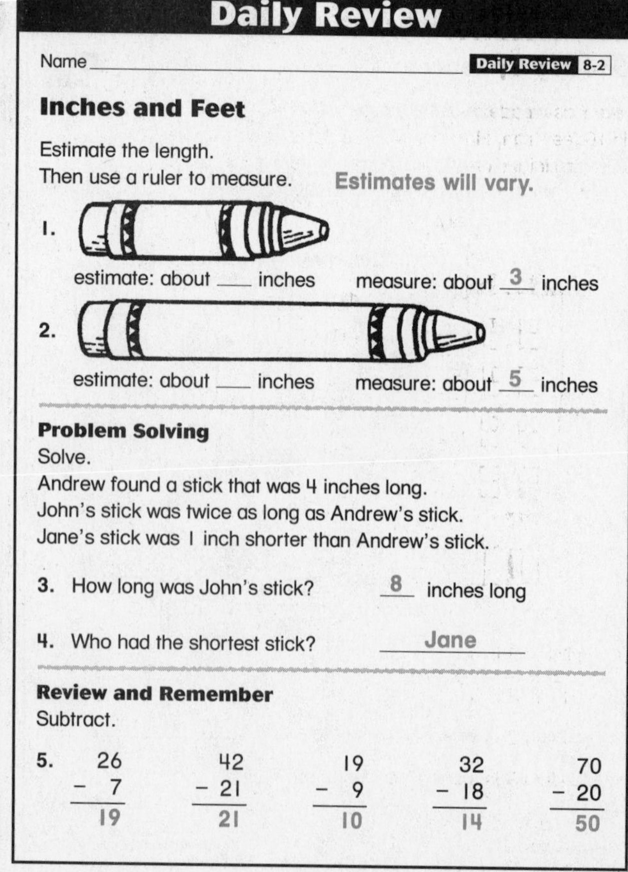

Daily Review

Name ______________ Daily Review 8-2

Inches and Feet

Estimate the length.
Then use a ruler to measure. Estimates will vary.

1. estimate: about ___ inches measure: about 3 inches
2. estimate: about ___ inches measure: about 5 inches

Problem Solving

Solve.
Andrew found a stick that was 4 inches long.
John's stick was twice as long as Andrew's stick.
Jane's stick was 1 inch shorter than Andrew's stick.

3. How long was John's stick? 8 inches long
4. Who had the shortest stick? Jane

Review and Remember

Subtract.

5. $26 - 7 = 19$ $42 - 21 = 21$ $19 - 9 = 10$ $32 - 18 = 14$ $70 - 20 = 50$

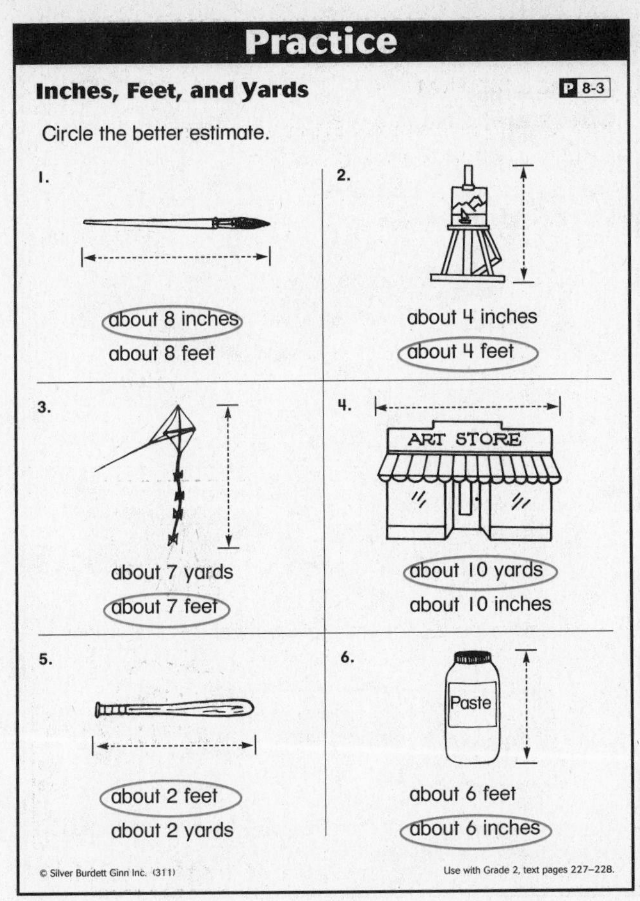

Practice

Inches, Feet, and Yards P 8-3

Circle the better estimate.

1. (about 8 inches) / about 8 feet
2. about 4 inches / (about 4 feet)
3. about 7 yards / (about 7 feet)
4. (about 10 yards) / about 10 inches
5. (about 2 feet) / about 2 yards
6. about 6 feet / (about 6 inches)

 Use with Grade 2, text pages 227–228.

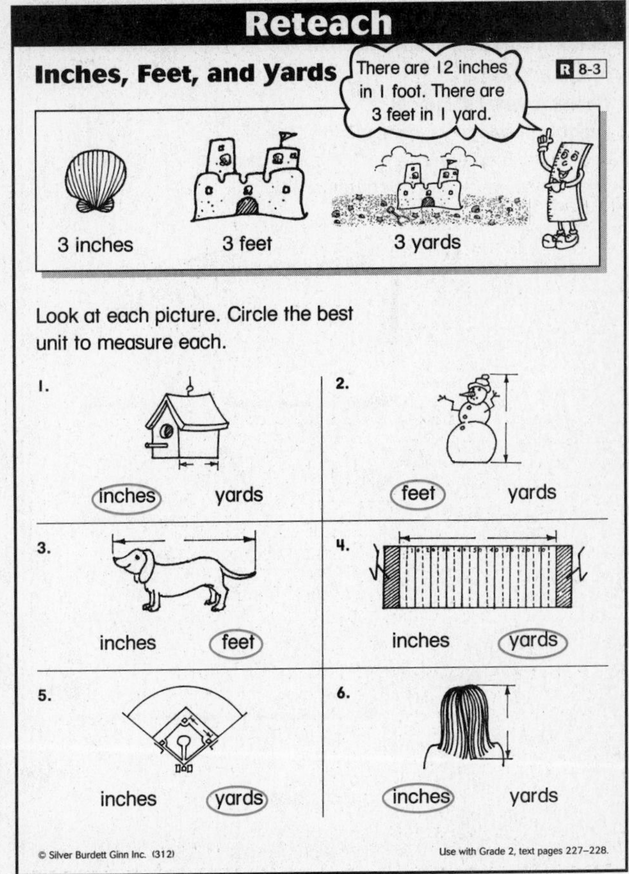

Reteach

Inches, Feet, and Yards R 8-3

There are 12 inches in 1 foot. There are 3 feet in 1 yard.
3 inches
3 feet
3 yards

Look at each picture. Circle the best unit to measure each.

1. (inches) yards
2. (feet) yards
3. inches (feet)
4. inches (yards)
5. inches (yards)
6. (inches) yards

 Use with Grade 2, text pages 227–228.

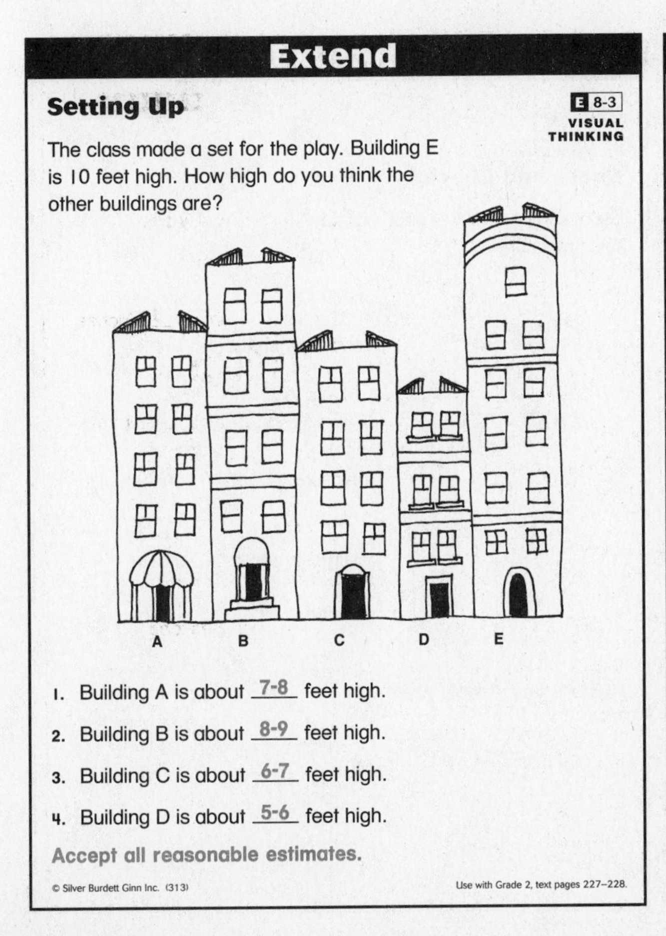

Extend

Setting Up E 8-3 VISUAL THINKING

The class made a set for the play. Building E is 10 feet high. How high do you think the other buildings are?

1. Building A is about 7-8 feet high.
2. Building B is about 8-9 feet high.
3. Building C is about 6-7 feet high.
4. Building D is about 5-6 feet high.

Accept all reasonable estimates.

 Use with Grade 2, text pages 227–228.

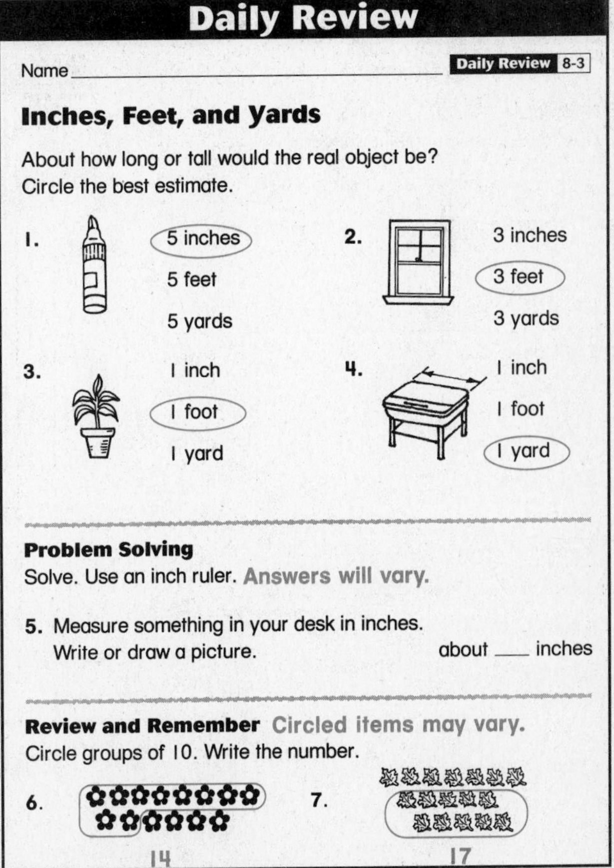

Daily Review

Name________________ Daily Review 8-3

Inches, Feet, and Yards

About how long or tall would the real object be? Circle the best estimate.

1. (5 inches) / 5 feet / 5 yards
2. 3 inches / (3 feet) / 3 yards
3. 1 inch / (1 foot) / 1 yard
4. 1 inch / 1 foot / (1 yard)

Problem Solving

Solve. Use an inch ruler. Answers will vary.

5. Measure something in your desk in inches. Write or draw a picture. about ___ inches

Review and Remember Circled items may vary.

Circle groups of 10. Write the number.

6. 14
7. 17

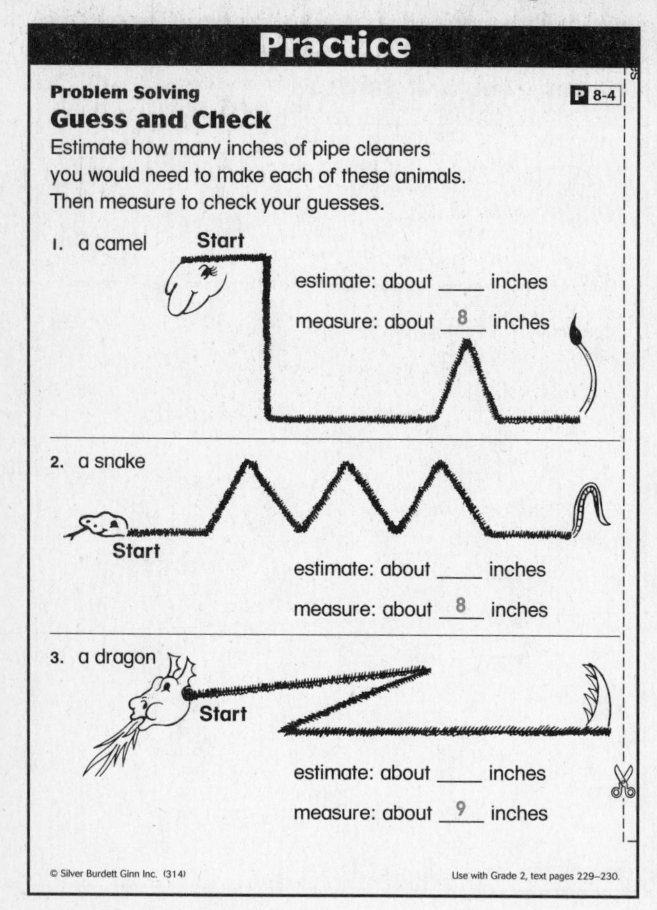

Practice

Problem Solving P 8-4

Guess and Check

Estimate how many inches of pipe cleaners you would need to make each of these animals. Then measure to check your guesses.

1. a camel (Start)
   estimate: about ____ inches
   measure: about 8 inches

2. a snake (Start)
   estimate: about ____ inches
   measure: about 8 inches

3. a dragon (Start)
   estimate: about ____ inches
   measure: about 9 inches

 Use with Grade 2, text pages 229–230.

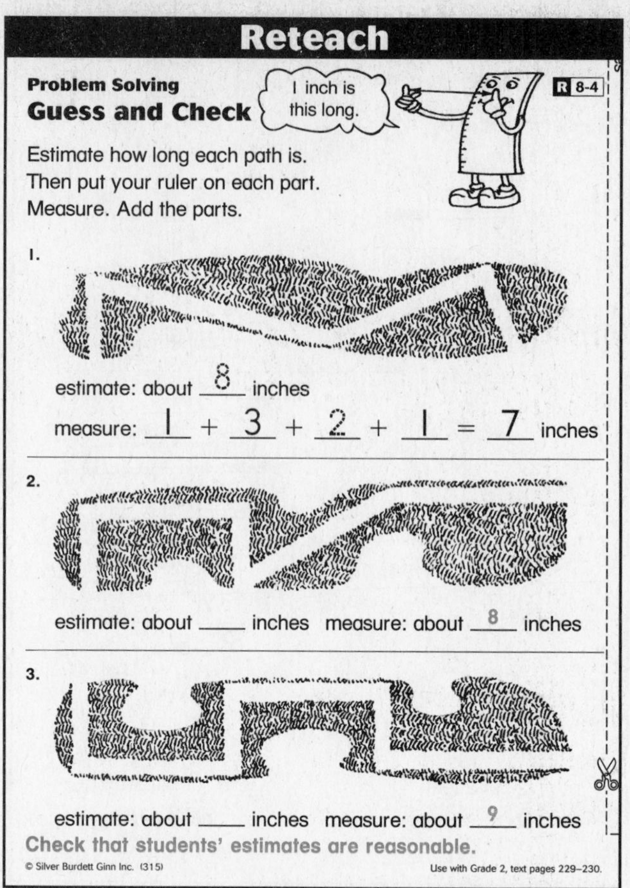

Reteach

Problem Solving R 8-4

Guess and Check

Estimate how long each path is. Then put your ruler on each part. Measure. Add the parts.

1. estimate: about 8 inches
   measure: 1 + 3 + 2 + 1 = 7 inches

2. estimate: about ____ inches measure: about 8 inches

3. estimate: about ____ inches measure: about 9 inches

Check that students' estimates are reasonable.

 Use with Grade 2, text pages 229–230.

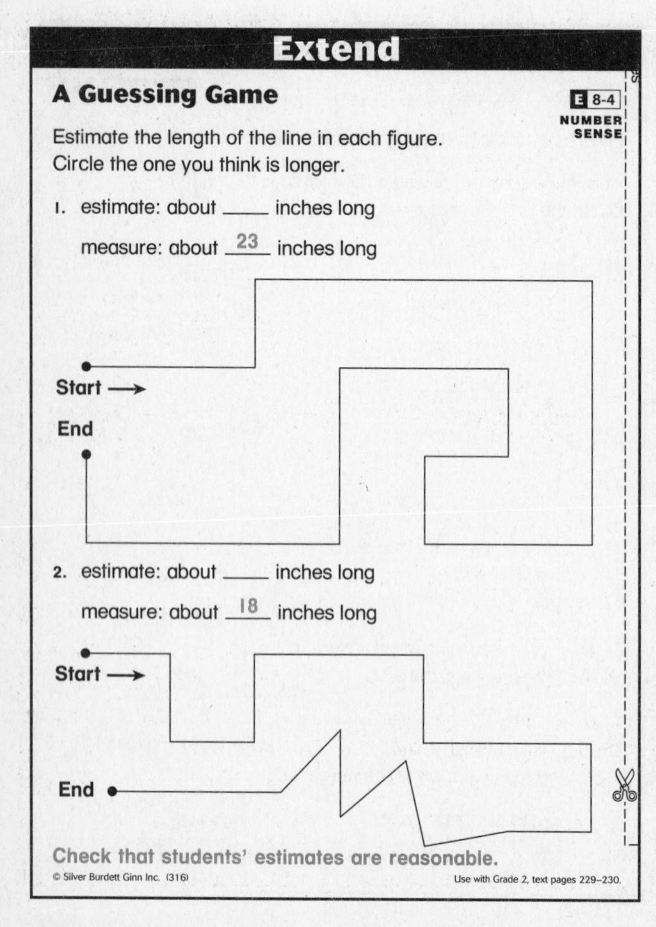

Extend

A Guessing Game

E 8-4 NUMBER SENSE

Estimate the length of the line in each figure. Circle the one you think is longer.

1. estimate: about ____ inches long
   measure: about 23 inches long
   Start → End

2. estimate: about ____ inches long
   measure: about 18 inches long
   Start → End

Check that students' estimates are reasonable.

 Use with Grade 2, text pages 229–230.

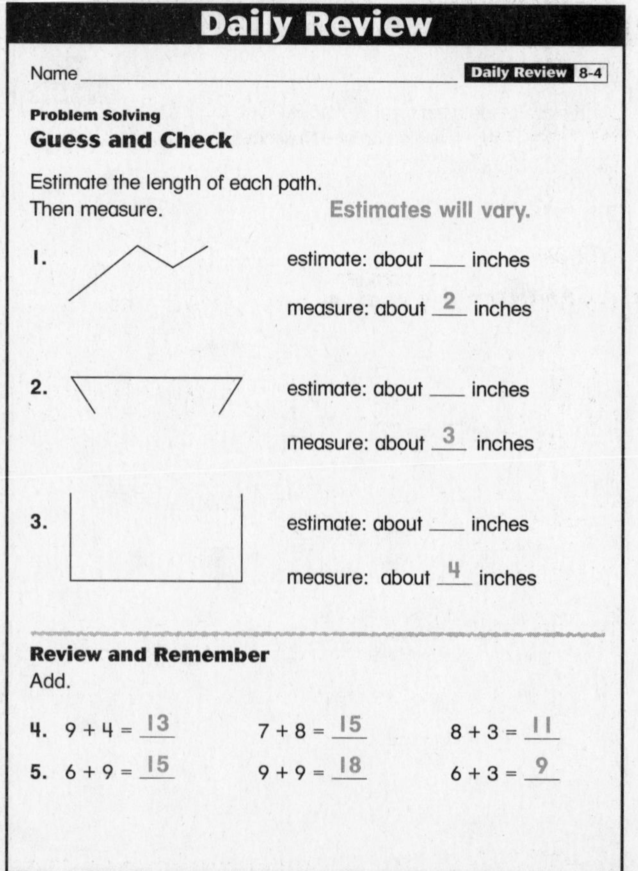

Daily Review

Name ______________________ Daily Review 8-4

Problem Solving

Guess and Check

Estimate the length of each path. Then measure. Estimates will vary.

1. estimate: about ____ inches
   measure: about 2 inches

2. estimate: about ____ inches
   measure: about 3 inches

3. estimate: about ____ inches
   measure: about 4 inches

Review and Remember

Add.

4. 9 + 4 = 13 7 + 8 = 15 8 + 3 = 11
5. 6 + 9 = 15 9 + 9 = 18 6 + 3 = 9

Chapter 8 • Lesson 5

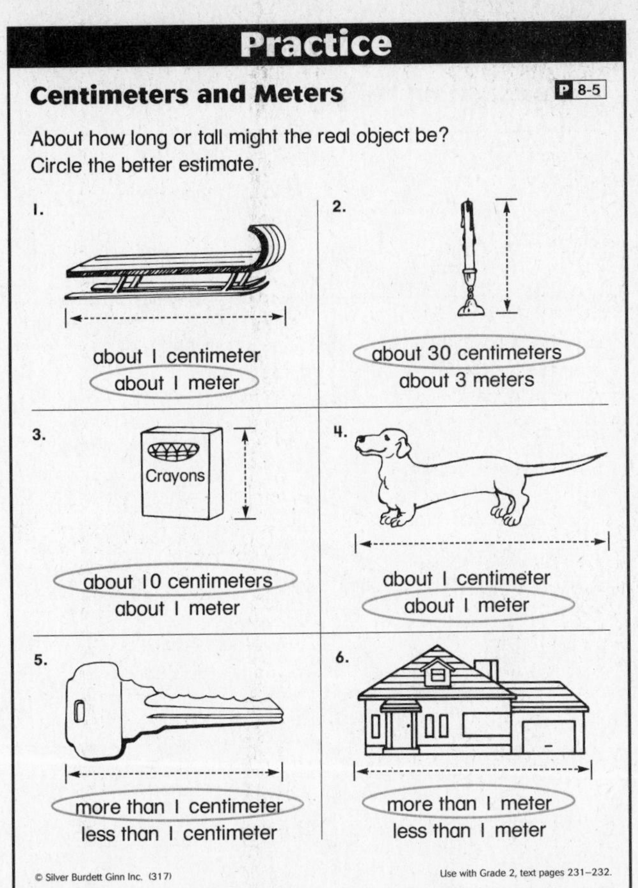

Practice

Centimeters and Meters P 8-5

About how long or tall might the real object be?
Circle the better estimate.

1. about 1 centimeter / (about 1 meter)
2. (about 30 centimeters) / about 3 meters
3. (about 10 centimeters) / about 1 meter
4. about 1 centimeter / (about 1 meter)
5. (more than 1 centimeter) / less than 1 centimeter
6. (more than 1 meter) / less than 1 meter

Use with Grade 2, text pages 231–232.

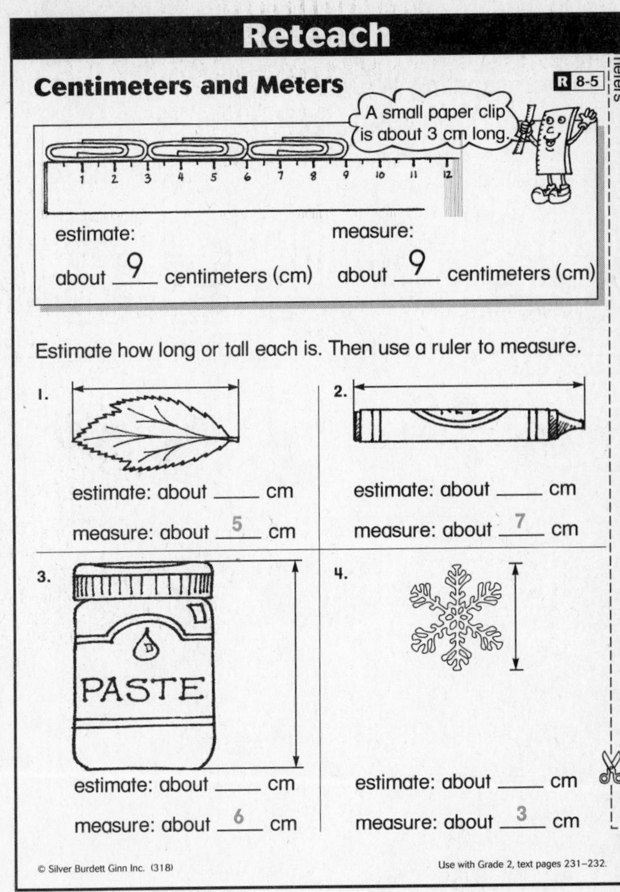

Reteach

Centimeters and Meters R 8-5

estimate: about 9 centimeters (cm) measure: about 9 centimeters (cm)

Estimate how long or tall each is. Then use a ruler to measure.

1. estimate: about ___ cm
   measure: about 5 cm
2. estimate: about ___ cm
   measure: about 7 cm
3.
   estimate: about ___ cm
   measure: about 6 cm
4. estimate: about ___ cm
   measure: about 3 cm

Use with Grade 2, text pages 231–232.

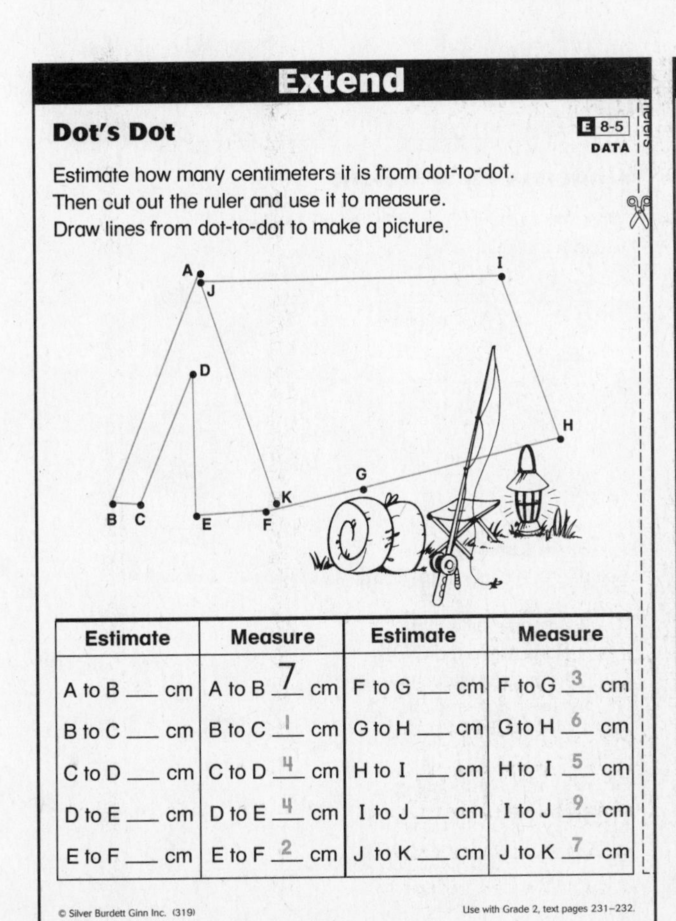

Extend

Dot's Dot E 8-5 DATA

Estimate how many centimeters it is from dot-to-dot.
Then cut out the ruler and use it to measure.
Draw lines from dot-to-dot to make a picture.

Estimate	Measure	Estimate	Measure
A to B ___ cm	A to B 7 cm	F to G ___ cm	F to G 3 cm
B to C ___ cm	B to C 1 cm	G to H ___ cm	G to H 6 cm
C to D ___ cm	C to D 4 cm	H to I ___ cm	H to I 5 cm
D to E ___ cm	D to E 4 cm	I to J ___ cm	I to J 9 cm
E to F ___ cm	E to F 2 cm	J to K ___ cm	J to K 7 cm

Use with Grade 2, text pages 231–232.

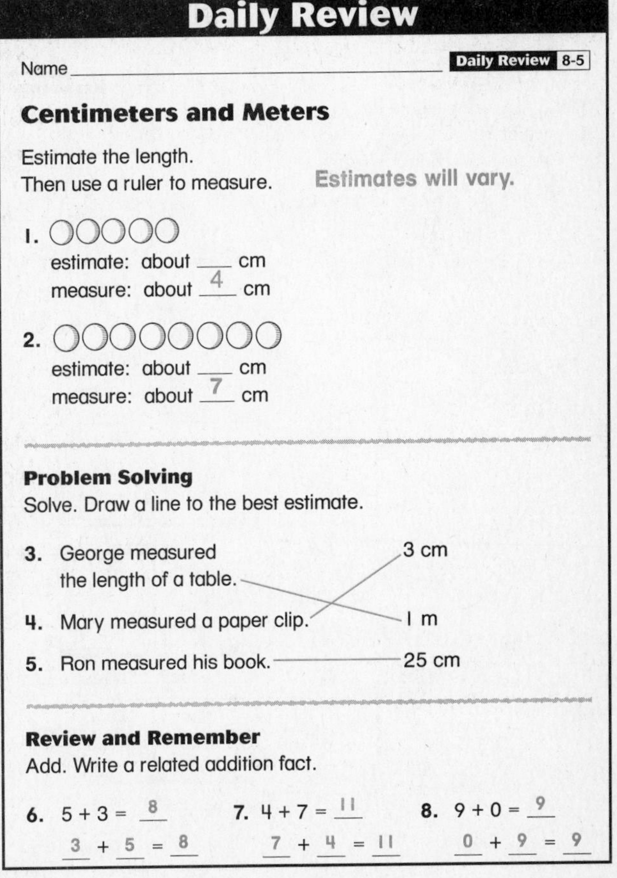

Daily Review

Name ______________________ Daily Review 8-5

Centimeters and Meters

Estimate the length.
Then use a ruler to measure. Estimates will vary.

1. estimate: about ___ cm
   measure: about 4 cm
2. estimate: about ___ cm
   measure: about 7 cm

Problem Solving

Solve. Draw a line to the best estimate.

3. George measured the length of a table. — 1 m
4. Mary measured a paper clip. — 3 cm
5. Ron measured his book. — 25 cm

Review and Remember

Add. Write a related addition fact.

6. 5 + 3 = 8   3 + 5 = 8
7. 4 + 7 = 11   7 + 4 = 11
8. 9 + 0 = 9   0 + 9 = 9

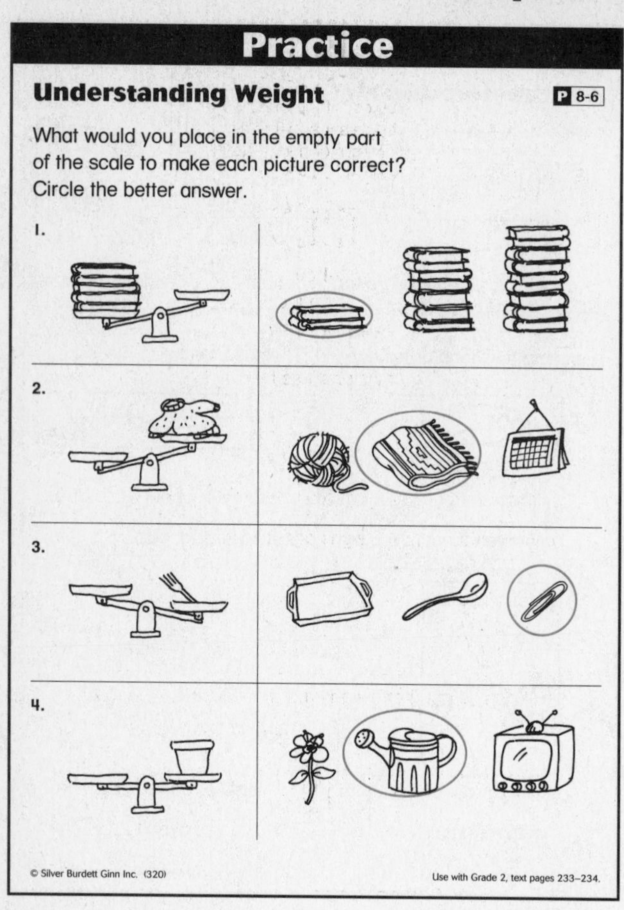

Practice

Understanding Weight

P 8-6

What would you place in the empty part of the scale to make each picture correct? Circle the better answer.

1.

2.

3.

4.

Use with Grade 2, text pages 233–234.

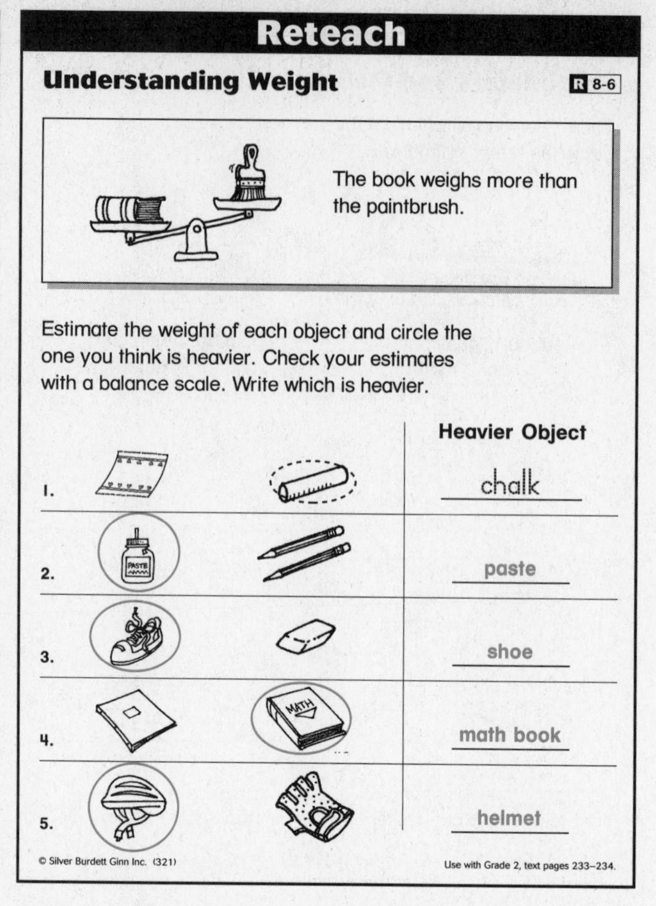

Reteach

Understanding Weight

R 8-6

The book weighs more than the paintbrush.

Estimate the weight of each object and circle the one you think is heavier. Check your estimates with a balance scale. Write which is heavier.

		Heavier Object
1.		chalk
2.		paste
3.		shoe
4.		math book
5.		helmet

Use with Grade 2, text pages 233–234.

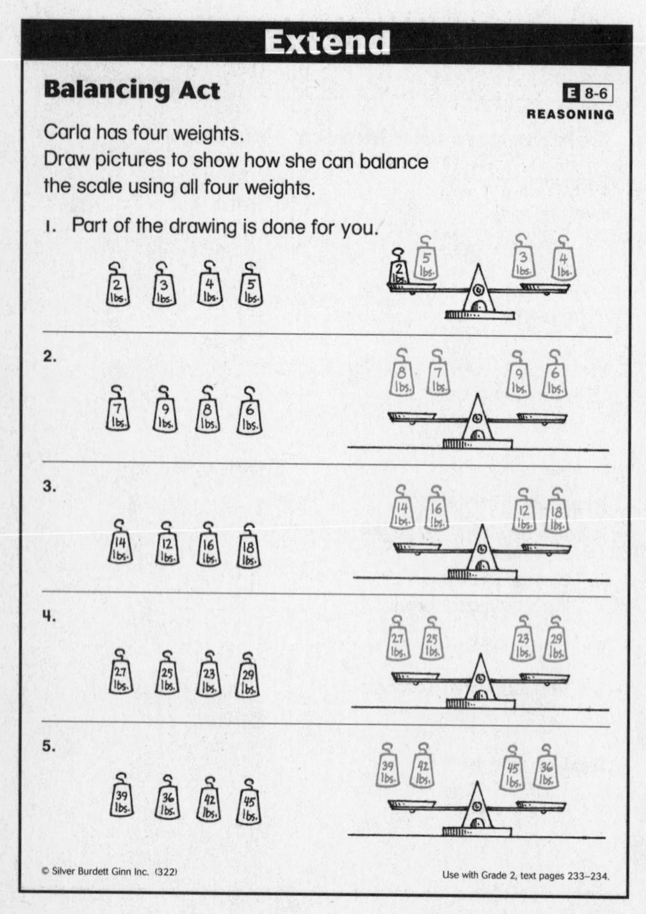

Extend

Balancing Act

E 8-6
REASONING

Carla has four weights.
Draw pictures to show how she can balance the scale using all four weights.

1. Part of the drawing is done for you.

2.

3.

4.

5.

Use with Grade 2, text pages 233–234.

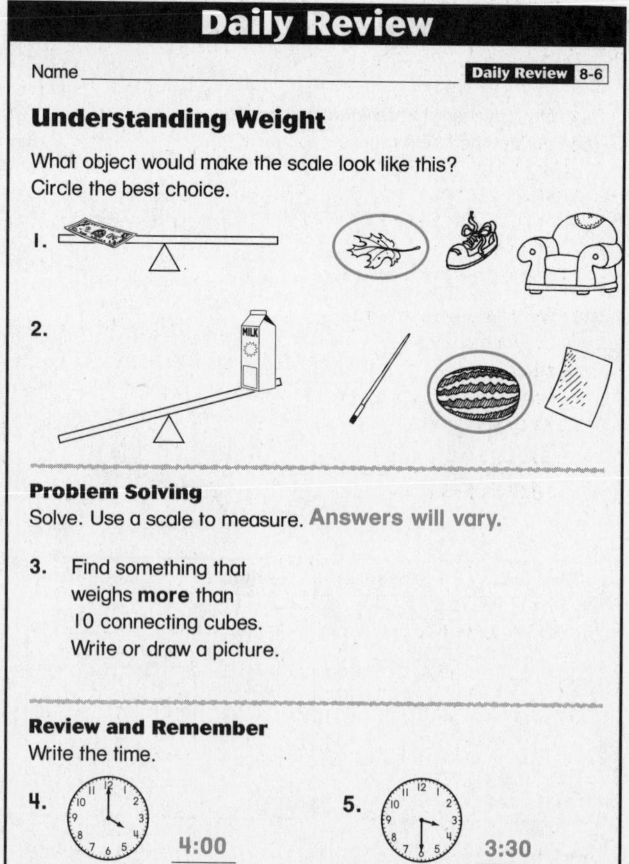

Daily Review

Name ____________________

Daily Review 8-6

Understanding Weight

What object would make the scale look like this?
Circle the best choice.

1.

2.

Problem Solving

Solve. Use a scale to measure. Answers will vary.

3. Find something that weighs **more** than 10 connecting cubes. Write or draw a picture.

Review and Remember

Write the time.

4. 4:00

5. 3:30

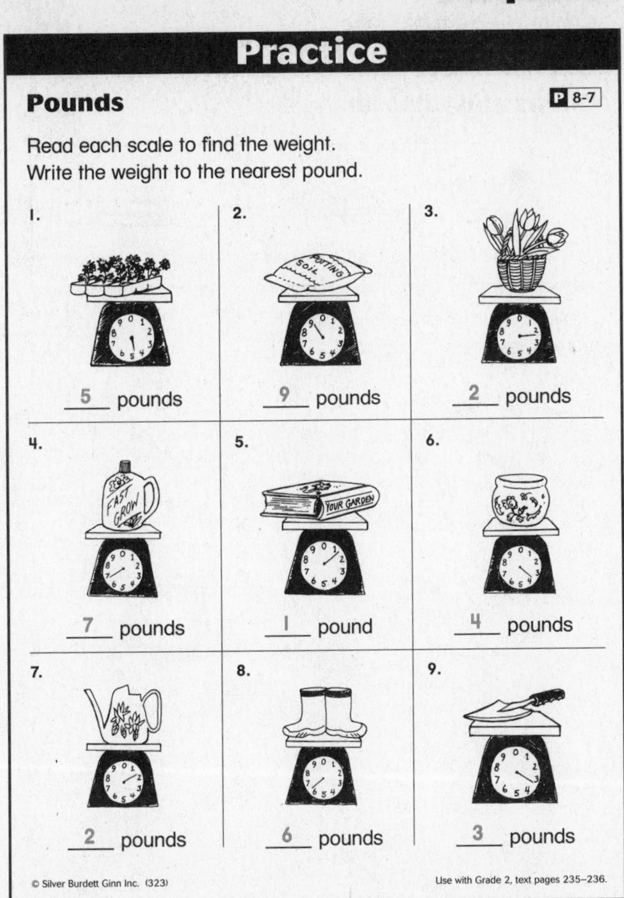

Practice

Pounds

P 8-7

Read each scale to find the weight.
Write the weight to the nearest pound.

1. 5 pounds
2. 9 pounds
3. 2 pounds
4. 7 pounds
5. 1 pound
6. 4 pounds
7. 2 pounds
8. 6 pounds
9. 3 pounds

 Use with Grade 2, text pages 235–236.

Reteach

Pounds

R 8-7

You can lift up these objects in the supermarket to see how light or heavy they are.

more than 1 pound | about 1 pound | less than 1 pound

1. Circle the object that weighs less than 1 pound.
2. Circle the object that weighs about 1 pound.
3. Circle the object that weighs more than 1 pound.

 Use with Grade 2, text pages 235–236.

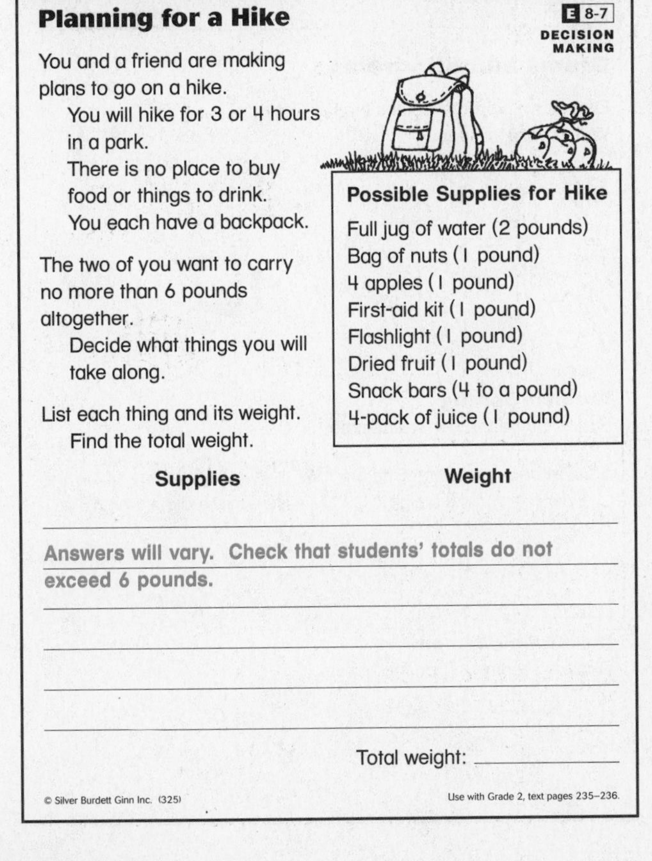

Extend

Planning for a Hike

E 8-7
DECISION MAKING

You and a friend are making plans to go on a hike.
You will hike for 3 or 4 hours in a park.
There is no place to buy food or things to drink.
You each have a backpack.

The two of you want to carry no more than 6 pounds altogether.
Decide what things you will take along.

List each thing and its weight.
Find the total weight.

Possible Supplies for Hike
- Full jug of water (2 pounds)
- Bag of nuts (1 pound)
- 4 apples (1 pound)
- First-aid kit (1 pound)
- Flashlight (1 pound)
- Dried fruit (1 pound)
- Snack bars (4 to a pound)
- 4-pack of juice (1 pound)

Supplies	Weight
Answers will vary. Check that students' totals do not exceed 6 pounds.	

Total weight: ______

 Use with Grade 2, text pages 235–236.

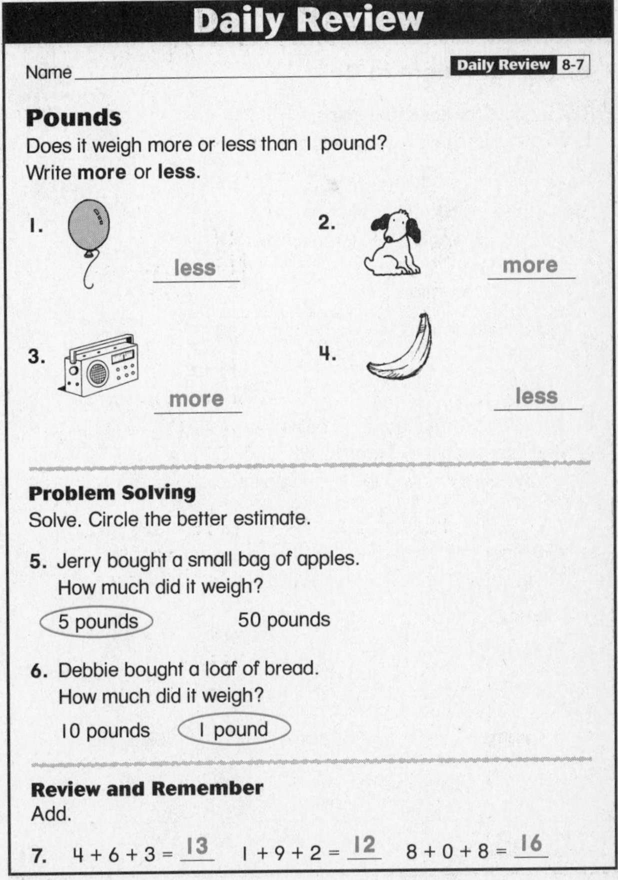

Daily Review

Name ______ Daily Review 8-7

Pounds

Does it weigh more or less than 1 pound?
Write **more** or **less**.

1. less
2. more
3. more
4. less

Problem Solving

Solve. Circle the better estimate.

5. Jerry bought a small bag of apples. How much did it weigh?
   (5 pounds) 50 pounds
6. Debbie bought a loaf of bread. How much did it weigh?
   10 pounds (1 pound)

Review and Remember

Add.

7. 4 + 6 + 3 = 13 1 + 9 + 2 = 12 8 + 0 + 8 = 16

Chapter 8 • Lesson 8

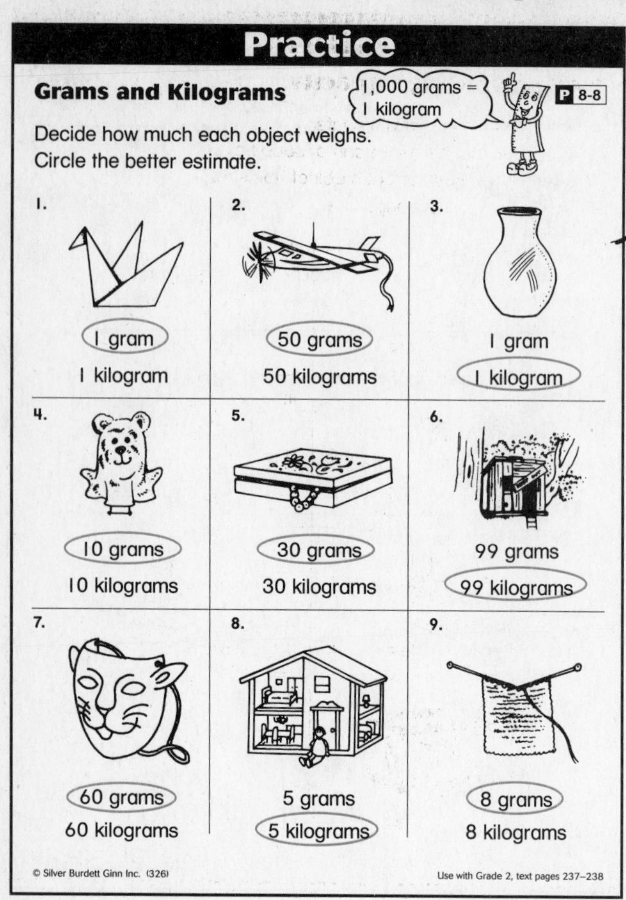

Practice

Grams and Kilograms P 8-8

1,000 grams = 1 kilogram

Decide how much each object weighs.
Circle the better estimate.

1. (1 gram) / 1 kilogram	2. (50 grams) / 50 kilograms	3. 1 gram / (1 kilogram)
4. (10 grams) / 10 kilograms	5. (30 grams) / 30 kilograms	6. 99 grams / (99 kilograms)
7. (60 grams) / 60 kilograms	8. 5 grams / (5 kilograms)	9. (8 grams) / 8 kilograms

Use with Grade 2, text pages 237–238

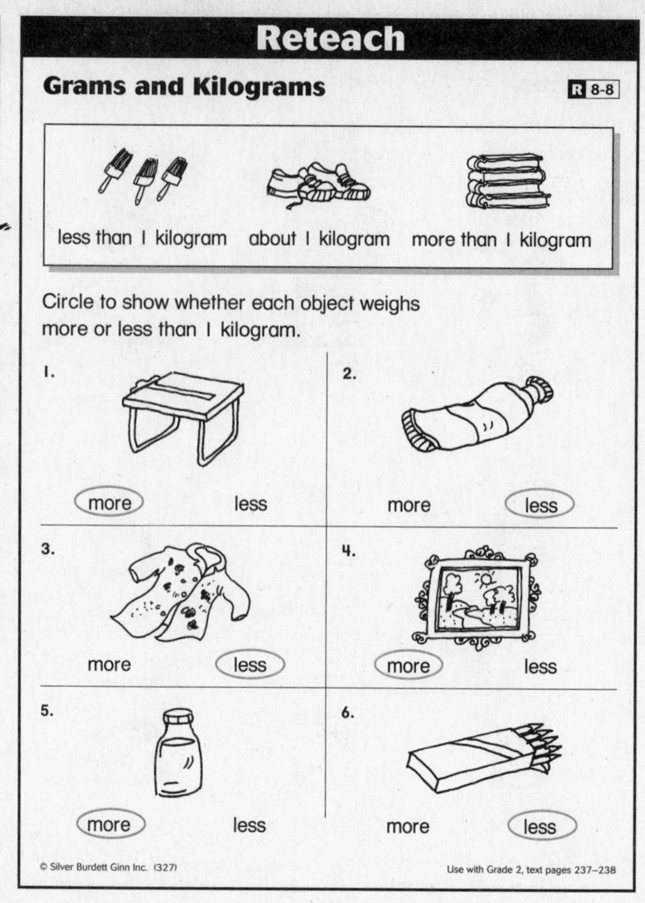

Reteach

Grams and Kilograms R 8-8

less than 1 kilogram — about 1 kilogram — more than 1 kilogram

Circle to show whether each object weighs more or less than 1 kilogram.

1. (more) less	2. more (less)
3. more (less)	4. (more) less
5. (more) less	6. more (less)

Use with Grade 2, text pages 237–238

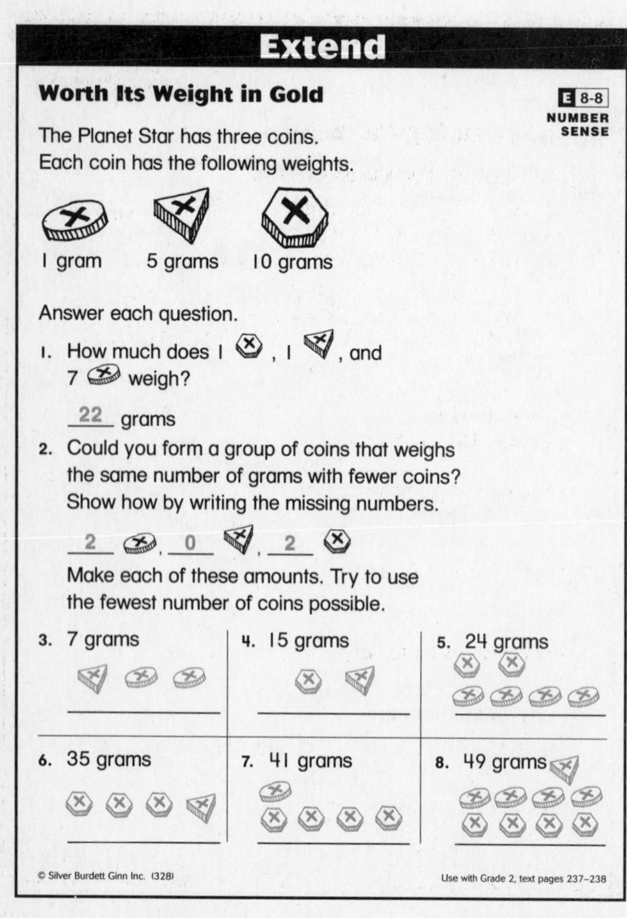

Extend

Worth Its Weight in Gold E 8-8 NUMBER SENSE

The Planet Star has three coins.
Each coin has the following weights.

1 gram — 5 grams — 10 grams

Answer each question.

1. How much does 1 [10-gram coin], 1 [5-gram coin], and 7 [1-gram coins] weigh?

   22 grams

2. Could you form a group of coins that weighs the same number of grams with fewer coins? Show how by writing the missing numbers.

   2 [1-gram], 0 [5-gram], 2 [10-gram]

Make each of these amounts. Try to use the fewest number of coins possible.

3. 7 grams	4. 15 grams	5. 24 grams
6. 35 grams	7. 41 grams	8. 49 grams

Use with Grade 2, text pages 237–238

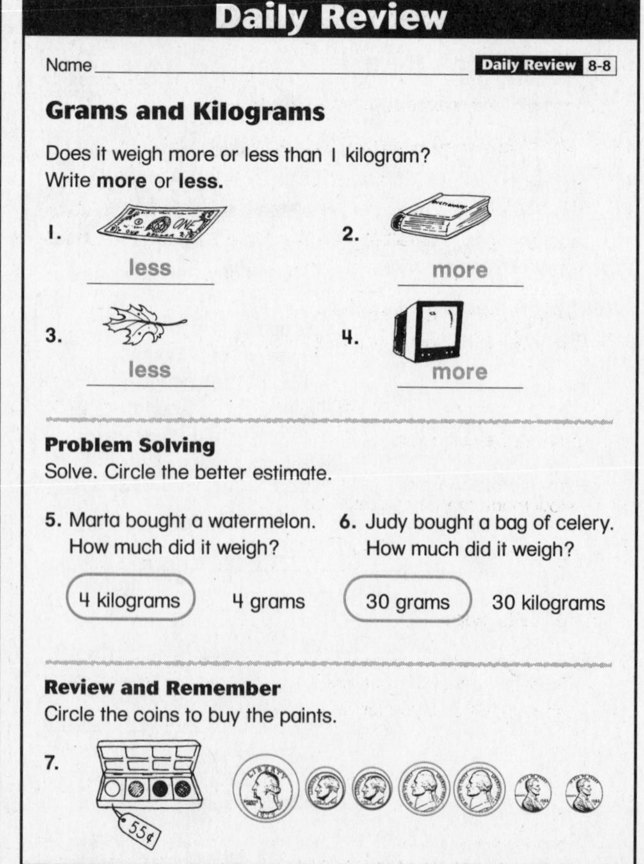

Daily Review

Name ____________________ Daily Review 8-8

Grams and Kilograms

Does it weigh more or less than 1 kilogram?
Write **more** or **less**.

1. less
2. more
3. less
4. more

Problem Solving

Solve. Circle the better estimate.

5. Marta bought a watermelon. How much did it weigh?

   (4 kilograms) 4 grams

6. Judy bought a bag of celery. How much did it weigh?

   (30 grams) 30 kilograms

Review and Remember

Circle the coins to buy the paints.

7. 55¢

Chapter 8 • Lesson 9

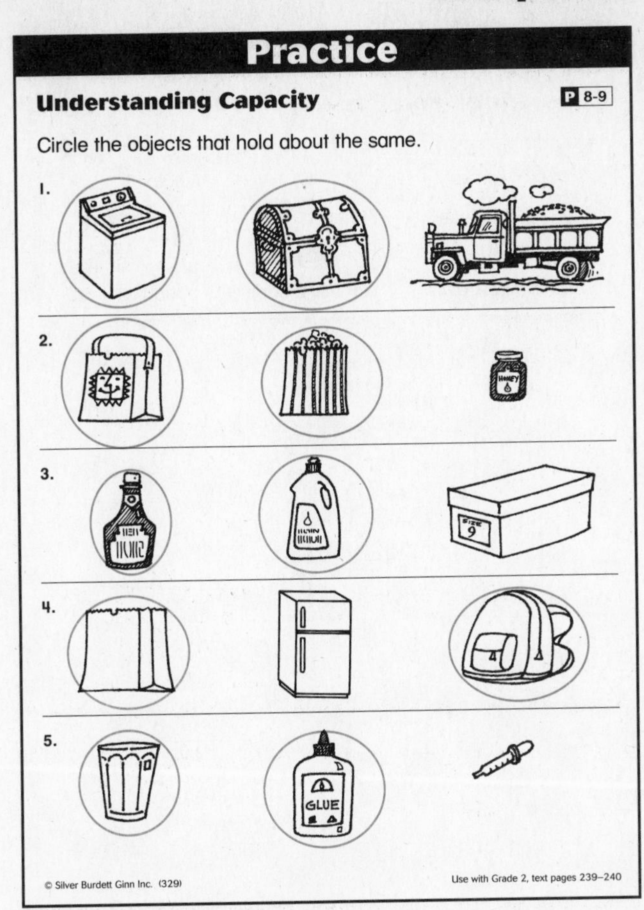

Practice

Understanding Capacity P 8-9

Circle the objects that hold about the same.

1.

2.

3.

4.

5.

© Silver Burdett Ginn Inc. (329)

Use with Grade 2, text pages 239–240

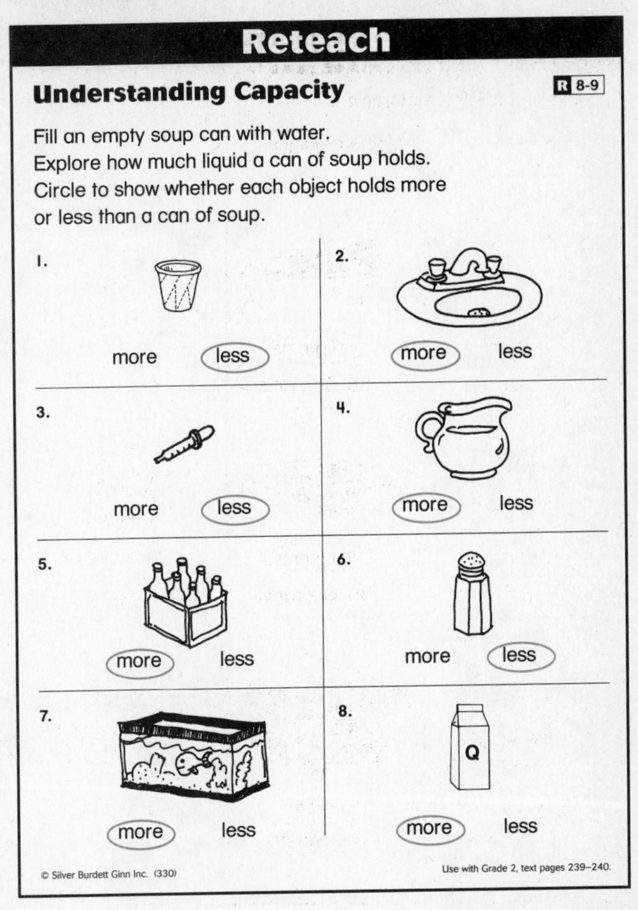

Reteach

Understanding Capacity R 8-9

Fill an empty soup can with water.
Explore how much liquid a can of soup holds.
Circle to show whether each object holds more or less than a can of soup.

1. more less
2. more less
3. more less
4. more less
5. more less
6. more less
7. more less
8. more less

© Silver Burdett Ginn Inc. (330)

Use with Grade 2, text pages 239–240.

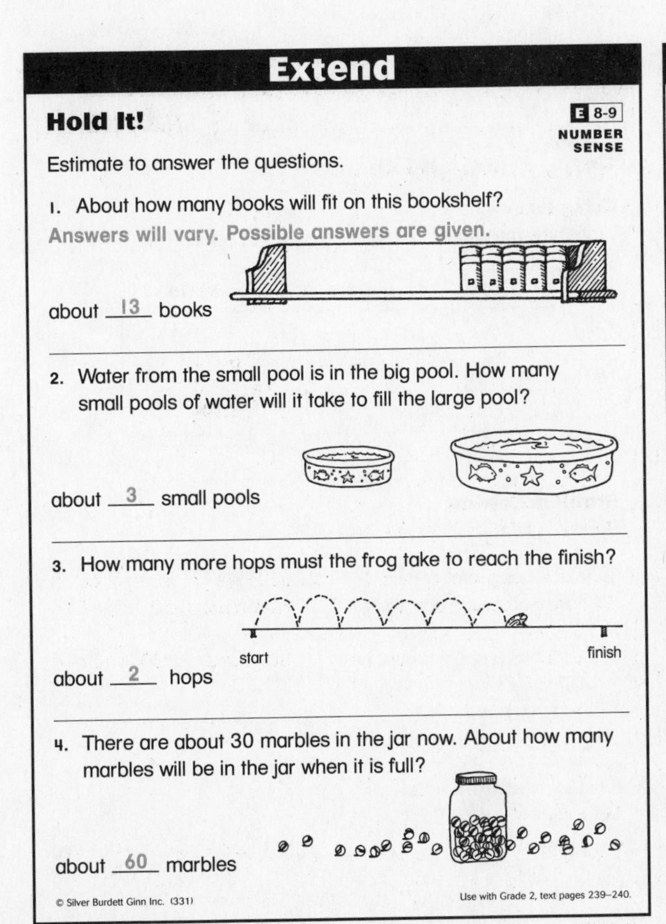

Extend

Hold It! E 8-9 NUMBER SENSE

Estimate to answer the questions.

1. About how many books will fit on this bookshelf?
Answers will vary. Possible answers are given.
about 13 books

2. Water from the small pool is in the big pool. How many small pools of water will it take to fill the large pool?
about 3 small pools

3. How many more hops must the frog take to reach the finish?
start finish
about 2 hops

4. There are about 30 marbles in the jar now. About how many marbles will be in the jar when it is full?
about 60 marbles

© Silver Burdett Ginn Inc. (331)

Use with Grade 2, text pages 239–240.

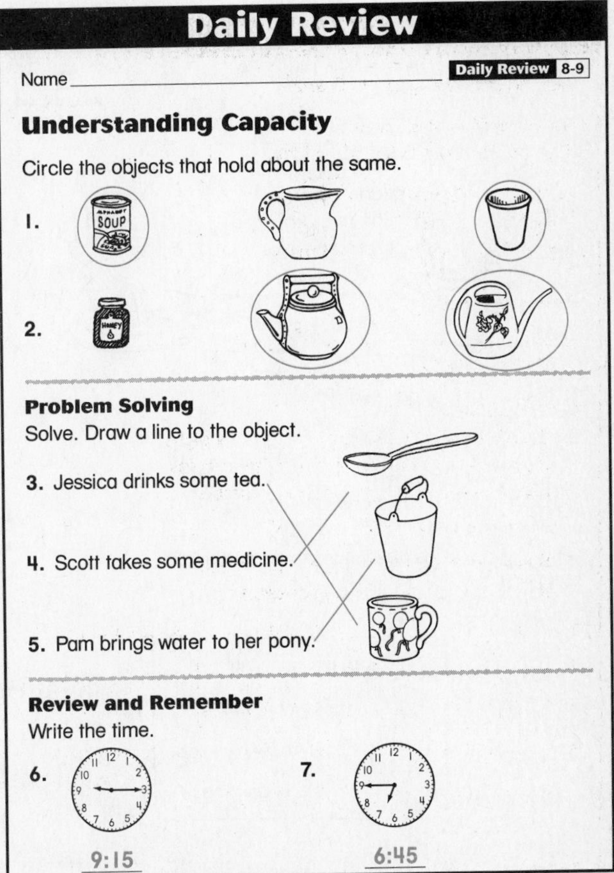

Daily Review

Name ______________________ Daily Review 8-9

Understanding Capacity

Circle the objects that hold about the same.

1.

2.

Problem Solving

Solve. Draw a line to the object.

3. Jessica drinks some tea.
4. Scott takes some medicine.
5. Pam brings water to her pony.

Review and Remember

Write the time.

6. 9:15
7. 6:45

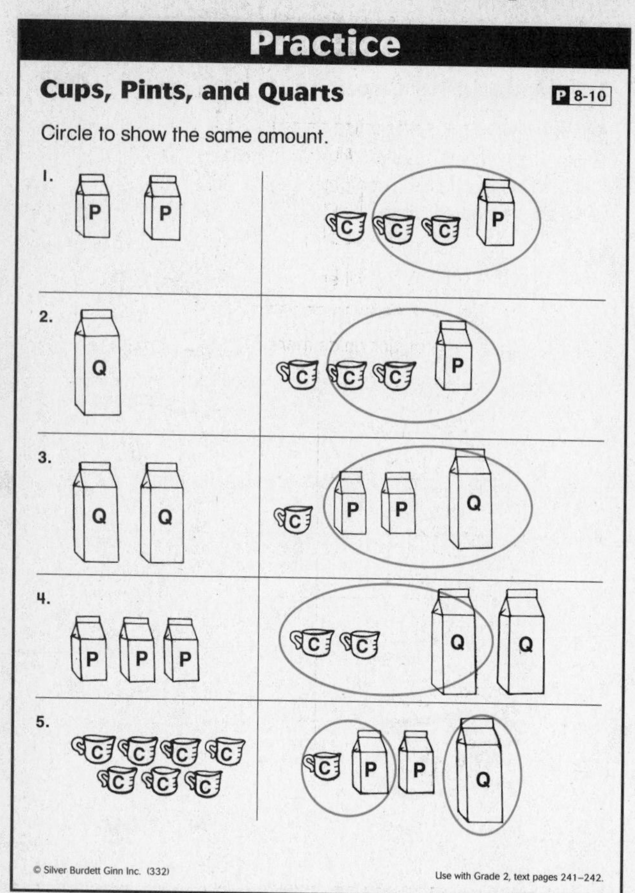

Practice
Cups, Pints, and Quarts
P 8-10
Circle to show the same amount.
© Silver Burdett Ginn Inc. (332)
Use with Grade 2, text pages 241–242.

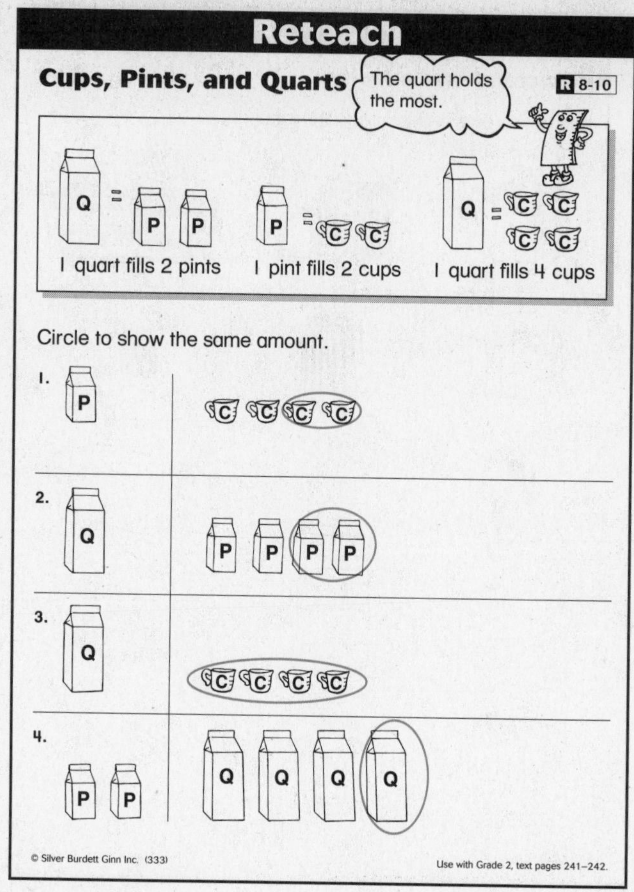

Reteach
Cups, Pints, and Quarts
R 8-10
The quart holds the most.
I quart fills 2 pints
I pint fills 2 cups
I quart fills 4 cups
Circle to show the same amount.
© Silver Burdett Ginn Inc. (333)
Use with Grade 2, text pages 241–242.

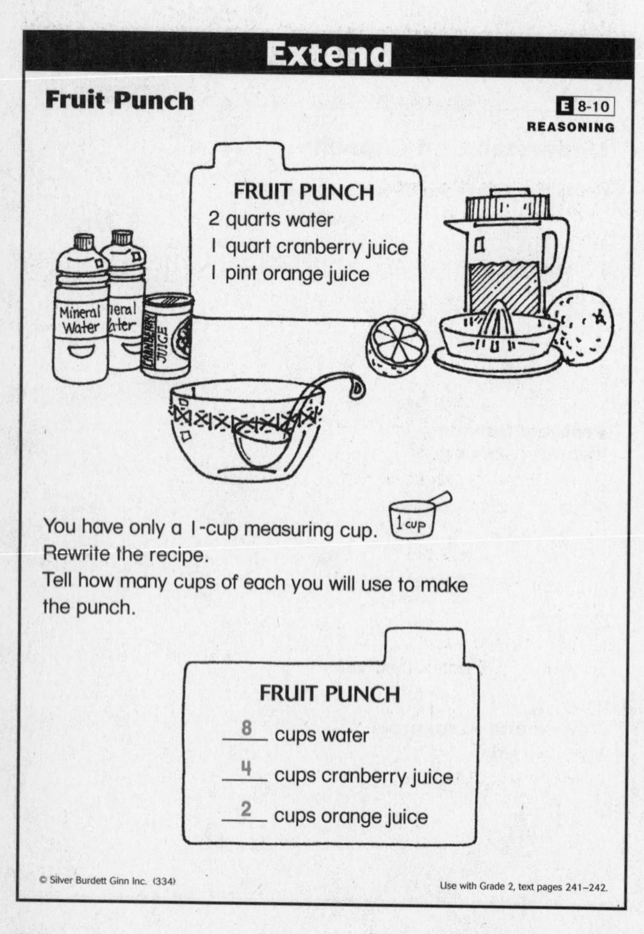

Extend
Fruit Punch
E 8-10
REASONING
FRUIT PUNCH
2 quarts water
I quart cranberry juice
I pint orange juice
Mineral Water
You have only a I-cup measuring cup.
Rewrite the recipe.
Tell how many cups of each you will use to make the punch.
FRUIT PUNCH
8 cups water
4 cups cranberry juice
2 cups orange juice

Daily Review

Name _____

Daily Review 8-10

Complete the chart.
Write how many cups, pints, or quarts.

Problem Solving
Solve.

4. Bruce has 1 pint of milk.
 How many cups can he fill? _2_ cups

5. Jerry has 3 cups of milk.
 Alice has 1 pint of milk.
 Who has more milk? _Jerry_

Review and Remember
Subtract.

6.
35	41	70	26	19
− 18	− 6	− 50	− 17	− 2
17	35	20	9	17

© Silver Burdett Ginn Inc. (334)
Use with Grade 2, text pages 241–242.

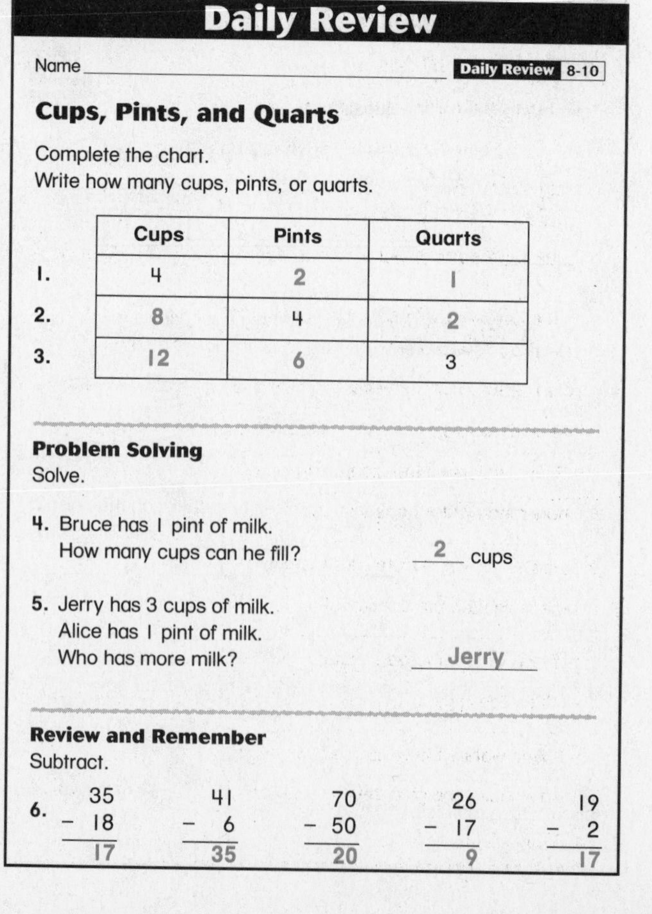

	Cups	Pints	Quarts
1.	4	2	I
2.	8	4	2
3.	12	6	3

Chapter 8 • Lesson 11

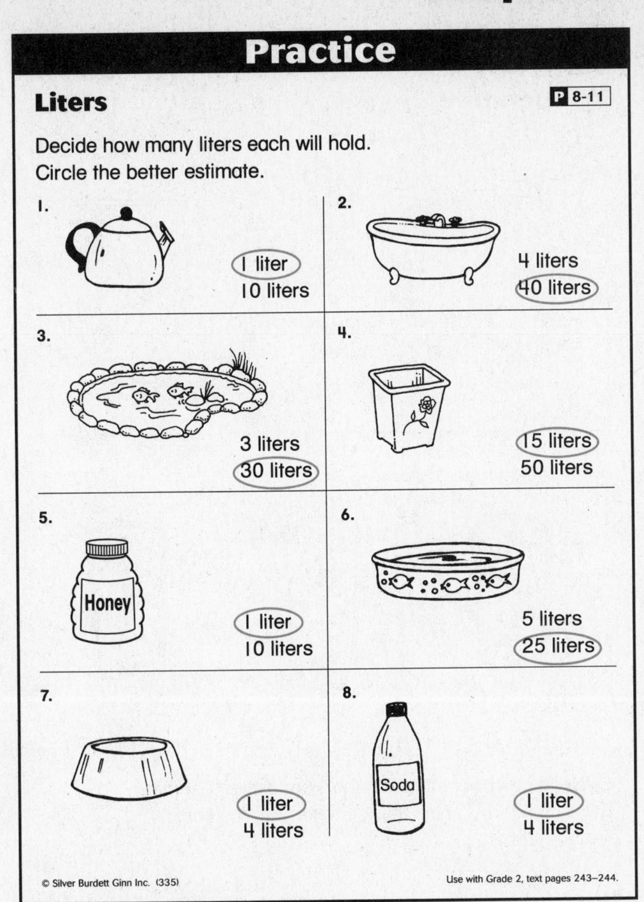

Practice

Liters P 8-11

Decide how many liters each will hold.
Circle the better estimate.

1. 1 liter / 10 liters (circled: 1 liter)
2. 4 liters / 40 liters (circled: 40 liters)
3. 3 liters / 30 liters (circled: 30 liters)
4. 15 liters / 50 liters (circled: 15 liters)
5. 1 liter / 10 liters (circled: 1 liter)
6. 5 liters / 25 liters (circled: 25 liters)
7. 1 liter / 4 liters (circled: 1 liter)
8. 1 liter / 4 liters (circled: 1 liter)

 Use with Grade 2, text pages 243–244.

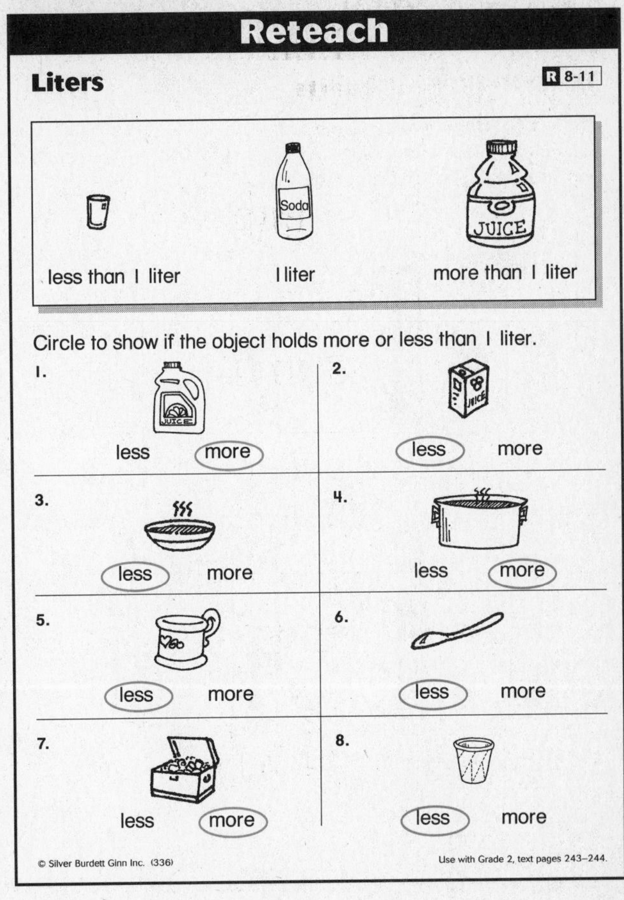

Reteach

Liters R 8-11

less than 1 liter | 1 liter | more than 1 liter

Circle to show if the object holds more or less than 1 liter.

1. less / more (circled: more)
2. less / more (circled: less)
3. less / more (circled: less)
4. less / more (circled: more)
5. less / more (circled: less)
6. less / more (circled: less)
7. less / more (circled: more)
8. less / more (circled: less)

 Use with Grade 2, text pages 243–244.

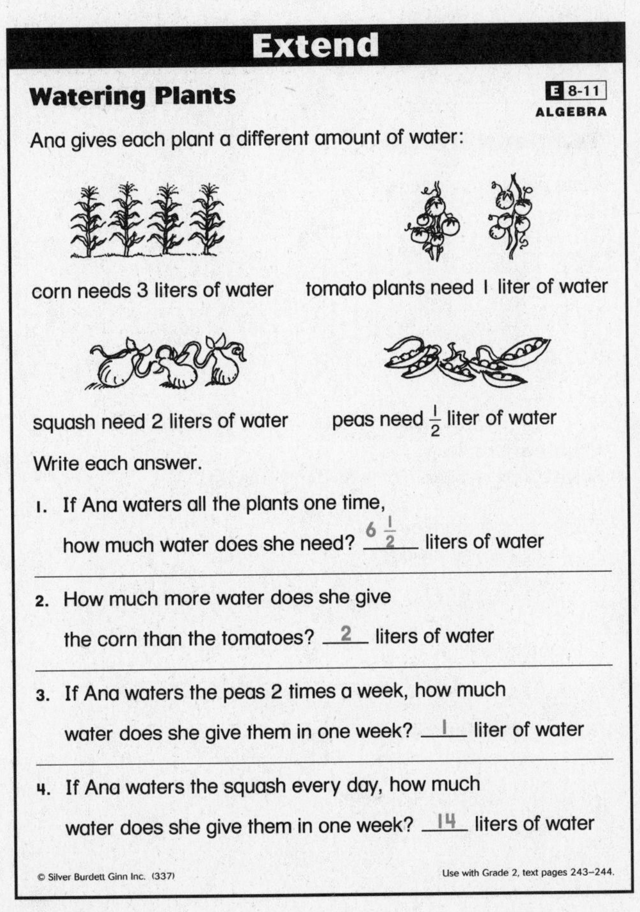

Extend

Watering Plants E 8-11 ALGEBRA

Ana gives each plant a different amount of water:

corn needs 3 liters of water

tomato plants need 1 liter of water

squash need 2 liters of water

peas need $\frac{1}{2}$ liter of water

Write each answer.

1. If Ana waters all the plants one time, how much water does she need? $6\frac{1}{2}$ liters of water
2. How much more water does she give the corn than the tomatoes? 2 liters of water
3. If Ana waters the peas 2 times a week, how much water does she give them in one week? 1 liter of water
4. If Ana waters the squash every day, how much water does she give them in one week? 14 liters of water

 Use with Grade 2, text pages 243–244.

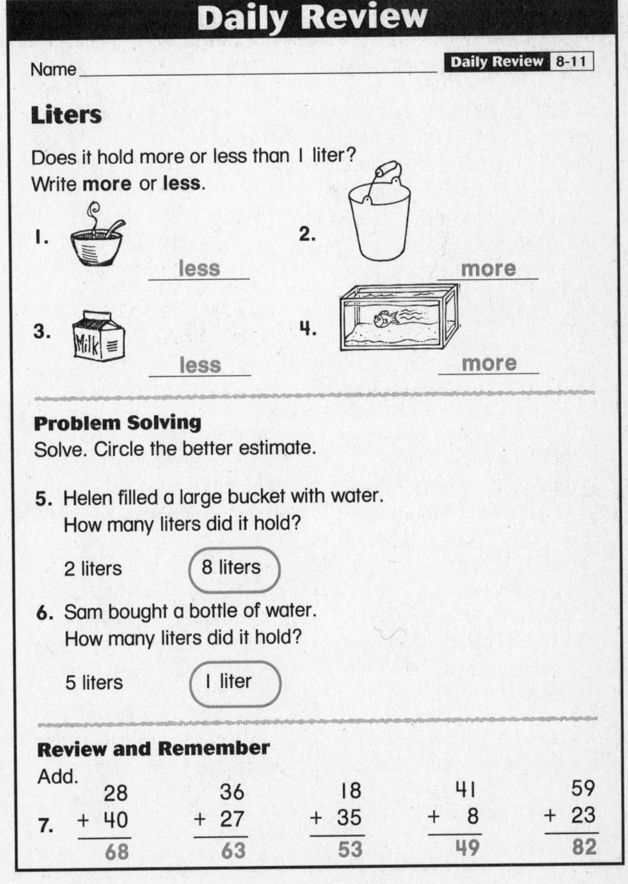

Daily Review

Name ______________________ Daily Review 8-11

Liters

Does it hold more or less than 1 liter?
Write **more** or **less**.

1. less
2. more
3. less
4. more

Problem Solving

Solve. Circle the better estimate.

5. Helen filled a large bucket with water. How many liters did it hold?
   2 liters / 8 liters (circled: 8 liters)
6. Sam bought a bottle of water. How many liters did it hold?
   5 liters / 1 liter (circled: 1 liter)

Review and Remember

Add.

7.

28	36	18	41	59
+ 40	+ 27	+ 35	+ 8	+ 23
68	63	53	49	82

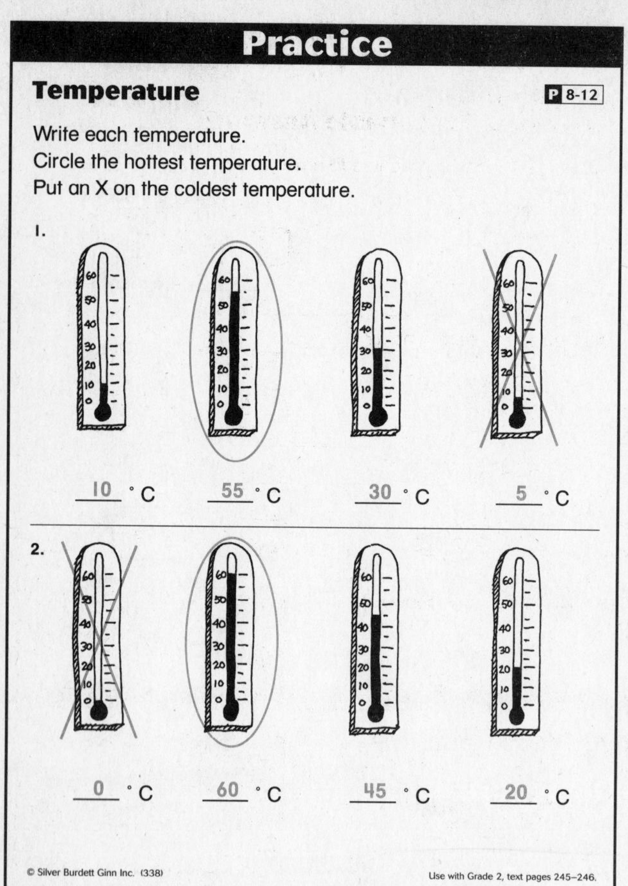

Practice

Temperature

P 8-12

Write each temperature.
Circle the hottest temperature.
Put an X on the coldest temperature.

1.

10 °C   55 °C   30 °C   5 °C

2.

0 °C   60 °C   45 °C   20 °C

Use with Grade 2, text pages 245–246.

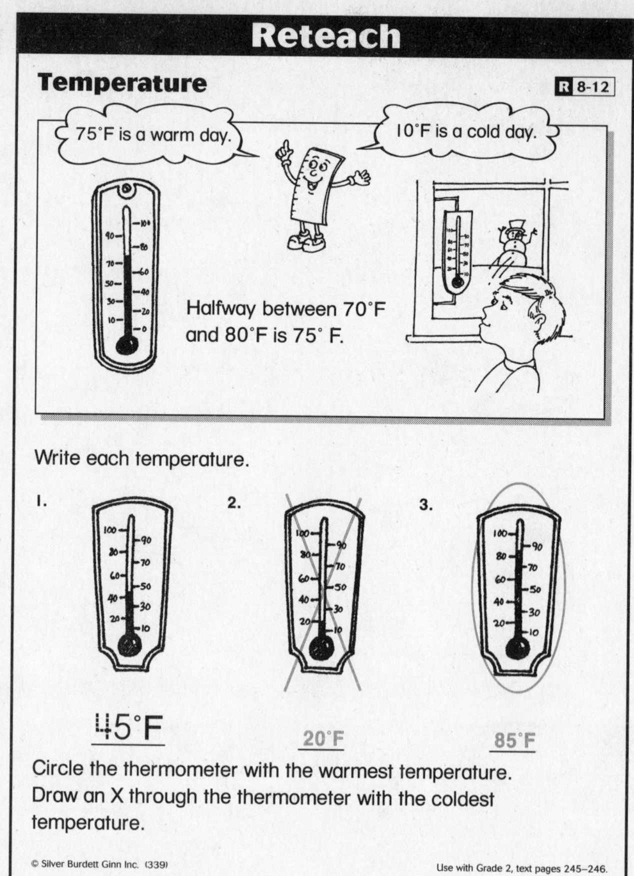

Reteach

Temperature

R 8-12

75°F is a warm day.
10°F is a cold day.
Halfway between 70°F and 80°F is 75° F.

Write each temperature.

1. 45°F
2. 20°F
3. 85°F

Circle the thermometer with the warmest temperature.
Draw an X through the thermometer with the coldest temperature.

Use with Grade 2, text pages 245–246.

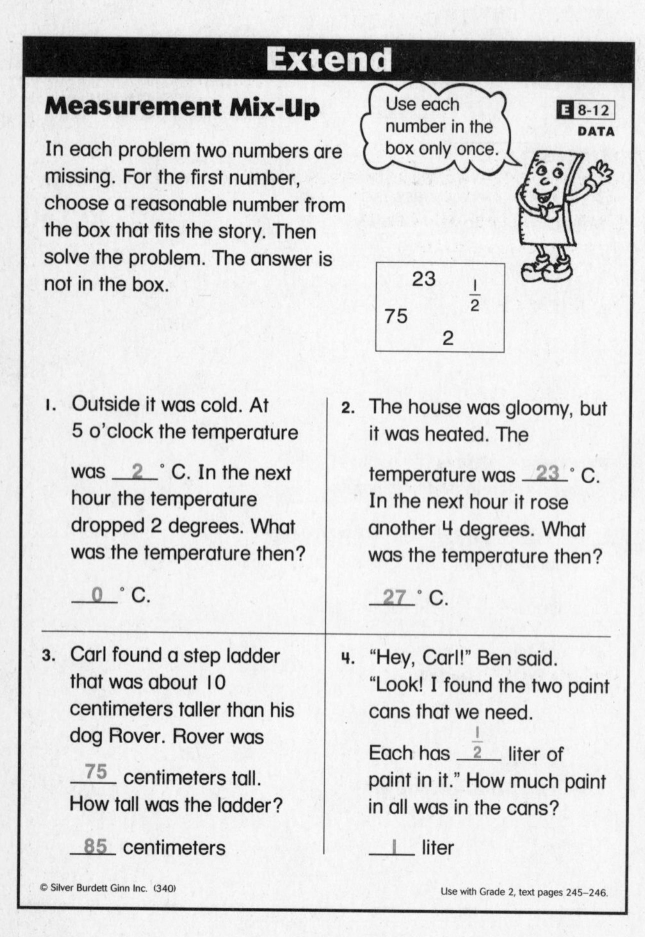

Extend

Measurement Mix-Up

E 8-12
DATA

Use each number in the box only once.

In each problem two numbers are missing. For the first number, choose a reasonable number from the box that fits the story. Then solve the problem. The answer is not in the box.

23   $\frac{1}{2}$ 75   2

1. Outside it was cold. At 5 o'clock the temperature was 2 ° C. In the next hour the temperature dropped 2 degrees. What was the temperature then?

   0 ° C.

2. The house was gloomy, but it was heated. The temperature was 23 ° C. In the next hour it rose another 4 degrees. What was the temperature then?

   27 ° C.

3. Carl found a step ladder that was about 10 centimeters taller than his dog Rover. Rover was 75 centimeters tall. How tall was the ladder?

   85 centimeters

4. "Hey, Carl!" Ben said. "Look! I found the two paint cans that we need. Each has $\frac{1}{2}$ liter of paint in it." How much paint in all was in the cans?

   1 liter

Use with Grade 2, text pages 245–246.

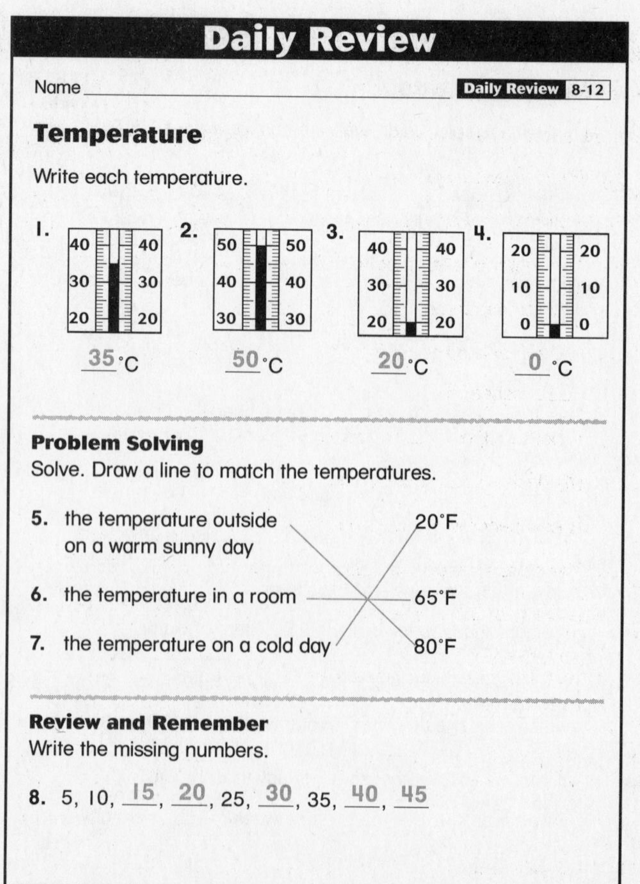

Daily Review

Name ____________________

Daily Review 8-12

Temperature

Write each temperature.

1. 35 °C
2. 50 °C
3. 20 °C
4. 0 °C

Problem Solving

Solve. Draw a line to match the temperatures.

5. the temperature outside on a warm sunny day — 80°F
6. the temperature in a room — 65°F
7. the temperature on a cold day — 20°F

Review and Remember

Write the missing numbers.

8. 5, 10, 15, 20, 25, 30, 35, 40, 45

Chapter 8 • Lesson 13

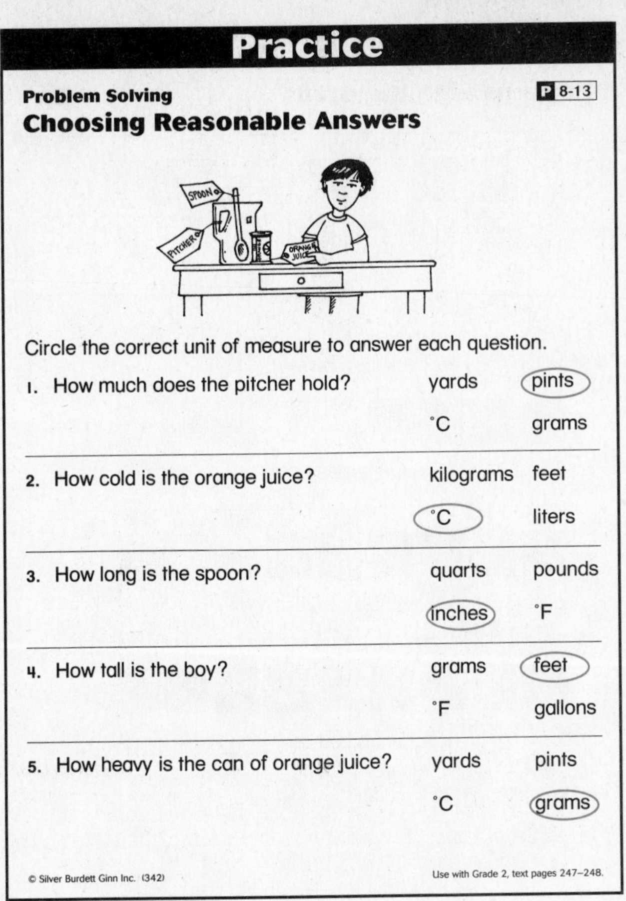

Practice

Problem Solving P 8-13

Choosing Reasonable Answers

Circle the correct unit of measure to answer each question.

1. How much does the pitcher hold? yards, (pints), °C, grams
2. How cold is the orange juice? kilograms, feet, (°C), liters
3. How long is the spoon? quarts, pounds, (inches), °F
4. How tall is the boy? grams, (feet), °F, gallons
5. How heavy is the can of orange juice? yards, pints, °C, (grams)

Use with Grade 2, text pages 247–248.

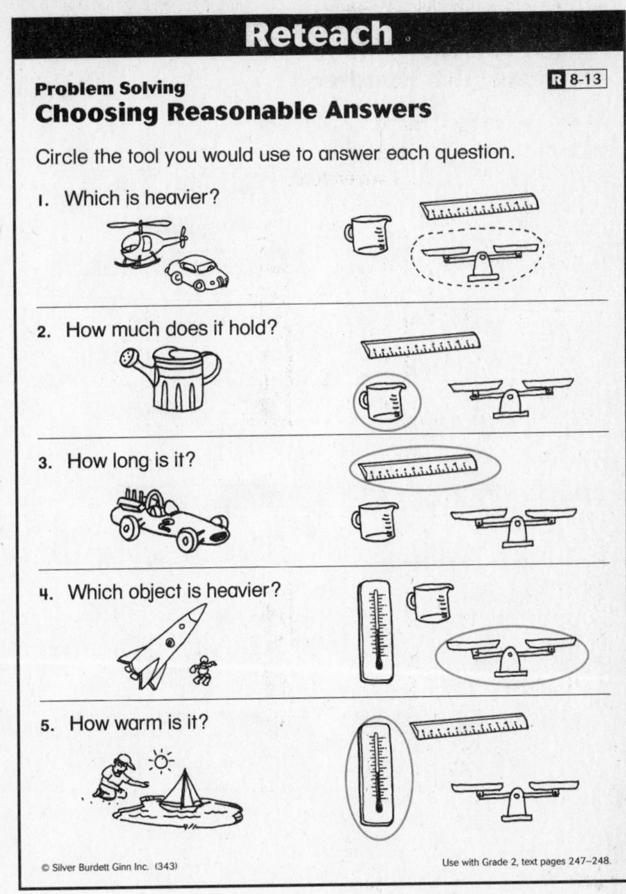

Reteach

Problem Solving R 8-13

Choosing Reasonable Answers

Circle the tool you would use to answer each question.

1. Which is heavier?
2. How much does it hold?
3. How long is it?
4. Which object is heavier?
5. How warm is it?

Use with Grade 2, text pages 247–248.

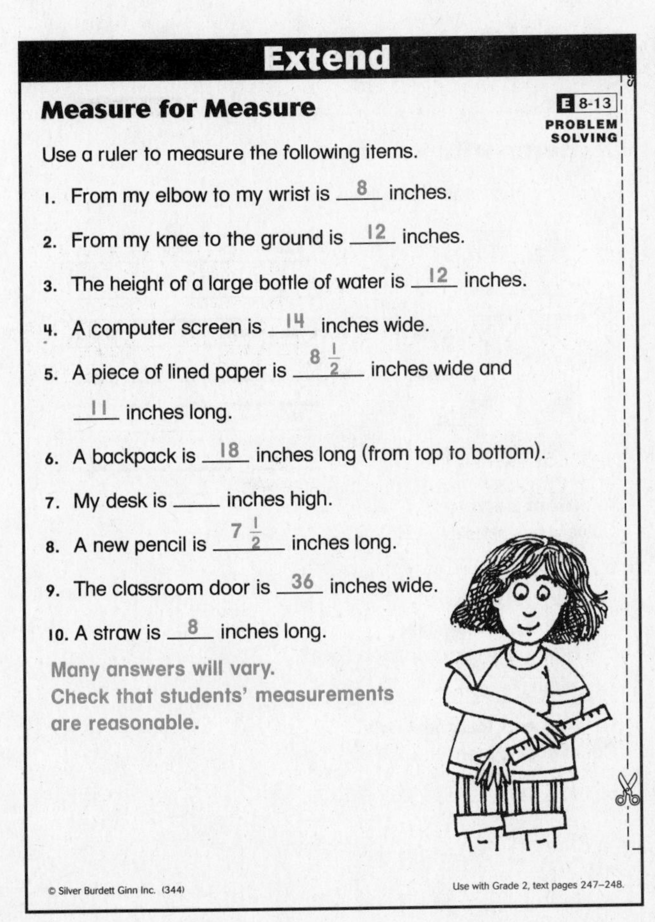

Extend

Measure for Measure E 8-13 PROBLEM SOLVING

Use a ruler to measure the following items.

1. From my elbow to my wrist is 8 inches.
2. From my knee to the ground is 12 inches.
3. The height of a large bottle of water is 12 inches.
4. A computer screen is 14 inches wide.
5. A piece of lined paper is $8\frac{1}{2}$ inches wide and 11 inches long.
6. A backpack is 18 inches long (from top to bottom).
7. My desk is ____ inches high.
8. A new pencil is $7\frac{1}{2}$ inches long.
9. The classroom door is 36 inches wide.
10. A straw is 8 inches long.

Many answers will vary. Check that students' measurements are reasonable.

Use with Grade 2, text pages 247–248.

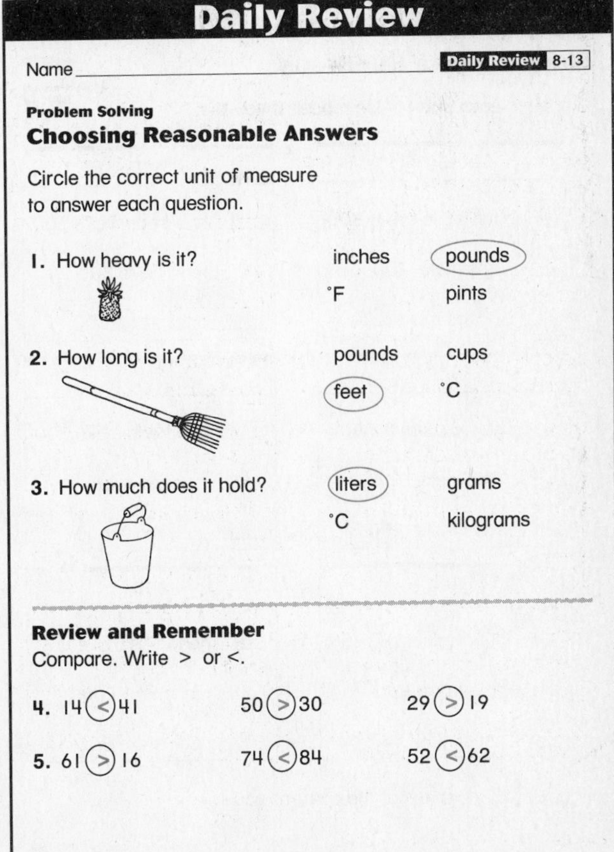

Daily Review

Name ____________________ Daily Review 8-13

Problem Solving

Choosing Reasonable Answers

Circle the correct unit of measure to answer each question.

1. How heavy is it? inches, (pounds), °F, pints
2. How long is it? pounds, cups, (feet), °C
3. How much does it hold? (liters), grams, °C, kilograms

Review and Remember

Compare. Write > or <.

4. 14 < 41　　50 > 30　　29 > 19
5. 61 > 16　　74 < 84　　52 < 62

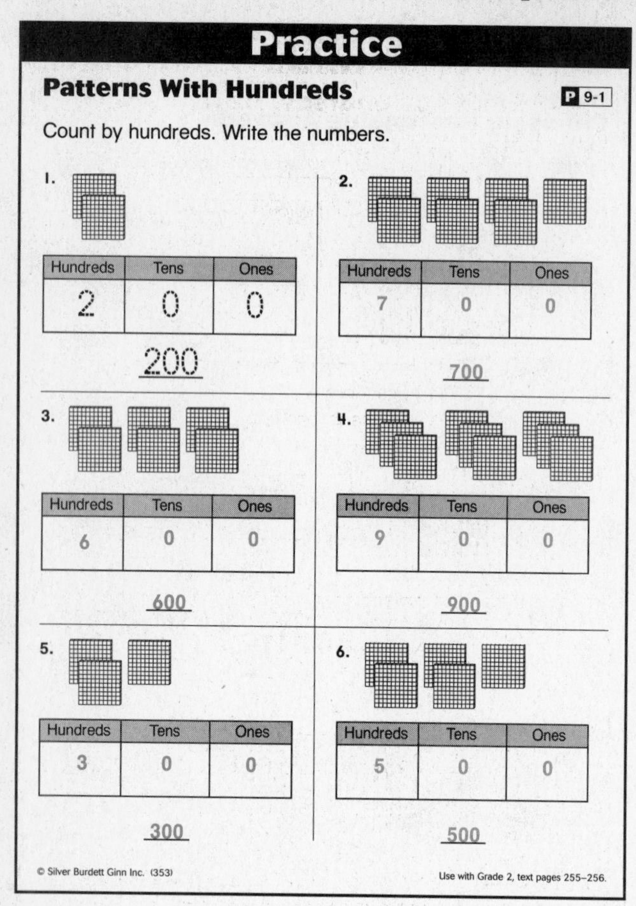

Practice

Patterns With Hundreds

P 9-1

Count by hundreds. Write the numbers.

1.

Hundreds	Tens	Ones
2	0	0

200

2.

Hundreds	Tens	Ones
7	0	0

700

3.

Hundreds	Tens	Ones
6	0	0

600

4.

Hundreds	Tens	Ones
9	0	0

900

5.

Hundreds	Tens	Ones
3	0	0

300

6.

Hundreds	Tens	Ones
5	0	0

500

 Use with Grade 2, text pages 255–256.

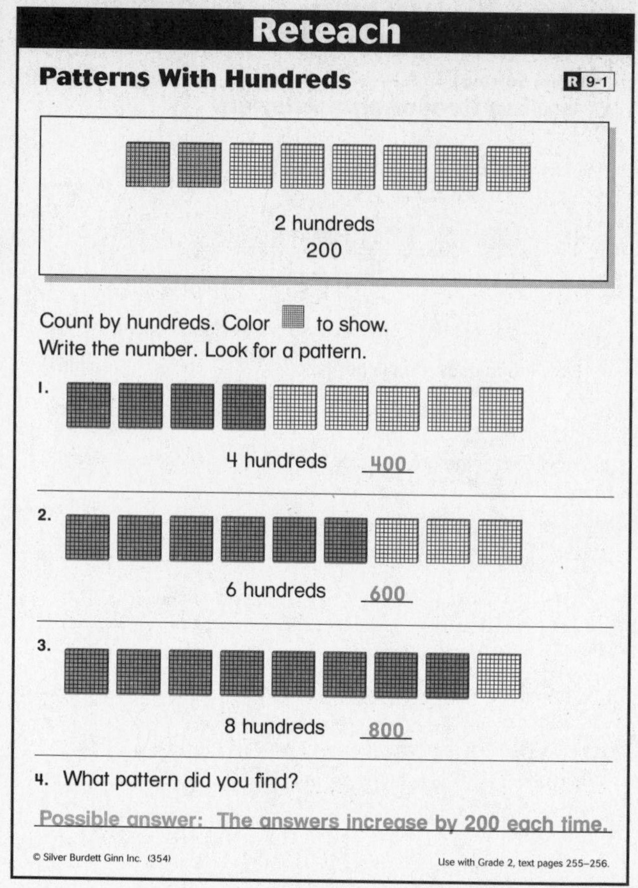

Reteach

Patterns With Hundreds

R 9-1

2 hundreds
200

Count by hundreds. Color to show.
Write the number. Look for a pattern.

1. 4 hundreds 400

2. 6 hundreds 600

3. 8 hundreds 800

4. What pattern did you find?
Possible answer: The answers increase by 200 each time.

 Use with Grade 2, text pages 255–256.

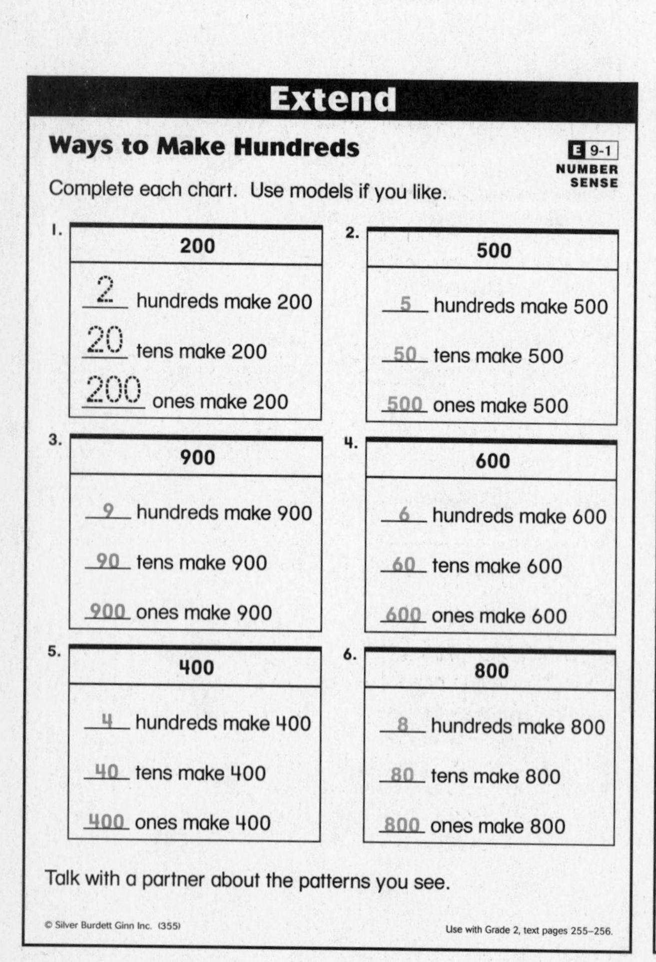

Extend

Ways to Make Hundreds

E 9-1 NUMBER SENSE

Complete each chart. Use models if you like.

1. **200**
2 hundreds make 200
20 tens make 200
200 ones make 200

2. **500**
5 hundreds make 500
50 tens make 500
500 ones make 500

3. **900**
9 hundreds make 900
90 tens make 900
900 ones make 900

4. **600**
6 hundreds make 600
60 tens make 600
600 ones make 600

5. **400**
4 hundreds make 400
40 tens make 400
400 ones make 400

6. **800**
8 hundreds make 800
80 tens make 800
800 ones make 800

Talk with a partner about the patterns you see.

 Use with Grade 2, text pages 255–256.

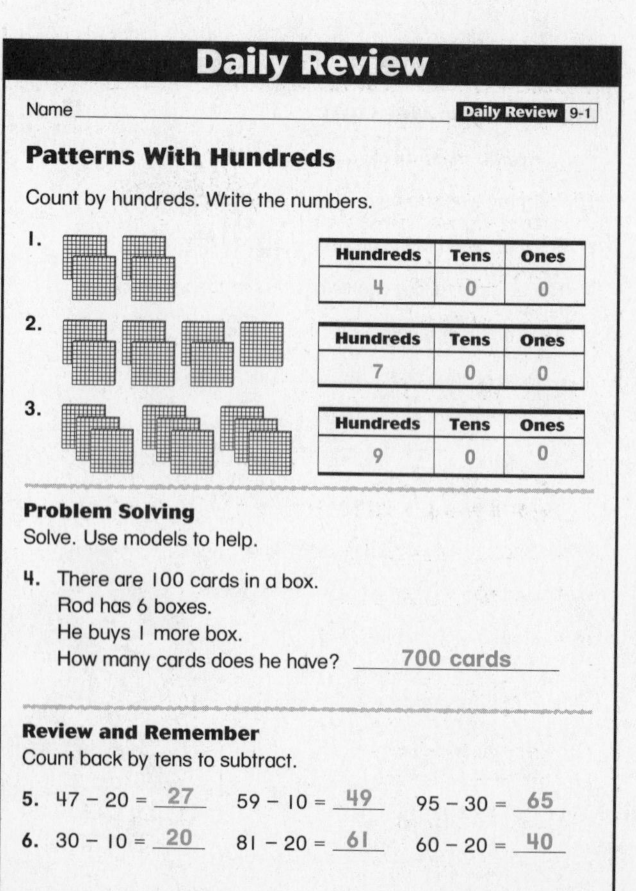

Daily Review

Name ____________ Daily Review 9-1

Patterns With Hundreds

Count by hundreds. Write the numbers.

1.

Hundreds	Tens	Ones
4	0	0

2.

Hundreds	Tens	Ones
7	0	0

3.

Hundreds	Tens	Ones
9	0	0

Problem Solving
Solve. Use models to help.

4. There are 100 cards in a box.
Rod has 6 boxes.
He buys 1 more box.
How many cards does he have? 700 cards

Review and Remember
Count back by tens to subtract.

5. 47 − 20 = 27 59 − 10 = 49 95 − 30 = 65

6. 30 − 10 = 20 81 − 20 = 61 60 − 20 = 40

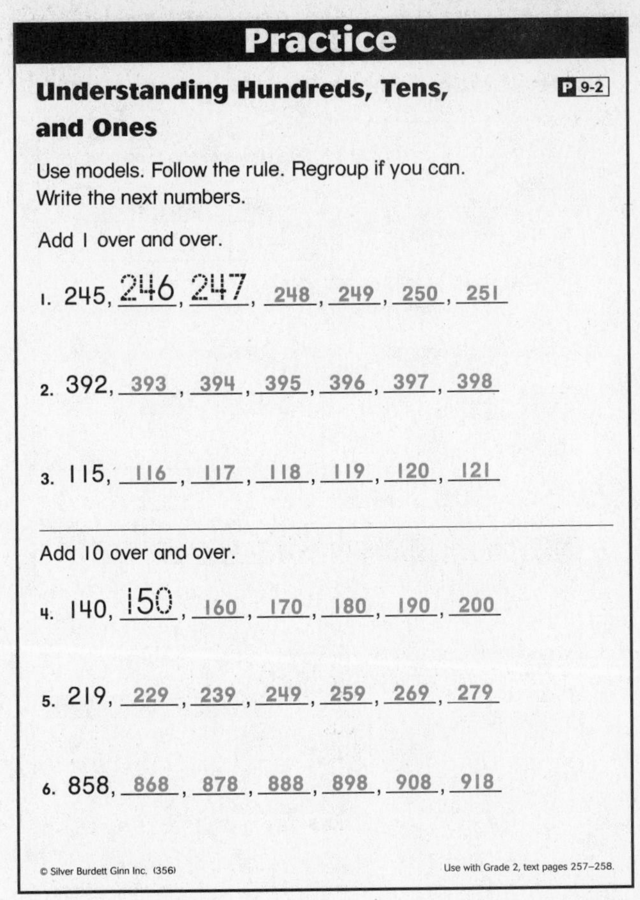

Practice

Understanding Hundreds, Tens, and Ones

P 9-2

Use models. Follow the rule. Regroup if you can.
Write the next numbers.

Add 1 over and over.

1. 245, 246, 247, 248, 249, 250, 251
2. 392, 393, 394, 395, 396, 397, 398
3. 115, 116, 117, 118, 119, 120, 121

Add 10 over and over.

4. 140, 150, 160, 170, 180, 190, 200
5. 219, 229, 239, 249, 259, 269, 279
6. 858, 868, 878, 888, 898, 908, 918

 Use with Grade 2, text pages 257–258.

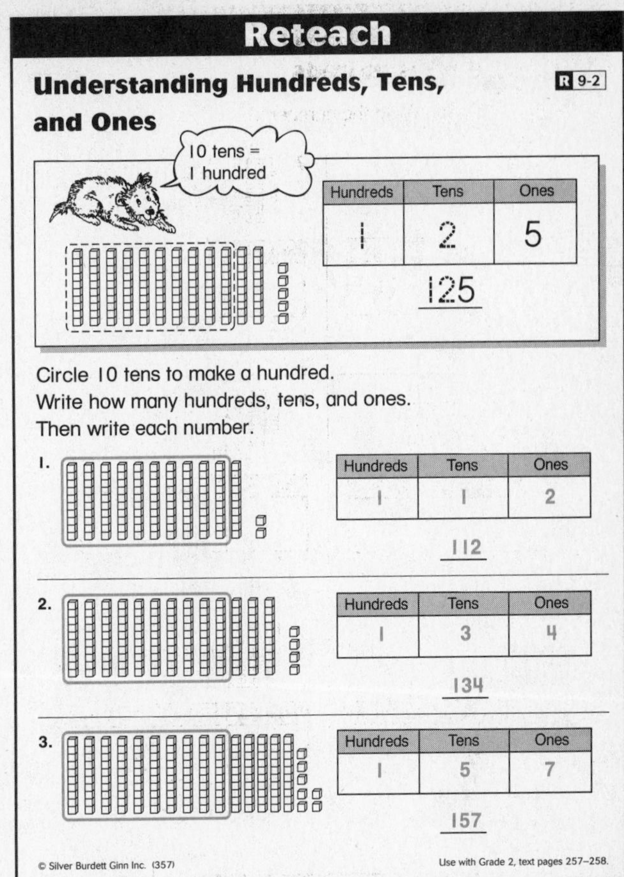

Reteach

Understanding Hundreds, Tens, and Ones

R 9-2

Hundreds	Tens	Ones
1	2	5

125

Circle 10 tens to make a hundred.
Write how many hundreds, tens, and ones.
Then write each number.

1.

Hundreds	Tens	Ones
1	1	2

112

2.

Hundreds	Tens	Ones
1	3	4

134

3.

Hundreds	Tens	Ones
1	5	7

157

 Use with Grade 2, text pages 257–258.

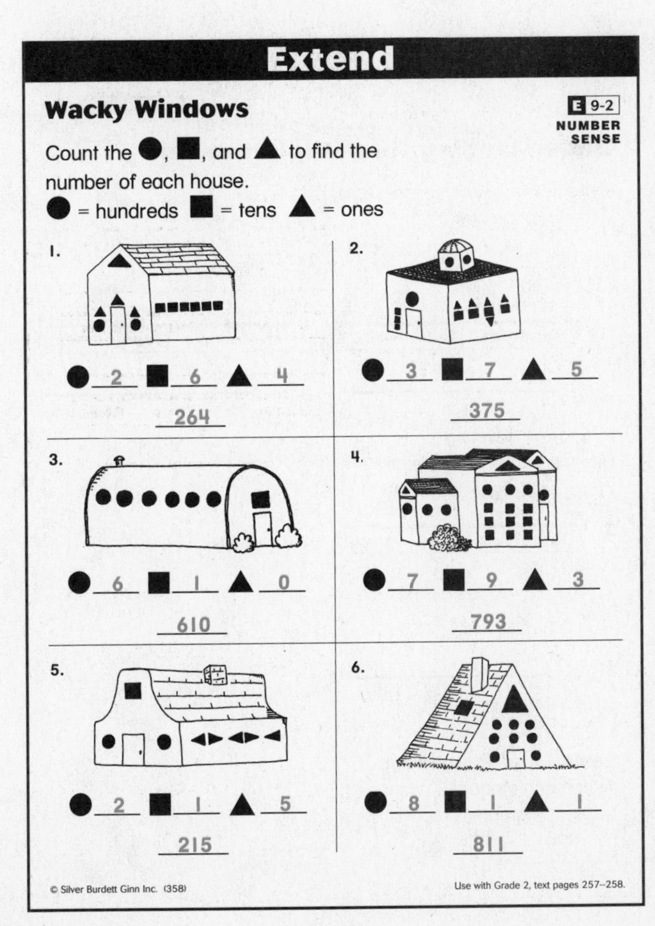

Extend

Wacky Windows

E 9-2 NUMBER SENSE

Count the ●, ■, and ▲ to find the number of each house.
● = hundreds ■ = tens ▲ = ones

1. ● 2 ■ 6 ▲ 4 — 264
2. ● 3 ■ 7 ▲ 5 — 375
3. ● 6 ■ 1 ▲ 0 — 610
4. ● 7 ■ 9 ▲ 3 — 793
5. ● 2 ■ 1 ▲ 5 — 215
6. ● 8 ■ 1 ▲ 1 — 811

 Use with Grade 2, text pages 257–258.

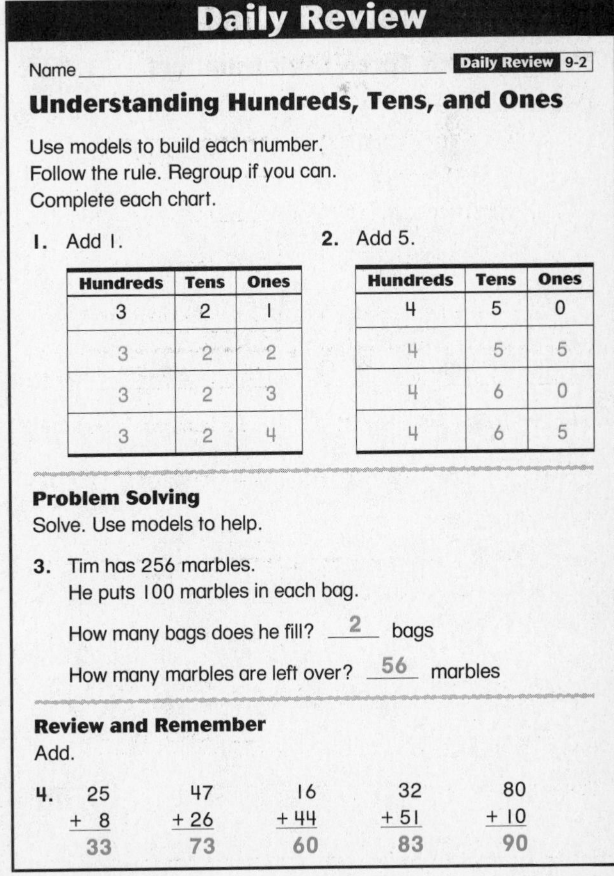

Daily Review

Name ____________ Daily Review 9-2

Understanding Hundreds, Tens, and Ones

Use models to build each number.
Follow the rule. Regroup if you can.
Complete each chart.

1. Add 1.

Hundreds	Tens	Ones
3	2	1
3	2	2
3	2	3
3	2	4

2. Add 5.

Hundreds	Tens	Ones
4	5	0
4	5	5
4	6	0
4	6	5

Problem Solving

Solve. Use models to help.

3. Tim has 256 marbles.
He puts 100 marbles in each bag.
How many bags does he fill? 2 bags
How many marbles are left over? 56 marbles

Review and Remember

Add.

4. $25 + 8 = 33$ $\quad 47 + 26 = 73$ $\quad 16 + 44 = 60$ $\quad 32 + 51 = 83$ $\quad 80 + 10 = 90$

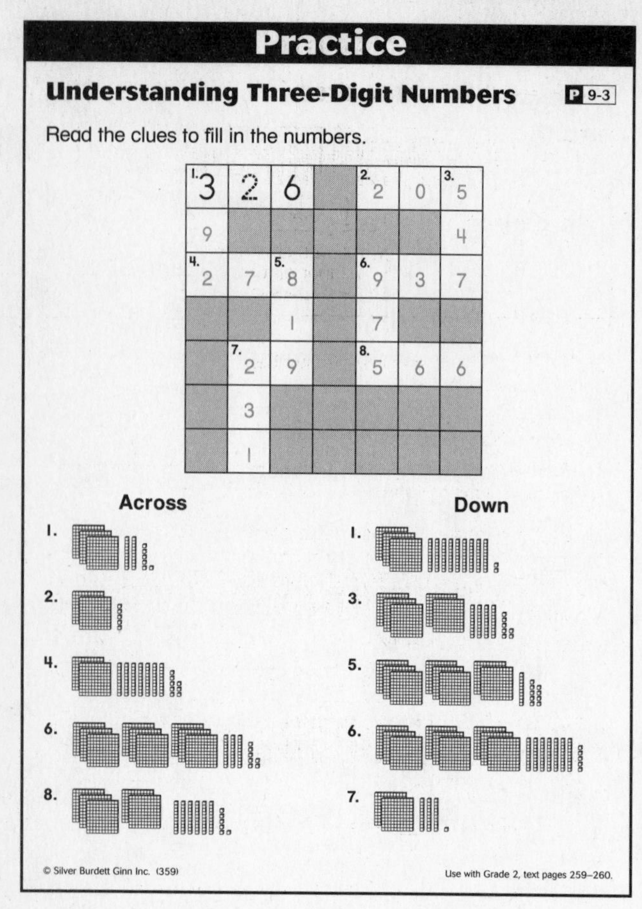

Practice

Understanding Three-Digit Numbers

P 9-3

Read the clues to fill in the numbers.

1. 3	2	6		2. 2	0	3. 5
9						4
4. 2	7	5. 8		6. 9	3	7
		1		7		
	7. 2	9		8. 5	6	6
	3					
	1					

Across

1.
2.
4.
6.
8.

Down

1.
3.
5.
6.
7.

 Use with Grade 2, text pages 259–260.

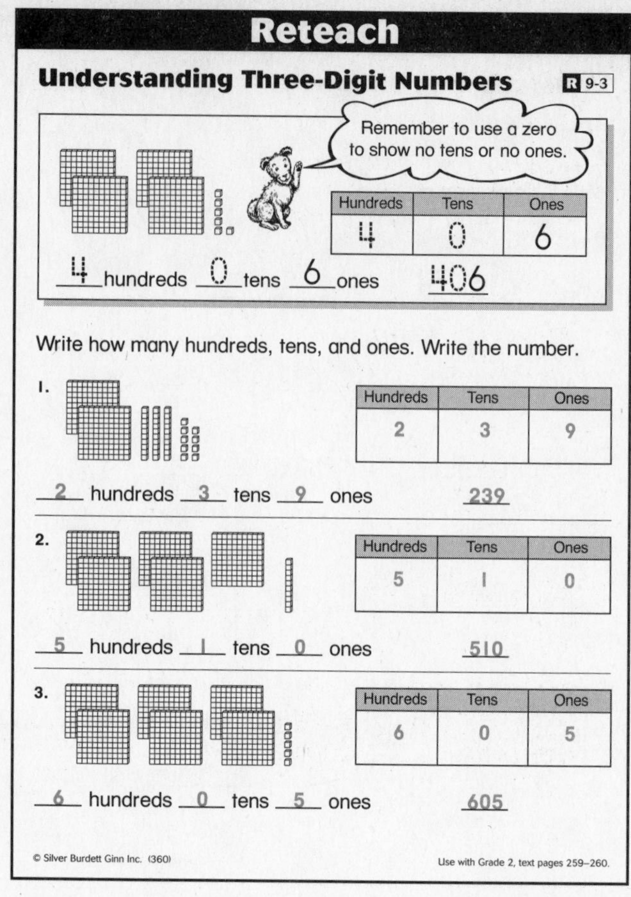

Reteach

Understanding Three-Digit Numbers

R 9-3

Hundreds	Tens	Ones
4	0	6

4 hundreds 0 tens 6 ones 406

Write how many hundreds, tens, and ones. Write the number.

1.

Hundreds	Tens	Ones
2	3	9

2 hundreds 3 tens 9 ones 239

2.

Hundreds	Tens	Ones
5	1	0

5 hundreds 1 tens 0 ones 510

3.

Hundreds	Tens	Ones
6	0	5

6 hundreds 0 tens 5 ones 605

 Use with Grade 2, text pages 259–260.

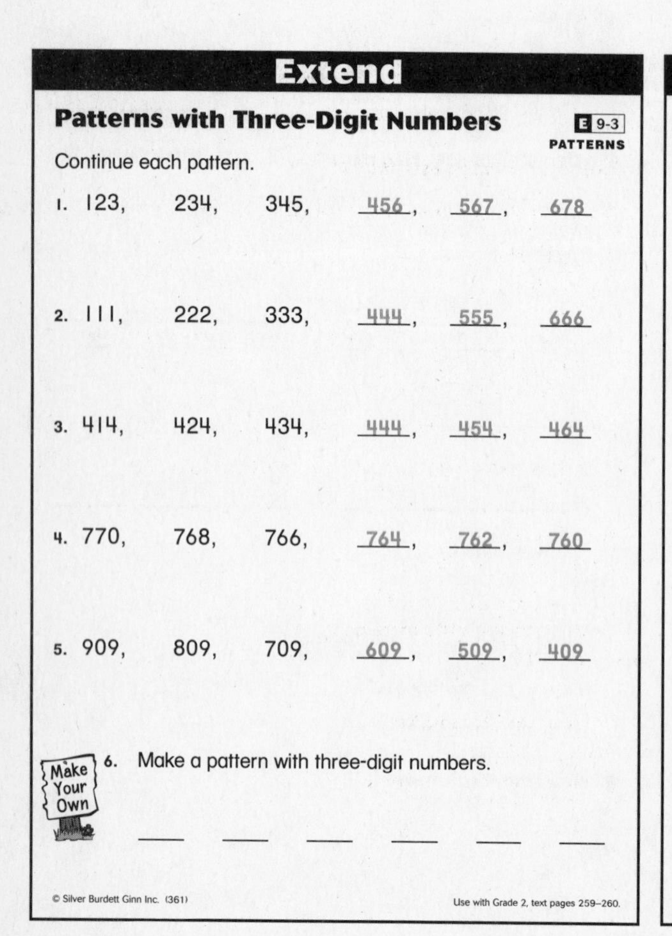

Extend

Patterns with Three-Digit Numbers

E 9-3 PATTERNS

Continue each pattern.

1. 123, 234, 345, 456, 567, 678
2. 111, 222, 333, 444, 555, 666
3. 414, 424, 434, 444, 454, 464
4. 770, 768, 766, 764, 762, 760
5. 909, 809, 709, 609, 509, 409

6. Make a pattern with three-digit numbers.

___ ___ ___ ___ ___ ___

 Use with Grade 2, text pages 259–260.

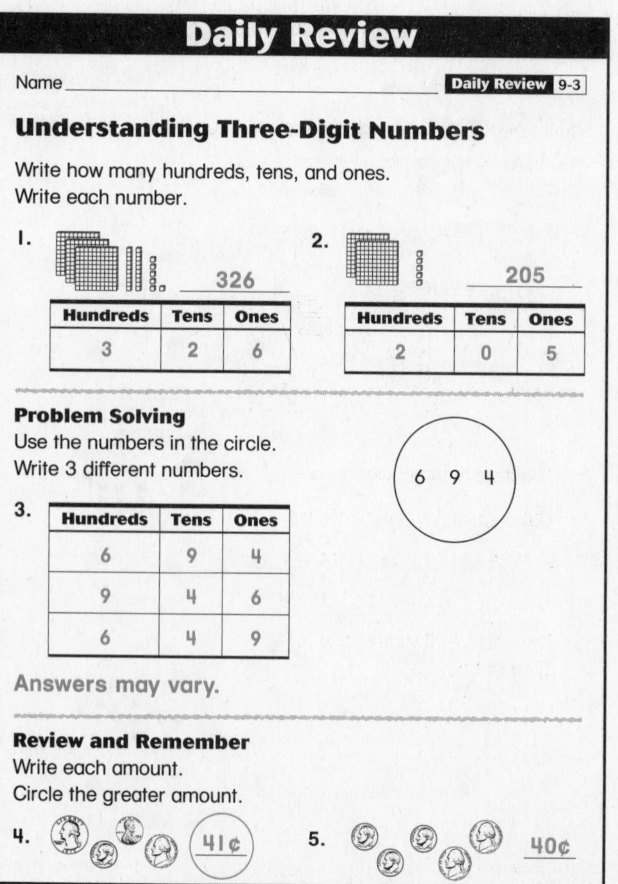

Daily Review

Name ____________________ Daily Review 9-3

Understanding Three-Digit Numbers

Write how many hundreds, tens, and ones.
Write each number.

1. 326

Hundreds	Tens	Ones
3	2	6

2. 205

Hundreds	Tens	Ones
2	0	5

Problem Solving

Use the numbers in the circle.
Write 3 different numbers.

3.

Hundreds	Tens	Ones
6	9	4
9	4	6
6	4	9

Answers may vary.

Review and Remember

Write each amount.
Circle the greater amount.

4. 41¢

5. 40¢

Chapter 9 • Lesson 4

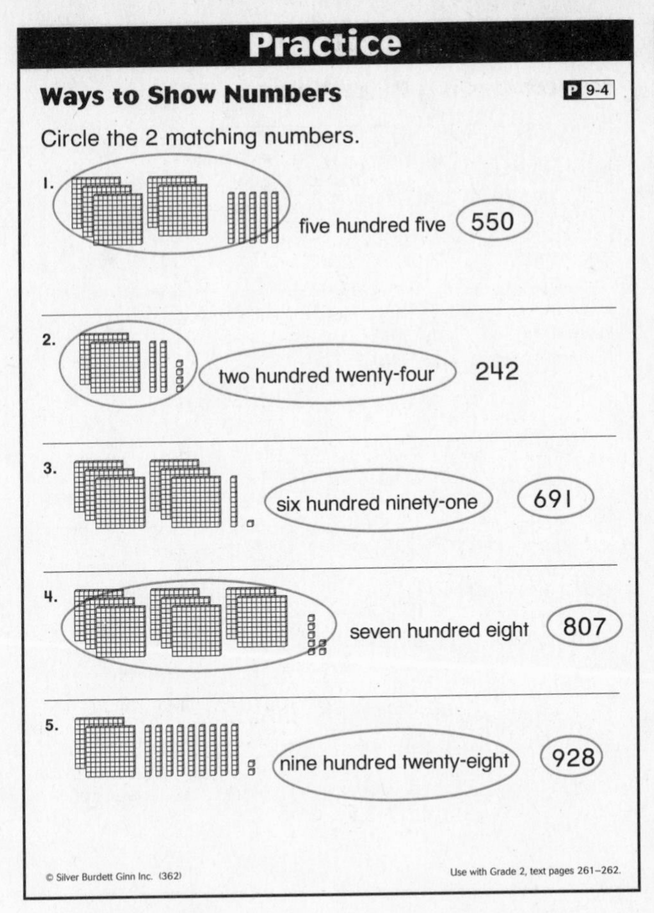

Practice

Ways to Show Numbers

P 9-4

Circle the 2 matching numbers.

1. five hundred five 550
2. two hundred twenty-four 242
3. six hundred ninety-one 691
4. seven hundred eight 807
5. nine hundred twenty-eight 928

Use with Grade 2, text pages 261–262.

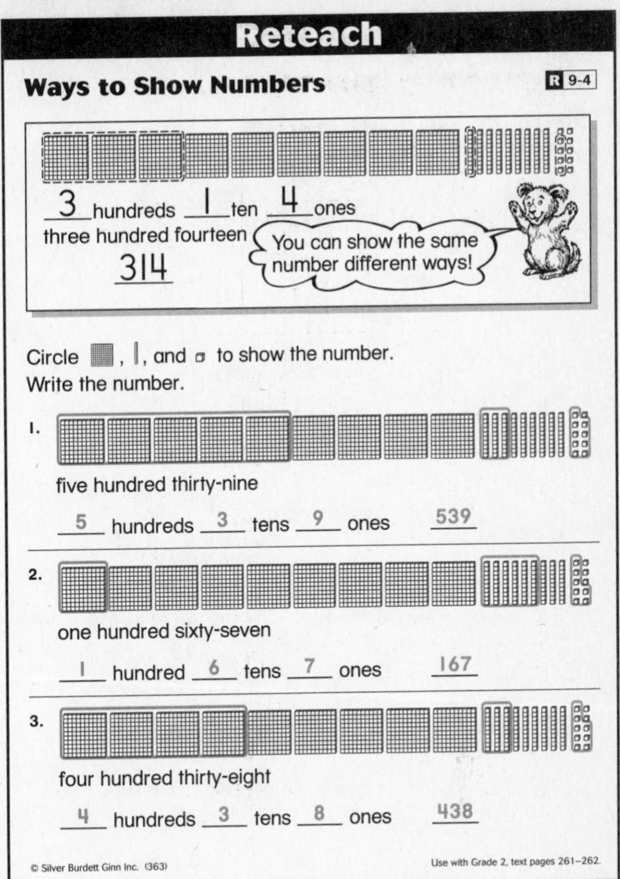

Reteach

Ways to Show Numbers

R 9-4

3 hundreds 1 ten 4 ones

three hundred fourteen

314

You can show the same number different ways!

Circle ▦, |, and ▫ to show the number.
Write the number.

1. five hundred thirty-nine

5 hundreds 3 tens 9 ones 539

2. one hundred sixty-seven

1 hundred 6 tens 7 ones 167

3. four hundred thirty-eight

4 hundreds 3 tens 8 ones 438

Use with Grade 2, text pages 261–262.

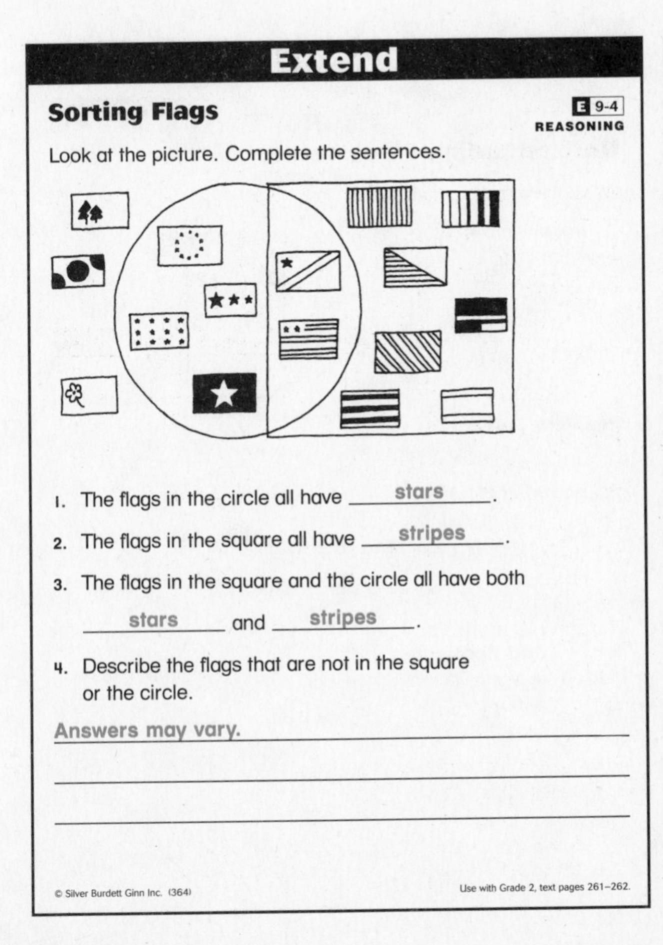

Extend

Sorting Flags

E 9-4
REASONING

Look at the picture. Complete the sentences.

1. The flags in the circle all have stars.
2. The flags in the square all have stripes.
3. The flags in the square and the circle all have both stars and stripes.
4. Describe the flags that are not in the square or the circle.

Answers may vary.

Use with Grade 2, text pages 261–262.

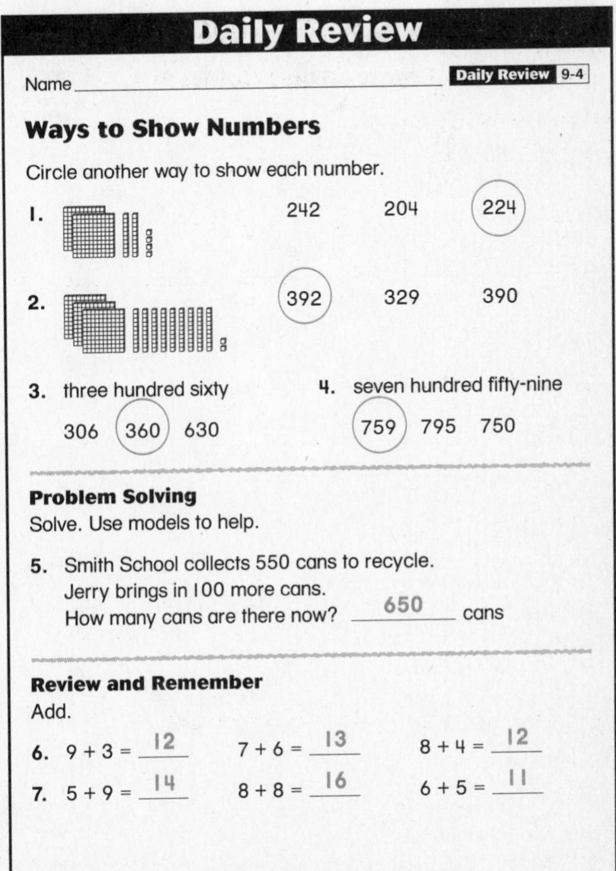

Daily Review

Name ____________

Daily Review 9-4

Ways to Show Numbers

Circle another way to show each number.

1. 242 204 (224)
2. (392) 329 390
3. three hundred sixty

306 (360) 630

4. seven hundred fifty-nine

(759) 795 750

Problem Solving

Solve. Use models to help.

5. Smith School collects 550 cans to recycle.
Jerry brings in 100 more cans.
How many cans are there now? 650 cans

Review and Remember

Add.

6. 9 + 3 = 12 7 + 6 = 13 8 + 4 = 12
7. 5 + 9 = 14 8 + 8 = 16 6 + 5 = 11

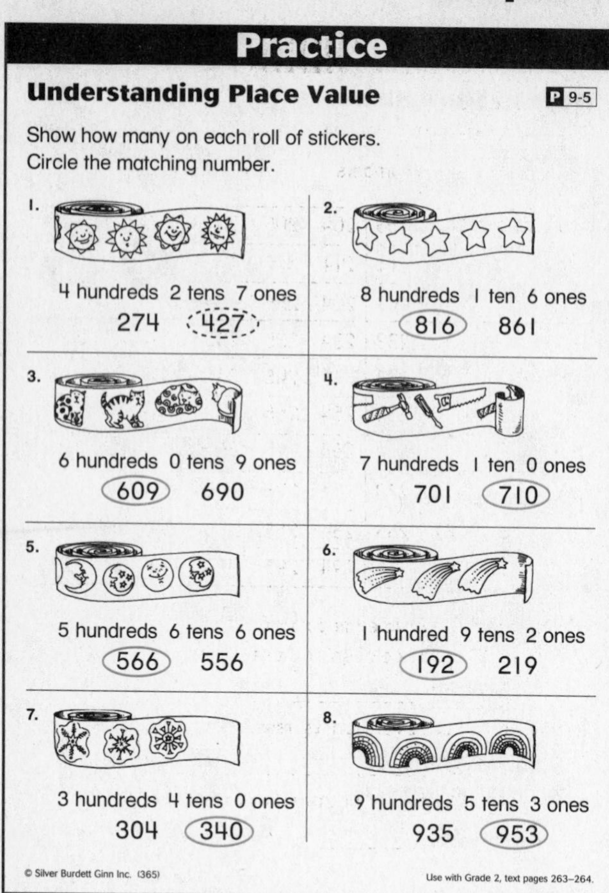

Practice

Understanding Place Value

P 9-5

Show how many on each roll of stickers.
Circle the matching number.

1. 4 hundreds 2 tens 7 ones
274 (427)

2. 8 hundreds 1 ten 6 ones
(816) 861

3. 6 hundreds 0 tens 9 ones
(609) 690

4. 7 hundreds 1 ten 0 ones
701 (710)

5. 5 hundreds 6 tens 6 ones
(566) 556

6. 1 hundred 9 tens 2 ones
(192) 219

7. 3 hundreds 4 tens 0 ones
304 (340)

8. 9 hundreds 5 tens 3 ones
935 (953)

Use with Grade 2, text pages 263–264.

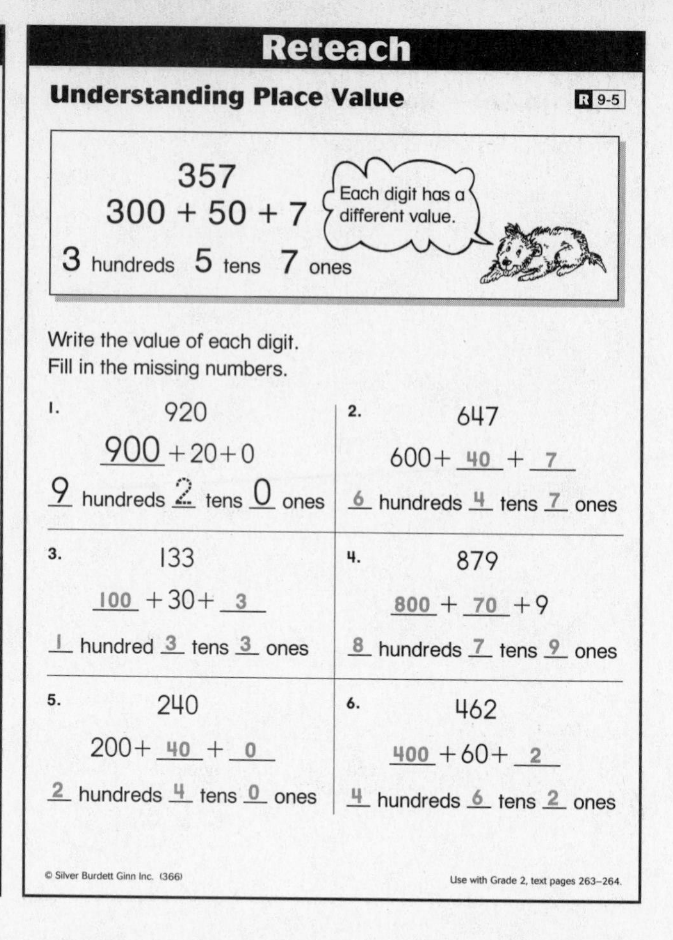

Reteach

Understanding Place Value

R 9-5

357
300 + 50 + 7
3 hundreds 5 tens 7 ones

Write the value of each digit.
Fill in the missing numbers.

1. 920
900 + 20 + 0
9 hundreds 2 tens 0 ones

2. 647
600 + 40 + 7
6 hundreds 4 tens 7 ones

3. 133
100 + 30 + 3
1 hundred 3 tens 3 ones

4. 879
800 + 70 + 9
8 hundreds 7 tens 9 ones

5. 240
200 + 40 + 0
2 hundreds 4 tens 0 ones

6. 462
400 + 60 + 2
4 hundreds 6 tens 2 ones

Use with Grade 2, text pages 263–264.

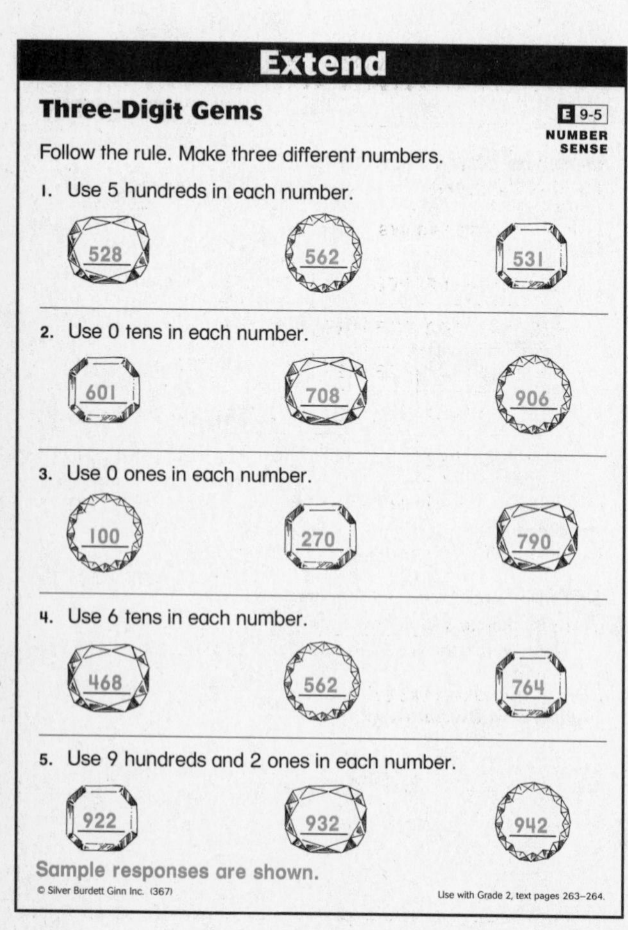

Extend

Three-Digit Gems

E 9-5
NUMBER SENSE

Follow the rule. Make three different numbers.

1. Use 5 hundreds in each number.
528 562 531

2. Use 0 tens in each number.
601 708 906

3. Use 0 ones in each number.
100 270 790

4. Use 6 tens in each number.
468 562 764

5. Use 9 hundreds and 2 ones in each number.
922 932 942

Sample responses are shown.

Use with Grade 2, text pages 263–264.

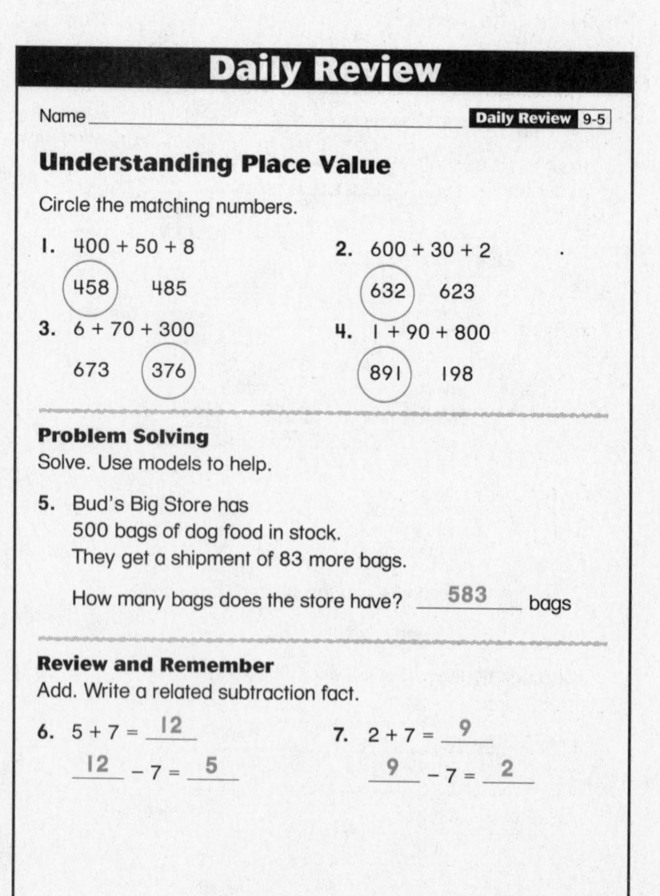

Daily Review

Name ____________________ Daily Review 9-5

Understanding Place Value

Circle the matching numbers.

1. 400 + 50 + 8
(458) 485

2. 600 + 30 + 2
(632) 623

3. 6 + 70 + 300
673 (376)

4. 1 + 90 + 800
(891) 198

Problem Solving
Solve. Use models to help.

5. Bud's Big Store has 500 bags of dog food in stock. They get a shipment of 83 more bags.
How many bags does the store have? 583 bags

Review and Remember
Add. Write a related subtraction fact.

6. 5 + 7 = 12
12 − 7 = 5

7. 2 + 7 = 9
9 − 7 = 2

Chapter 9 • Lesson 6

Practice

Problem Solving P 9-6

Find a Pattern

1. Write the missing numbers.

100	101	102	103	104	105	106	107	108	109
110	111	112	113	114	115	116	117	118	119
120	121	122	123	124	125	126	127	128	129
130	131	132	133	134	135	136	137	138	139
140	141	142	143	144	145	146	147	148	149
150	151	152	153	154	155	156	157	158	159
160	161	162	163	164	165	166	167	168	169
170	171	172	173	174	175	176	177	178	179
180	181	182	183	184	185	186	187	188	189
190	191	192	193	194	195	196	197	198	199

Use the chart to complete each pattern.

2. 100, 111, 122, 133, 144, 155, 166, 177, 188
3. 109, 119, 129, 139, 149, 159, 169, 179, 189

4. Make your own pattern of numbers from the chart.

____, ____, ____, ____, ____, ____, ____

 Use with Grade 2, text pages 265–266.

Reteach

Problem Solving R 9-6

Find a Pattern

1. Write the missing numbers.

200	201	202	203	204	205	206	207	208	209
210	211	212	213	214	215	216	217	218	219
220	221	222	223	224	225	226	227	228	229
230	231	232	233	234	235	236	237	238	239
240	241	242	243	244	245	246	247	248	249
250	251	252	253	254	255	256	257	258	259
260	261	262	263	264	265	266	267	268	269
270	271	272	273	274	275	276	277	278	279
280	281	282	283	284	285	286	287	288	289
290	291	292	293	294	295	296	297	298	299

Use the chart to complete the pattern.

2. Start at 200 and skip count by fives.
   200, 205, 210, 215, 220, 225, 230, 235
3. Start at 204 and skip count by tens.
   204, 214, 224, 234, 244, 254, 264, 274
4. Start at 299 and count backward by ones.
   299, 298, 297, 296, 295, 294, 293, 292

 Use with Grade 2, text pages 265–266.

Extend

Place Value with the Calculator

E 9-6 CALCULATOR

Use the numbers in the shapes. Use a calculator to follow each rule. Write the numbers you see each time.

1. □3 ○4  △2

Add 1 over and over.
□ △ ○, 325, 326, 327, 328

Add 10 over and over.
○ □ △, 442, 452, 462, 472

Add 100 over and over.
△ □ ○, 334, 434, 534, 634

2. □1 ○0 △5

Add 1 over and over.
△ ○ □, 502, 503, 504, 505

Add 10 over and over.
□ △ ○, 160, 170, 180, 190

Add 100 over and over.
△ □ ○, 610, 710, 810, 910

 Use with Grade 2, text pages 265–266.

Daily Review

Name ________________ Daily Review 9-6

Problem Solving

Find a Pattern

Write the missing numbers.

1.

400	401	402	403	404	405	406	407	408	409
410	411	412	413	414	415	416	417	418	419
420	421	422	423	424	425	426	427	428	429
430	431	432	433	434	435	436	437	438	439
440	441	442	443	444	445	446	447	448	449

Use the chart to continue each pattern.

2. 400, 410, 420, 430, 440
3. 403, 413, 423, 433, 443
4. 448, 438, 428, 418, 408

Review and Remember

Write each time. Look for a pattern.

5.  1:00  2:00  3:00  4:00

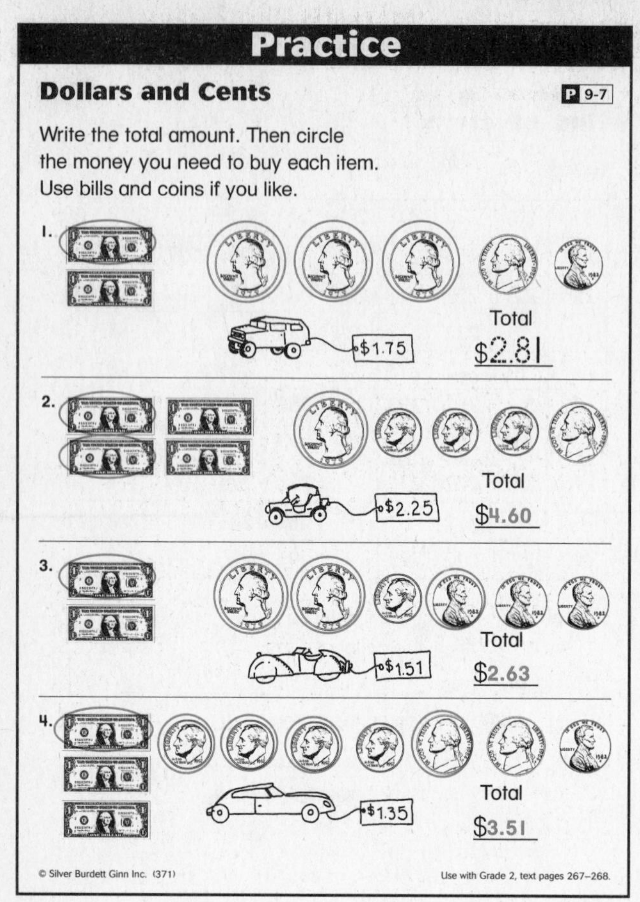

Chapter 9 • Lesson 7

Practice

Dollars and Cents P 9-7

Write the total amount. Then circle
the money you need to buy each item.
Use bills and coins if you like.

1. Total $2.81 $1.75
2. Total $4.60 $2.25
3. Total $2.63 $1.51
4. Total $3.51 $1.35

© Silver Burdett Ginn Inc. (371) Use with Grade 2, text pages 267–268.

Reteach

Dollars and Cents R 9-7

$1.00 $1.25 $1.35 $1.40 $1.41 $1.42

Count on to find the total amount.

1. $2.00 $2.25 $2.35 $2.45 $2.50 Total
2. $3.00 $3.10 $3.20 $3.30 $3.35 $3.36 Total
3. $3.00 $3.25 $3.50 $3.75 $3.80 $3.81 Total

© Silver Burdett Ginn Inc. (372) Use with Grade 2, text pages 267–268.

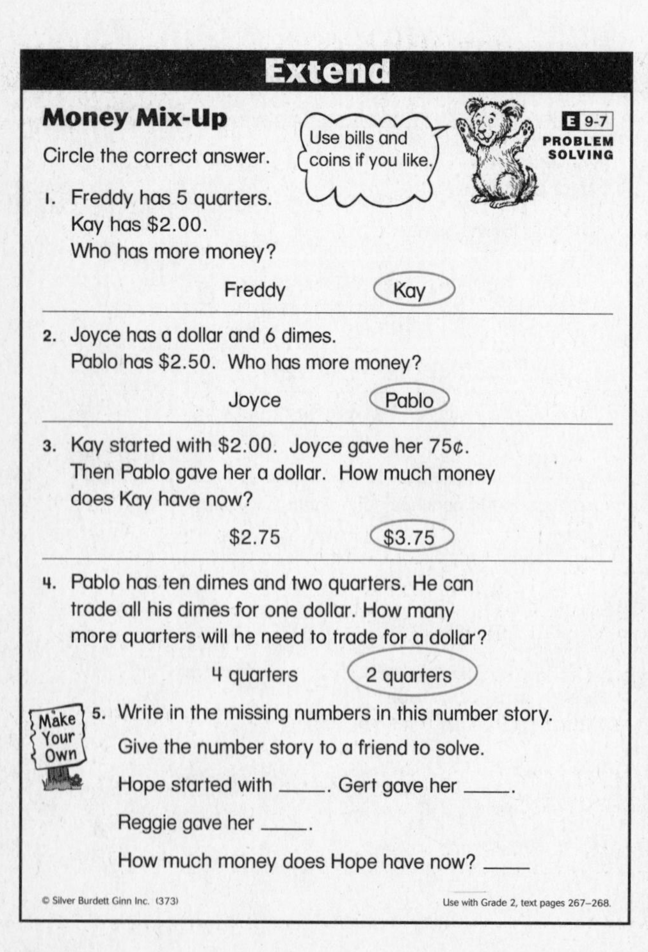

Extend

Money Mix-Up E 9-7 PROBLEM SOLVING

Use bills and coins if you like.

Circle the correct answer.

1. Freddy has 5 quarters. Kay has $2.00. Who has more money?
 Freddy (Kay)

2. Joyce has a dollar and 6 dimes. Pablo has $2.50. Who has more money?
 Joyce (Pablo)

3. Kay started with $2.00. Joyce gave her 75¢. Then Pablo gave her a dollar. How much money does Kay have now?
 $2.75 ($3.75)

4. Pablo has ten dimes and two quarters. He can trade all his dimes for one dollar. How many more quarters will he need to trade for a dollar?
 4 quarters (2 quarters)

Make Your Own 5. Write in the missing numbers in this number story. Give the number story to a friend to solve.

 Hope started with _____. Gert gave her _____.

 Reggie gave her _____.

 How much money does Hope have now? _____

© Silver Burdett Ginn Inc. (373) Use with Grade 2, text pages 267–268.

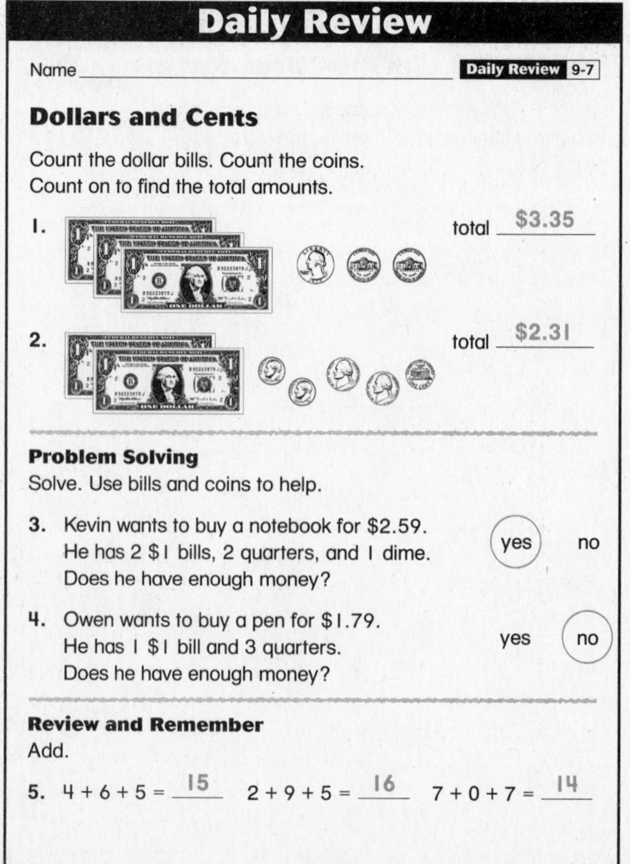

Daily Review

Name _____ Daily Review 9-7

Dollars and Cents

Count the dollar bills. Count the coins. Count on to find the total amounts.

1. total $3.35
2. total $2.31

Problem Solving
Solve. Use bills and coins to help.

3. Kevin wants to buy a notebook for $2.59. He has 2 $1 bills, 2 quarters, and 1 dime. Does he have enough money? (yes) no

4. Owen wants to buy a pen for $1.79. He has 1 $1 bill and 3 quarters. Does he have enough money? yes (no)

Review and Remember
Add.

5. 4 + 6 + 5 = 15 2 + 9 + 5 = 16 7 + 0 + 7 = 14

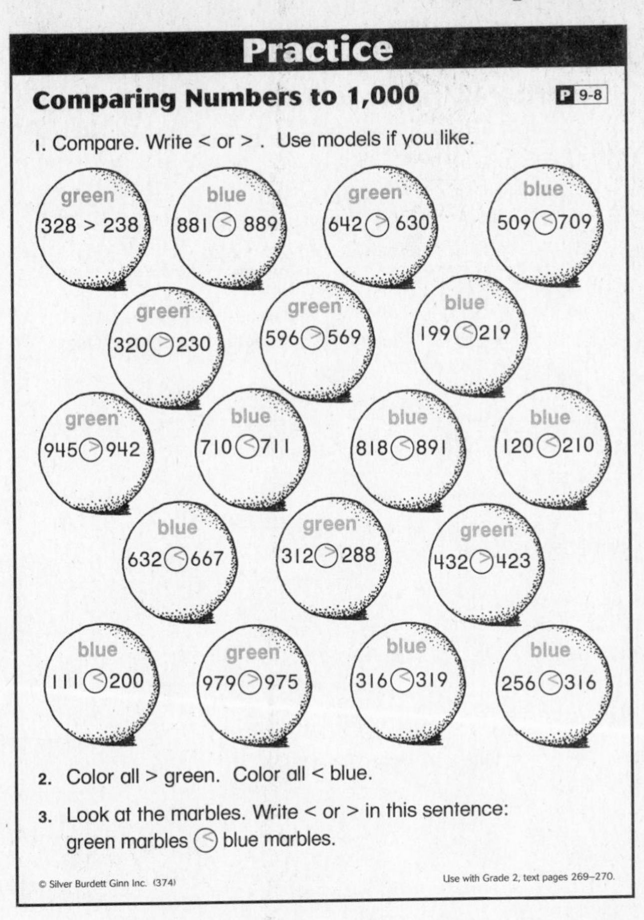

Practice

Comparing Numbers to 1,000

P 9-8

1. Compare. Write < or > . Use models if you like.

green 328 > 238	blue 881 < 889	green 642 > 630	blue 509 < 709
green 320 > 230	green 596 > 569	blue 199 < 219	
green 945 > 942	blue 710 < 711	blue 818 < 891	blue 120 < 210
blue 632 < 667	green 312 > 288	green 432 > 423	
blue 111 < 200	green 979 > 975	blue 316 < 319	blue 256 < 316

2. Color all > green. Color all < blue.
3. Look at the marbles. Write < or > in this sentence:
green marbles < blue marbles.

Use with Grade 2, text pages 269–270.

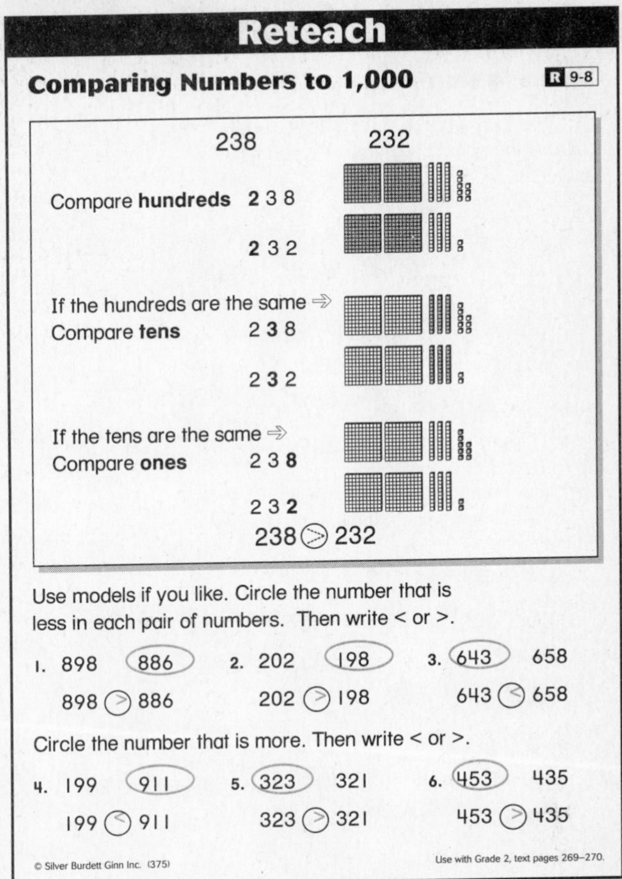

Reteach

Comparing Numbers to 1,000

R 9-8

238 232

Compare **hundreds** **2** 3 8
2 3 2

If the hundreds are the same ⇒
Compare **tens** 2 **3** 8
2 **3** 2

If the tens are the same ⇒
Compare **ones** 2 3 **8**
2 3 **2**

238 > 232

Use models if you like. Circle the number that is less in each pair of numbers. Then write < or >.

1. 898 (886)
898 > 886
2. 202 (198)
202 > 198
3. (643) 658
643 < 658

Circle the number that is more. Then write < or >.

4. 199 (911)
199 < 911
5. (323) 321
323 > 321
6. (453) 435
453 > 435

Use with Grade 2, text pages 269–270.

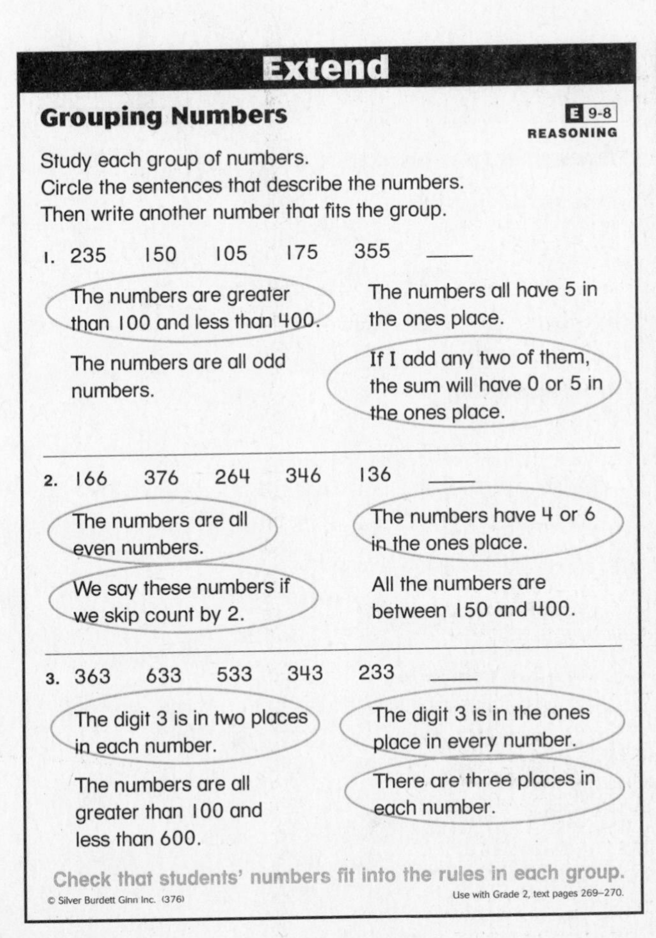

Extend

Grouping Numbers

E 9-8
REASONING

Study each group of numbers.
Circle the sentences that describe the numbers.
Then write another number that fits the group.

1. 235 150 105 175 355 ____

(The numbers are greater than 100 and less than 400.)
The numbers all have 5 in the ones place.
The numbers are all odd numbers.
(If I add any two of them, the sum will have 0 or 5 in the ones place.)

2. 166 376 264 346 136 ____

(The numbers are all even numbers.)
(The numbers have 4 or 6 in the ones place.)
(We say these numbers if we skip count by 2.)
All the numbers are between 150 and 400.

3. 363 633 533 343 233 ____

(The digit 3 is in two places in each number.)
(The digit 3 is in the ones place in every number.)
The numbers are all greater than 100 and less than 600.
(There are three places in each number.)

Check that students' numbers fit into the rules in each group.

Use with Grade 2, text pages 269–270.

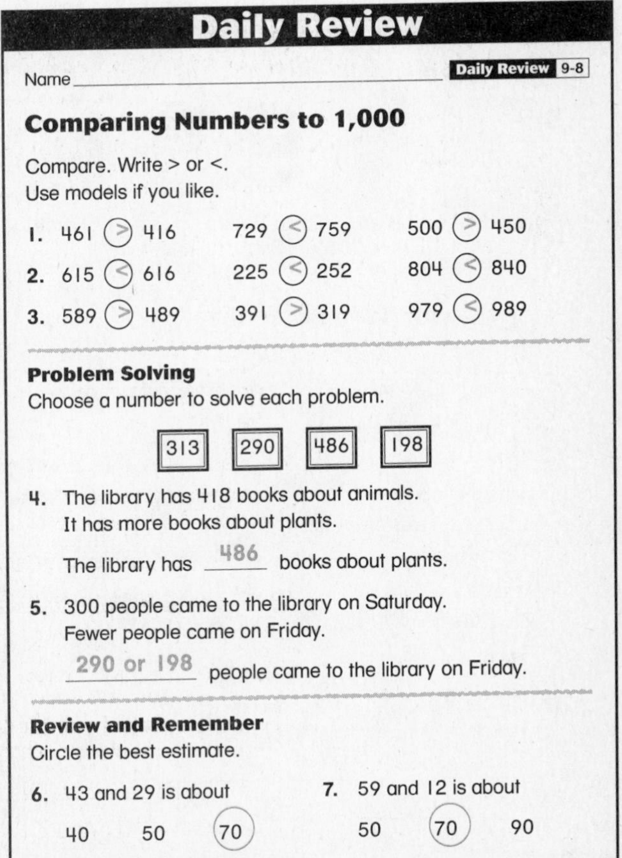

Daily Review

Name ____________________

Daily Review 9-8

Comparing Numbers to 1,000

Compare. Write > or <.
Use models if you like.

1. 461 > 416 729 < 759 500 > 450
2. 615 < 616 225 < 252 804 < 840
3. 589 > 489 391 > 319 979 < 989

Problem Solving
Choose a number to solve each problem.

313 290 486 198

4. The library has 418 books about animals.
It has more books about plants.
The library has 486 books about plants.
5. 300 people came to the library on Saturday.
Fewer people came on Friday.
290 or 198 people came to the library on Friday.

Review and Remember
Circle the best estimate.

6. 43 and 29 is about
40 50 (70)
7. 59 and 12 is about
50 (70) 90

Chapter 9 • Lesson 9

Practice

Ordering Numbers to 1,000

P 9-9

1. Follow the numbers in order from 784 to 799.
   Color the path to help the bear find the cave.

	784			
758	785	786	787	688
783	782	767	788	889
792	791	790	789	780
793	774	891	890	781
794	795	796	797	
775	895	769	798	799

2. Follow the numbers in order from 301 to 319.
   Color the path to help the bee find the hive.

	301			
303	302	330	310	311
304	203	308	309	312
305	306	307	334	313
603	103	136	315	314
613	418	317	316	351
	319	318	617	352

Use with Grade 2, text pages 271–272.

Reteach

Ordering Numbers to 1,000

R 9-9

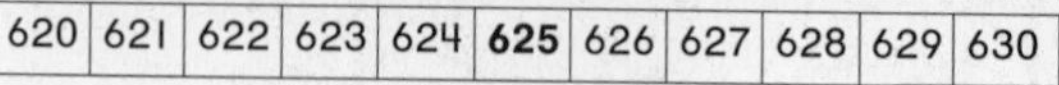

620	621	622	623	624	**625**	626	627	628	629	630

626 is after 625.
624 is before 625.
625 is between 624 and 626.

Write the number that comes before.		Write the number that comes between.			Write the number that comes after.	
1. 618	619	620	621	622	623	624
2. 782	783	784	785	786	787	788
3. 333	334	335	336	337	338	339
4. 504	505	506	507	508	509	510
5. 294	295	296	297	298	299	300
6. 109	110	111	112	113	114	115
7. 897	898	899	900	901	902	903
8. 441	442	443	444	445	446	447
9. 994	995	996	997	998	999	1000

Use with Grade 2, text pages 271–272.

Extend

Animal Parade

E 9-9
REASONING

Beaver	Ostrich	Tiger	Giant Panda	Lion	Eagle
65 pounds	300 pounds	600 pounds	350 pounds	550 pounds	14 pounds

Use the picture and the information to complete each sentence.

1. The animal that weighs the most is the Tiger.
   It weighs 600 pounds.

2. The animal that weighs the least is the Eagle.
   It weighs 14 pounds.

3. All of the animals weigh more than 13 pounds, and less than 601 pounds.

4. None of the animals weighs more than 600 pounds, or less than 14 pounds.

5. Think of a way to sort the animals shown.
   Explain your way of sorting. Check students' methods.

Use with Grade 2, text pages 271–272.

Daily Review

Name ______________________ Daily Review 9-9

Ordering Numbers to 1,000

Write the missing numbers.

1. 427, 428, 429, 430, 431, 432, 433
2. 750, 751, 752, 753, 754, 755, 756
3. 696, 697, 698, 699, 700, 701, 702

Problem Solving
Solve.

4. The theater seats are numbered in order.
   Elaine's seat is between 113 and 115.
   What is her seat number? 114

5. Dan's seat is right after 228.
   What is his seat number? 229

Review and Remember
Circle the amounts that equal the same as a half dollar.

6.

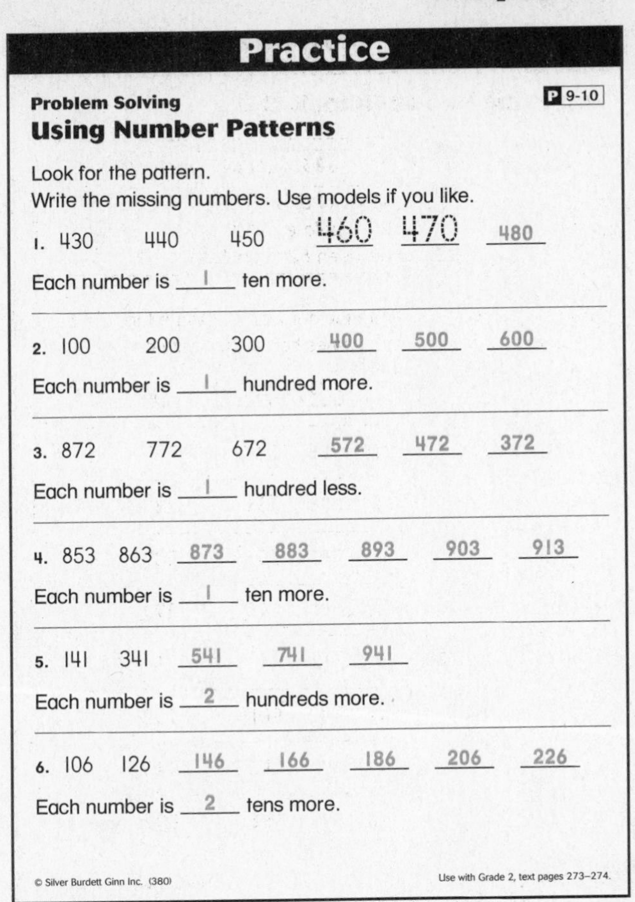

Practice

Problem Solving P 9-10

Using Number Patterns

Look for the pattern.
Write the missing numbers. Use models if you like.

1. 430 440 450 460 470 480

Each number is 1 ten more.

2. 100 200 300 400 500 600

Each number is 1 hundred more.

3. 872 772 672 572 472 372

Each number is 1 hundred less.

4. 853 863 873 883 893 903 913

Each number is 1 ten more.

5. 141 341 541 741 941

Each number is 2 hundreds more.

6. 106 126 146 166 186 206 226

Each number is 2 tens more.

 Use with Grade 2, text pages 273–274.

Reteach

Problem Solving R 9-10

Using Number Patterns

Write the missing numbers. Use models if you like.
Count on and back by tens.

1.

100	110	120	130	140	150	160
+ 10	+ 10	+ 10	+ 10	+ 10	+ 10	+ 10

2.

300	290	280	270	260	250	240
- 10	- 10	- 10	- 10	- 10	- 10	- 10

3.

211	221	231	241	251	261	271
+ 10	+ 10	+ 10	+ 10	+ 10	+ 10	+ 10

Count on and back by hundreds.

4.

100	200	300	400	500	600	700
+ 100	+ 100	+ 100	+ 100	+ 100	+ 100	+ 100

5.

320	420	520	620	720	820	920
+ 100	+ 100	+ 100	+ 100	+ 100	+ 100	+ 100

6.

837	737	637	537	437	337	237
- 100	- 100	- 100	- 100	- 100	- 100	- 100

 Use with Grade 2, text pages 273–274.

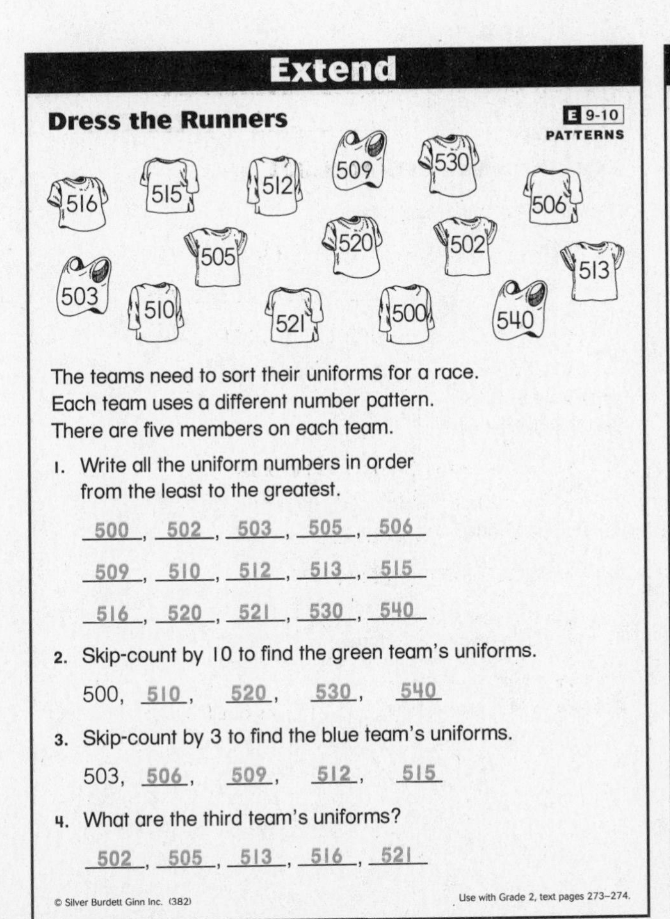

Extend

Dress the Runners

E 9-10 PATTERNS

The teams need to sort their uniforms for a race.
Each team uses a different number pattern.
There are five members on each team.

1. Write all the uniform numbers in order from the least to the greatest.

500, 502, 503, 505, 506

509, 510, 512, 513, 515

516, 520, 521, 530, 540

2. Skip-count by 10 to find the green team's uniforms.

500, 510, 520, 530, 540

3. Skip-count by 3 to find the blue team's uniforms.

503, 506, 509, 512, 515

4. What are the third team's uniforms?

502, 505, 513, 516, 521

 Use with Grade 2, text pages 273–274.

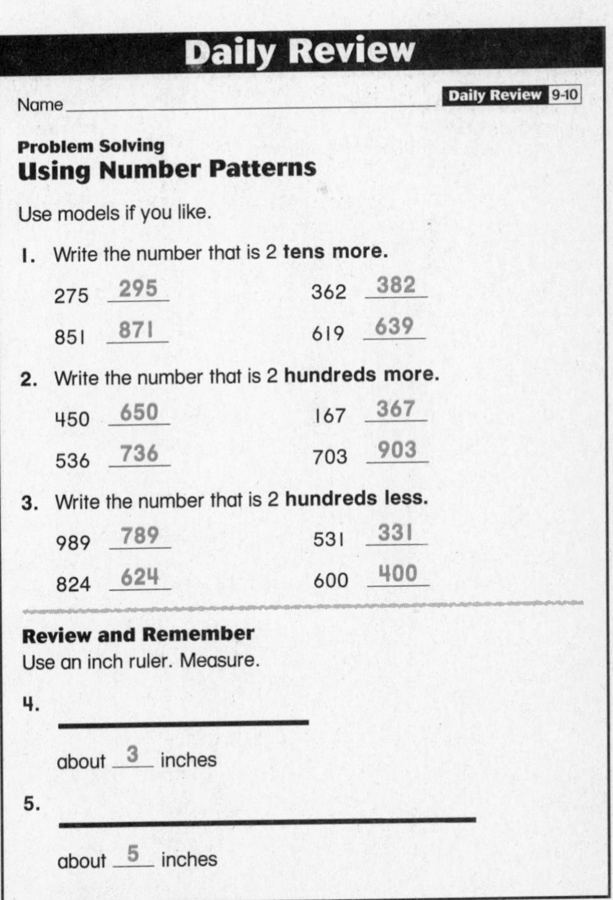

Daily Review

Name ______________ Daily Review 9-10

Problem Solving

Using Number Patterns

Use models if you like.

1. Write the number that is 2 **tens more.**

275 295 362 382

851 871 619 639

2. Write the number that is 2 **hundreds more.**

450 650 167 367

536 736 703 903

3. Write the number that is 2 **hundreds less.**

989 789 531 331

824 624 600 400

Review and Remember

Use an inch ruler. Measure.

4. ______________

about 3 inches

5. ______________________

about 5 inches

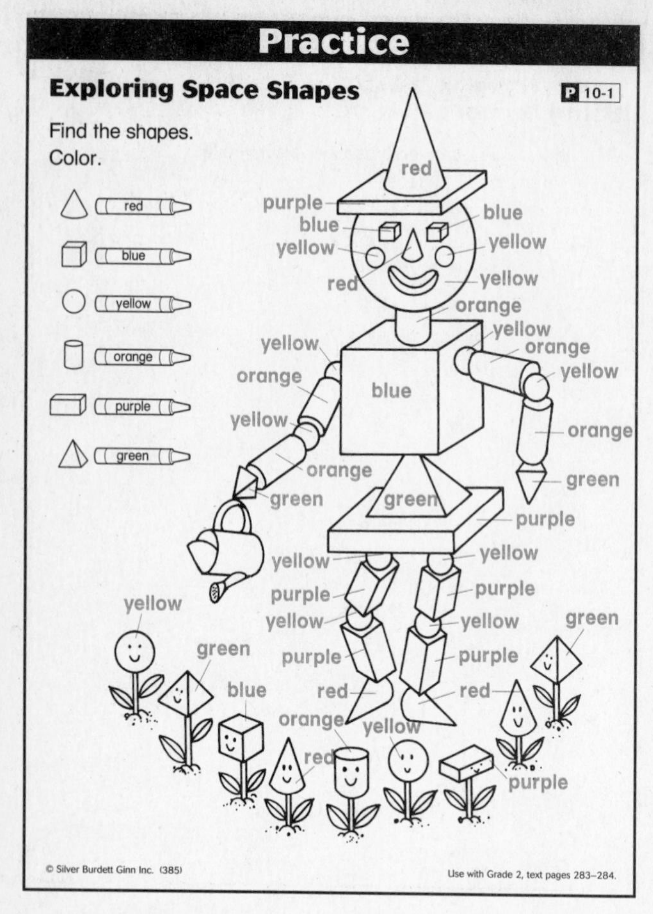

Practice

Exploring Space Shapes

P 10-1

Find the shapes.
Color.

© Silver Burdett Ginn Inc. (385) Use with Grade 2, text pages 283–284.

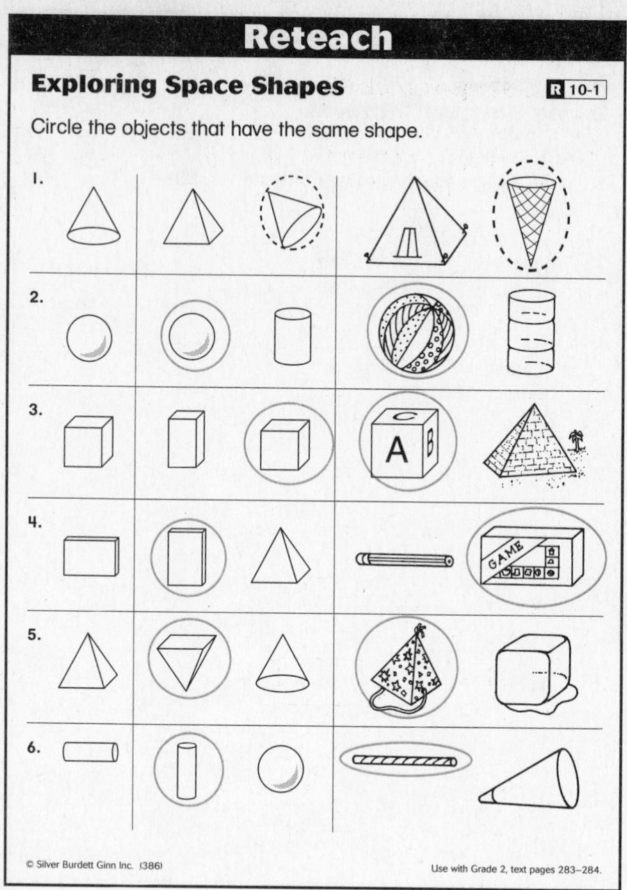

Reteach

Exploring Space Shapes

R 10-1

Circle the objects that have the same shape.

1.
2.
3.
4.
5.
6.

© Silver Burdett Ginn Inc. (386) Use with Grade 2, text pages 283–284.

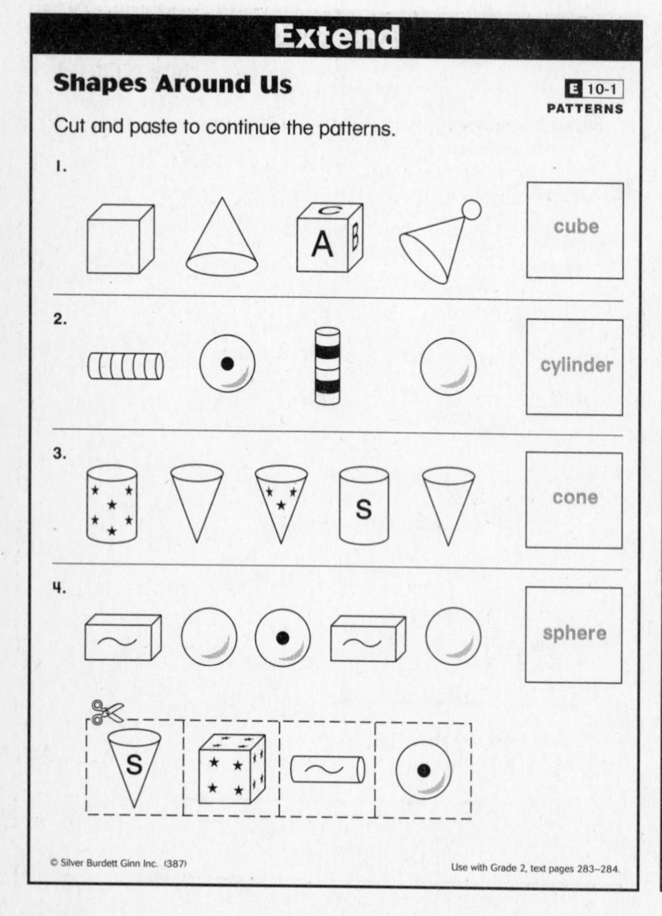

Extend

Shapes Around Us

E 10-1
PATTERNS

Cut and paste to continue the patterns.

1. cube
2. cylinder
3. cone
4. sphere

© Silver Burdett Ginn Inc. (387) Use with Grade 2, text pages 283–284.

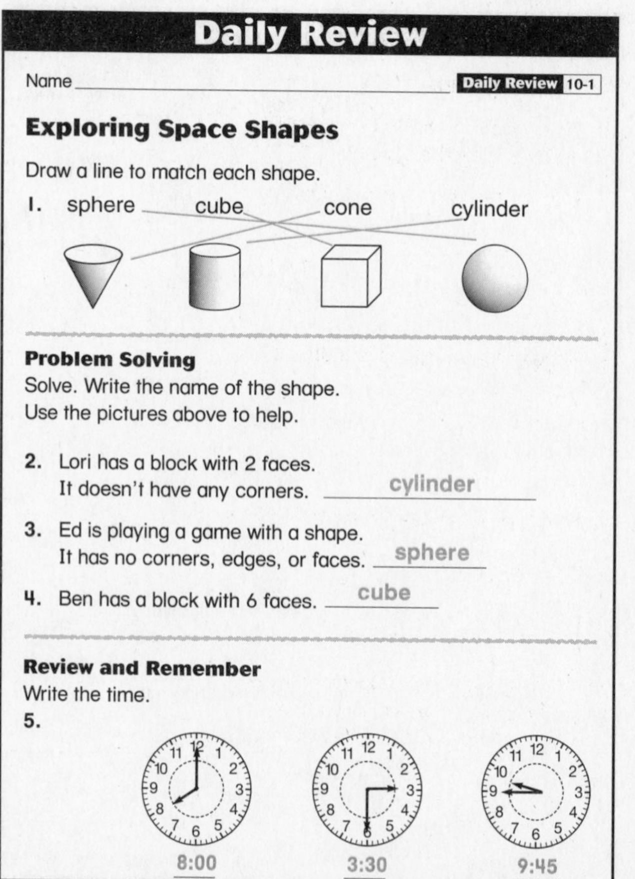

Daily Review

Name____________________ Daily Review 10-1

Exploring Space Shapes

Draw a line to match each shape.

1. sphere cube cone cylinder

Problem Solving

Solve. Write the name of the shape.
Use the pictures above to help.

2. Lori has a block with 2 faces.
   It doesn't have any corners. cylinder
3. Ed is playing a game with a shape.
   It has no corners, edges, or faces. sphere
4. Ben has a block with 6 faces. cube

Review and Remember

Write the time.

5. 8:00 3:30 9:45

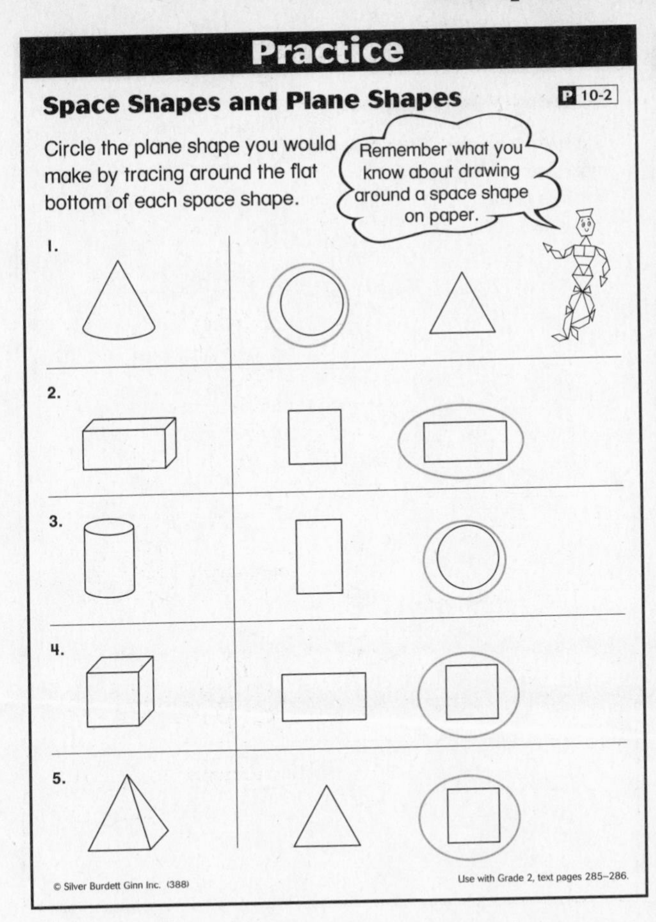

Practice
Space Shapes and Plane Shapes
P 10-2
Circle the plane shape you would make by tracing around the flat bottom of each space shape.
Remember what you know about drawing around a space shape on paper.
1.
2.
3.
4.
5.
© Silver Burdett Ginn Inc. (388)
Use with Grade 2, text pages 285–286.

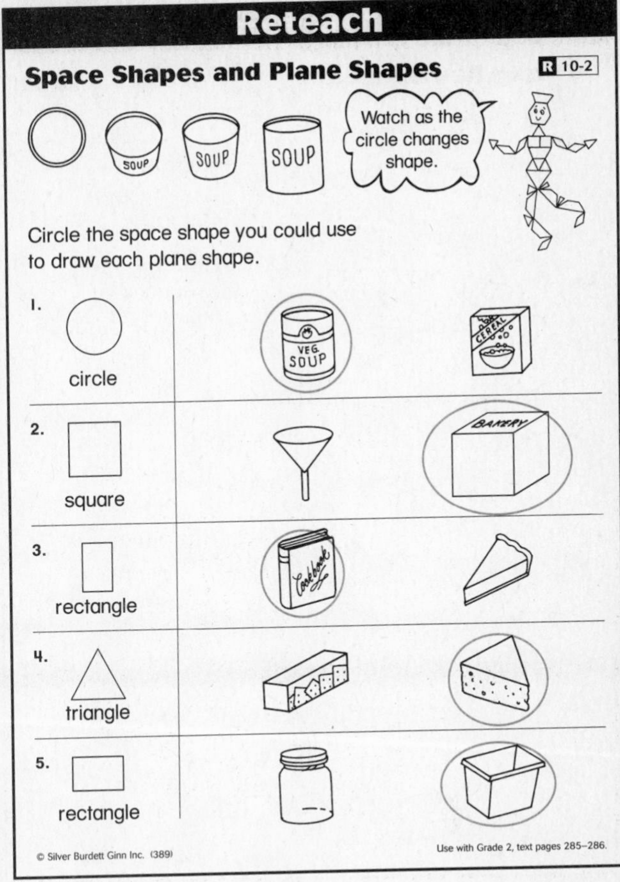

Reteach
Space Shapes and Plane Shapes
R 10-2
SOUP
SOUP
SOUP
Watch as the circle changes shape.
Circle the space shape you could use to draw each plane shape.
1.
circle
VEG. SOUP
CEREAL
2.
square
BAKERY
3.
rectangle
Cookbook
4.
triangle
5.
rectangle
© Silver Burdett Ginn Inc. (389)
Use with Grade 2, text pages 285–286.

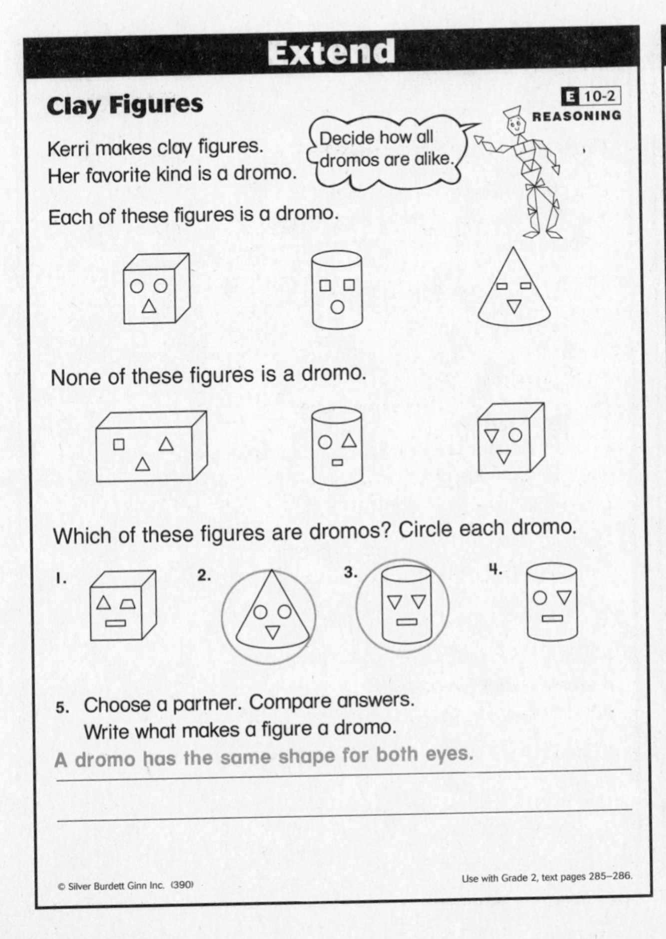

Extend
Clay Figures
E 10-2
REASONING
Kerri makes clay figures.
Her favorite kind is a dromo.
Decide how all dromos are alike.
Each of these figures is a dromo.
None of these figures is a dromo.
Which of these figures are dromos? Circle each dromo.
1.
2.
3.
4.
5. Choose a partner. Compare answers.
Write what makes a figure a dromo.
A dromo has the same shape for both eyes.
© Silver Burdett Ginn Inc. (390)
Use with Grade 2, text pages 285–286.

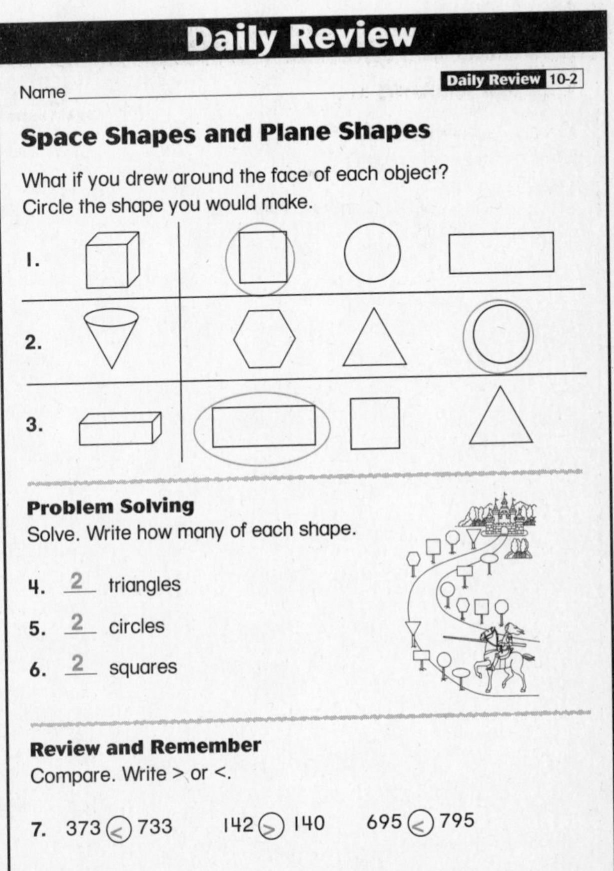

Daily Review
Name
Daily Review 10-2
Space Shapes and Plane Shapes
What if you drew around the face of each object?
Circle the shape you would make.
1.
2.
3.
Problem Solving
Solve. Write how many of each shape.
4. 2 triangles
5. 2 circles
6. 2 squares
Review and Remember
Compare. Write > or <.
7. 373 < 733 142 > 140 695 < 795

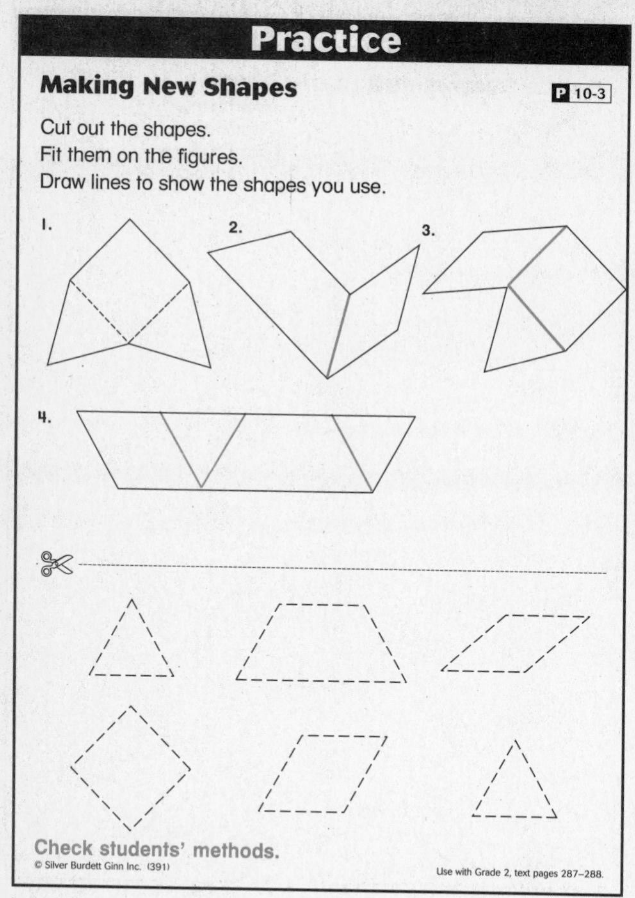

Practice

Making New Shapes

P 10-3

Cut out the shapes.
Fit them on the figures.
Draw lines to show the shapes you use.

1. 2. 3.

4.

Check students' methods.

Use with Grade 2, text pages 287–288.

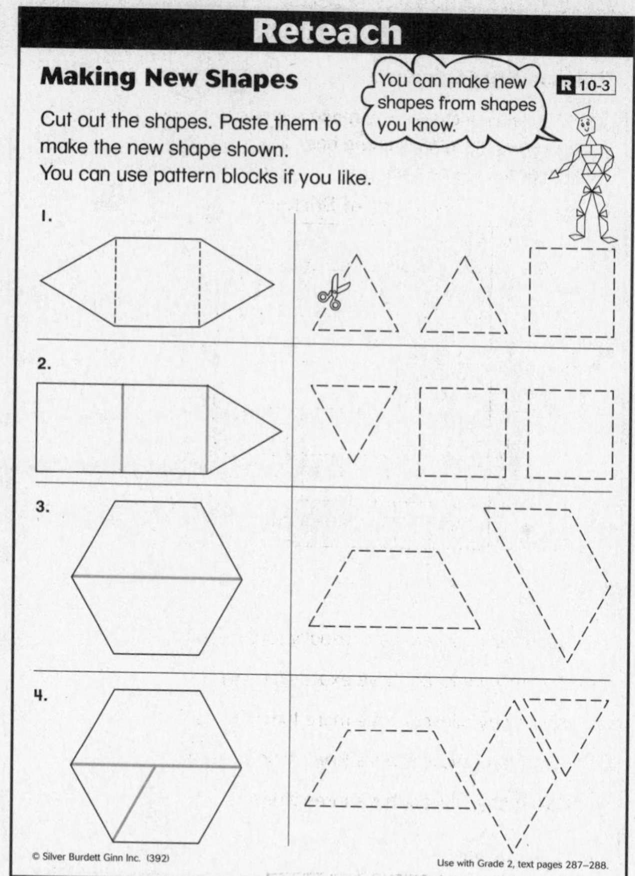

Reteach

Making New Shapes

R 10-3

You can make new shapes from shapes you know.

Cut out the shapes. Paste them to make the new shape shown.
You can use pattern blocks if you like.

1.

2.

3.

4.

Use with Grade 2, text pages 287–288.

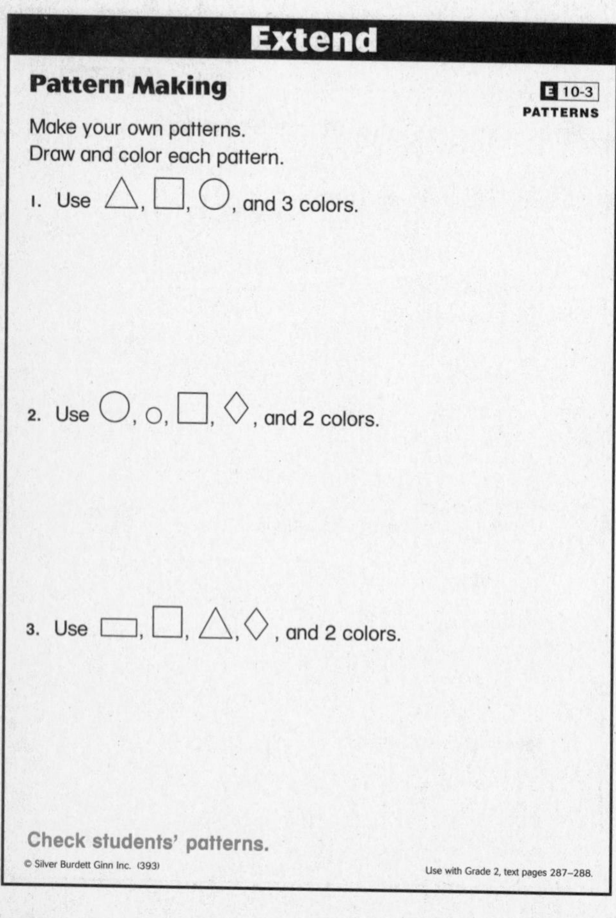

Extend

Pattern Making

E 10-3
PATTERNS

Make your own patterns.
Draw and color each pattern.

1. Use △, □, ○, and 3 colors.

2. Use ○, ○, □, ◇, and 2 colors.

3. Use ▭, □, △, ◇, and 2 colors.

Check students' patterns.

Use with Grade 2, text pages 287–288.

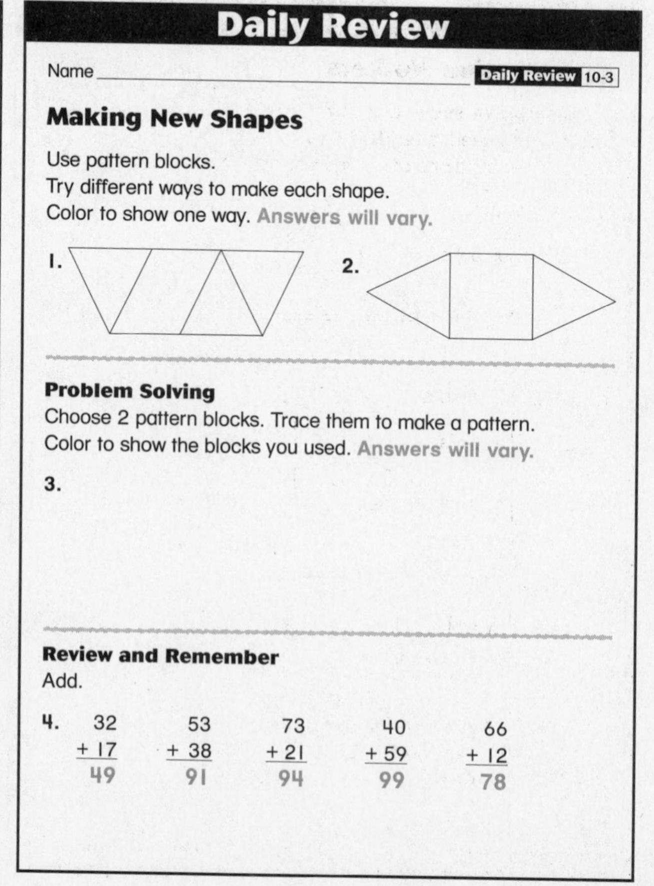

Daily Review

Name ______________________ Daily Review 10-3

Making New Shapes

Use pattern blocks.
Try different ways to make each shape.
Color to show one way. Answers will vary.

1. 2.

Problem Solving

Choose 2 pattern blocks. Trace them to make a pattern.
Color to show the blocks you used. Answers will vary.

3.

Review and Remember

Add.

4. 32 + 17 = 49   53 + 38 = 91   73 + 21 = 94   40 + 59 = 99   66 + 12 = 78

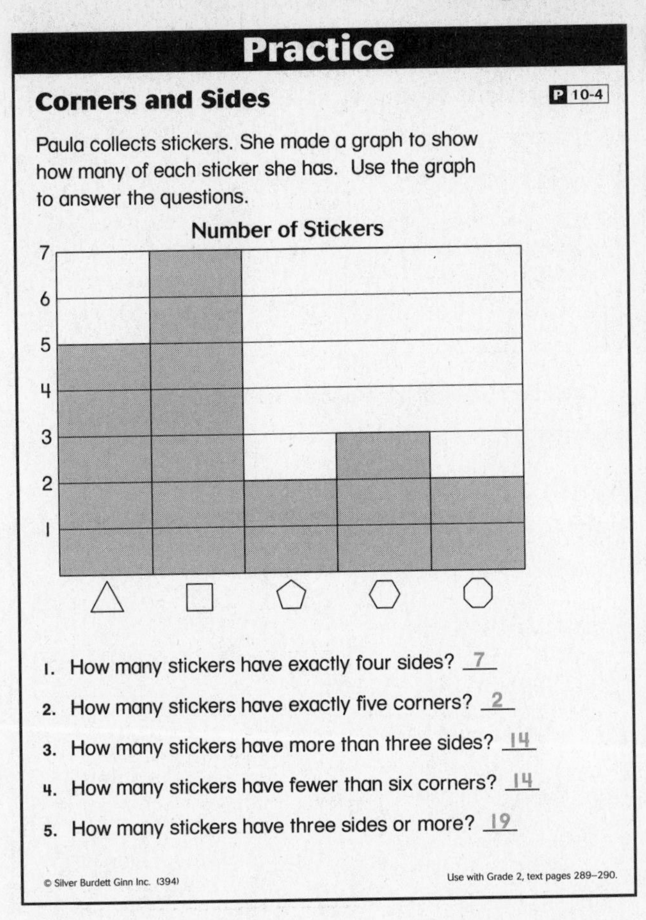

Practice

Corners and Sides

P 10-4

Paula collects stickers. She made a graph to show how many of each sticker she has. Use the graph to answer the questions.

1. How many stickers have exactly four sides? 7
2. How many stickers have exactly five corners? 2
3. How many stickers have more than three sides? 14
4. How many stickers have fewer than six corners? 14
5. How many stickers have three sides or more? 19

Use with Grade 2, text pages 289–290.

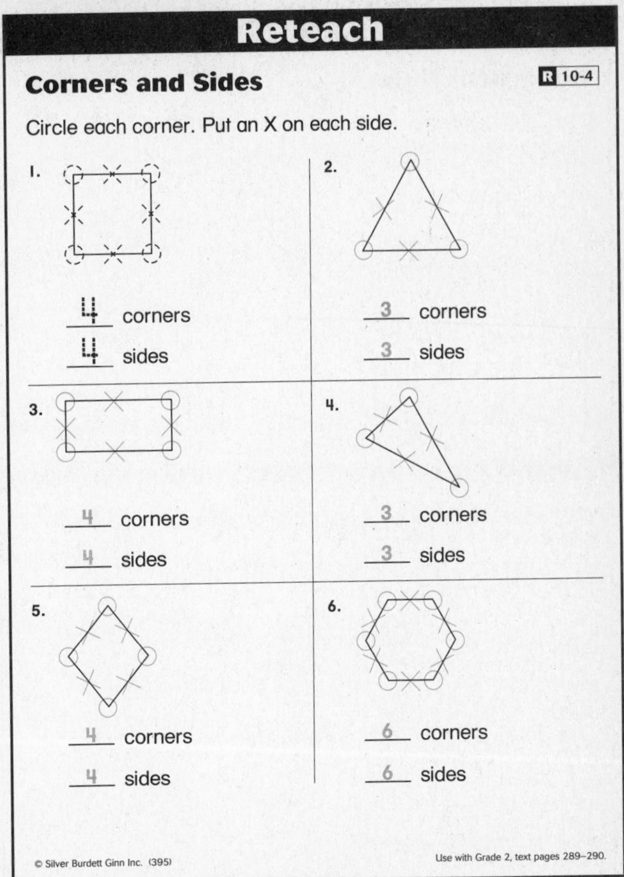

Reteach

Corners and Sides

R 10-4

Circle each corner. Put an X on each side.

1. 4 corners
   4 sides
2. 3 corners
   3 sides
3. 4 corners
   4 sides
4. 3 corners
   3 sides
5. 4 corners
   4 sides
6. 6 corners
   6 sides

Use with Grade 2, text pages 289–290.

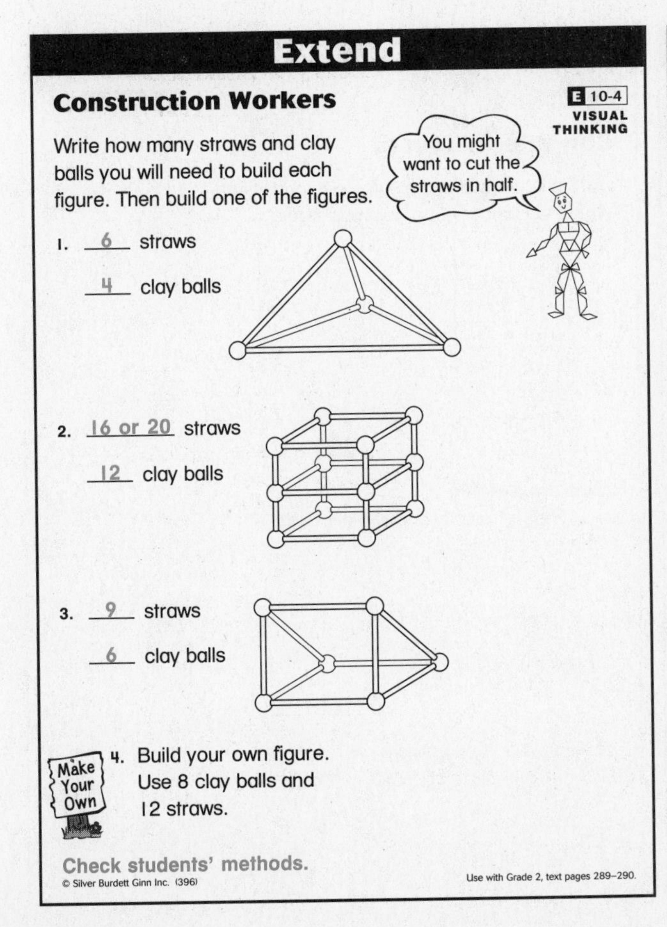

Extend

Construction Workers

E 10-4 VISUAL THINKING

Write how many straws and clay balls you will need to build each figure. Then build one of the figures.

You might want to cut the straws in half.

1. 6 straws
   4 clay balls
2. 16 or 20 straws
   12 clay balls
3. 9 straws
   6 clay balls

4. Build your own figure. Use 8 clay balls and 12 straws.

Check students' methods.

Use with Grade 2, text pages 289–290.

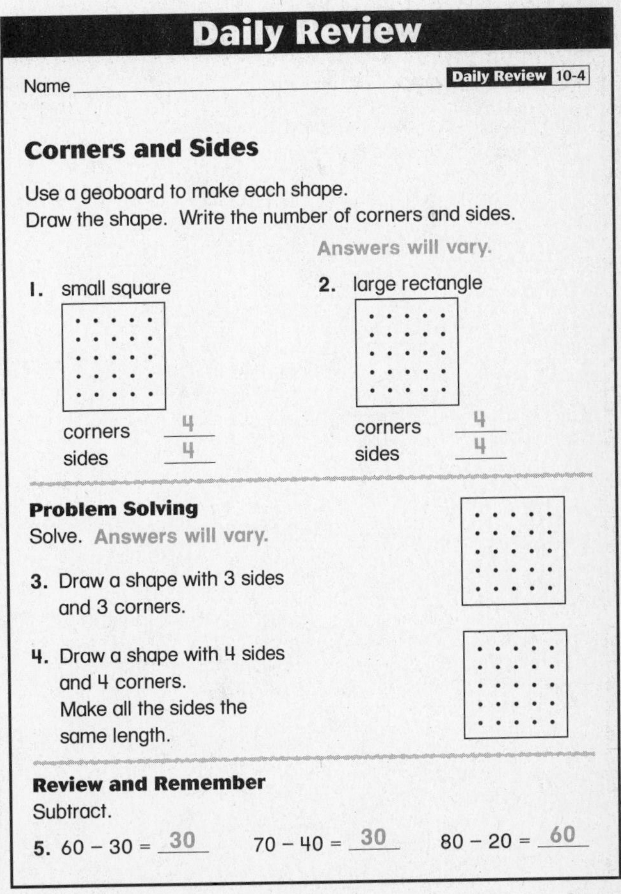

Daily Review

Name ______________________

Daily Review 10-4

Corners and Sides

Use a geoboard to make each shape.
Draw the shape. Write the number of corners and sides.

Answers will vary.

1. small square
   corners 4
   sides 4
2. large rectangle
   corners 4
   sides 4

Problem Solving

Solve. Answers will vary.

3. Draw a shape with 3 sides and 3 corners.
4. Draw a shape with 4 sides and 4 corners. Make all the sides the same length.

Review and Remember

Subtract.

5. 60 – 30 = 30   70 – 40 = 30   80 – 20 = 60

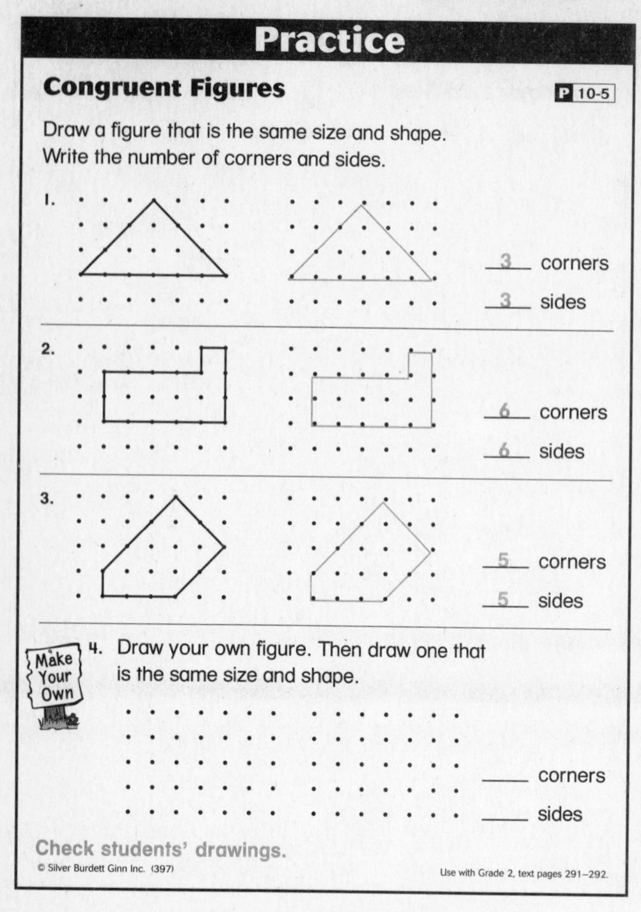

Practice

Congruent Figures

P 10-5

Draw a figure that is the same size and shape.
Write the number of corners and sides.

1. 3 corners
3 sides

2. 6 corners
6 sides

3. 5 corners
5 sides

Make Your Own

4. Draw your own figure. Then draw one that is the same size and shape.

____ corners
____ sides

Check students' drawings.

Use with Grade 2, text pages 291–292.

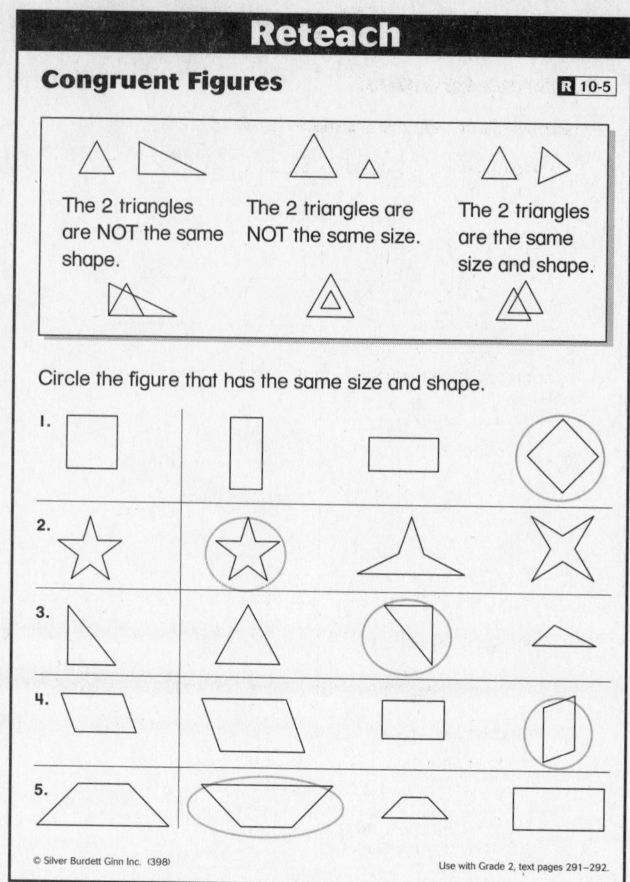

Reteach

Congruent Figures

R 10-5

The 2 triangles are NOT the same shape.

The 2 triangles are NOT the same size.

The 2 triangles are the same size and shape.

Circle the figure that has the same size and shape.

1.

2.

3.

4.

5.

Use with Grade 2, text pages 291–292.

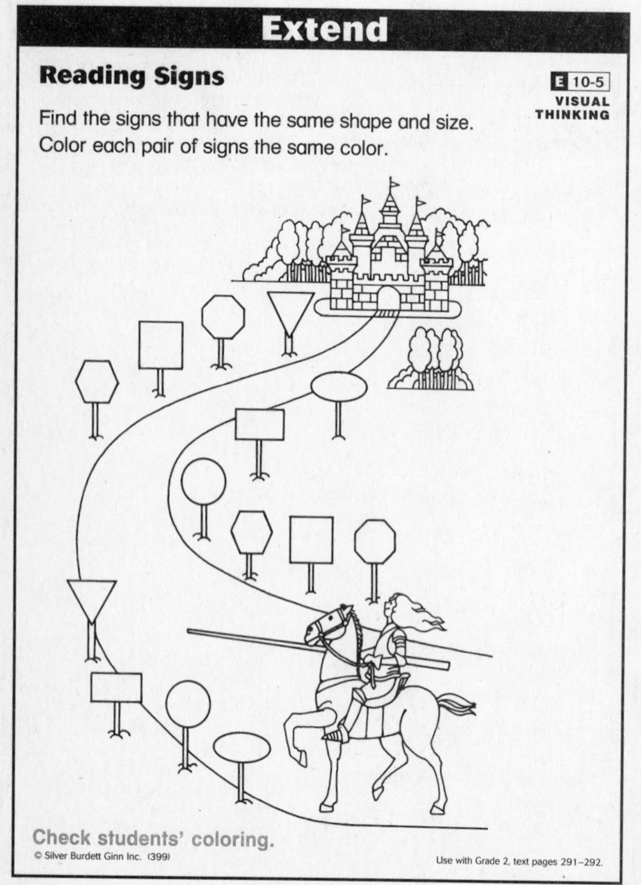

Extend

Reading Signs

E 10-5
VISUAL THINKING

Find the signs that have the same shape and size.
Color each pair of signs the same color.

Check students' coloring.

Use with Grade 2, text pages 291–292.

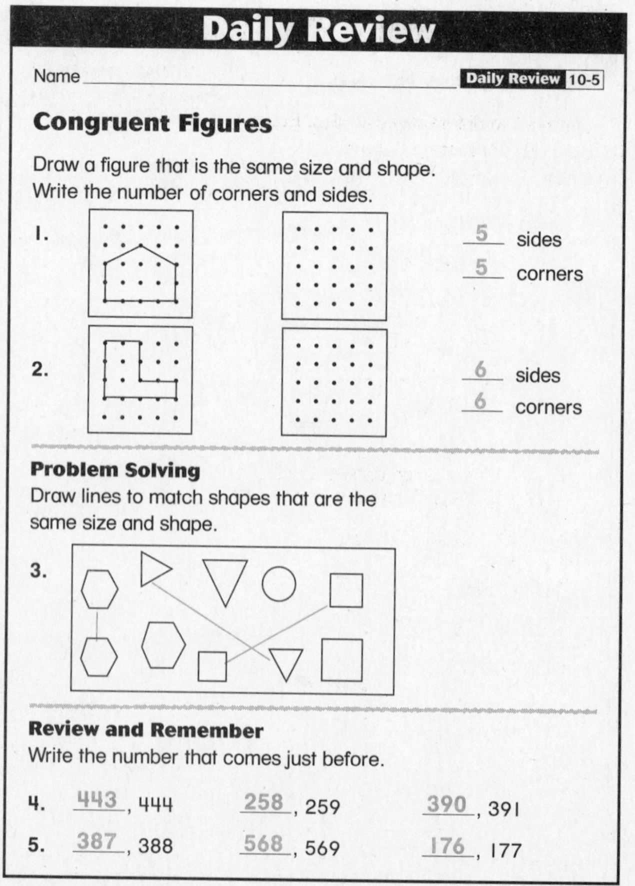

Daily Review

Name ______________________

Daily Review 10-5

Congruent Figures

Draw a figure that is the same size and shape.
Write the number of corners and sides.

1. 5 sides
5 corners

2. 6 sides
6 corners

Problem Solving

Draw lines to match shapes that are the same size and shape.

3.

Review and Remember

Write the number that comes just before.

4. 443, 444   258, 259   390, 391

5. 387, 388   568, 569   176, 177

Chapter 10 • Lesson 6

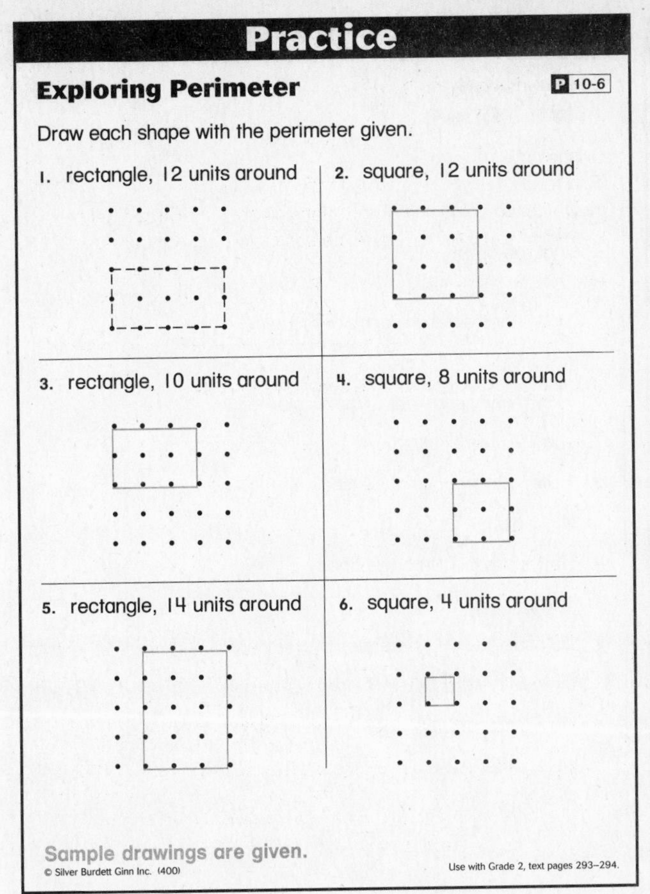

Practice
Exploring Perimeter
P 10-6
Draw each shape with the perimeter given.
1. rectangle, 12 units around
2. square, 12 units around
3. rectangle, 10 units around
4. square, 8 units around
5. rectangle, 14 units around
6. square, 4 units around
Sample drawings are given.
© Silver Burdett Ginn Inc. (400)
Use with Grade 2, text pages 293–294.

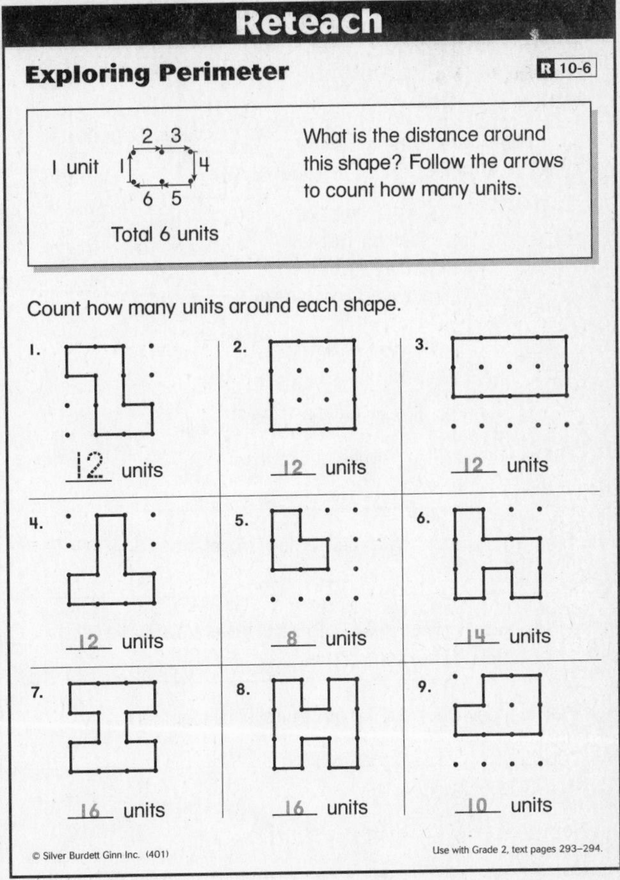

Reteach
Exploring Perimeter
R 10-6
1 unit
2 3
1 4
6 5
Total 6 units
What is the distance around this shape? Follow the arrows to count how many units.
Count how many units around each shape.
1. 12 units
2. 12 units
3. 12 units
4. 12 units
5. 8 units
6. 14 units
7. 16 units
8. 16 units
9. 10 units
© Silver Burdett Ginn Inc. (401)
Use with Grade 2, text pages 293–294.

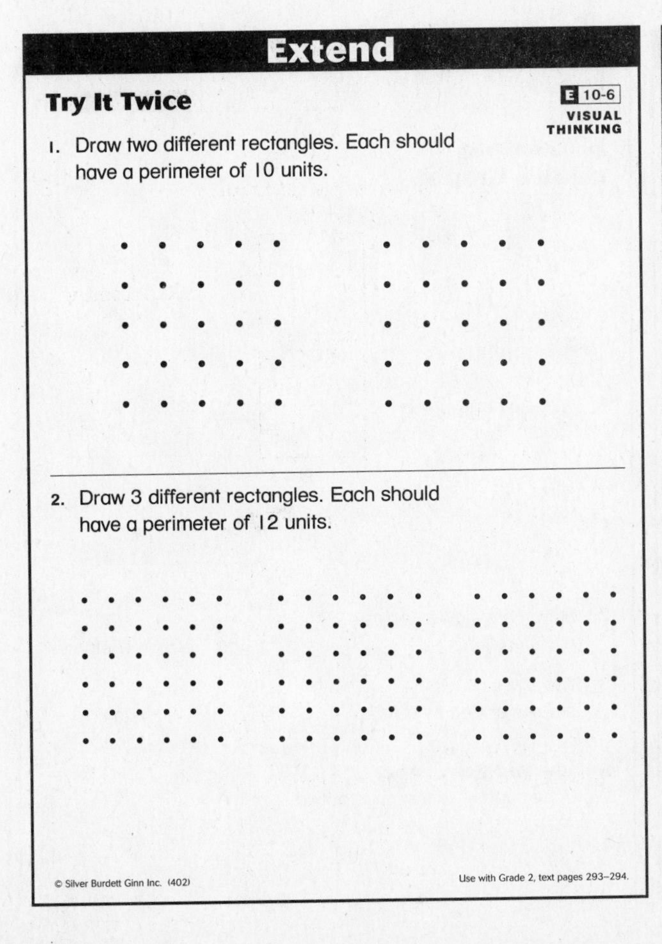

Extend
Try It Twice
E 10-6
VISUAL THINKING
1. Draw two different rectangles. Each should have a perimeter of 10 units.
2. Draw 3 different rectangles. Each should have a perimeter of 12 units.
© Silver Burdett Ginn Inc. (402)
Use with Grade 2, text pages 293–294.

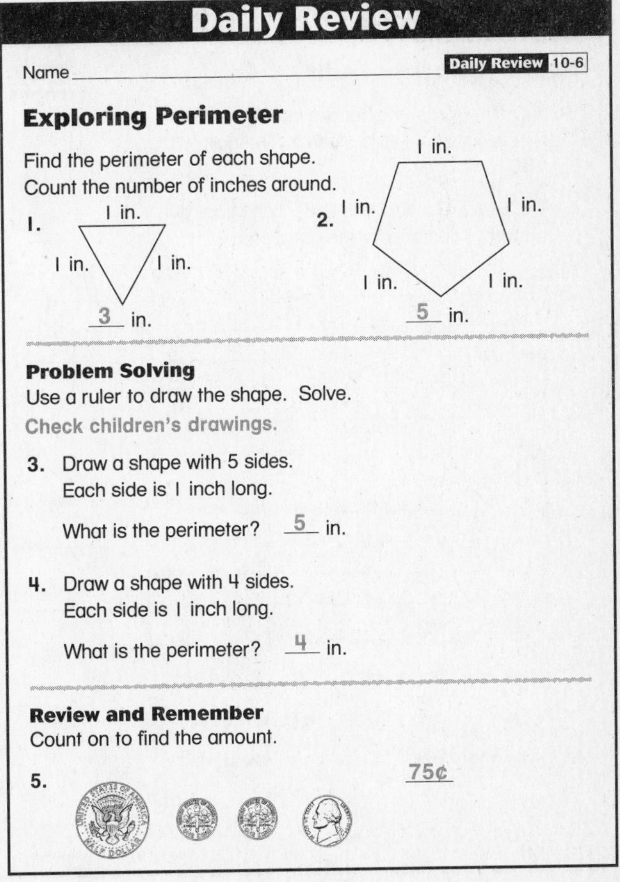

Daily Review
Name
Daily Review 10-6
Exploring Perimeter
Find the perimeter of each shape.
Count the number of inches around.
1.
1 in.
1 in.
1 in.
3 in.
2.
1 in.
1 in.
1 in.
1 in.
1 in.
5 in.
Problem Solving
Use a ruler to draw the shape. Solve.
Check children's drawings.
3. Draw a shape with 5 sides.
Each side is 1 inch long.
What is the perimeter? 5 in.
4. Draw a shape with 4 sides.
Each side is 1 inch long.
What is the perimeter? 4 in.
Review and Remember
Count on to find the amount.
5.
75¢

Practice

Problem Solving P 10-7

Make a Graph

Sea turtles travel many miles.
Here's how far four turtles traveled:

Turtle A traveled 4 miles. Turtle B traveled 1 more mile than Turtle A. Turtle C traveled 3 more miles than Turtle A. Turtle D traveled only 1 mile.

Miles Traveled

8, 7, 6, 5, 4, 3, 2, 1, 0

A B C D

1. Finish the graph to show how far each turtle traveled.

Use the graph to answer the questions.

2. Which two turtles traveled the farthest?
   Turtle B and Turtle C
3. How many more miles did Turtle B travel than Turtle D?
   4 more miles
4. How many more miles did Turtle C travel than Turtle B?
   2 more miles
5. How many miles did the turtles travel all together?
   17 miles

 Use with Grade 2, text pages 295–296.

Reteach

Problem Solving R 10-7

Make a Graph

Trisha collects models.
She made this graph to show how many models she has.

Look at the graph.
Answer the questions.

Models

7, 6, 5, 4, 3, 2, 1, 0

1. How many different kinds of models are shown on the graph? 4
2. How many spaces did Trisha color to show 7 cars? 7
3. How many spaces did Trisha color to show planes? 3
4. How many boat models does Trisha have? 5
5. If Trisha had 10 boats, could she show that on this graph? no
6. How many models does Trisha have all together? 16

 Use with Grade 2, text pages 295–296.

Extend

Make Your Own Quilt

E 10-7 PATTERNS

Rosa and her grandmother are making a quilt. They have finished Rows 1 and 2. The quilt will have 10 rows in all.

Look at Rows 1 and 2. See if you can figure out the pattern. Then answer the questions.

Row											
1	☆	○	☽	□	◇	~	☆	○	☽	□	◇
2	~	☆	○	☽	□	◇	~	☆	○	☽	□
3											
4											
5	☽						☽				
6											
7											
8		☆						☆			
9											
10											

1. What shape does row 3 begin with? diamond
2. Which row begins with a ○ ? row 6
3. Draw where every ☆ will be in Row 8.
4. Draw where every ☽ will be in Row 5.

 Use with Grade 2, text pages 295–296.

Daily Review

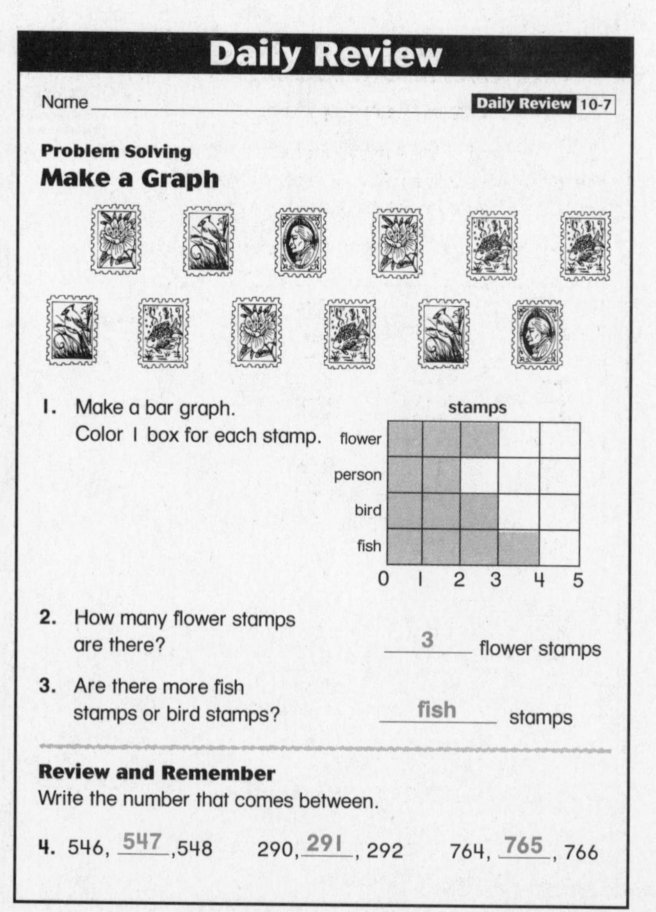

Name ______________________ Daily Review 10-7

Problem Solving

Make a Graph

1. Make a bar graph.
   Color 1 box for each stamp.

stamps

flower, person, bird, fish

0 1 2 3 4 5

2. How many flower stamps are there? 3 flower stamps
3. Are there more fish stamps or bird stamps? fish stamps

Review and Remember

Write the number that comes between.

4. 546, 547, 548   290, 291, 292   764, 765, 766

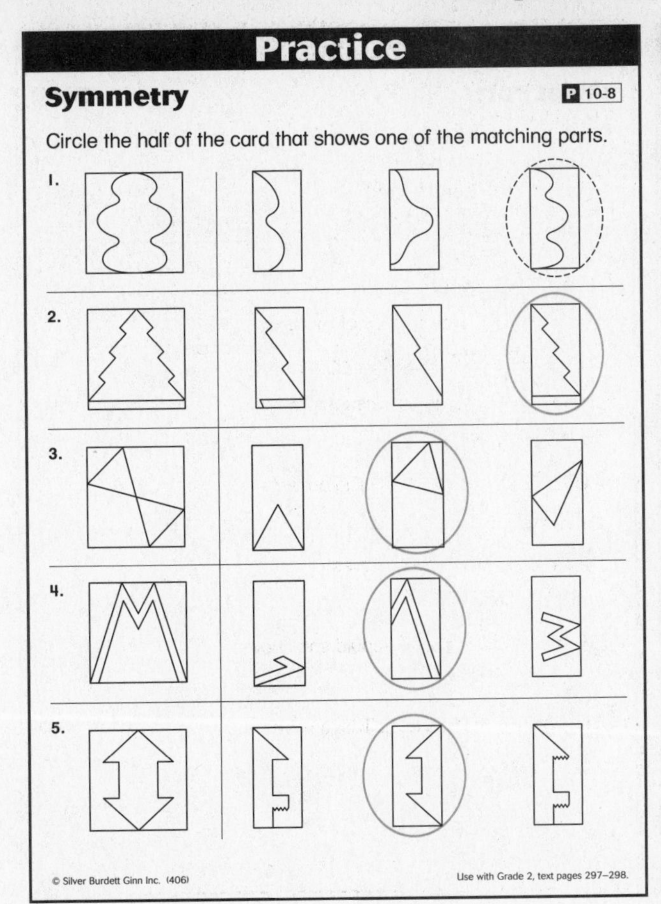

Practice

Symmetry P 10-8

Circle the half of the card that shows one of the matching parts.

1.
2.
3.
4.
5.

Use with Grade 2, text pages 297–298.

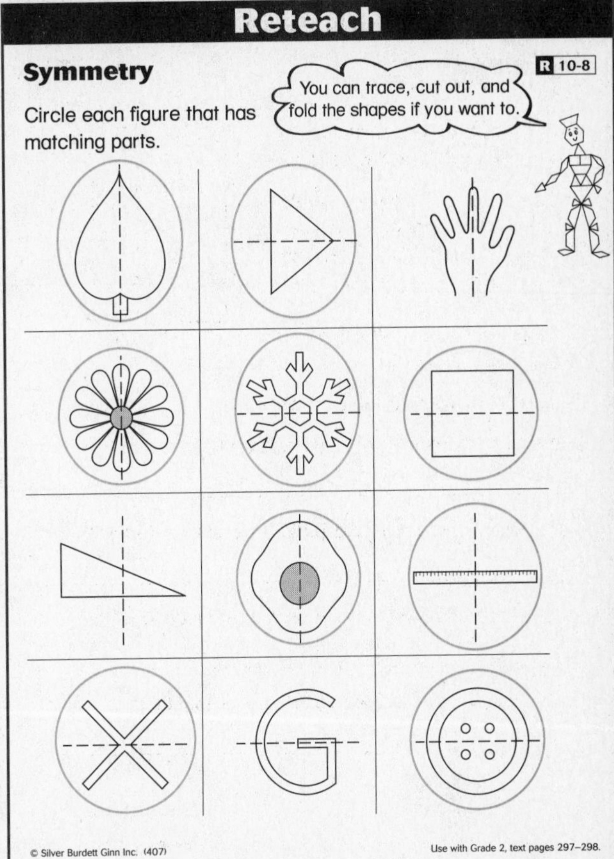

Reteach

Symmetry R 10-8

You can trace, cut out, and fold the shapes if you want to.

Circle each figure that has matching parts.

Use with Grade 2, text pages 297–298.

Extend

Letters With Matching Parts E 10-8 VISUAL THINKING

Some letters have a line of symmetry.
The letter O has 2 lines of symmetry.
Each line makes two matching parts.

1. Draw the lines of symmetry if you can.

A	B	C	D	E
F	G	H	I	J
K	L	M	N	P
Q	R	S	T	U
V	W	X	Y	Z

2. Which letters have only 1 line of symmetry?
A, B, C, D, E, M, T, U, V, W, Y

3. Besides the letter O, which letters have 2 lines of symmetry?
H, I, X

Use with Grade 2, text pages 297–298.

Daily Review

Name ______________________ Daily Review 10-8

Symmetry

Draw a line of symmetry if you can. Check children's drawings. All drawings are symmetrical except P and plant.

1.

2. P

Problem Solving
Solve.

3. Amy says every letter in her name has a line of symmetry. Draw lines of symmetry if you can. Is she right?
AMY
yes

4. Jim says every letter in his name has a line of symmetry. Draw lines of symmetry if you can. Is he right?
JIM
no

Review and Remember
Subtract.

5. $57 - 13 = 44$ $36 - 28 = 8$ $89 - 62 = 27$ $25 - 9 = 16$ $67 - 36 = 31$

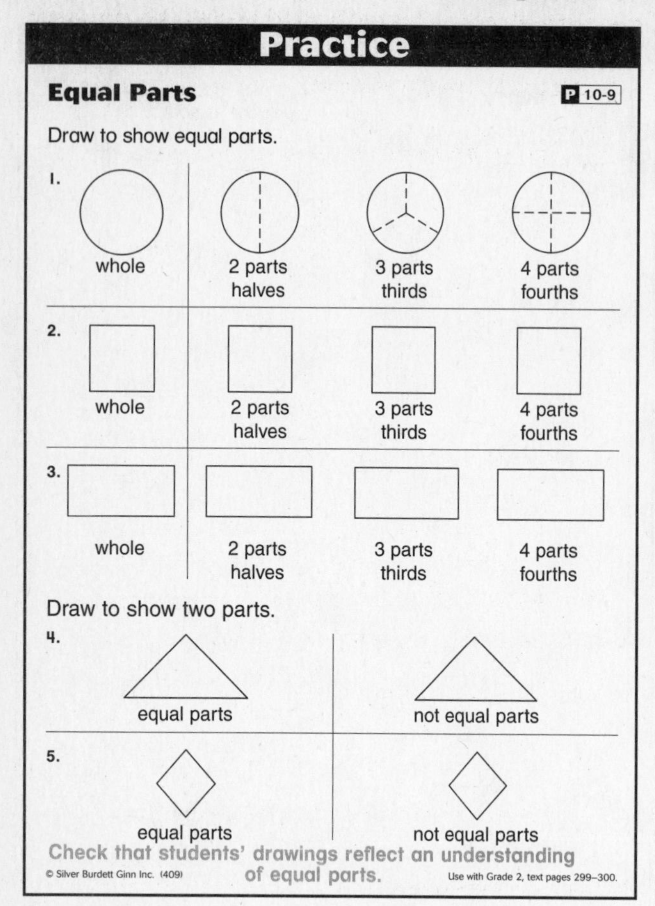

Practice

Equal Parts

P 10-9

Draw to show equal parts.

1. whole | 2 parts halves | 3 parts thirds | 4 parts fourths

2. whole | 2 parts halves | 3 parts thirds | 4 parts fourths

3. whole | 2 parts halves | 3 parts thirds | 4 parts fourths

Draw to show two parts.

4. equal parts | not equal parts

5. equal parts | not equal parts

Check that students' drawings reflect an understanding of equal parts.

 Use with Grade 2, text pages 299–300.

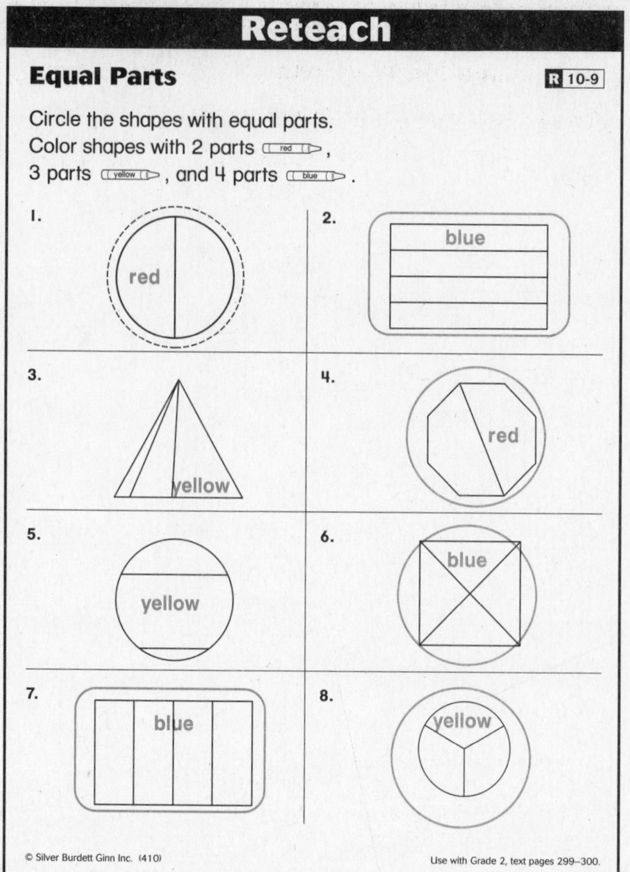

Reteach

Equal Parts

R 10-9

Circle the shapes with equal parts.
Color shapes with 2 parts red, 3 parts yellow, and 4 parts blue.

1. red
2. blue
3. yellow
4. red
5. yellow
6. blue
7. blue
8. yellow

 Use with Grade 2, text pages 299–300.

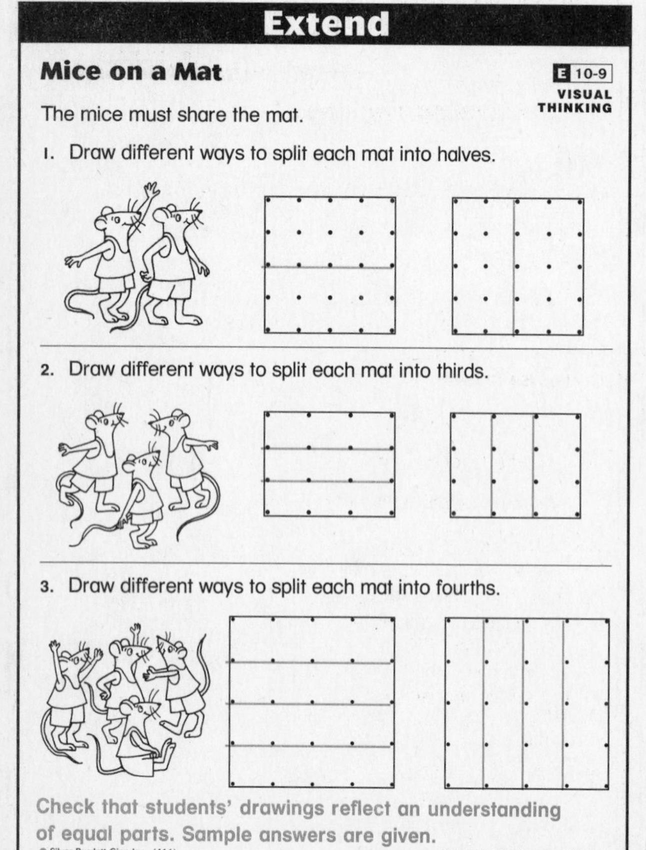

Extend

Mice on a Mat

E 10-9 VISUAL THINKING

The mice must share the mat.

1. Draw different ways to split each mat into halves.
2. Draw different ways to split each mat into thirds.
3. Draw different ways to split each mat into fourths.

Check that students' drawings reflect an understanding of equal parts. Sample answers are given.

 Use with Grade 2, text pages 299–300.

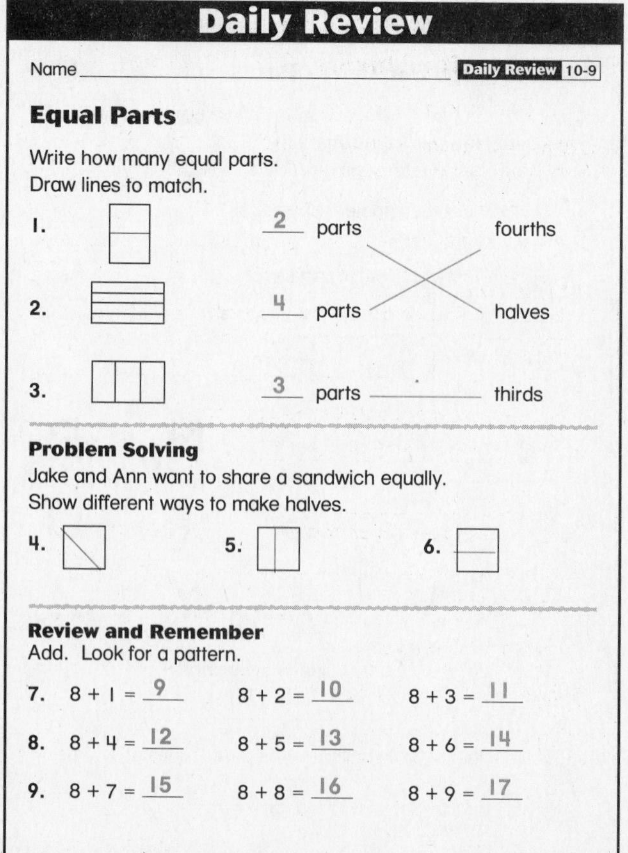

Daily Review

Name__________ Daily Review 10-9

Equal Parts

Write how many equal parts.
Draw lines to match.

1. 2 parts — fourths
2. 4 parts — halves
3. 3 parts — thirds

Problem Solving

Jake and Ann want to share a sandwich equally.
Show different ways to make halves.

4. 5. 6.

Review and Remember

Add. Look for a pattern.

7. 8 + 1 = 9 8 + 2 = 10 8 + 3 = 11
8. 8 + 4 = 12 8 + 5 = 13 8 + 6 = 14
9. 8 + 7 = 15 8 + 8 = 16 8 + 9 = 17

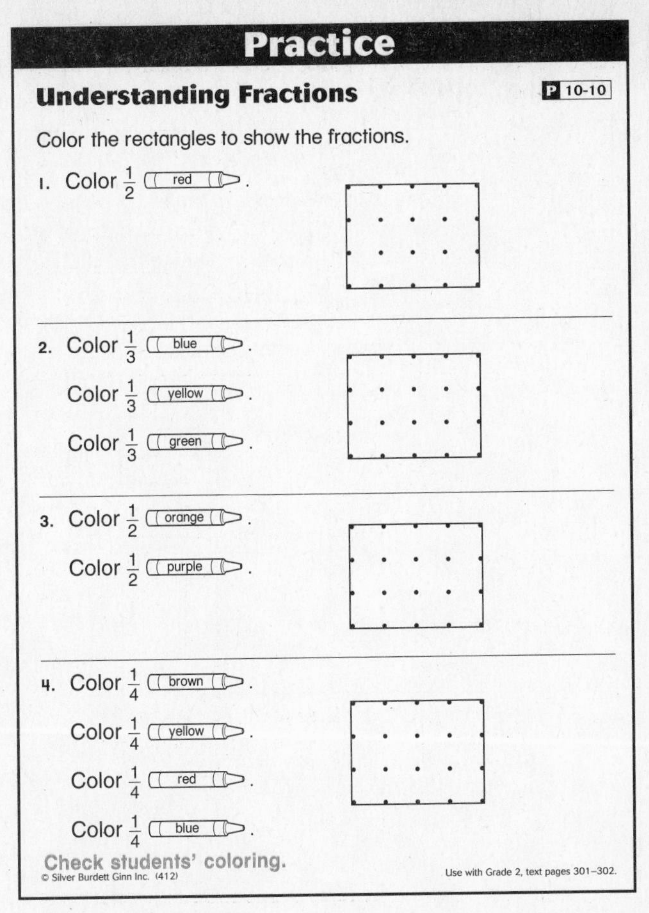

Practice

Understanding Fractions

P 10-10

Color the rectangles to show the fractions.

1. Color $\frac{1}{2}$ red.

2. Color $\frac{1}{3}$ blue.
   Color $\frac{1}{3}$ yellow.
   Color $\frac{1}{3}$ green.

3. Color $\frac{1}{2}$ orange.
   Color $\frac{1}{2}$ purple.

4. Color $\frac{1}{4}$ brown.
   Color $\frac{1}{4}$ yellow.
   Color $\frac{1}{4}$ red.
   Color $\frac{1}{4}$ blue.

Check students' coloring.

 Use with Grade 2, text pages 301–302.

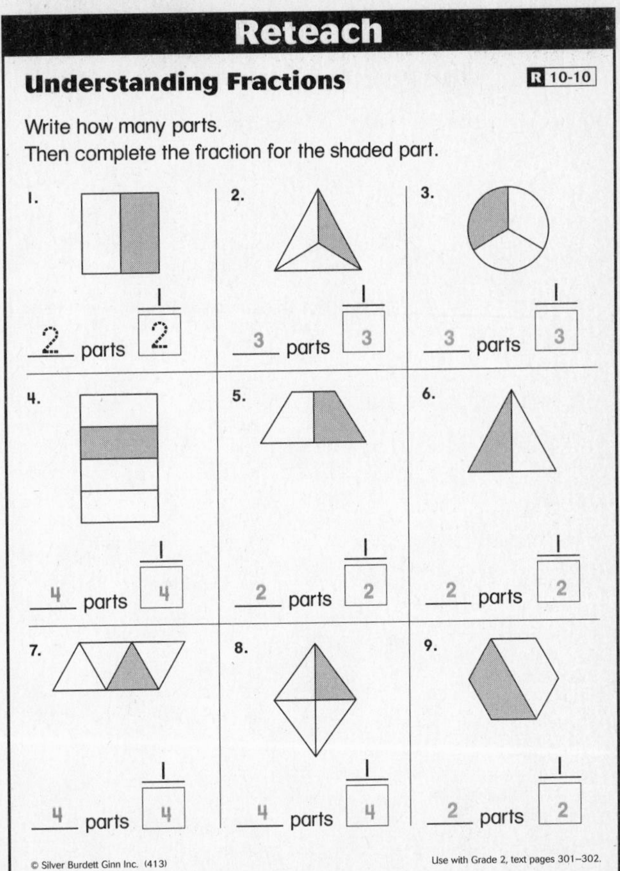

Reteach

Understanding Fractions

R 10-10

Write how many parts.
Then complete the fraction for the shaded part.

1. 2 parts $\frac{1}{2}$
2. 3 parts $\frac{1}{3}$
3. 3 parts $\frac{1}{3}$
4. 4 parts $\frac{1}{4}$
5. 2 parts $\frac{1}{2}$
6. 2 parts $\frac{1}{2}$
7. 4 parts $\frac{1}{4}$
8. 4 parts $\frac{1}{4}$
9. 2 parts $\frac{1}{2}$

 Use with Grade 2, text pages 301–302.

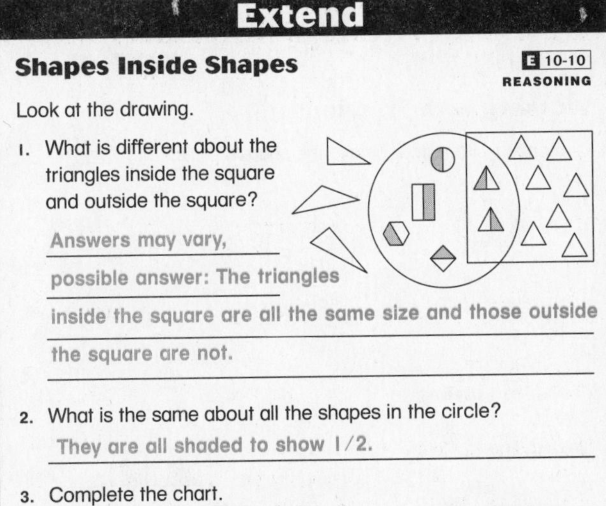

Extend

Shapes Inside Shapes

E 10-10
REASONING

Look at the drawing.

1. What is different about the triangles inside the square and outside the square?
   Answers may vary, possible answer: The triangles inside the square are all the same size and those outside the square are not.

2. What is the same about all the shapes in the circle?
   They are all shaded to show 1/2.

3. Complete the chart.

Places for triangles	Number of triangles
Triangles in the circle	2
Triangles in the square	9
Triangles in both the circle and the square	2
Triangles not in the circle or the square	3
Triangles in all	12

 Use with Grade 2, text pages 301–302.

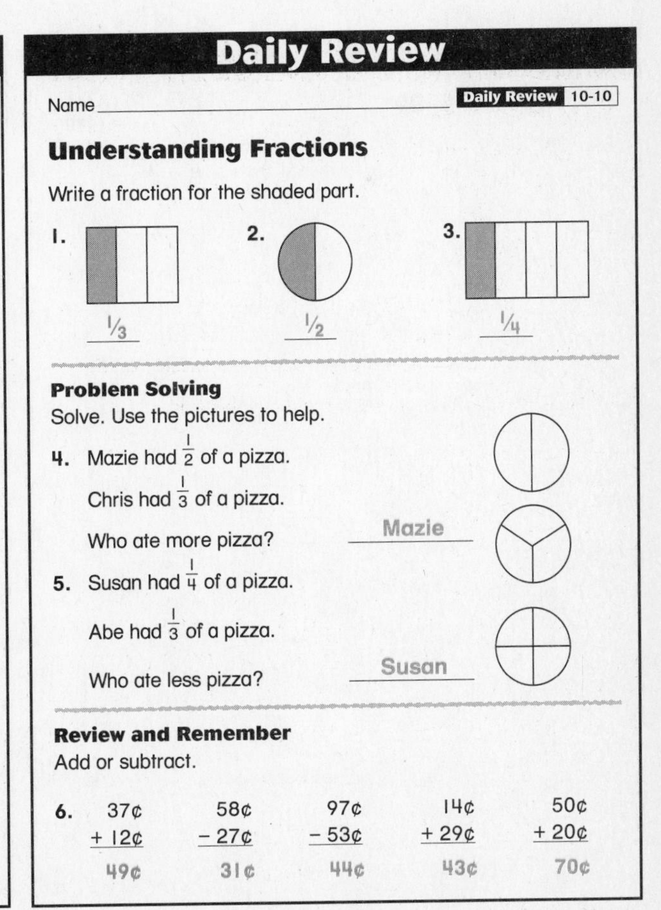

Daily Review

Name ____________________ Daily Review 10-10

Understanding Fractions

Write a fraction for the shaded part.

1. $\frac{1}{3}$
2. $\frac{1}{2}$
3. $\frac{1}{4}$

Problem Solving

Solve. Use the pictures to help.

4. Mazie had $\frac{1}{2}$ of a pizza.
   Chris had $\frac{1}{3}$ of a pizza.
   Who ate more pizza? Mazie

5. Susan had $\frac{1}{4}$ of a pizza.
   Abe had $\frac{1}{3}$ of a pizza.
   Who ate less pizza? Susan

Review and Remember

Add or subtract.

6. 37¢ + 12¢ = 49¢ 58¢ − 27¢ = 31¢ 97¢ − 53¢ = 44¢ 14¢ + 29¢ = 43¢ 50¢ + 20¢ = 70¢

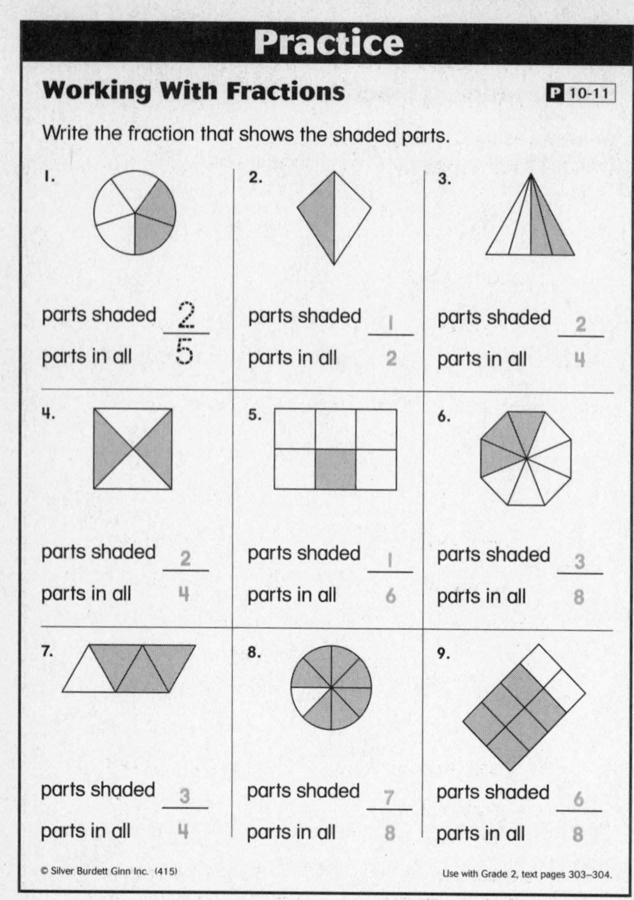

Practice

Working With Fractions

P 10-11

Write the fraction that shows the shaded parts.

1. parts shaded 2 / parts in all 5
2. parts shaded 1 / parts in all 2
3. parts shaded 2 / parts in all 4
4. parts shaded 2 / parts in all 4
5. parts shaded 1 / parts in all 6
6. parts shaded 3 / parts in all 8
7. parts shaded 3 / parts in all 4
8. parts shaded 7 / parts in all 8
9. parts shaded 6 / parts in all 8

Use with Grade 2, text pages 303–304.

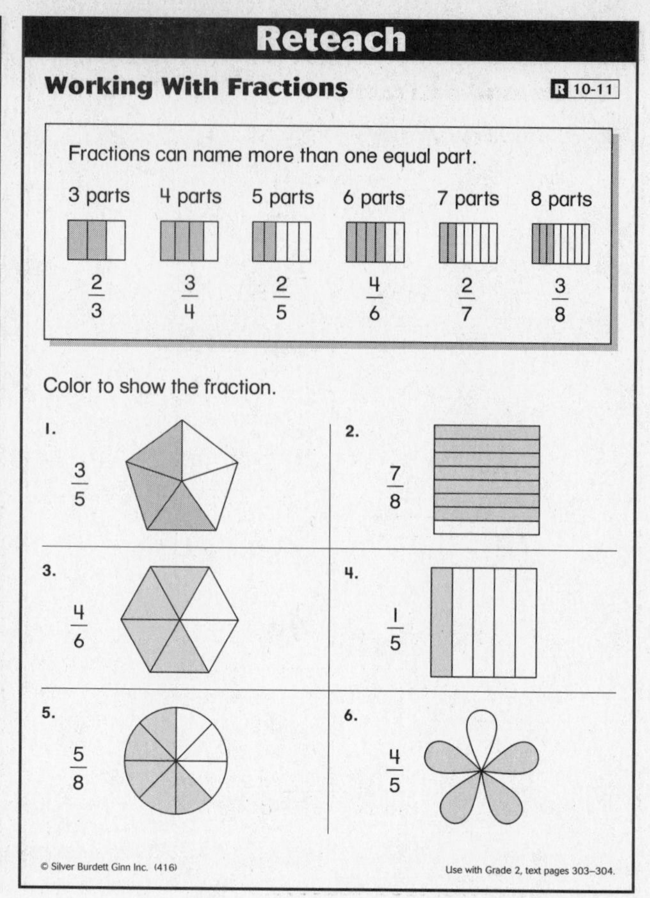

Reteach

Working With Fractions

R 10-11

Fractions can name more than one equal part.

3 parts	4 parts	5 parts	6 parts	7 parts	8 parts
$\frac{2}{3}$	$\frac{3}{4}$	$\frac{2}{5}$	$\frac{4}{6}$	$\frac{2}{7}$	$\frac{3}{8}$

Color to show the fraction.

1. $\frac{3}{5}$
2. $\frac{7}{8}$
3. $\frac{4}{6}$
4. $\frac{1}{5}$
5. $\frac{5}{8}$
6. $\frac{4}{5}$

Use with Grade 2, text pages 303–304.

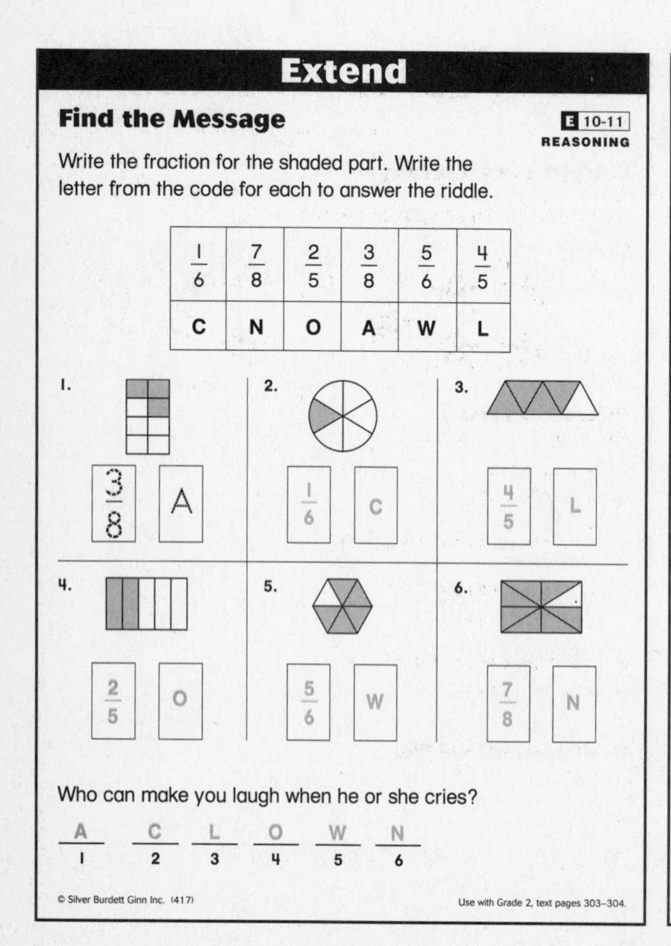

Extend

Find the Message

E 10-11 REASONING

Write the fraction for the shaded part. Write the letter from the code for each to answer the riddle.

$\frac{1}{6}$	$\frac{7}{8}$	$\frac{2}{5}$	$\frac{3}{8}$	$\frac{5}{6}$	$\frac{4}{5}$
C	N	O	A	W	L

1. $\frac{3}{8}$ A
2. $\frac{1}{6}$ C
3. $\frac{4}{5}$ L
4. $\frac{2}{5}$ O
5. $\frac{5}{6}$ W
6. $\frac{7}{8}$ N

Who can make you laugh when he or she cries?

A (1) C (2) L (3) O (4) W (5) N (6)

Use with Grade 2, text pages 303–304.

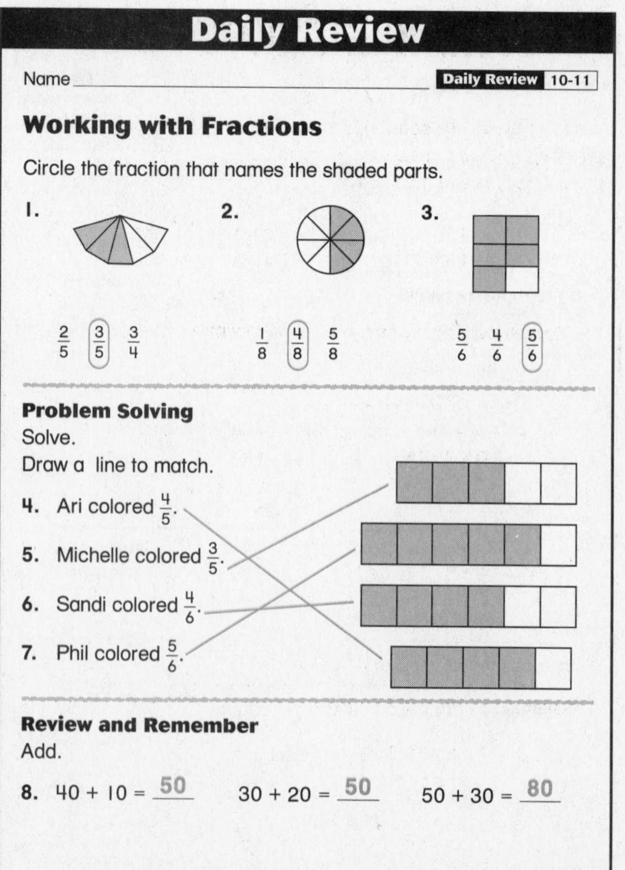

Daily Review

Name ____________________ Daily Review 10-11

Working with Fractions

Circle the fraction that names the shaded parts.

1. $\frac{2}{5}$ ($\frac{3}{5}$) $\frac{3}{4}$
2. $\frac{1}{8}$ ($\frac{4}{8}$) $\frac{5}{8}$
3. $\frac{5}{6}$ $\frac{4}{6}$ ($\frac{5}{6}$)

Problem Solving

Solve.
Draw a line to match.

4. Ari colored $\frac{4}{5}$.
5. Michelle colored $\frac{3}{5}$.
6. Sandi colored $\frac{4}{6}$.
7. Phil colored $\frac{5}{6}$.

Review and Remember

Add.

8. 40 + 10 = 50 30 + 20 = 50 50 + 30 = 80

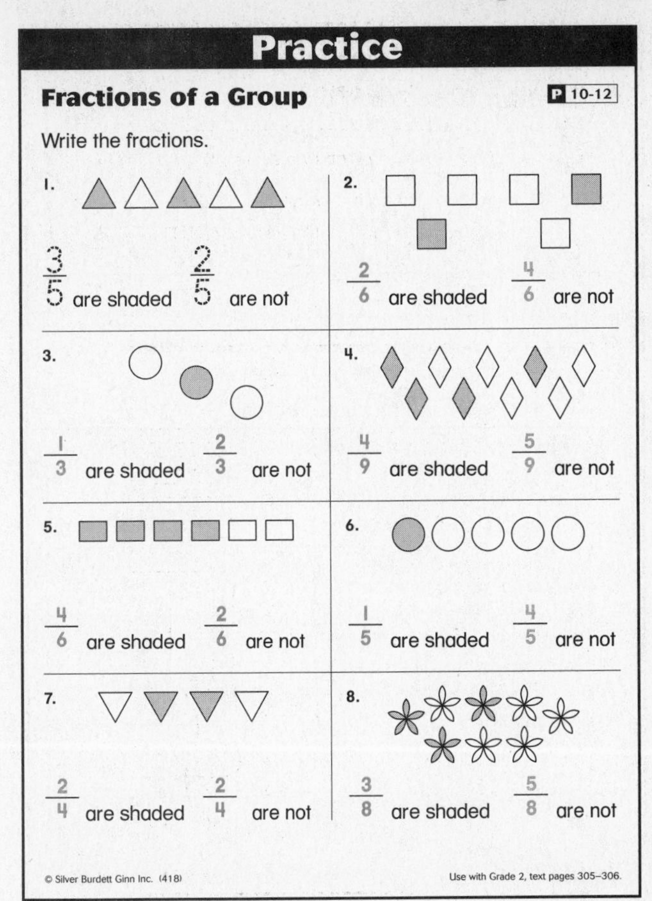

Practice

Fractions of a Group

P 10-12

Write the fractions.

1. 3/5 are shaded 2/5 are not
2. 2/6 are shaded 4/6 are not
3. 1/3 are shaded 2/3 are not
4. 4/9 are shaded 5/9 are not
5. 4/6 are shaded 2/6 are not
6. 1/5 are shaded 4/5 are not
7. 2/4 are shaded 2/4 are not
8. 3/8 are shaded 5/8 are not

 Use with Grade 2, text pages 305–306.

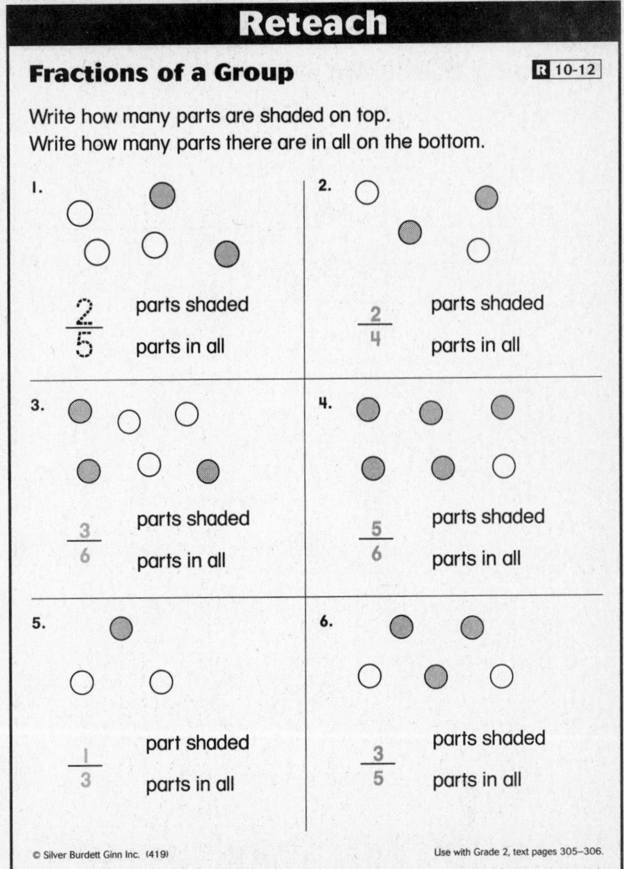

Reteach

Fractions of a Group

R 10-12

Write how many parts are shaded on top.
Write how many parts there are in all on the bottom.

1. 2/5 parts shaded / parts in all
2. 2/4 parts shaded / parts in all
3. 3/6 parts shaded / parts in all
4. 5/6 parts shaded / parts in all
5. 1/3 part shaded / parts in all
6. 3/5 parts shaded / parts in all

 Use with Grade 2, text pages 305–306.

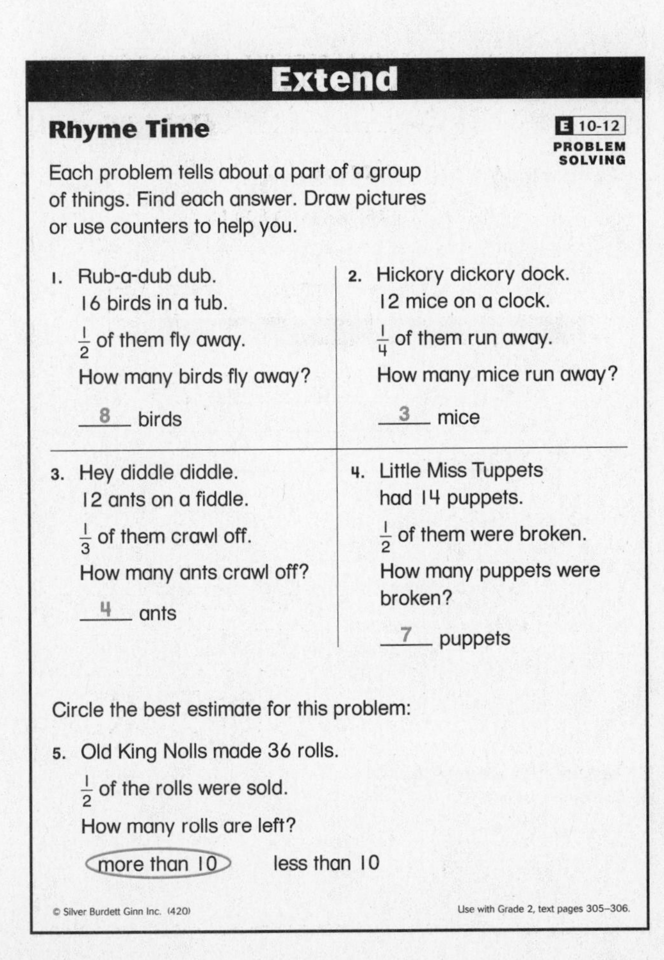

Extend

Rhyme Time

E 10-12 PROBLEM SOLVING

Each problem tells about a part of a group of things. Find each answer. Draw pictures or use counters to help you.

1. Rub-a-dub dub.
   16 birds in a tub.
   $\frac{1}{2}$ of them fly away.
   How many birds fly away?
   8 birds

2. Hickory dickory dock.
   12 mice on a clock.
   $\frac{1}{4}$ of them run away.
   How many mice run away?
   3 mice

3. Hey diddle diddle.
   12 ants on a fiddle.
   $\frac{1}{3}$ of them crawl off.
   How many ants crawl off?
   4 ants

4. Little Miss Tuppets
   had 14 puppets.
   $\frac{1}{2}$ of them were broken.
   How many puppets were broken?
   7 puppets

Circle the best estimate for this problem:

5. Old King Nolls made 36 rolls.
   $\frac{1}{2}$ of the rolls were sold.
   How many rolls are left?
   (more than 10) less than 10

 Use with Grade 2, text pages 305–306.

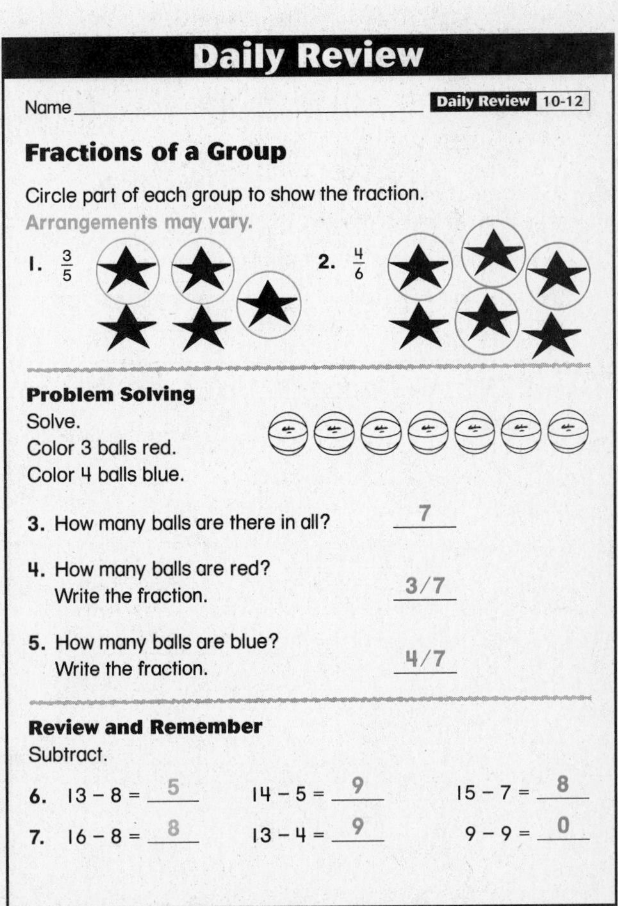

Daily Review

Name ______________________ Daily Review 10-12

Fractions of a Group

Circle part of each group to show the fraction.
Arrangements may vary.

1. $\frac{3}{5}$
2. $\frac{4}{6}$

Problem Solving

Solve.
Color 3 balls red.
Color 4 balls blue.

3. How many balls are there in all? 7
4. How many balls are red? Write the fraction. 3/7
5. How many balls are blue? Write the fraction. 4/7

Review and Remember

Subtract.

6. 13 − 8 = 5 14 − 5 = 9 15 − 7 = 8
7. 16 − 8 = 8 13 − 4 = 9 9 − 9 = 0

Practice

Recording Data From a Survey

P 10-13

1. Take a survey. First, write four activities on the chart. Then ask classmates which activity they like best. Tally the answers. Then write the total.

Activities

Activity	Tally	Total

2. Make a bar graph. Color one box for each time an activity was chosen.

Activities

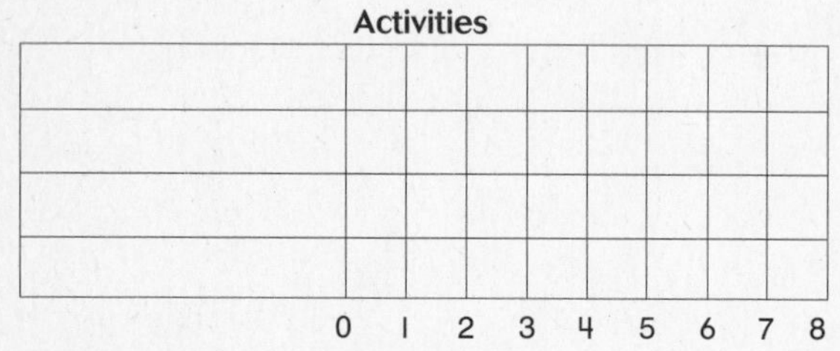

3. What activity do children like the best?

Check students' charts and graphs.

 Use with Grade 2, text pages 307–308.

Reteach

Recording Data From a Survey

R 10-13

Tallies are made in groups of 5. Count by 5s to get the number of tallies.

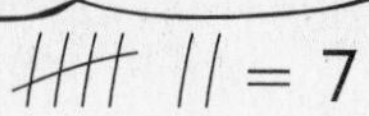

1. Andrea asks 10 classmates if they like football. She makes a tally mark to show each answer. Fill in the totals for those who like and dislike football.

Who Likes Football?

Answer	Tally	Total
Yes	卌 |	6
No	||||	4

2. Make a bar graph to show how many children like football. Color one box for every child who likes football. Then color one box for every child who does NOT like football.

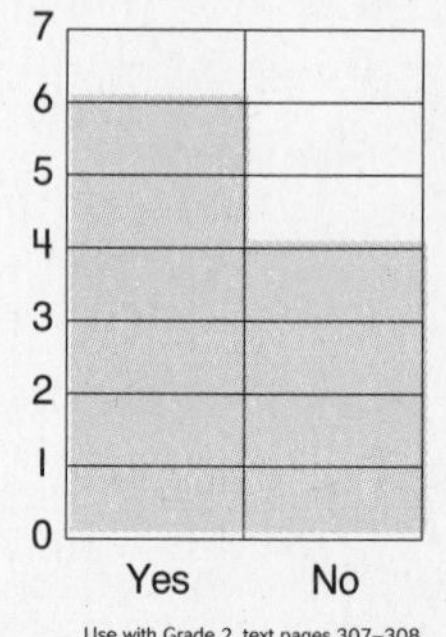

 Use with Grade 2, text pages 307–308.

Extend

Tally-Ho!

E 10-13 REASONING

1. Use these clues to finish the tally chart.

The total of children who like soccer is one more than the total of children who like jogging.

Twice as many children like baseball as like soccer.

The total number of children who like ice-skating is one less than the total number of children who like baseball.

Activity	Tally	Total
baseball	卌 |||	8
soccer		4
jogging		3
ice-skating		7

2. Make a graph of the results.

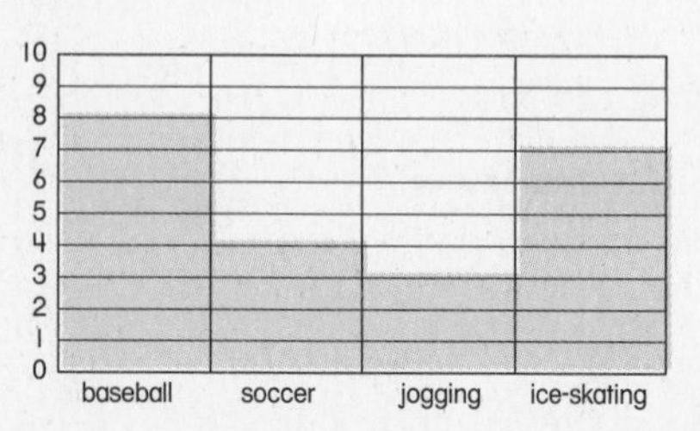

 Use with Grade 2, text pages 307–308.

Daily Review

Name ____________________ Daily Review 10-13

Recording Data from a Survey

Matt took a survey. He asked his friends to choose the sport they liked best.

1. Complete the chart to show what his friends said.

Sport	Tally	Total
Baseball	卌 |	6
Football	|||	3
Soccer	卌 ||	7
Basketball	||	2

Problem Solving

Solve. Use the chart.

2. Which sport was chosen the most? soccer
3. Which sport was chosen the least? basketball
4. How many friends liked baseball? 6 friends
5. How many friends did Matt survey? 18 friends

Review and Remember

Add.

6. 35 + 14 = 49   12 + 8 = 20   28 + 27 = 55   47 + 36 = 83   52 + 15 = 67

Practice

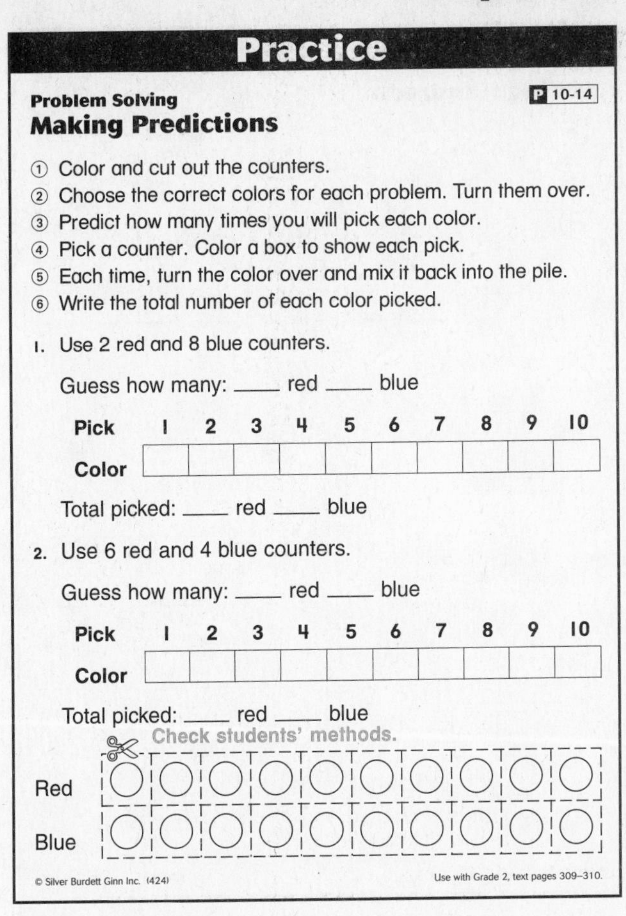

Problem Solving **P 10-14**

Making Predictions

① Color and cut out the counters.
② Choose the correct colors for each problem. Turn them over.
③ Predict how many times you will pick each color.
④ Pick a counter. Color a box to show each pick.
⑤ Each time, turn the color over and mix it back into the pile.
⑥ Write the total number of each color picked.

1. Use 2 red and 8 blue counters.

Guess how many: ____ red ____ blue

Pick	1	2	3	4	5	6	7	8	9	10
Color										

Total picked: ____ red ____ blue

2. Use 6 red and 4 blue counters.

Guess how many: ____ red ____ blue

Pick	1	2	3	4	5	6	7	8	9	10
Color										

Total picked: ____ red ____ blue

Check students' methods.

Red ○ ○ ○ ○ ○ ○ ○ ○ ○ ○

Blue ○ ○ ○ ○ ○ ○ ○ ○ ○ ○

 Use with Grade 2, text pages 309–310.

Reteach

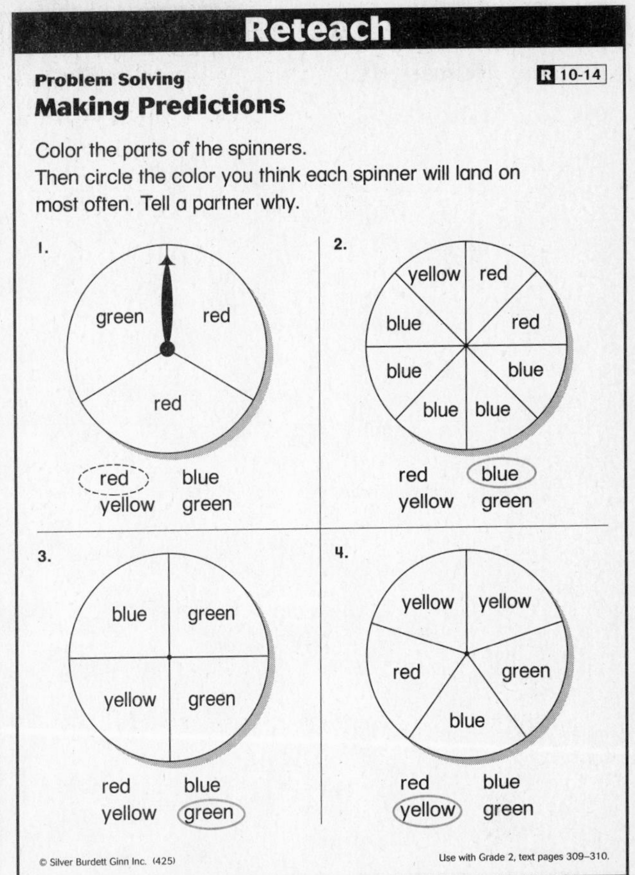

Problem Solving **R 10-14**

Making Predictions

Color the parts of the spinners.
Then circle the color you think each spinner will land on most often. Tell a partner why.

1.
(red) blue
yellow green

2.
red (blue)
yellow green

3.
red blue
yellow (green)

4.
red blue
(yellow) green

 Use with Grade 2, text pages 309–310.

Extend

More Probability

E 10-14 PROBABILITY

1. Put the same number of red and blue markers into a bag. Out of 10 picks, how many do you predict will be red? Circle your choice below.

0, 1, 2, or 3 (4, 5, or 6) 7, 8, 9, or 10

Now pick 10 times. Be sure to put your marker back each time.

How many red markers did you pick? ____

2. This time put 2 red markers and 8 blue markers in the bag. Out of 10 picks, how many do you predict will be red? Circle your choice below.

(0, 1, 2, or 3) 4, 5, or 6 7, 8, 9, or 10

Now pick 10 times. How many red markers did you pick? ____

Check students' methods.

 Use with Grade 2, text pages 309–310.

Daily Review

Name ______________________ **Daily Review 10-14**

Problem Solving

Making Predictions

Put red and blue cubes in a bag.
Predict how many times you will pick each color.
Pick 1 cube at a time. Color a box to show your pick.

1. Put 7 red and 3 blue cubes in the bag. Answers will vary.

prediction ______ red ______ blue

Pick	1	2	3	4	5	6	7	8	9	10
Color										

2. Put 4 red and 6 blue cubes in the bag.

prediction ______ red ______ blue

Pick	1	2	3	4	5	6	7	8	9	10
Color										

Review and Remember

Write the total amount.

3. 51¢

4. 100¢

Practice

Adding Hundreds

P 11-1

Add. Look for a pattern.

1.	2.	3.	4.
1 + 3 = 4	5 + 3 = 8	6 + 2 = 8	1 + 8 = 9
10 + 30 = 40	50 + 30 = 80	60 + 20 = 80	10 + 80 = 90
100 + 300 = 400	500 + 300 = 800	600 + 200 = 800	100 + 800 = 900

5.	6.	7.	8.
6 + 3 = 9	2 + 5 = 7	3 + 2 = 5	5 + 1 = 6
60 + 30 = 90	20 + 50 = 70	30 + 20 = 50	50 + 10 = 60
600 + 300 = 900	200 + 500 = 700	300 + 200 = 500	500 + 100 = 600

Use with Grade 2, text pages 317–318.

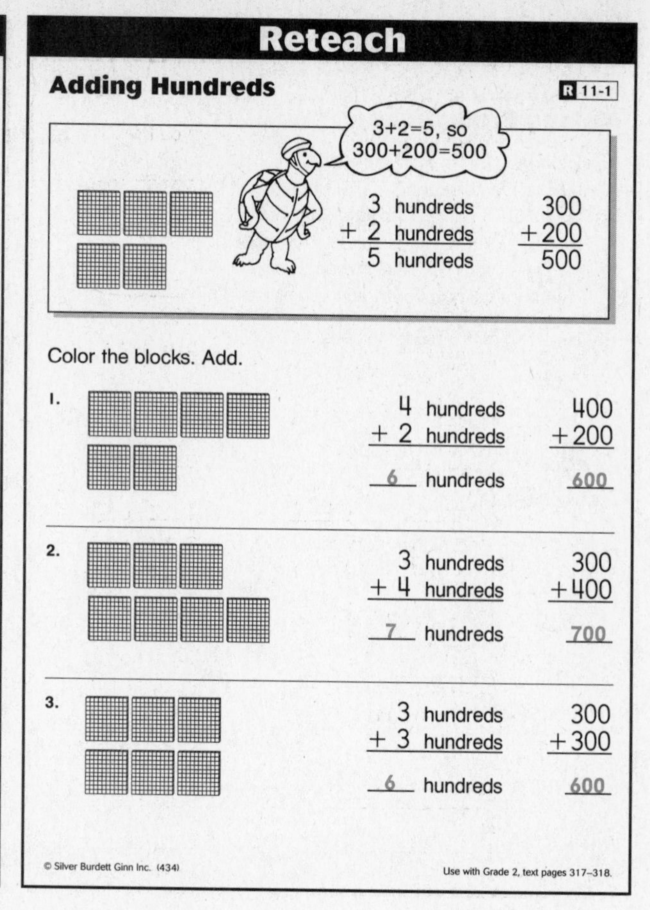

Reteach

Adding Hundreds

R 11-1

3 hundreds + 2 hundreds = 5 hundreds
300 + 200 = 500

Color the blocks. Add.

1. 4 hundreds + 2 hundreds = 6 hundreds; 400 + 200 = 600
2. 3 hundreds + 4 hundreds = 7 hundreds; 300 + 400 = 700
3. 3 hundreds + 3 hundreds = 6 hundreds; 300 + 300 = 600

Use with Grade 2, text pages 317–318.

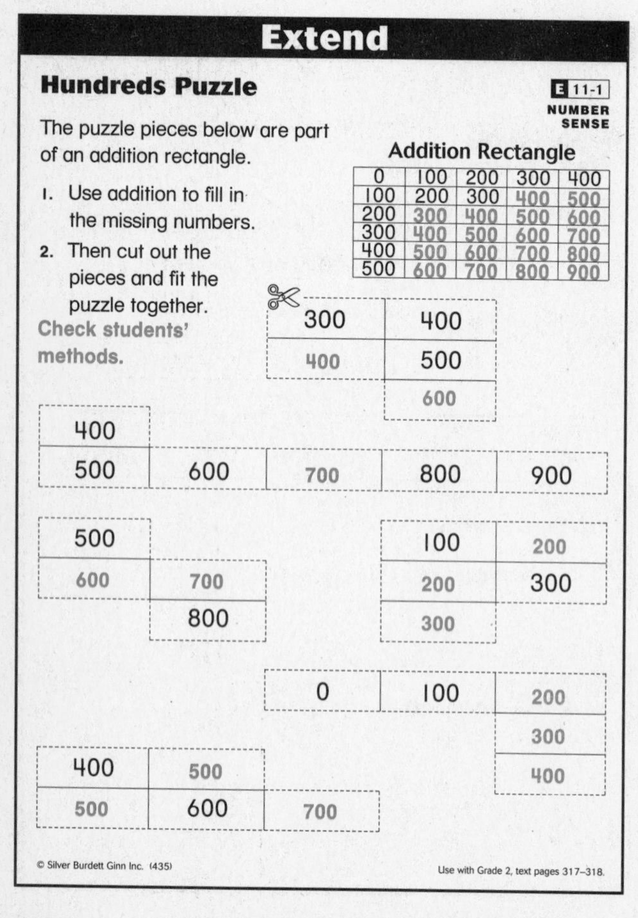

Extend

Hundreds Puzzle

E 11-1 NUMBER SENSE

The puzzle pieces below are part of an addition rectangle.

1. Use addition to fill in the missing numbers.
2. Then cut out the pieces and fit the puzzle together.

Check students' methods.

Addition Rectangle

0	100	200	300	400
100	200	300	400	500
200	300	400	500	600
300	400	500	600	700
400	500	600	700	800
500	600	700	800	900

Puzzle pieces:

- 300, 400 / 400, 500 / 600
- 400 / 500, 600, 700, 800, 900
- 500 / 600, 700 / 800
- 100, 200 / 200, 300 / 300
- 0, 100, 200 / 300 / 400
- 400, 500 / 500, 600, 700

Use with Grade 2, text pages 317–318.

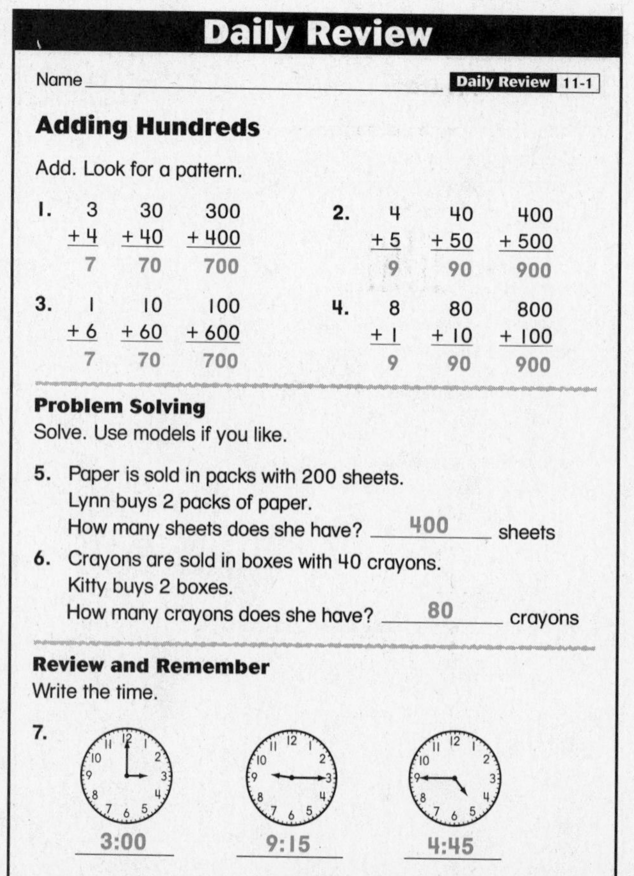

Daily Review

Name ____________ Daily Review 11-1

Adding Hundreds

Add. Look for a pattern.

1. 3 + 4 = 7; 30 + 40 = 70; 300 + 400 = 700
2. 4 + 5 = 9; 40 + 50 = 90; 400 + 500 = 900
3. 1 + 6 = 7; 10 + 60 = 70; 100 + 600 = 700
4. 8 + 1 = 9; 80 + 10 = 90; 800 + 100 = 900

Problem Solving

Solve. Use models if you like.

5. Paper is sold in packs with 200 sheets. Lynn buys 2 packs of paper. How many sheets does she have? 400 sheets
6. Crayons are sold in boxes with 40 crayons. Kitty buys 2 boxes. How many crayons does she have? 80 crayons

Review and Remember

Write the time.

7. 3:00 9:15 4:45

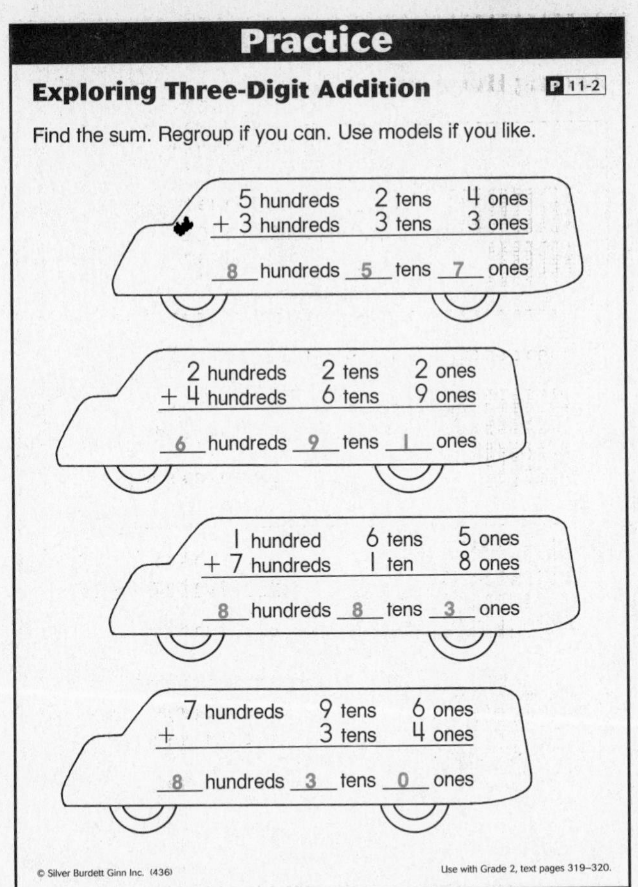

Practice

Exploring Three-Digit Addition

P 11-2

Find the sum. Regroup if you can. Use models if you like.

5 hundreds	2 tens	4 ones
+ 3 hundreds	3 tens	3 ones
8 hundreds	5 tens	7 ones

2 hundreds	2 tens	2 ones
+ 4 hundreds	6 tens	9 ones
6 hundreds	9 tens	1 ones

1 hundred	6 tens	5 ones
+ 7 hundreds	1 ten	8 ones
8 hundreds	8 tens	3 ones

7 hundreds	9 tens	6 ones
+	3 tens	4 ones
8 hundreds	3 tens	0 ones

Use with Grade 2, text pages 319–320.

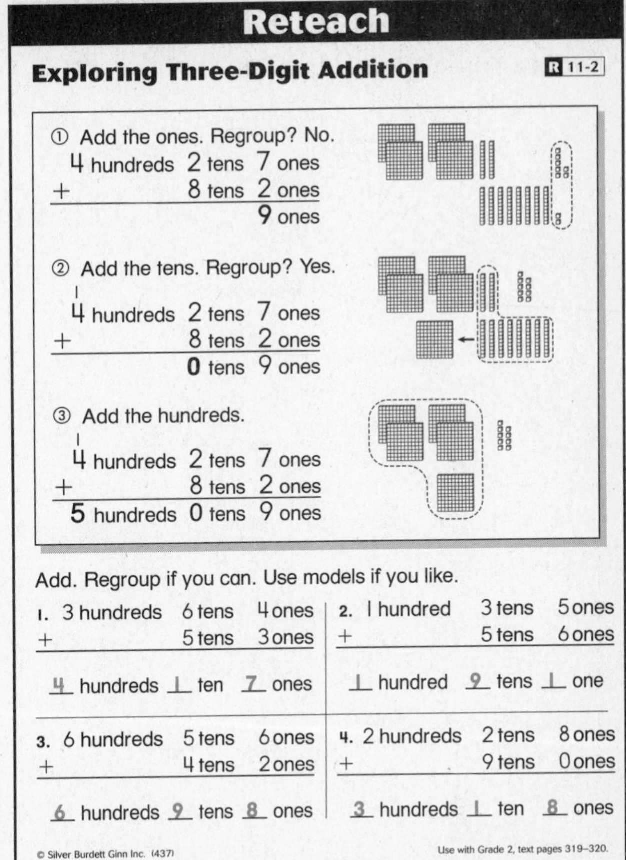

Reteach

Exploring Three-Digit Addition

R 11-2

① Add the ones. Regroup? No.

	4 hundreds	2 tens	7 ones
+		8 tens	2 ones
			9 ones

② Add the tens. Regroup? Yes.

	1 4 hundreds	2 tens	7 ones
+		8 tens	2 ones
		0 tens	9 ones

③ Add the hundreds.

	1 4 hundreds	2 tens	7 ones
+		8 tens	2 ones
	5 hundreds	0 tens	9 ones

Add. Regroup if you can. Use models if you like.

1. 3 hundreds 6 tens 4 ones
   \+ 5 tens 3 ones
   4 hundreds 1 ten 7 ones

2. 1 hundred 3 tens 5 ones
   \+ 5 tens 6 ones
   1 hundred 9 tens 1 one

3. 6 hundreds 5 tens 6 ones
   \+ 4 tens 2 ones
   6 hundreds 9 tens 8 ones

4. 2 hundreds 2 tens 8 ones
   \+ 9 tens 0 ones
   3 hundreds 1 ten 8 ones

Use with Grade 2, text pages 319–320.

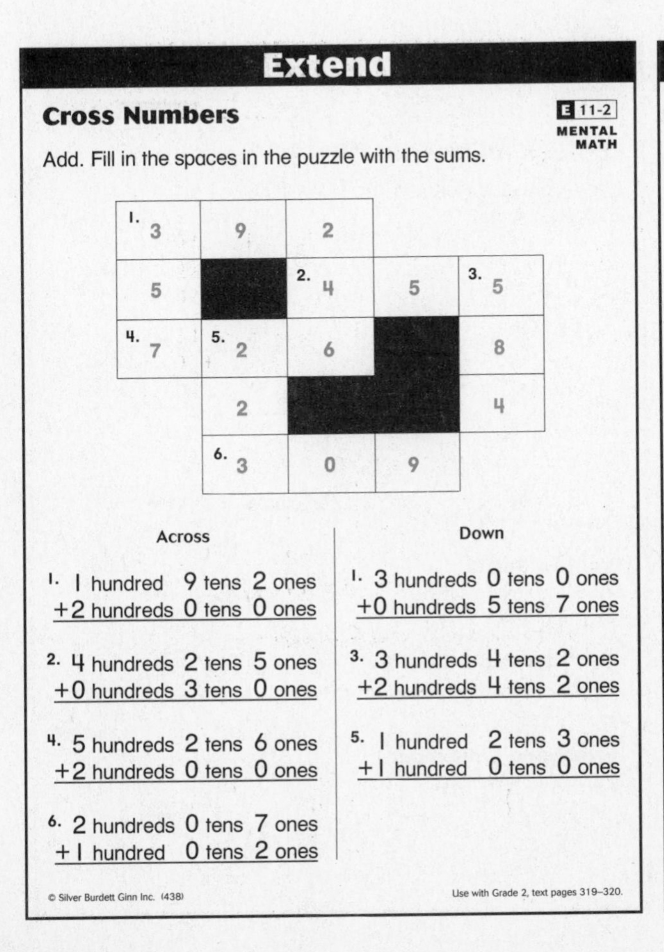

Extend

Cross Numbers

E 11-2
MENTAL MATH

Add. Fill in the spaces in the puzzle with the sums.

1. 3	9	2		
5	■	2. 4	5	3. 5
4. 7	5. 2	6	■	8
	2	■	■	4
	6. 3	0	9	

Across

1. 1 hundred 9 tens 2 ones
   +2 hundreds 0 tens 0 ones

2. 4 hundreds 2 tens 5 ones
   +0 hundreds 3 tens 0 ones

4. 5 hundreds 2 tens 6 ones
   +2 hundreds 0 tens 0 ones

6. 2 hundreds 0 tens 7 ones
   +1 hundred 0 tens 2 ones

Down

1. 3 hundreds 0 tens 0 ones
   +0 hundreds 5 tens 7 ones

3. 3 hundreds 4 tens 2 ones
   +2 hundreds 4 tens 2 ones

5. 1 hundred 2 tens 3 ones
   +1 hundred 0 tens 0 ones

Use with Grade 2, text pages 319–320.

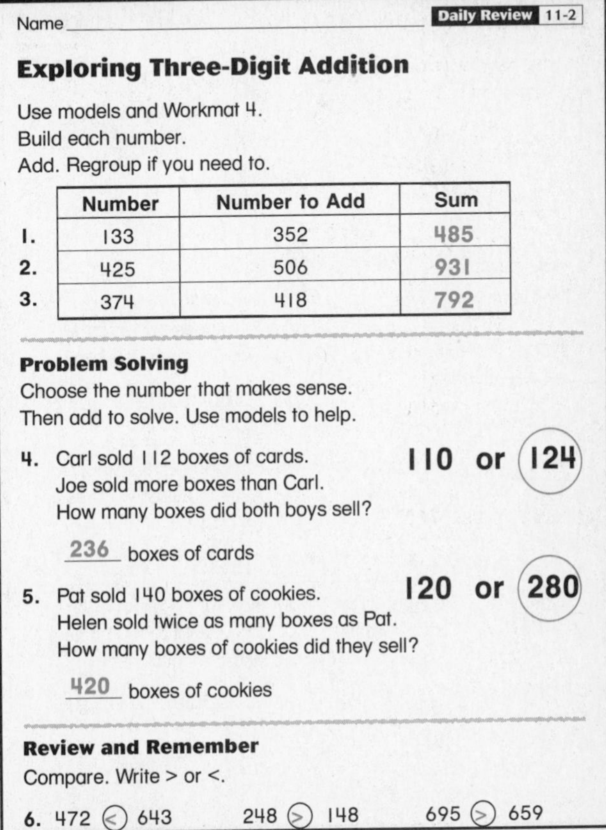

Daily Review

Name ______________________

Daily Review 11-2

Exploring Three-Digit Addition

Use models and Workmat 4.
Build each number.
Add. Regroup if you need to.

	Number	Number to Add	Sum
1.	133	352	485
2.	425	506	931
3.	374	418	792

Problem Solving

Choose the number that makes sense.
Then add to solve. Use models to help.

4. Carl sold 112 boxes of cards.
   Joe sold more boxes than Carl.
   How many boxes did both boys sell?   110 or (124)

   236 boxes of cards

5. Pat sold 140 boxes of cookies.
   Helen sold twice as many boxes as Pat.
   How many boxes of cookies did they sell?   120 or (280)

   420 boxes of cookies

Review and Remember

Compare. Write > or <.

6. 472 (<) 643   248 (>) 148   695 (>) 659

Chapter 11 • Lesson 3

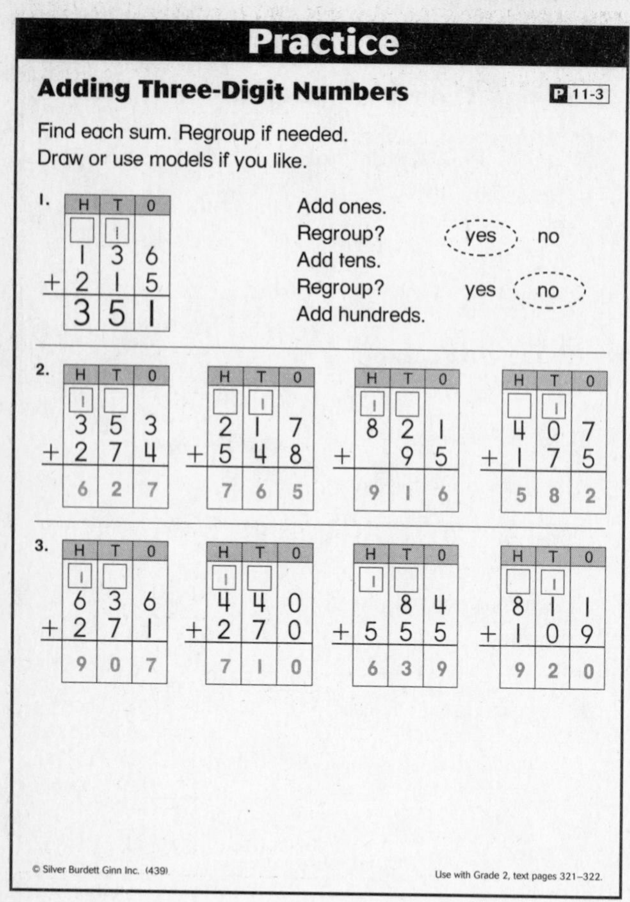

Practice

Adding Three-Digit Numbers

P 11-3

Find each sum. Regroup if needed.
Draw or use models if you like.

1.

H	T	O
	1	
1	3	6
+ 2	1	5
3	5	1

Add ones.
Regroup? (yes) no
Add tens.
Regroup? yes (no)
Add hundreds.

2. 353 + 274 = 627; 217 + 548 = 765; 821 + 95 = 916; 407 + 175 = 582

3. 636 + 271 = 907; 440 + 270 = 710; 84 + 555 = 639; 811 + 109 = 920

© Silver Burdett Ginn Inc. (439) Use with Grade 2, text pages 321–322.

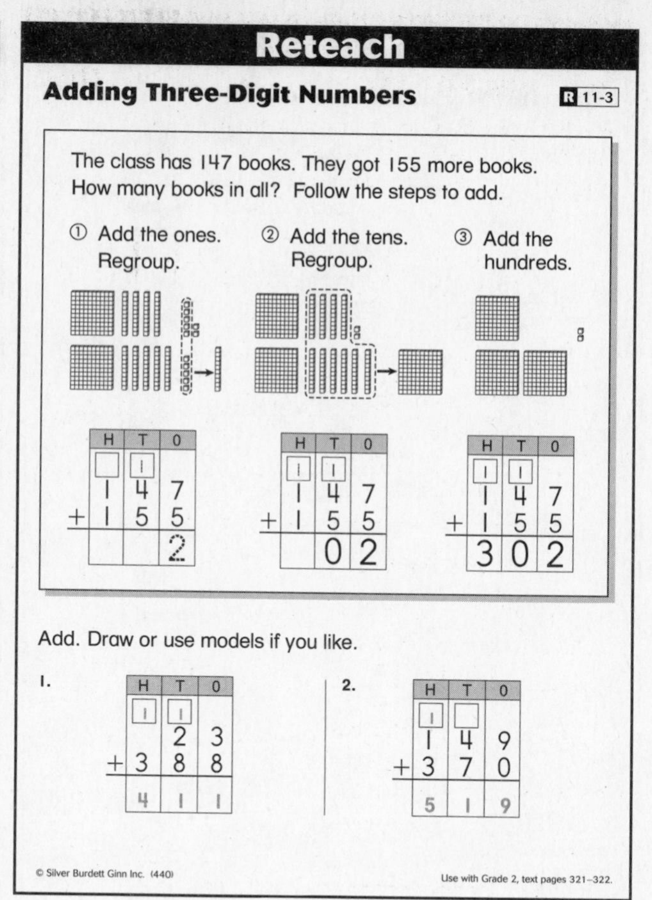

Reteach

Adding Three-Digit Numbers

R 11-3

The class has 147 books. They got 155 more books.
How many books in all? Follow the steps to add.

① Add the ones. Regroup.
② Add the tens. Regroup.
③ Add the hundreds.

H	T	O
	1	
1	4	7
+ 1	5	5
		2

H	T	O
1	1	
1	4	7
+ 1	5	5
	0	2

H	T	O
1	1	
1	4	7
+ 1	5	5
3	0	2

Add. Draw or use models if you like.

1. 23 + 388 = 411

2. 149 + 370 = 519

© Silver Burdett Ginn Inc. (440) Use with Grade 2, text pages 321–322.

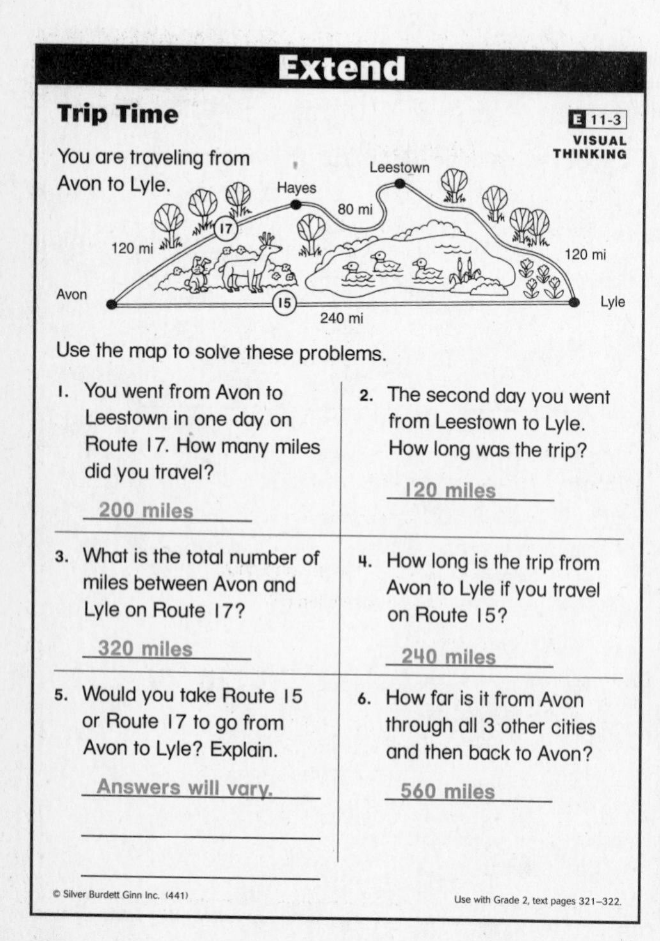

Extend

Trip Time

E 11-3
VISUAL THINKING

You are traveling from Avon to Lyle.

Use the map to solve these problems.

1. You went from Avon to Leestown in one day on Route 17. How many miles did you travel? 200 miles

2. The second day you went from Leestown to Lyle. How long was the trip? 120 miles

3. What is the total number of miles between Avon and Lyle on Route 17? 320 miles

4. How long is the trip from Avon to Lyle if you travel on Route 15? 240 miles

5. Would you take Route 15 or Route 17 to go from Avon to Lyle? Explain. Answers will vary.

6. How far is it from Avon through all 3 other cities and then back to Avon? 560 miles

© Silver Burdett Ginn Inc. (441) Use with Grade 2, text pages 321–322.

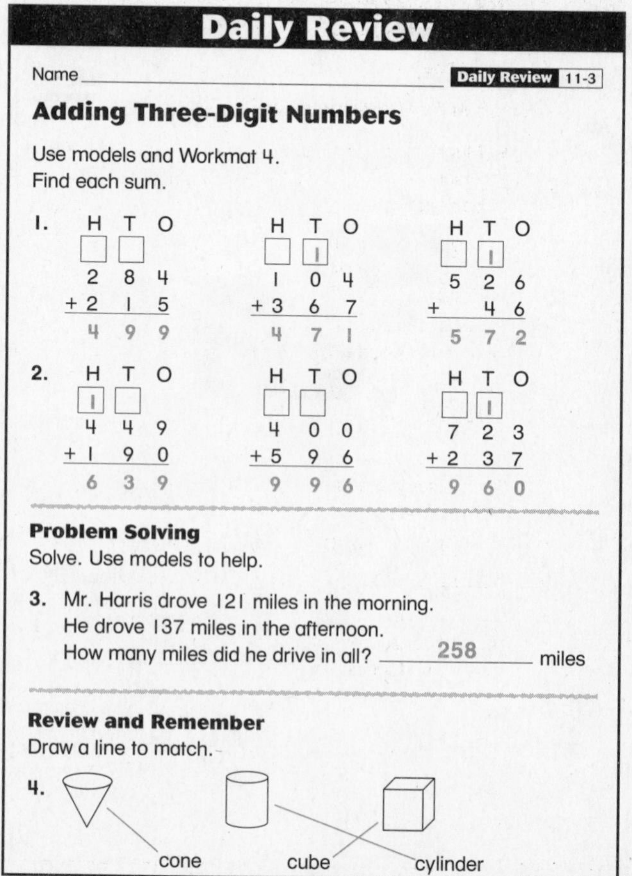

Daily Review

Name ______________________ Daily Review 11-3

Adding Three-Digit Numbers

Use models and Workmat 4.
Find each sum.

1. 284 + 215 = 499; 104 + 367 = 471; 526 + 46 = 572

2. 449 + 190 = 639; 400 + 596 = 996; 723 + 237 = 960

Problem Solving
Solve. Use models to help.

3. Mr. Harris drove 121 miles in the morning.
He drove 137 miles in the afternoon.
How many miles did he drive in all? 258 miles

Review and Remember
Draw a line to match.

4. cone cube cylinder

Practice

Practicing Addition

P 11-4

Find each sum. Draw or use models if you like. Then use the code to write the letter for each number in the sum. Each sum makes a word.

Code

0	1	2	3	4	5	6	7	8	9
A	D	G	R	H	U	S	E	N	T

1.

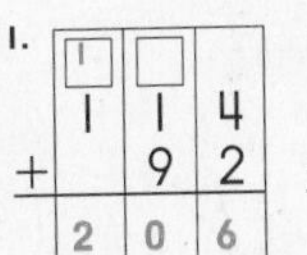

114 + 92 = 206 — G A S

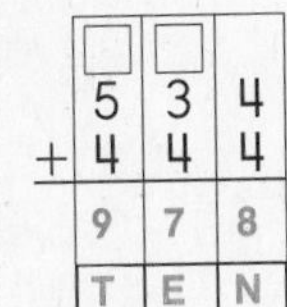

534 + 444 = 978 — T E N

301 + 300 = 601 — S A D

583 + 296 = 879 — N E T

These sums make a sentence.

2.

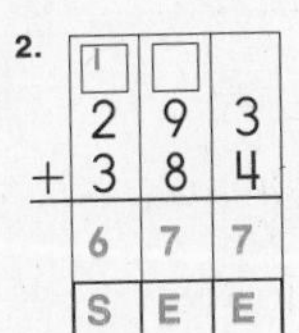

293 + 384 = 677 — S E E

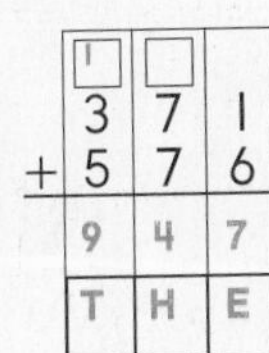

371 + 576 = 947 — T H E

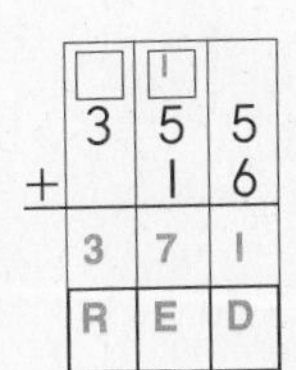

355 + 16 = 371 — R E D

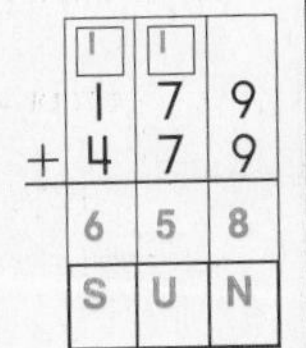

179 + 479 = 658 — S U N

 Use with Grade 2, text pages 323–324.

Reteach

Practicing Addition

R 11-4

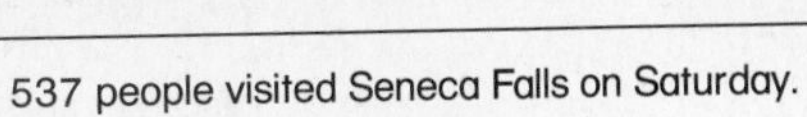

537 people visited Seneca Falls on Saturday.
324 people visited on Sunday.
How many visited in all?

① Add the ones. Regroup? Yes.

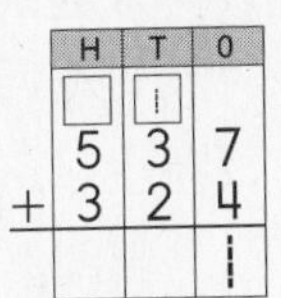

② Add the tens. Regroup? No.

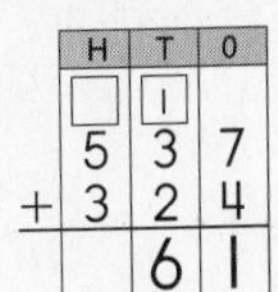

③ Add the hundreds.

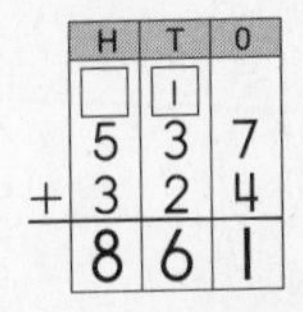

Add. Use models if you like.

1. 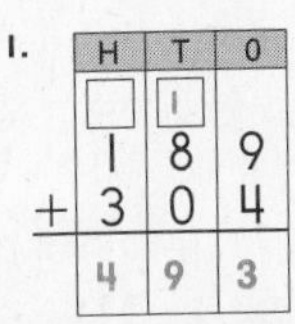

189 + 304 = 493

2. 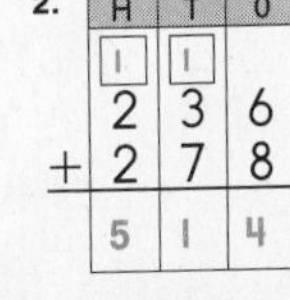

236 + 278 = 514

3. 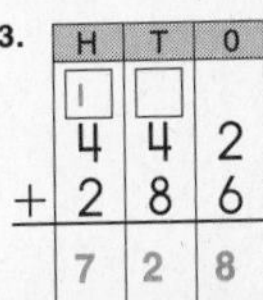

442 + 286 = 728

4. 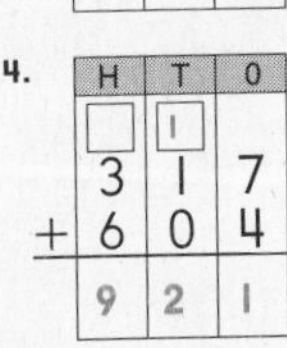

317 + 604 = 921

5. 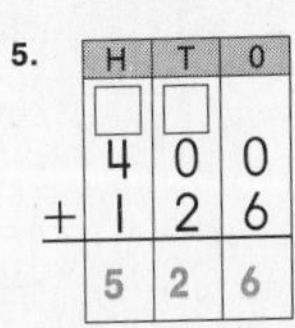

400 + 126 = 526

6. 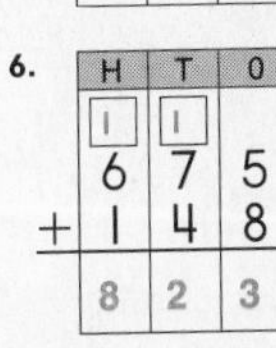

675 + 148 = 823

 Use with Grade 2, text pages 323–324.

Extend

Sum Machine!

E 11-4 REASONING

Which sums can the Sum Machine find?

1. The Sum Machine will find the sum of these problems.

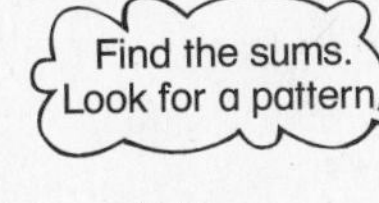

128	201	864	172
+427	+132	+135	+ 50
555	333	999	222

2. It will not find these sums.

507	342	110	289
+215	+469	+ 87	+605
722	811	197	894

3. Circle the problems that the Sum Machine will add.

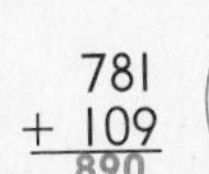
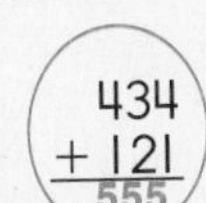
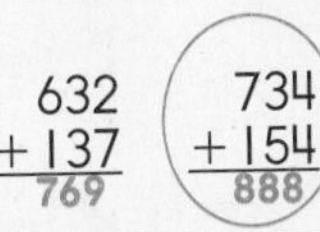
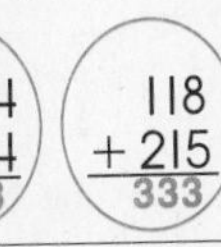

305	781	434	632	734	118
+472	+ 109	+ 121	+ 137	+ 154	+ 215
777	890	555	769	888	333

4. Write two different problems that the Sum Machine will solve. Check that students write two addition problems in which the sum has 3 digits. Each digit should be the same number.

+ ____ + ____

 Use with Grade 2, text pages 323–324.

Daily Review

Name ____________________

Daily Review 11-4

Practicing Addition

Add. Use models if you like.

1.

475	314	284	502	628
+ 116	+ 493	+ 517	+ 79	+ 131
591	807	801	581	759

2.

634	482	750	361	584
+ 129	+ 37	+ 152	+ 208	+ 163
763	519	902	569	747

Problem Solving

Solve. Use models if you like.

3. Max's Movies sold 192 tickets for the first show. They sold 341 tickets for the second show. How many tickets did they sell in all?

533 tickets

Review and Remember

Draw a shape with 3 sides and 3 corners.

4. Answers may vary. Students should draw a triangle.

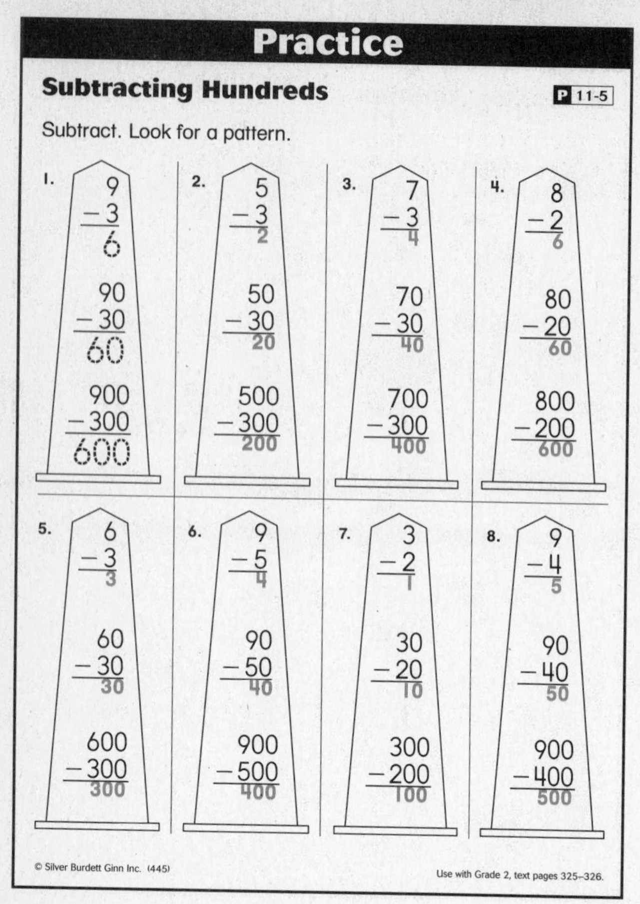

Practice

Subtracting Hundreds

P 11-5

Subtract. Look for a pattern.

1. 9 − 3 = 6; 90 − 30 = 60; 900 − 300 = 600
2. 5 − 3 = 2; 50 − 30 = 20; 500 − 300 = 200
3. 7 − 3 = 4; 70 − 30 = 40; 700 − 300 = 400
4. 8 − 2 = 6; 80 − 20 = 60; 800 − 200 = 600
5. 6 − 3 = 3; 60 − 30 = 30; 600 − 300 = 300
6. 9 − 5 = 4; 90 − 50 = 40; 900 − 500 = 400
7. 3 − 2 = 1; 30 − 20 = 10; 300 − 200 = 100
8. 9 − 4 = 5; 90 − 40 = 50; 900 − 400 = 500

Use with Grade 2, text pages 325–326.

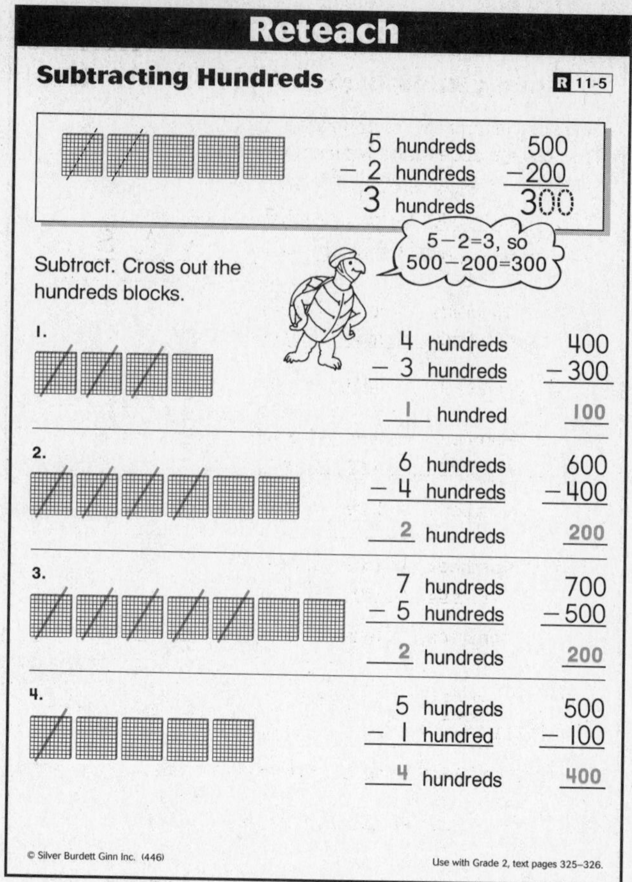

Reteach

Subtracting Hundreds

R 11-5

5 hundreds − 2 hundreds = 3 hundreds; 500 − 200 = 300

Subtract. Cross out the hundreds blocks.

1. 4 hundreds − 3 hundreds = 1 hundred; 400 − 300 = 100
2. 6 hundreds − 4 hundreds = 2 hundreds; 600 − 400 = 200
3. 7 hundreds − 5 hundreds = 2 hundreds; 700 − 500 = 200
4. 5 hundreds − 1 hundred = 4 hundreds; 500 − 100 = 400

Use with Grade 2, text pages 325–326.

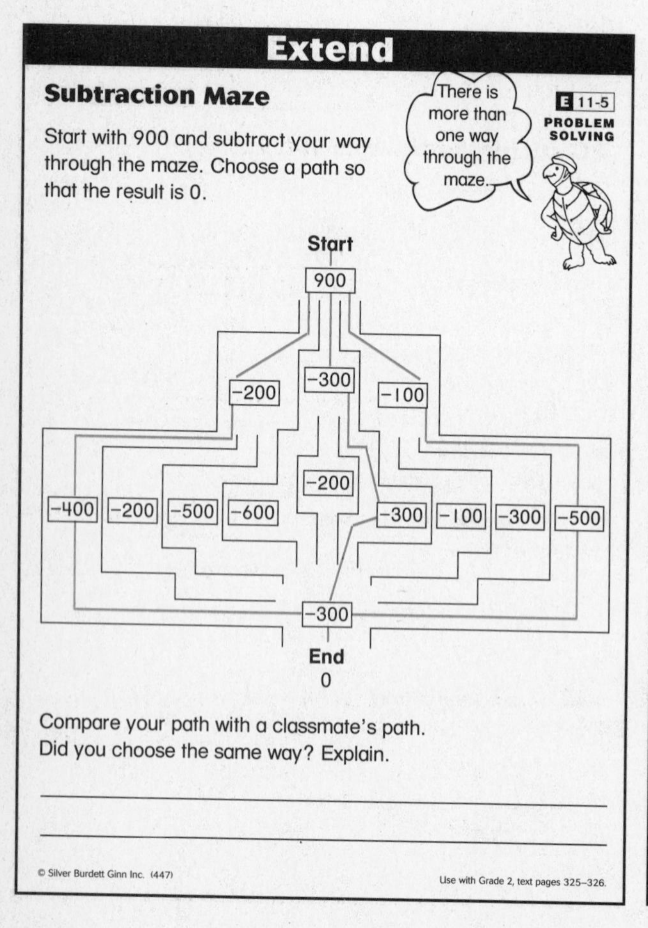

Extend

Subtraction Maze

E 11-5 PROBLEM SOLVING

Start with 900 and subtract your way through the maze. Choose a path so that the result is 0.

Compare your path with a classmate's path. Did you choose the same way? Explain.

Use with Grade 2, text pages 325–326.

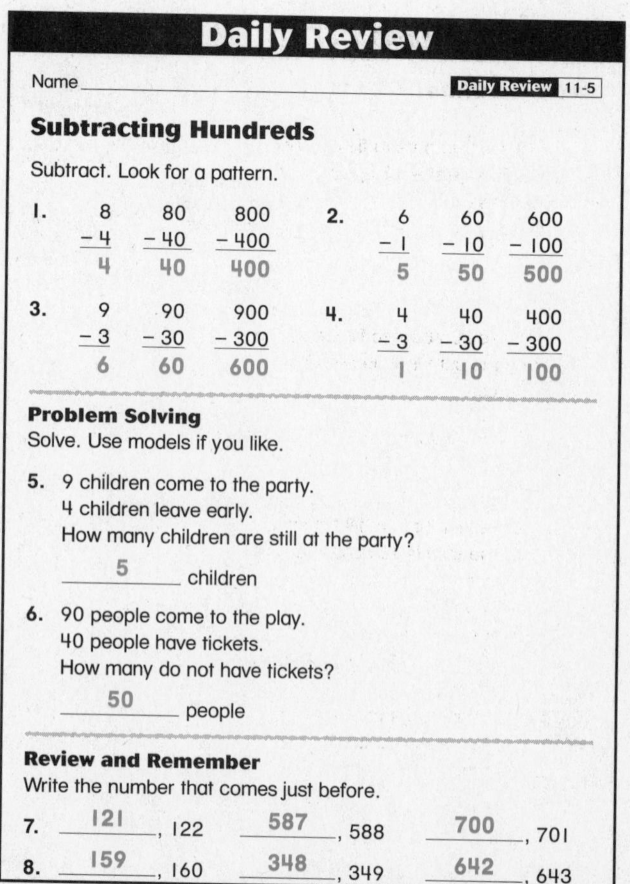

Daily Review

Name ____________________ Daily Review 11-5

Subtracting Hundreds

Subtract. Look for a pattern.

1. 8 − 4 = 4; 80 − 40 = 40; 800 − 400 = 400
2. 6 − 1 = 5; 60 − 10 = 50; 600 − 100 = 500
3. 9 − 3 = 6; 90 − 30 = 60; 900 − 300 = 600
4. 4 − 3 = 1; 40 − 30 = 10; 400 − 300 = 100

Problem Solving

Solve. Use models if you like.

5. 9 children come to the party. 4 children leave early. How many children are still at the party? 5 children
6. 90 people come to the play. 40 people have tickets. How many do not have tickets? 50 people

Review and Remember

Write the number that comes just before.

7. 121, 122 — 587, 588 — 700, 701
8. 159, 160 — 348, 349 — 642, 643

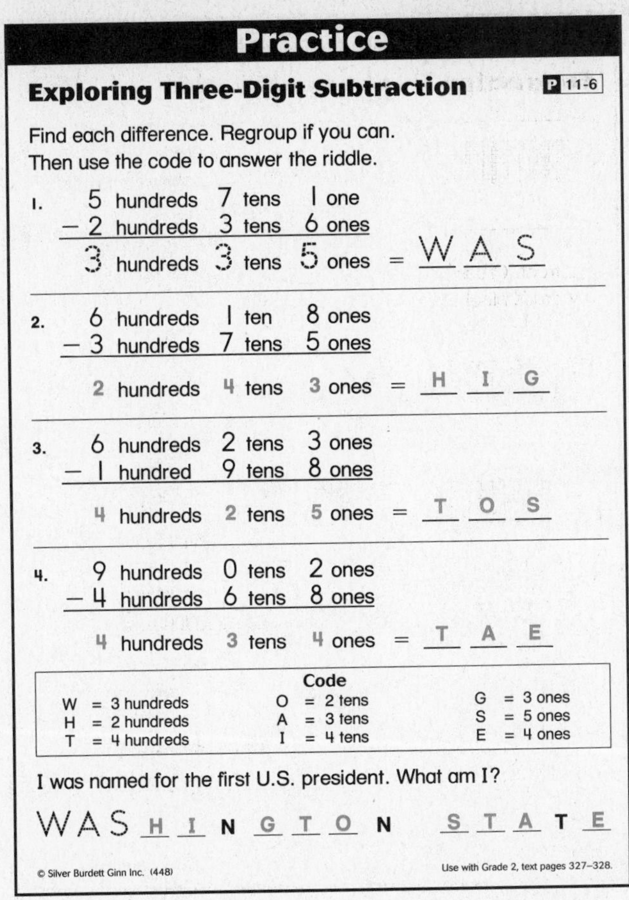

Practice

Exploring Three-Digit Subtraction

P 11-6

Find each difference. Regroup if you can.
Then use the code to answer the riddle.

1. 5 hundreds 7 tens 1 one
 − 2 hundreds 3 tens 6 ones
 3 hundreds 3 tens 5 ones = W A S

2. 6 hundreds 1 ten 8 ones
 − 3 hundreds 7 tens 5 ones
 2 hundreds 4 tens 3 ones = H I G

3. 6 hundreds 2 tens 3 ones
 − 1 hundred 9 tens 8 ones
 4 hundreds 2 tens 5 ones = T O S

4. 9 hundreds 0 tens 2 ones
 − 4 hundreds 6 tens 8 ones
 4 hundreds 3 tens 4 ones = T A E

Code		
W = 3 hundreds	O = 2 tens	G = 3 ones
H = 2 hundreds	A = 3 tens	S = 5 ones
T = 4 hundreds	I = 4 tens	E = 4 ones

I was named for the first U.S. president. What am I?

WAS H I N G T O N S T A T E

 Use with Grade 2, text pages 327–328.

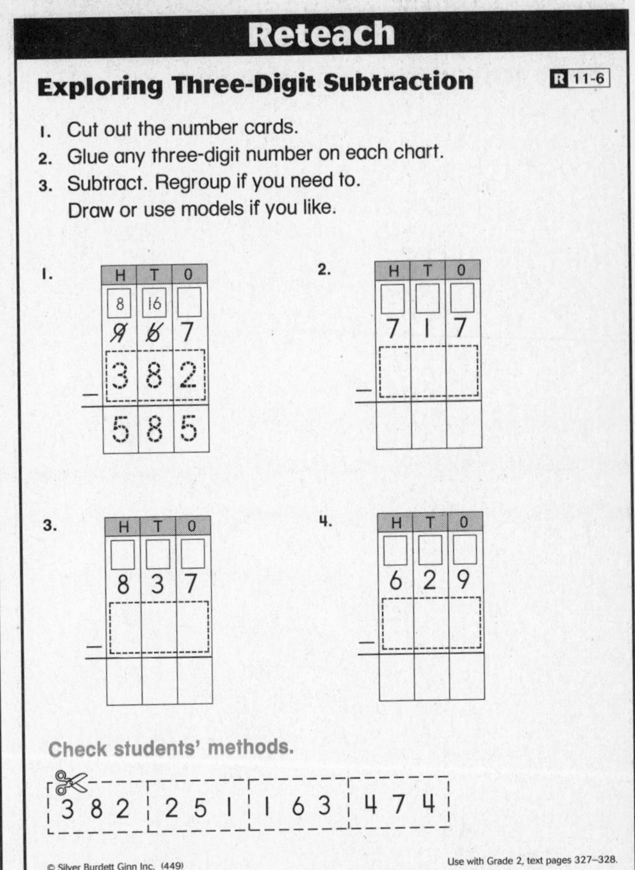

Reteach

Exploring Three-Digit Subtraction

R 11-6

1. Cut out the number cards.
2. Glue any three-digit number on each chart.
3. Subtract. Regroup if you need to.
 Draw or use models if you like.

1. H T O: 8 16 / 9̸ 6̸ 7 / − 3 8 2 / 5 8 5

2. H T O: 7 1 7 / −

3. H T O: 8 3 7 / −

4. H T O: 6 2 9 / −

Check students' methods.

3 8 2 | 2 5 1 | 1 6 3 | 4 7 4

 Use with Grade 2, text pages 327–328.

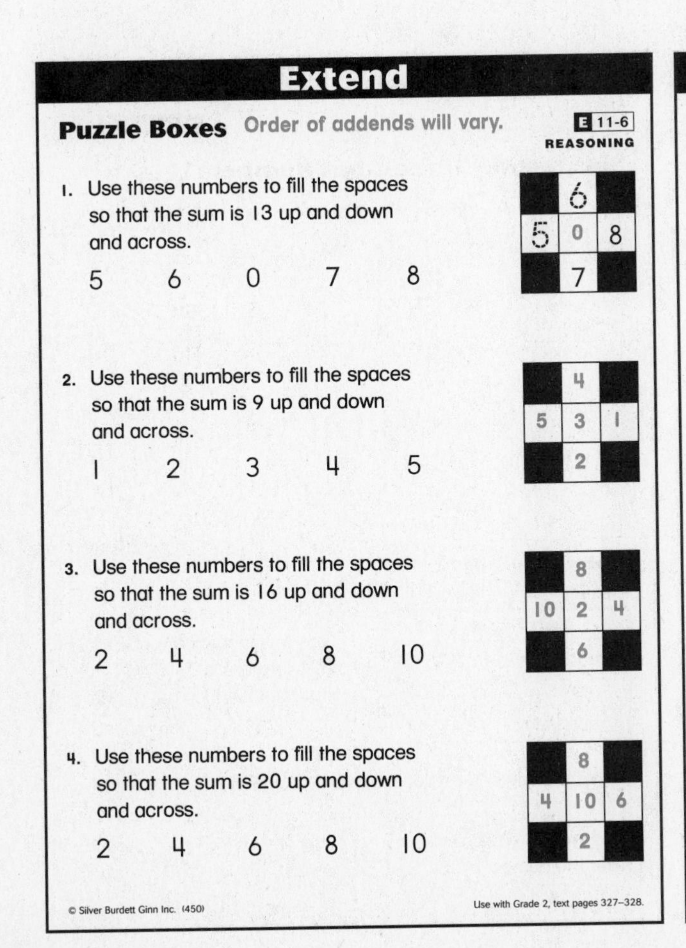

Extend

Puzzle Boxes

Order of addends will vary.

E 11-6 REASONING

1. Use these numbers to fill the spaces so that the sum is 13 up and down and across.
 5 6 0 7 8
 (Answer: 6 / 5 0 8 / 7)

2. Use these numbers to fill the spaces so that the sum is 9 up and down and across.
 1 2 3 4 5
 (Answer: 4 / 5 3 1 / 2)

3. Use these numbers to fill the spaces so that the sum is 16 up and down and across.
 2 4 6 8 10
 (Answer: 8 / 10 2 4 / 6)

4. Use these numbers to fill the spaces so that the sum is 20 up and down and across.
 2 4 6 8 10
 (Answer: 8 / 4 10 6 / 2)

 Use with Grade 2, text pages 327–328.

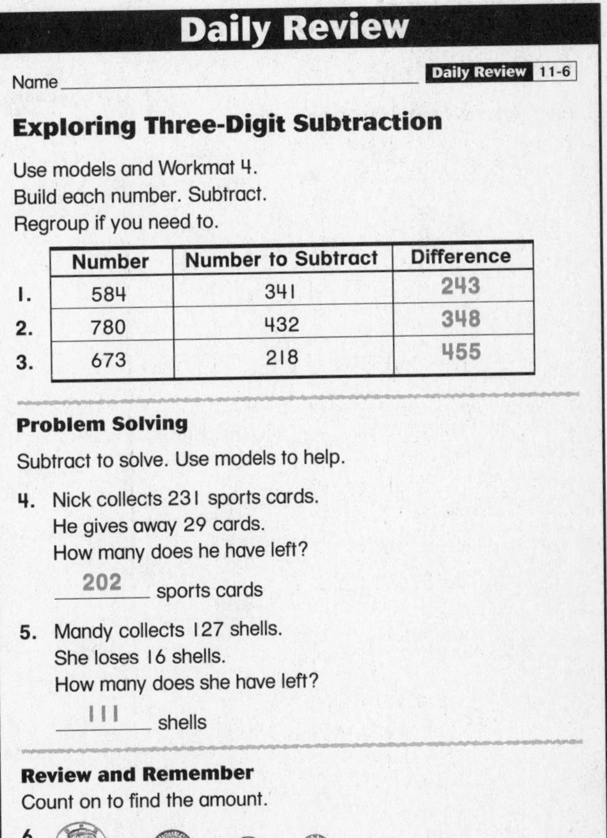

Daily Review

Name ____________

Daily Review 11-6

Exploring Three-Digit Subtraction

Use models and Workmat 4.
Build each number. Subtract.
Regroup if you need to.

	Number	Number to Subtract	Difference
1.	584	341	243
2.	780	432	348
3.	673	218	455

Problem Solving

Subtract to solve. Use models to help.

4. Nick collects 231 sports cards.
 He gives away 29 cards.
 How many does he have left?
 202 sports cards

5. Mandy collects 127 shells.
 She loses 16 shells.
 How many does she have left?
 111 shells

Review and Remember

Count on to find the amount.

6. 86¢

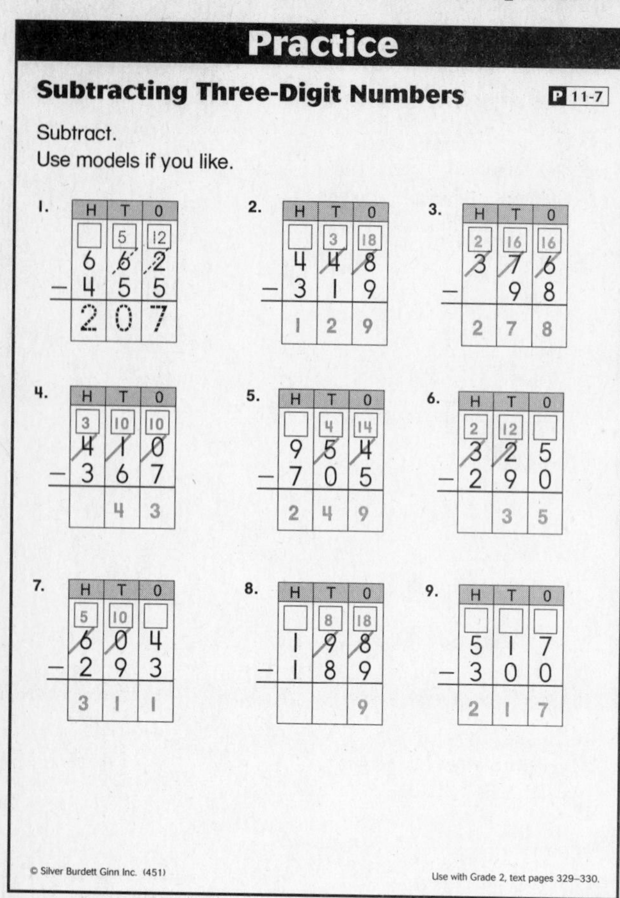

Practice

Subtracting Three-Digit Numbers

P 11-7

Subtract.
Use models if you like.

1. 662 − 455 = 207
2. 448 − 319 = 129
3. 376 − 98 = 278
4. 410 − 367 = 43
5. 954 − 705 = 249
6. 325 − 290 = 35
7. 604 − 293 = 311
8. 198 − 189 = 9
9. 517 − 300 = 217

© Silver Burdett Ginn Inc. (451)

Use with Grade 2, text pages 329–330.

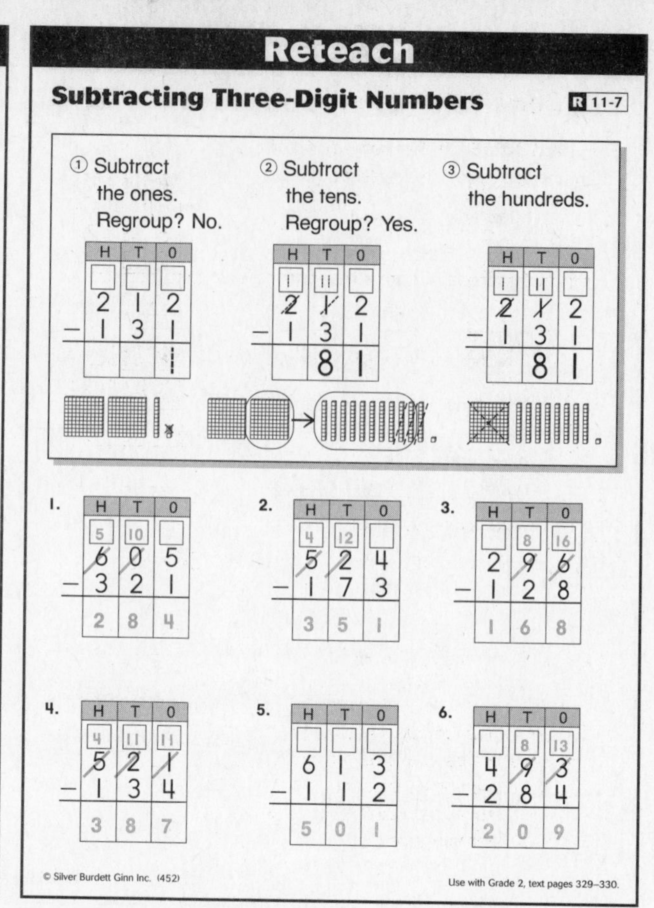

Reteach

Subtracting Three-Digit Numbers

R 11-7

① Subtract the ones. Regroup? No.
② Subtract the tens. Regroup? Yes.
③ Subtract the hundreds.

212 − 131 = 81

1. 605 − 321 = 284
2. 524 − 173 = 351
3. 296 − 128 = 168
4. 521 − 134 = 387
5. 613 − 112 = 501
6. 493 − 284 = 209

© Silver Burdett Ginn Inc. (452)

Use with Grade 2, text pages 329–330.

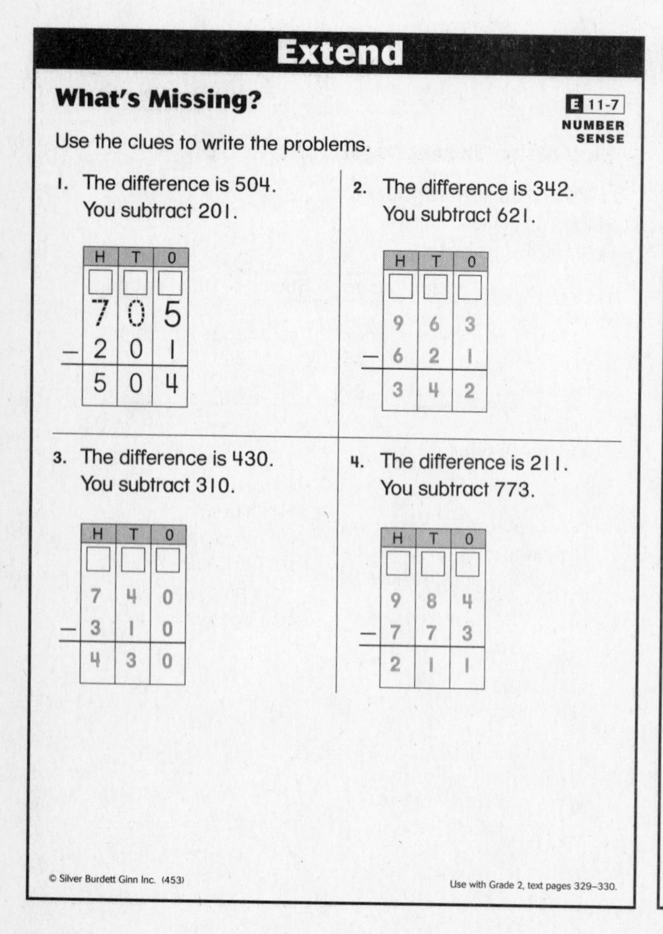

Extend

What's Missing?

E 11-7 NUMBER SENSE

Use the clues to write the problems.

1. The difference is 504. You subtract 201.
   705 − 201 = 504
2. The difference is 342. You subtract 621.
   963 − 621 = 342
3. The difference is 430. You subtract 310.
   740 − 310 = 430
4. The difference is 211. You subtract 773.
   984 − 773 = 211

© Silver Burdett Ginn Inc. (453)

Use with Grade 2, text pages 329–330.

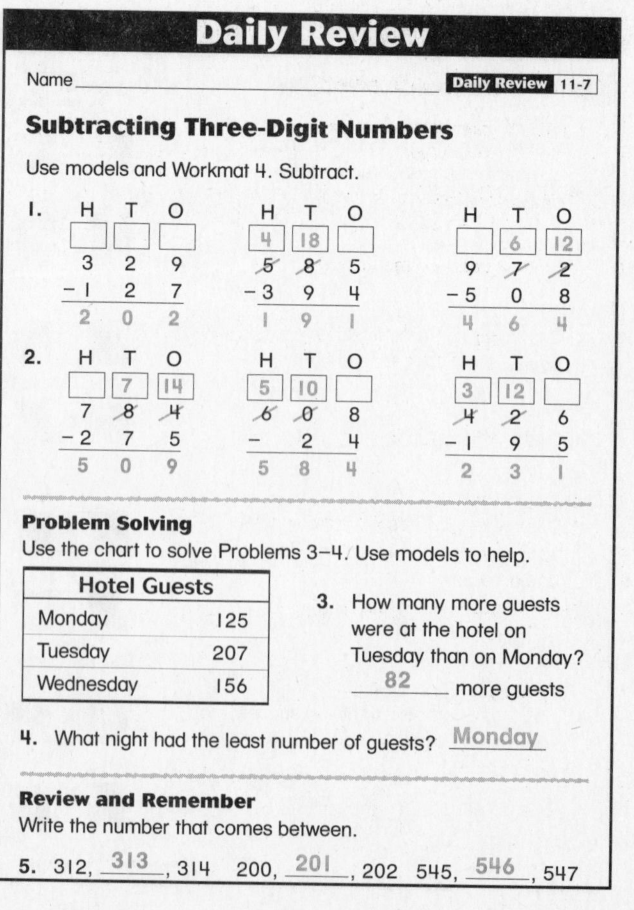

Daily Review

Name ______________ Daily Review 11-7

Subtracting Three-Digit Numbers

Use models and Workmat 4. Subtract.

1. 329 − 127 = 202 | 585 − 394 = 191 | 972 − 508 = 464
2. 784 − 275 = 509 | 608 − 24 = 584 | 426 − 195 = 231

Problem Solving

Use the chart to solve Problems 3–4. Use models to help.

Hotel Guests	
Monday	125
Tuesday	207
Wednesday	156

3. How many more guests were at the hotel on Tuesday than on Monday? 82 more guests
4. What night had the least number of guests? Monday

Review and Remember

Write the number that comes between.

5. 312, 313, 314   200, 201, 202   545, 546, 547

Chapter 11 • Lesson 8

Practice

Practicing Subtraction

P 11-8

Subtract. Draw or use models if you like.

1. 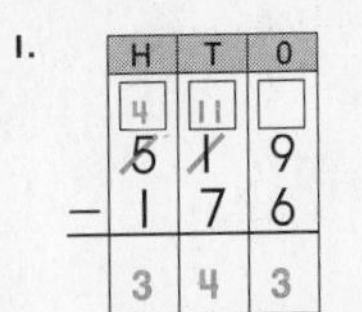

2. 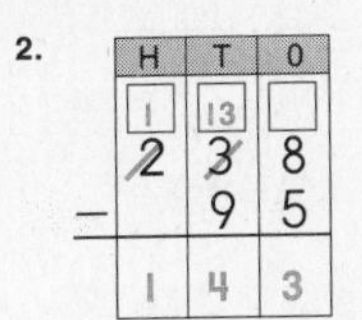

3.

H	T	O
	5	17
5	6	7
− 2	3	9
3	2	8

4. 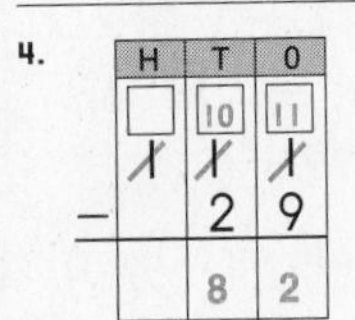

5. 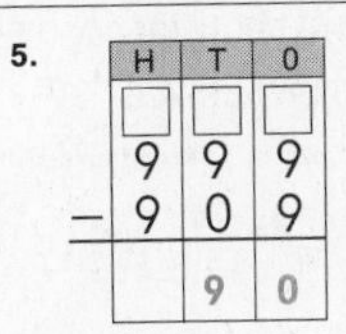

6. 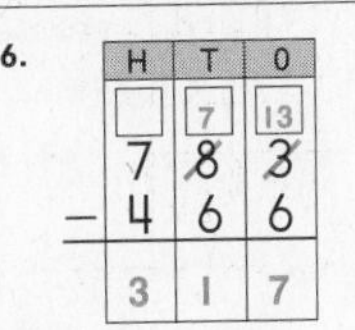

Write in vertical form. Subtract.

7. 222 − 171   222 − 171 = 51

8. 419 − 277   419 − 277 = 142

9. 342 − 56   342 − 56 = 286

10. Eamon helped ice cupcakes for the school bake sale. He used chocolate icing for 172 cupcakes and vanilla icing for 169 cupcakes. How many more chocolate cupcakes than vanilla did Eamon have?

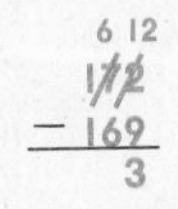

Use with Grade 2, text pages 331–332.

Reteach

Practicing Subtraction

R 11-8

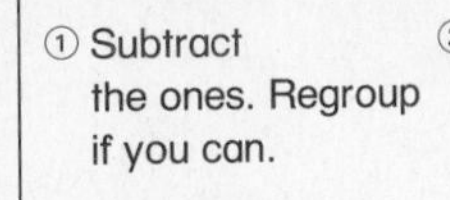

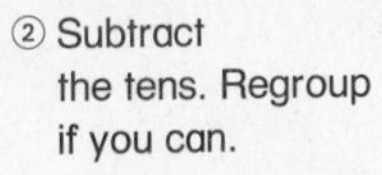

① Subtract the ones. Regroup if you can.

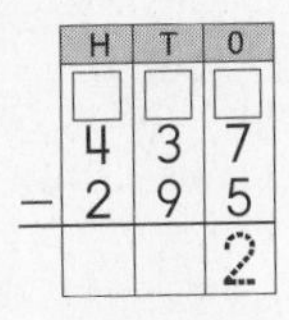

② Subtract the tens. Regroup if you can.

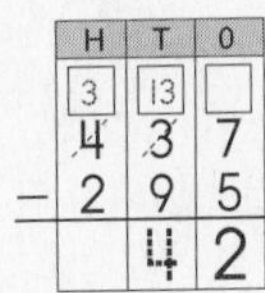

③ Subtract the hundreds.

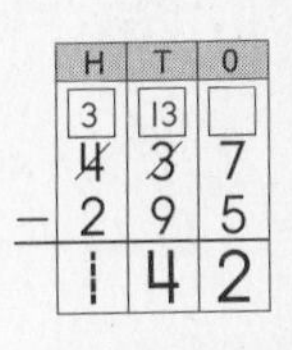

Subtract. Use models if you like.

1. 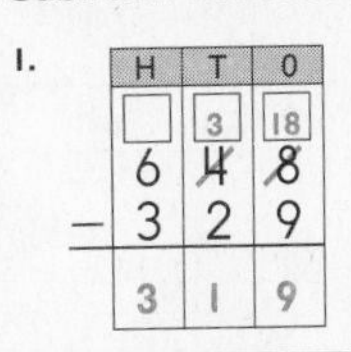

2. 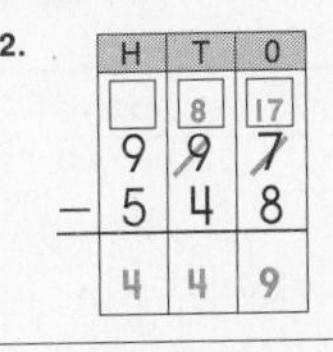

3. 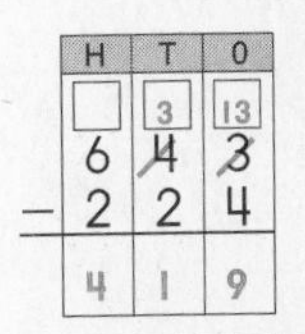

4. 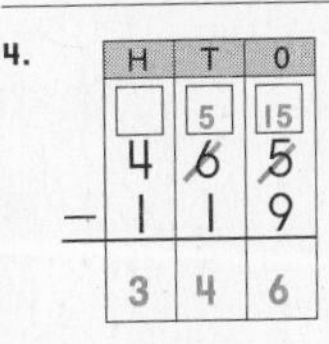

5. 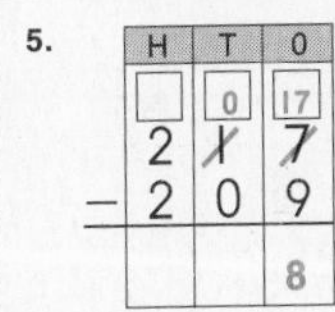

6. 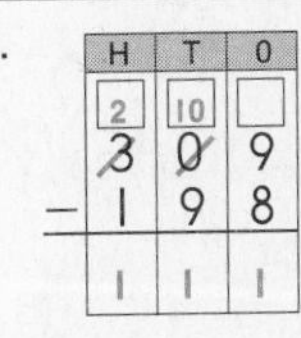

Use with Grade 2, text pages 331–332.

Extend

How Many Hundreds?

E 11-8 MENTAL MATH

Sometimes you can add or subtract hundreds in your head.

218 + 300 = 518
365 − 100 = 265

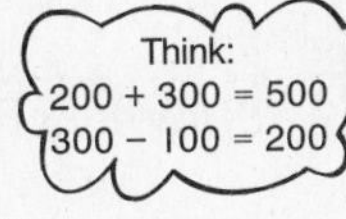

Add or subtract. Use mental math.

1. 459 + 300 = 759
2. 777 − 200 = 577
3. 123 + 700 = 823
4. 456 − 100 = 356
5. 210 + 400 = 610
6. 789 − 600 = 189
7. 222 + 500 = 722
8. 592 − 500 = 92
9. 136 + 800 = 936
10. 636 − 300 = 336
11. 294 + 400 = 694
12. 837 − 100 = 737
13. 199 + 200 = 399
14. 853 − 500 = 353
15. 269 + 600 = 869
16. 999 − 100 = 899
17. 182 + 700 = 882
18. 582 − 300 = 282

Use with Grade 2, text pages 331–332.

Daily Review

Name ______________________

Daily Review 11-8

Practicing Subtraction

Subtract. Use models if you like.

1. 436 − 129 = 307   709 − 206 = 503   562 − 381 = 181   385 − 294 = 91   663 − 437 = 226

2. 957 − 728 = 229   473 − 251 = 222   681 − 490 = 191   526 − 384 = 142   394 − 106 = 288

Problem Solving

Solve. Use models if you like.

3. Jim sells 275 bookmarks at the craft sale. He sells 159 picture frames. How many more bookmarks than frames does he sell?

116 more bookmarks

4. Michelle sells 182 bracelets. She sells 141 necklaces. How many more bracelets than necklaces does she sell?

41 more bracelets

Review and Remember

Ring the shapes that show equal parts.

5. 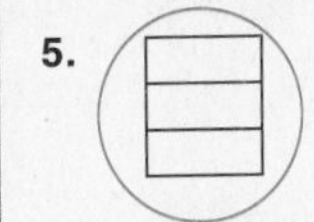 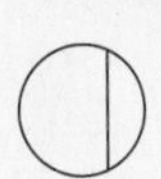 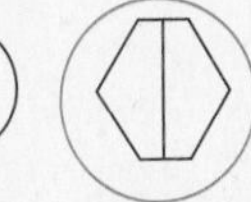 

Practice

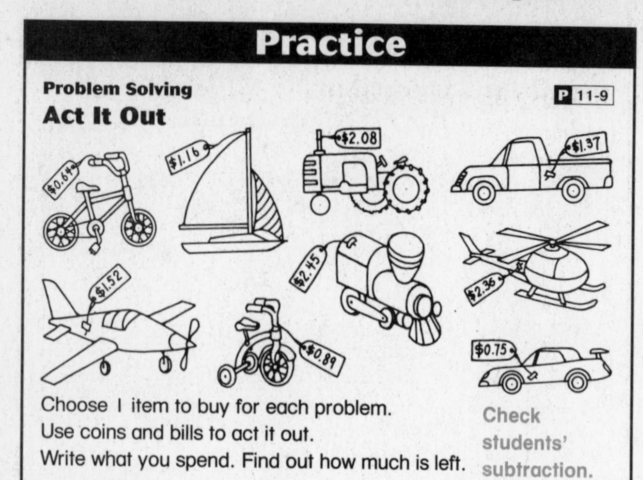

Problem Solving P 11-9

Act It Out

Choose 1 item to buy for each problem.
Use coins and bills to act it out.
Write what you spend. Find out how much is left.

Check students' subtraction.

You have	You spend	Amount left
(3 one-dollar bills)	\$ ___.___	\$ ___.___
(1 one-dollar bill)	\$ ___.___	\$ ___.___
(2 one-dollar bills)	\$ ___.___	\$ ___.___
(3 one-dollar bills)	\$ ___.___	\$ ___.___

 Use with Grade 2, text pages 333–334.

Reteach

Problem Solving R 11-9

Act It Out

Gabo has this much money. He buys a cup.

The coins crossed out show the money he spent.
This is how much Gabo has left. $1.96

Use and cross out bills and coins to show money spent.

1. Claudia has this much money. She buys postcards.

   Write how much Claudia has left. $ 2.81

2. Carlos has this much money. He buys a toy train.

   Write how much Carlos has left. $ 0.20

 Use with Grade 2, text pages 333–334.

Extend

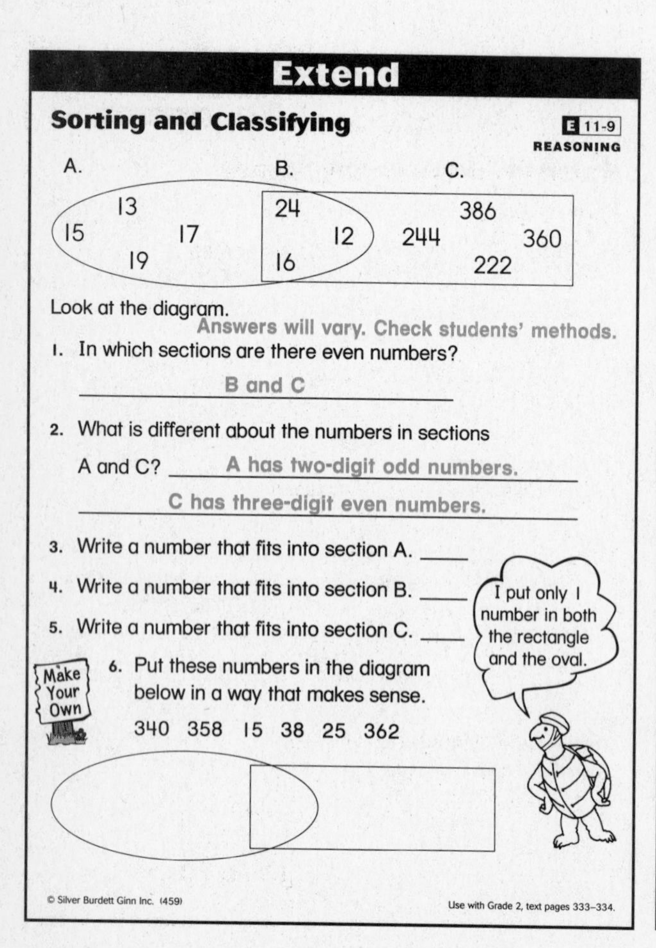

Sorting and Classifying

E 11-9
REASONING

Look at the diagram.
Answers will vary. Check students' methods.

1. In which sections are there even numbers?
   B and C
2. What is different about the numbers in sections A and C? A has two-digit odd numbers.
   C has three-digit even numbers.
3. Write a number that fits into section A. ____
4. Write a number that fits into section B. ____
5. Write a number that fits into section C. ____
6. Put these numbers in the diagram below in a way that makes sense.
   340 358 15 38 25 362

 Use with Grade 2, text pages 333–334.

Daily Review

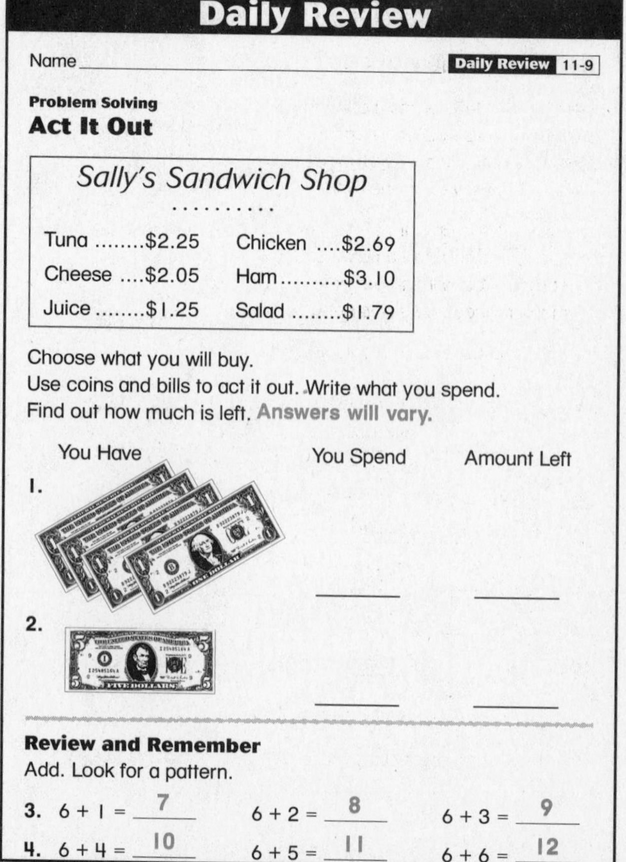

Name ________________ Daily Review 11-9

Problem Solving

Act It Out

Sally's Sandwich Shop

Tuna \$2.25	Chicken \$2.69
Cheese \$2.05	Ham..........\$3.10
Juice \$1.25	Salad \$1.79

Choose what you will buy.
Use coins and bills to act it out. Write what you spend.
Find out how much is left. Answers will vary.

	You Have	You Spend	Amount Left
1.	(4 one-dollar bills)	____	____
2.	(1 five-dollar bill)	____	____

Review and Remember

Add. Look for a pattern.

3. 6 + 1 = 7 6 + 2 = 8 6 + 3 = 9
4. 6 + 4 = 10 6 + 5 = 11 6 + 6 = 12

Practice

Adding and Subtracting Money

P 11-10

You can buy these blocks.

Find the cost for each set of 2 blocks.

1. 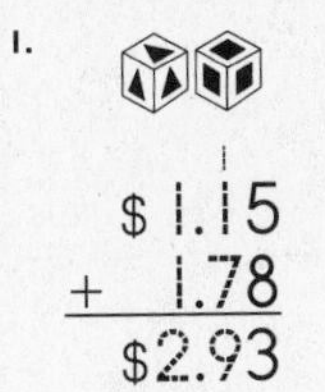
$1.15 + 1.78 = $2.93

2. 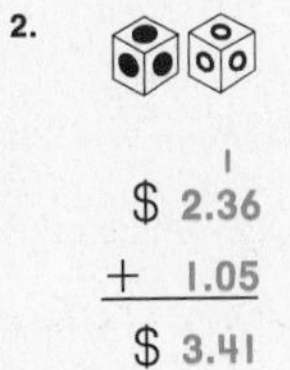
$2.36 + 1.05 = $3.41

3. 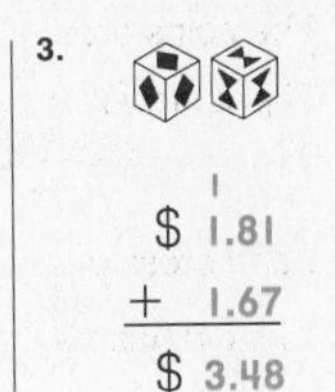
$1.81 + 1.67 = $3.48

Find the cost of the two blocks. Then find how much you have left after you buy them.

4. 
You have $6.45.
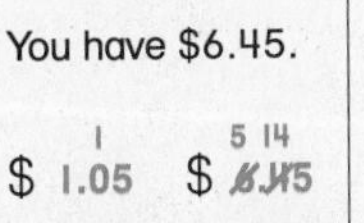
$1.05 + 1.78 = $2.83; $6.45 − 2.83 = $3.62

5. 
You have $5.17.
$1.67 + 2.36 = $4.03; $5.17 − 4.03 = $1.14

6. 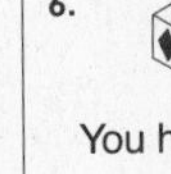
You have $5.04.
$1.81 + 1.78 = $3.59; $5.04 − 3.59 = $1.45

Use with Grade 2, text pages 335–336.

Reteach

Adding and Subtracting Money

Add $1.19 + $2.23
$ 1.19
+ 2.23
$ 3.42
Make sure you put the cents point in your answer.
Subtract $2.73 − $0.69
$ 2.73
− 0.69
$ 2.04

Add or subtract.

1. $2.78 + 0.94 = $3.72	2. $2.92 + 0.74 = $3.66	3. $5.60 − 1.25 = $4.35	4. $0.99 + 2.49 = $3.48
5. $7.15 − 5.09 = $2.06	6. $2.30 + 1.95 = $4.25	7. $6.55 + 3.35 = $9.90	8. $4.84 − 1.36 = $3.48
9. $9.11 + 0.09 = $9.20	10. $8.42 − 2.08 = $6.34	11. $6.35 − 1.16 = $5.19	12. $5.03 + 3.58 = $8.61
13. $7.40 − 1.26 = $6.14	14. $3.58 + 0.29 = $3.87	15. $4.31 − 4.07 = $0.24	16. $5.68 + 0.90 = $6.58

Use with Grade 2, text pages 335–336.

Extend

Keeping Track

E 11-10
CALCULATOR

Every week Delia earns money for doing chores. She spends some money and saves the rest. Find out how much money Delia saved in one month.

Add the money for weeks 1 and 2 and then weeks 3 and 4. Then add those sums together.

1. Subtract the amount of money she spent from the amount she earned. You will find out how much money she saves each week.
2. Fill in the table. Use a calculator if you like.

Week	Money earned	Money spent	Money saved
Week 1	$2.75	$1.45	$1.30
Week 2	$3.68	$3.60	$0.08
Week 3	$1.98	$1.09	$0.89
Week 4	$5.23	$3.75	$1.48
Total	$13.64	$9.89	$3.75

3. How much more money did Delia spend than save? $ 6.14
4. How much more money did Delia earn than spend? $ 3.75

Use with Grade 2, text pages 335–336.

Daily Review

Name ____________

Daily Review 11-10

Adding and Subtracting Money

Add or subtract.

1. $4.35 + 1.17 = $5.52; $9.56 − 3.48 = $6.08; $3.37 + 4.06 = $7.43; $8.50 − 6.43 = $2.07; $0.64 + 0.24 = $0.88
2. $5.62 − 1.26 = $4.36; $7.81 − 3.47 = $4.34; $6.30 + 1.07 = $7.37; $2.24 + 3.66 = $5.90; $7.36 − 4.36 = $3.00

Problem Solving

Solve. Use bills and coins if you need to.

3. Sandra buys a book for $2.79. She gives the clerk 2 $1 bills, 3 quarters, and 1 dime. What change does she get? 6¢
4. Erin buys a notebook for $3.30. She gives the clerk 3 $1 bills and 2 quarters. What change does she get? 20¢

Review and Remember

Write the number.

5. 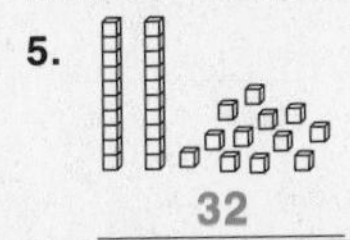
32

6. 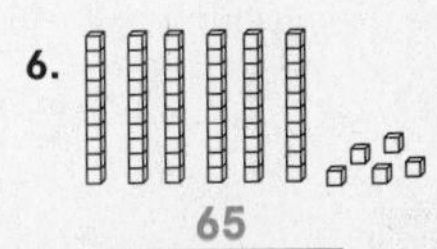
65

Practice

Choosing a Computation Method

P 11-11

Think about ways to solve each problem.
Add or subtract. Then write the letter of the way you used.

A. models
B. pencil and paper
C. mental math
D. calculator

1. 576 + 392 = 968 I used ___.
   643 − 200 = 443 I used ___.
   234 + 456 = 690 I used ___.
   973 + 14 = 987 I used ___.

2. 100 + 825 = 925 I used ___.
   666 + 166 = 832 I used ___.
   75 + 170 = 245 I used ___.
   676 − 392 = 284 I used ___.

3. 679 − 402 = 277 I used ___.
   999 − 111 = 888 I used ___.
   821 − 557 = 264 I used ___.
   784 − 200 = 584 I used ___.

Check students' methods.

 Use with Grade 2, text pages 337–338.

Reteach

Choosing a Computation Method

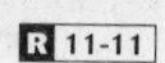

You can add or subtract in different ways.

You can use mental math.
300 + 200 → Think 3 + 2 = 5
So, 300 + 200 = 500

You can use a calculator.

You can use paper and pencil.
321 − 219 = 102

You can use models.
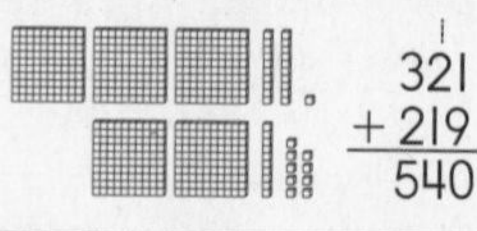
321 + 219 = 540

Add or subtract. Choose your own method.

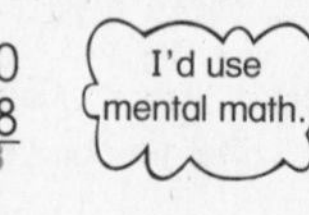

I'd use mental math.

1. 200 + 700 = 900
   420 − 300 = 120
   600 + 108 = 708

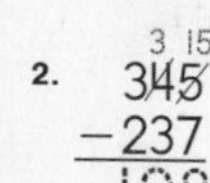

2. 345 − 237 = 108
   789 + 123 = 912
   431 − 134 = 297

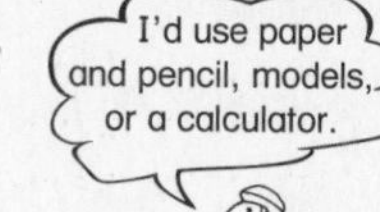

I'd use paper and pencil, models, or a calculator.

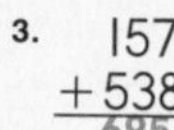

3. 157 + 538 = 695
   222 − 74 = 148
   649 + 307 = 956
   872 − 444 = 428

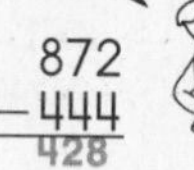

 Use with Grade 2, text pages 337–338.

Extend

Comparing Rivers

DATA

River	Length in miles
Powder	375
Salmon	420
Noatak	350
Gila	649
Susquehanna	444
Wabash	512
Tombigbee	525

Use the information on the chart to answer the questions.

1. How much shorter is the Powder River than the Gila River? 274 miles
2. How much longer is the Wabash River than the Salmon River? 92 miles
3. What is the difference in length between the longest and the shortest river on the chart? 299 miles
4. Which river is 137 miles shorter than the Gila River? Wabash
5. Which river is 24 miles longer than the Salmon River? Susquehanna

 Use with Grade 2, text pages 337–338.

Daily Review

Name ______________________ Daily Review 11-11

Choosing a Computation Method

Add or subtract.
Draw a line to show how you solved each problem.

1. 328 + 127 = 455
   734 − 206 = 528
   829 − 471 = 358
   462 + 523 = 985
   581 − 65 = 516

models   paper and pencil   mental math   calculator

Methods will vary.

Problem Solving
Solve.

2. Drew gets paid $2.25 an hour to babysit. He works for 2 hours. How much money does he make? $4.50
3. Olivia gets paid $1.10 a day to walk her neighbor's dog. How much does she get paid for 2 days? $2.20

Review and Remember
Circle the shapes that are open.

4.

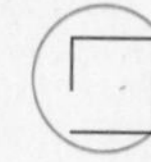
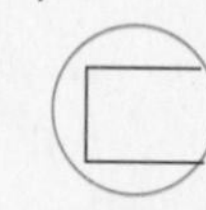
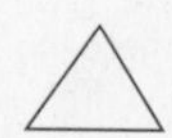

Practice

Problem Solving P 11-12

Too Much Information

Cross out the information you do not need. Solve.

1. In Colorado, we visited Rocky Mountain National Park. There were 346 campers in campground B. ~~My family camped in site 362.~~ There were 320 campers in campground D. How many people were camped in areas B and D?

   346
   +320
   666 campers

2. We went fishing in Cape Cod with my cousins and caught 437 fish. ~~You can drive the whole way around Cape Cod in 2 and a half hours.~~ We also trapped 136 lobsters. How many more fish than lobsters did we get?

   437
   − 136
   301 more fish

3. On my aunt's farm in Ohio we counted 208 corn plants. There were 83 pumpkins in the pumpkin patch. ~~The cornfield was 23 feet longer than the pumpkin patch.~~ How many more corn plants than pumpkins did we count?

   208
   − 83
   125 more corn plants

 Use with Grade 2, text pages 339–340.

Reteach

Problem Solving R 11-12

Too Much Information

Read the question. Then read the information in the boxes. Cross out the information you do not need. Solve.

1. How much more rain does Astoria, Oregon, get in a year than Yuma, Arizona?

Astoria, OR, gets about 70 inches of rain a year.	~~Miami, FL, is one of the wettest cities. It gets about 60 inches of rain a year.~~	Yuma, AZ, is very dry. It gets only about 3 inches of rain a year.

70 inches in Astoria
− 3 inches in Yuma
Astoria gets 67 inches more rain.

2. How many more historic places does Philadelphia, Pennsylvania, have than Providence, Rhode Island?

~~Philadelphia, PA, was the capital of the U.S. in 1790.~~	Philadelphia, PA, has 470 historic places.	There are 126 historic places in Providence, RI.

470 places in Philadelphia
− 126 places in Providence
Philadelphia has 344 more places.

 Use with Grade 2, text pages 339–340.

Extend

Hidden Patterns

E 11-12 PATTERNS

Continue each pattern.

1. 967 867 767 667 567 467
2. 843 793 743 693 643 593
3. 124 249 374 499 624 749
4. 135 307 479 651 823 995
5. 312+78 317+73 322+68 327+63 332+58
6. 956−85 944−72 932−59 920−46 908−33
7. 145+366 150+341 155+316 160+291 165+266

8. Make a pattern with three-digit numbers.

Check students' patterns.

 Use with Grade 2, text pages 339–340.

Daily Review

Name ____________ Daily Review 11-12

Problem Solving

Too Much Information

Cross out the information you do not need. Solve.

1. Bill's Bike Shop has 125 10-speed bikes. They have 92 5-speed bikes. ~~45 of the bikes are red.~~ How many more 10-speed than 5-speed bikes do they have?

   125
   − 92
   33

   33 more 10-speed bikes

2. The Bike Shop has a raffle. ~~They have 35 prizes to give away.~~ They sell 223 raffle tickets on Friday. They sell 347 tickets on Saturday. How many raffle tickets are sold?

   223
   + 347
   570

   570 tickets

Review and Remember

Write the number.

3. 812

4. 232

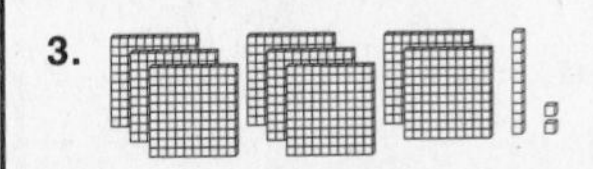

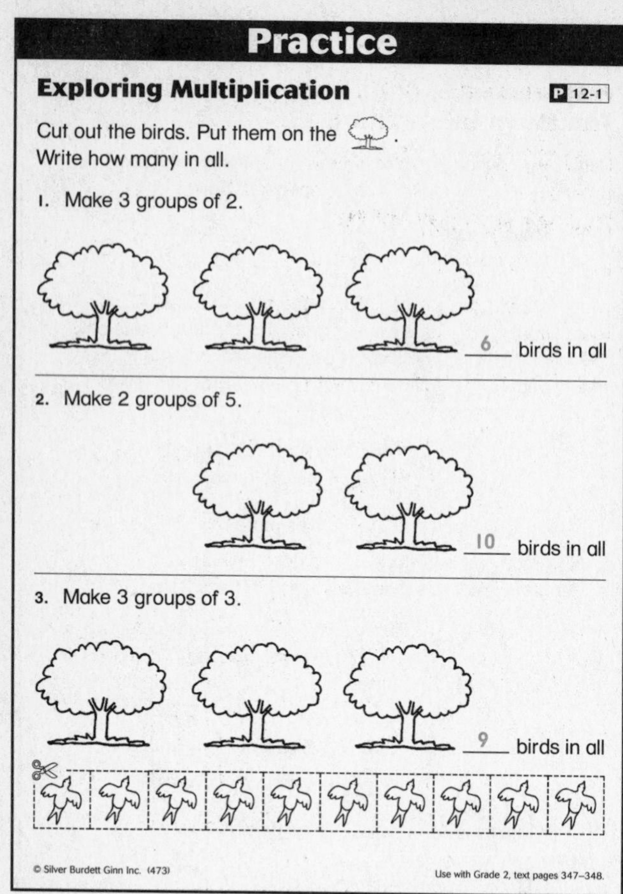

Practice

Exploring Multiplication

P 12-1

Cut out the birds. Put them on the tree.
Write how many in all.

1. Make 3 groups of 2.

6 birds in all

2. Make 2 groups of 5.

10 birds in all

3. Make 3 groups of 3.

9 birds in all

© Silver Burdett Ginn Inc. (473)

Use with Grade 2, text pages 347–348.

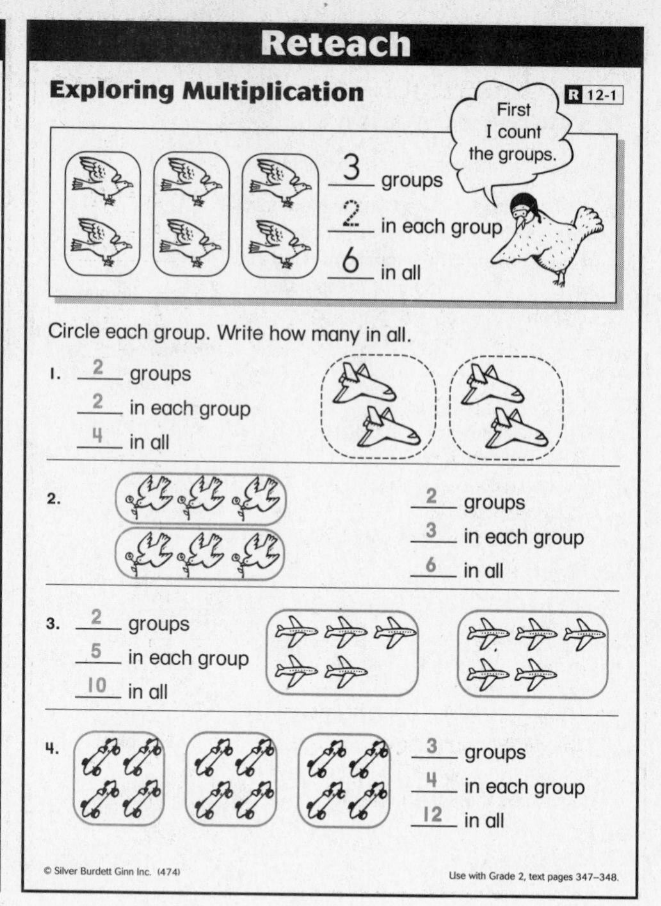

Reteach

Exploring Multiplication

R 12-1

First
I count
the groups.

3 groups
2 in each group
6 in all

Circle each group. Write how many in all.

1. 2 groups
2 in each group
4 in all

2. 2 groups
3 in each group
6 in all

3. 2 groups
5 in each group
10 in all

4. 3 groups
4 in each group
12 in all

© Silver Burdett Ginn Inc. (474)

Use with Grade 2, text pages 347–348.

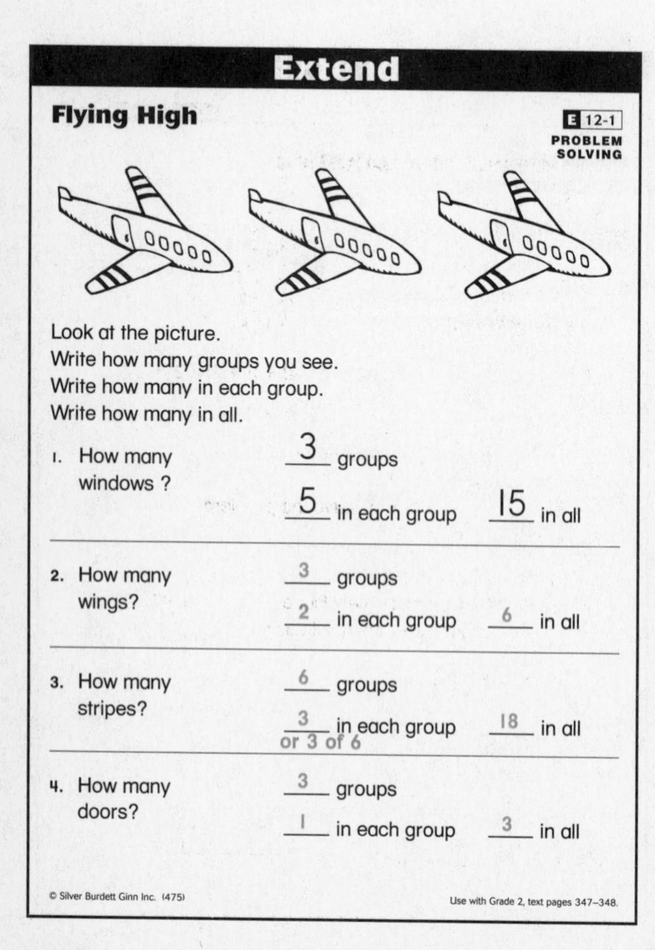

Extend

Flying High

E 12-1
PROBLEM SOLVING

Look at the picture.
Write how many groups you see.
Write how many in each group.
Write how many in all.

1. How many windows ? 3 groups
5 in each group 15 in all

2. How many wings? 3 groups
2 in each group 6 in all

3. How many stripes? 6 groups
3 in each group 18 in all
or 3 of 6

4. How many doors? 3 groups
1 in each group 3 in all

© Silver Burdett Ginn Inc. (475)

Use with Grade 2, text pages 347–348.

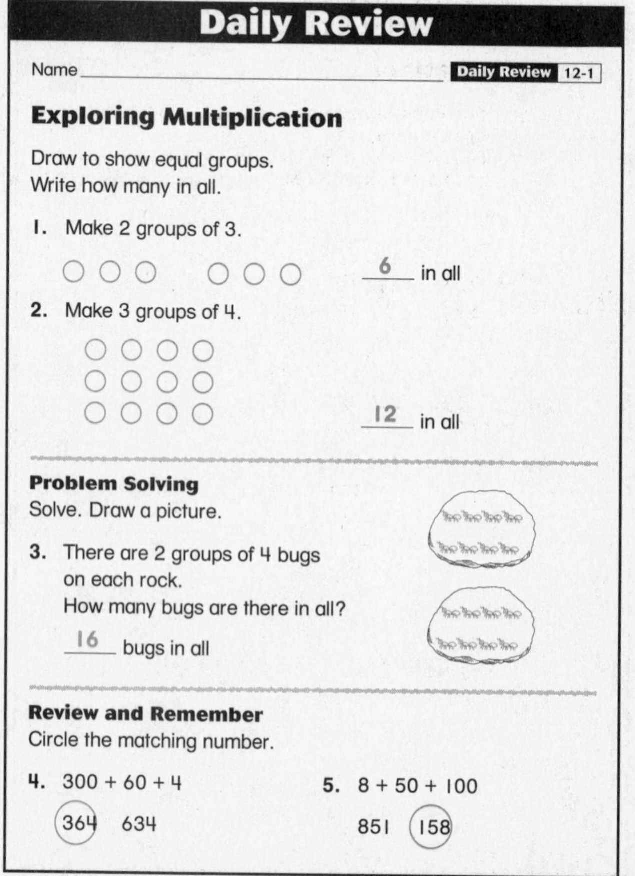

Daily Review

Name ________________ Daily Review 12-1

Exploring Multiplication

Draw to show equal groups.
Write how many in all.

1. Make 2 groups of 3.

6 in all

2. Make 3 groups of 4.

12 in all

Problem Solving
Solve. Draw a picture.

3. There are 2 groups of 4 bugs on each rock.
How many bugs are there in all?
16 bugs in all

Review and Remember
Circle the matching number.

4. 300 + 60 + 4
(364) 634

5. 8 + 50 + 100
851 (158)

Practice

Addition and Multiplication

P 12-2

Add. Then multiply. Circle groups if you like.

1. $3 + 3 = 6$
   $2 \times 3 = 6$

2. $3 + 3 + 3 = 9$
   $3 \times 3 = 9$

3. $2 + 2 + 2 + 2 = 8$
   $4 \times 2 = 8$

4. $4 + 4 + 4 = 12$
   $3 \times 4 = 12$

5. $5 + 5 = 10$
   $2 \times 5 = 10$

6. $3 + 3 + 3 + 3 = 12$
   $4 \times 3 = 12$

Use with Grade 2, text pages 349–350.

Reteach

Addition and Multiplication

R 12-2

groups of 3

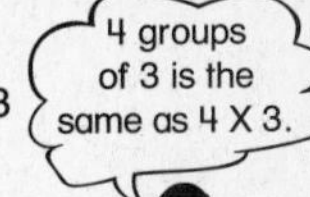

4 groups of 3 is the same as 4 X 3.

Add. $3 + 3 + 3 + 3 = 12$

Multiply. $4 \times 3 = 12$

Add. Then multiply. Use counters if you like.

1. Circle groups of 2.

Add. $2+2+2+2 = 8$

Multiply. $4 \times 2 = 8$

2. Circle groups of 6.

Add. $6 + 6 = 12$

Multiply. $2 \times 6 = 12$

3. Circle groups of 4.

Add. $4+4+4 = 12$

Multiply. $3 \times 4 = 12$

Use with Grade 2, text pages 349–350.

Extend

Kite Combinations

E 12-2 REASONING

All the numbers in each kite can be made with groups of the least number.
Use the numbers in the kite to fill in the chart.
Use a calculator to check your answers.

1.

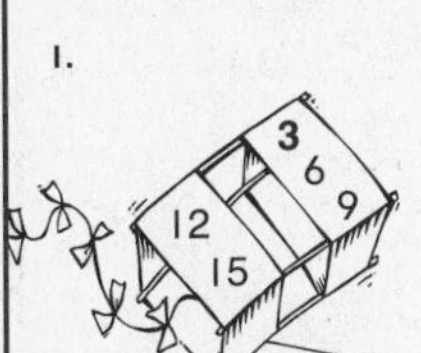

2.

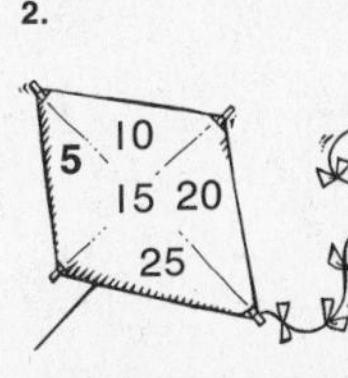

3.

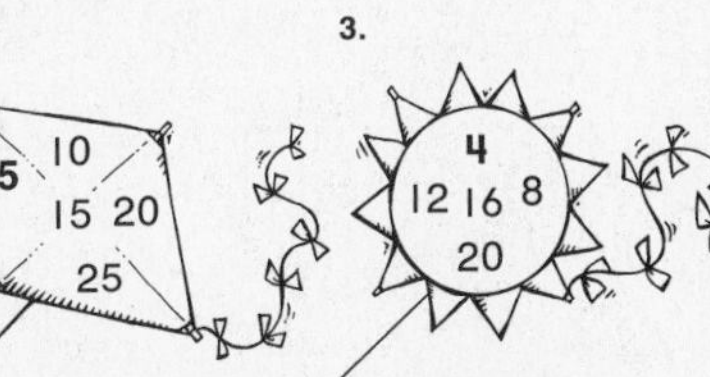

Groups of 3	
Number in each group	Total number
1	3
2	6
3	9
4	12
5	15

Groups of 5	
Number in each group	Total number
1	5
2	10
3	15
4	20
5	25

Groups of 4	
Number in each group	Total number
1	4
2	8
3	12
4	16
5	20

Use with Grade 2, text pages 349–350.

Daily Review

Name ____________________

Daily Review 12-2

Addition and Multiplication

Add. Then multiply.
Use counters if you like.

1. $5 + 5 = 10$
   $2 \times 5 = 10$

2. $2 + 2 + 2 + 2 = 8$
   $4 \times 2 = 8$

Problem Solving

Circle the number sentence to solve the problem.
Use counters to help.

3. Gina makes 4 necklaces.
   She puts 3 beads on each necklace.
   How many beads does she use in all?

   $4 \times 2 = 8$

   $4 \times 3 = 12$

   12 beads in all

Review and Remember

Write how many equal parts.

4.

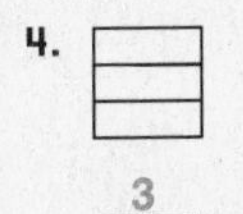

3

2

4

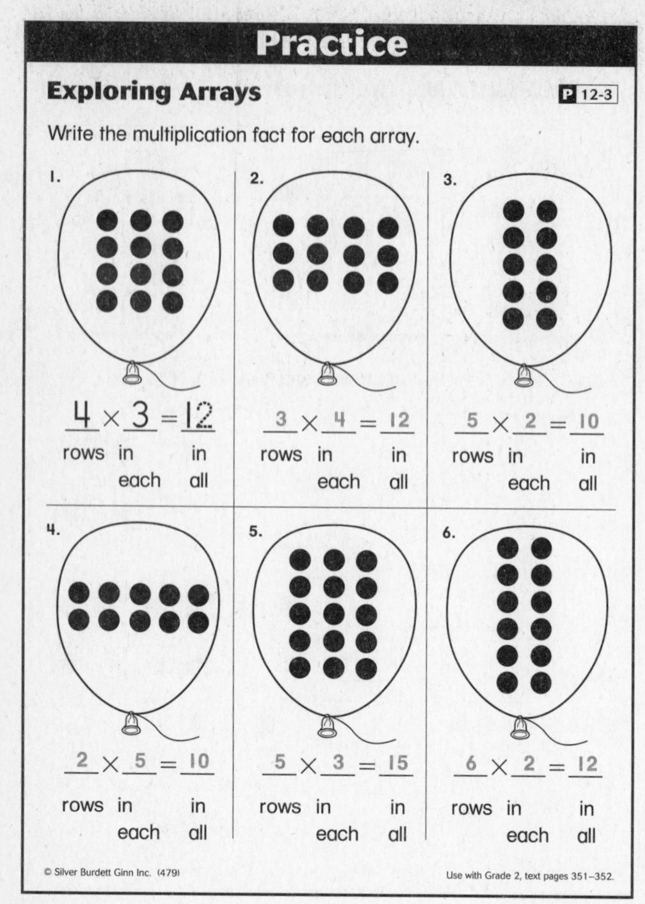

Practice

Exploring Arrays

P 12-3

Write the multiplication fact for each array.

1. 4 × 3 = 12
rows in each in all

2. 3 × 4 = 12
rows in each in all

3. 5 × 2 = 10
rows in each in all

4. 2 × 5 = 10
rows in each in all

5. 5 × 3 = 15
rows in each in all

6. 6 × 2 = 12
rows in each in all

 Use with Grade 2, text pages 351–352.

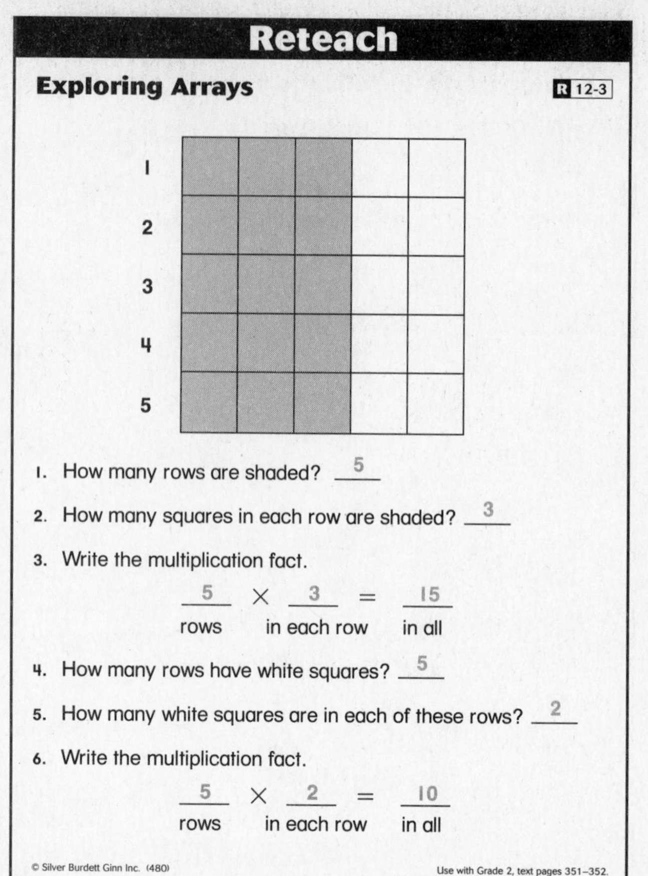

Reteach

Exploring Arrays

R 12-3

1. How many rows are shaded? 5
2. How many squares in each row are shaded? 3
3. Write the multiplication fact.
5 × 3 = 15
rows in each row in all
4. How many rows have white squares? 5
5. How many white squares are in each of these rows? 2
6. Write the multiplication fact.
5 × 2 = 10
rows in each row in all

 Use with Grade 2, text pages 351–352.

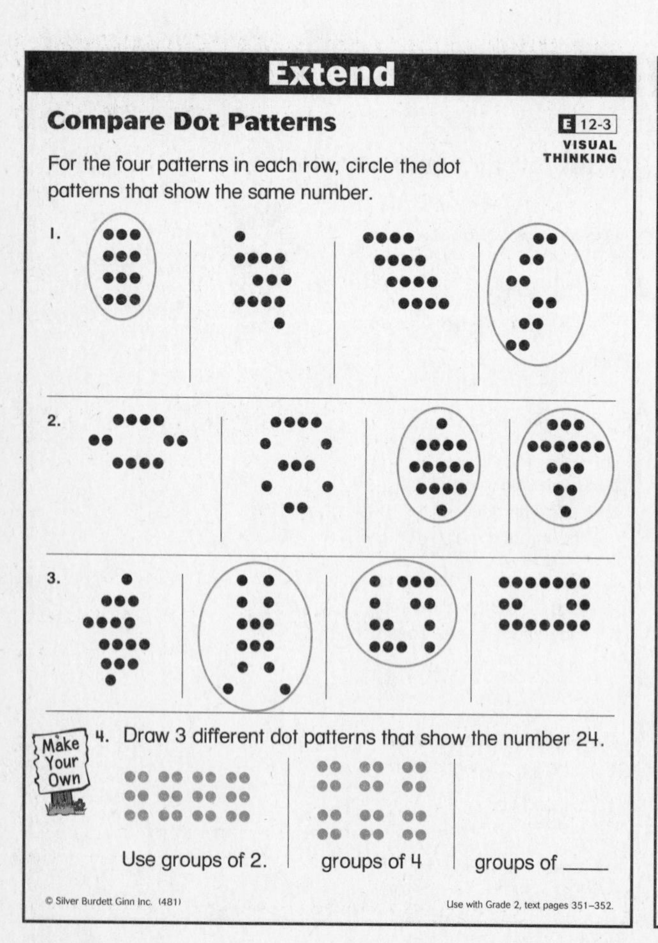

Extend

Compare Dot Patterns

E 12-3 VISUAL THINKING

For the four patterns in each row, circle the dot patterns that show the same number.

1.

2.

3.

Make Your Own

4. Draw 3 different dot patterns that show the number 24.

Use groups of 2. groups of 4 groups of ____

 Use with Grade 2, text pages 351–352.

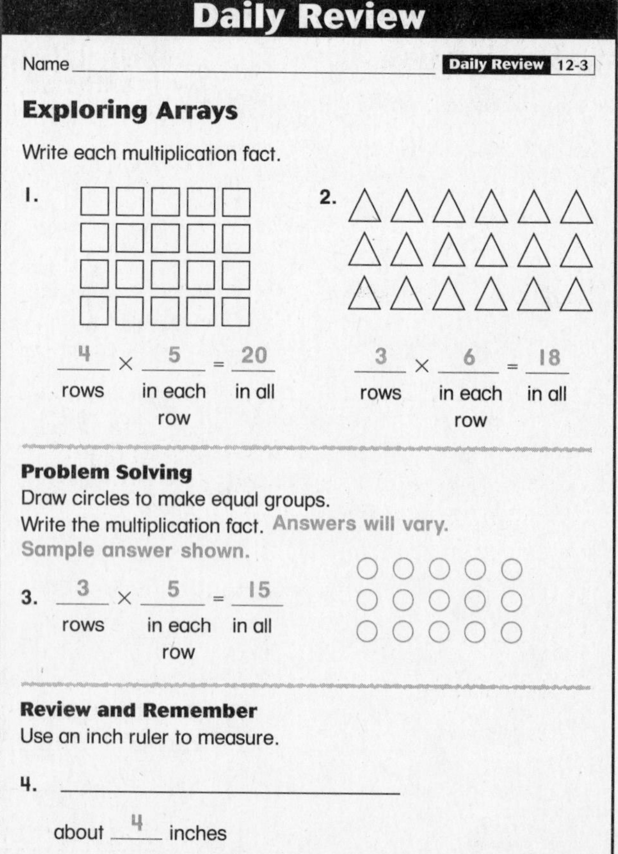

Daily Review

Name ____________________ Daily Review 12-3

Exploring Arrays

Write each multiplication fact.

1. 4 × 5 = 20
rows in each row in all

2. 3 × 6 = 18
rows in each row in all

Problem Solving

Draw circles to make equal groups.
Write the multiplication fact. Answers will vary. Sample answer shown.

3. 3 × 5 = 15
rows in each row in all

Review and Remember

Use an inch ruler to measure.

4. ____________________

about 4 inches

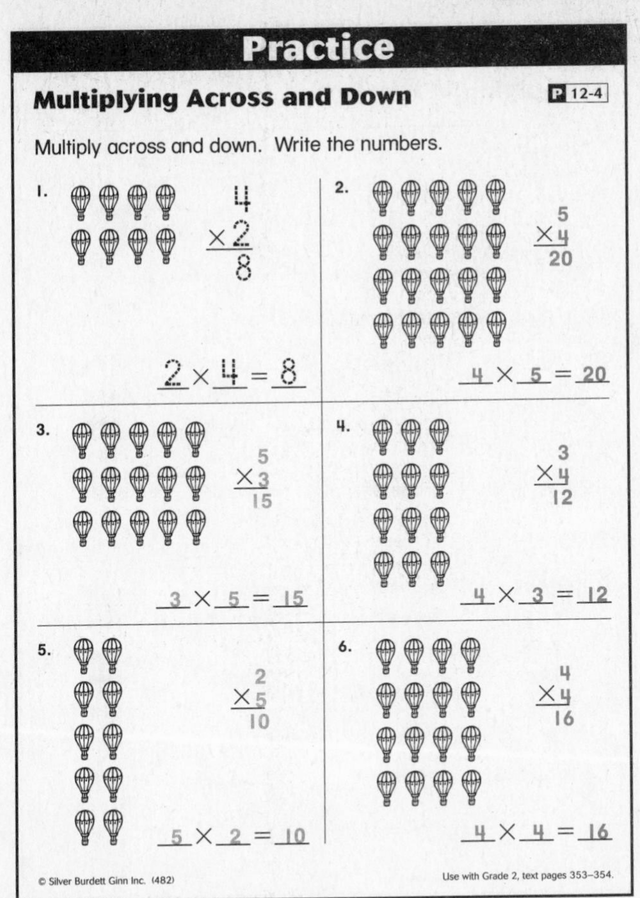

Practice

Multiplying Across and Down

P 12-4

Multiply across and down. Write the numbers.

1. $4 \times 2 = 8$ (down: 4, ×2, 8) — $2 \times 4 = 8$

2. 5, ×4, 20 — $4 \times 5 = 20$

3. 5, ×3, 15 — $3 \times 5 = 15$

4. 3, ×4, 12 — $4 \times 3 = 12$

5. 2, ×5, 10 — $5 \times 2 = 10$

6. 4, ×4, 16 — $4 \times 4 = 16$

Use with Grade 2, text pages 353–354.

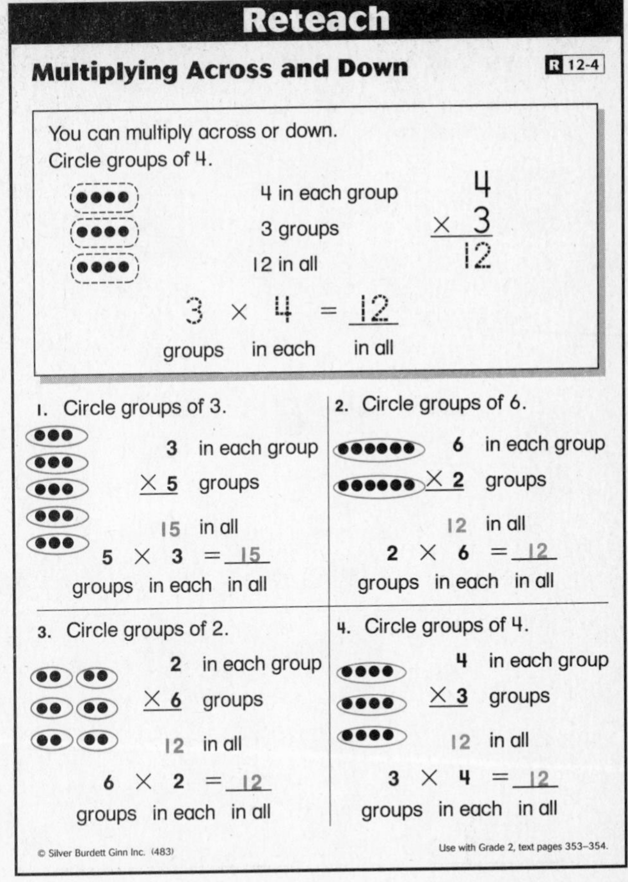

Reteach

Multiplying Across and Down

R 12-4

You can multiply across or down.
Circle groups of 4.

4 in each group
3 groups
12 in all

4
× 3
12

3 × 4 = 12
groups in each in all

1. Circle groups of 3.
3 in each group
× 5 groups
15 in all
5 × 3 = 15
groups in each in all

2. Circle groups of 6.
6 in each group
× 2 groups
12 in all
2 × 6 = 12
groups in each in all

3. Circle groups of 2.
2 in each group
× 6 groups
12 in all
6 × 2 = 12
groups in each in all

4. Circle groups of 4.
4 in each group
× 3 groups
12 in all
3 × 4 = 12
groups in each in all

Use with Grade 2, text pages 353–354.

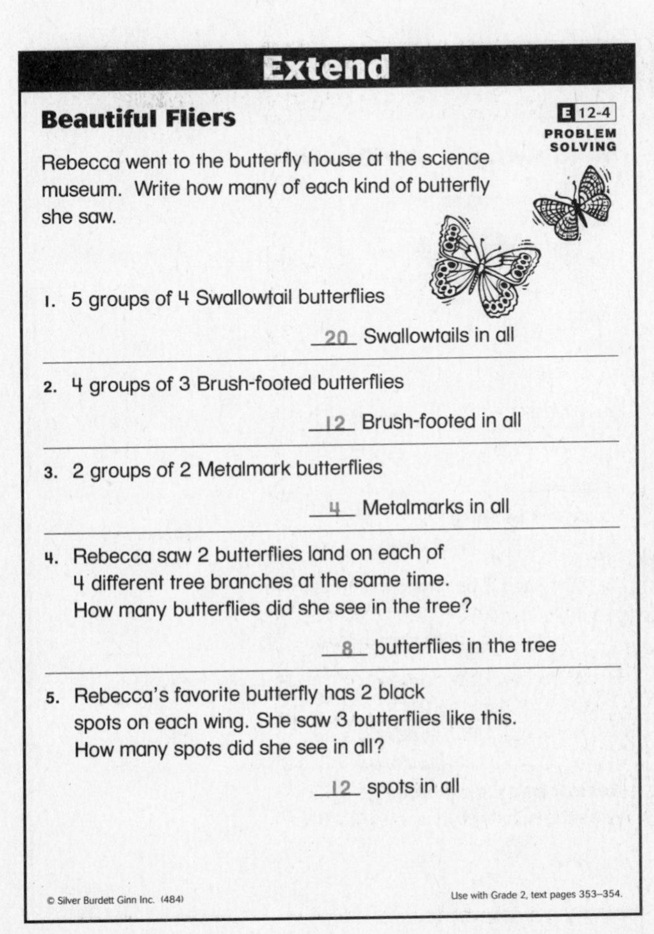

Extend

Beautiful Fliers

E 12-4
PROBLEM SOLVING

Rebecca went to the butterfly house at the science museum. Write how many of each kind of butterfly she saw.

1. 5 groups of 4 Swallowtail butterflies
20 Swallowtails in all

2. 4 groups of 3 Brush-footed butterflies
12 Brush-footed in all

3. 2 groups of 2 Metalmark butterflies
4 Metalmarks in all

4. Rebecca saw 2 butterflies land on each of 4 different tree branches at the same time. How many butterflies did she see in the tree?
8 butterflies in the tree

5. Rebecca's favorite butterfly has 2 black spots on each wing. She saw 3 butterflies like this. How many spots did she see in all?
12 spots in all

Use with Grade 2, text pages 353–354.

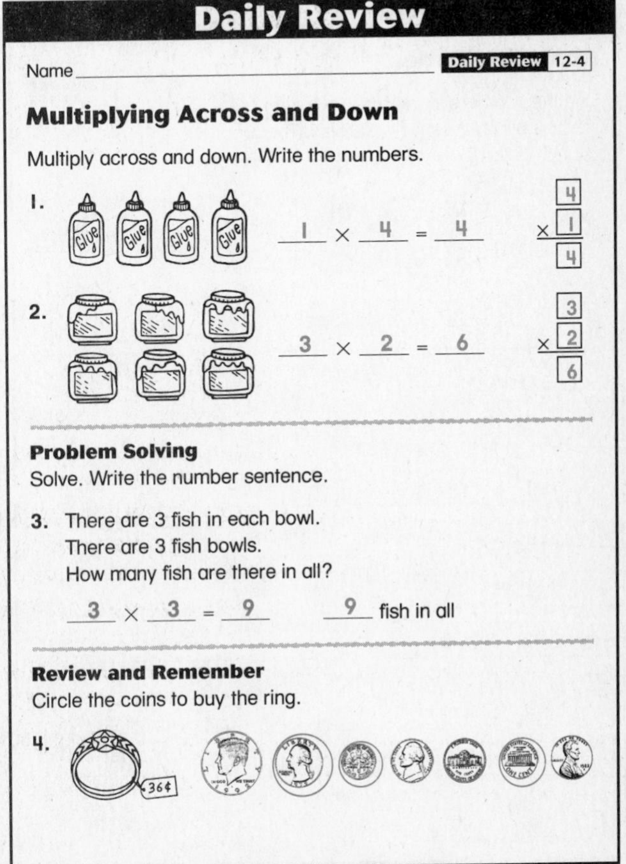

Daily Review

Name ____________

Daily Review 12-4

Multiplying Across and Down

Multiply across and down. Write the numbers.

1. 1 × 4 = 4 (down: 4, ×1, 4)

2. 3 × 2 = 6 (down: 3, ×2, 6)

Problem Solving
Solve. Write the number sentence.

3. There are 3 fish in each bowl.
There are 3 fish bowls.
How many fish are there in all?
3 × 3 = 9   9 fish in all

Review and Remember
Circle the coins to buy the ring.

4. 36¢

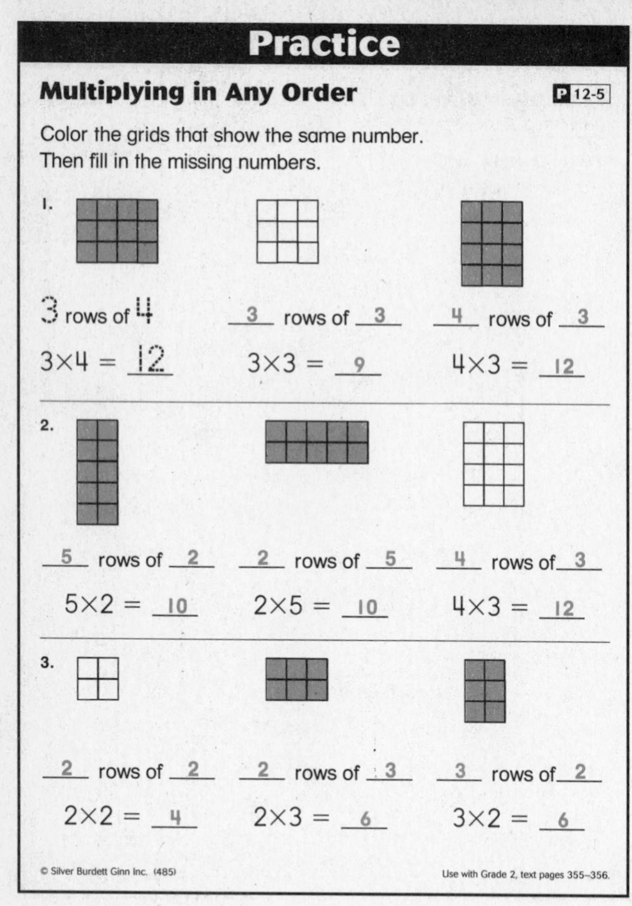

Practice

Multiplying in Any Order

P 12-5

Color the grids that show the same number.
Then fill in the missing numbers.

1.
3 rows of 4 — 3 × 4 = 12
3 rows of 3 — 3 × 3 = 9
4 rows of 3 — 4 × 3 = 12

2.
5 rows of 2 — 5 × 2 = 10
2 rows of 5 — 2 × 5 = 10
4 rows of 3 — 4 × 3 = 12

3.
2 rows of 2 — 2 × 2 = 4
2 rows of 3 — 2 × 3 = 6
3 rows of 2 — 3 × 2 = 6

Use with Grade 2, text pages 355–356.

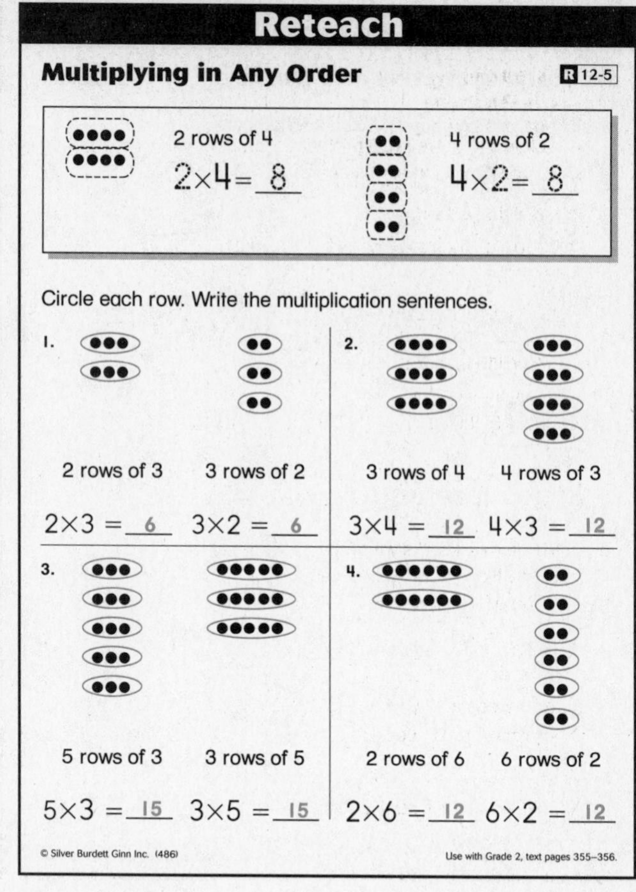

Reteach

Multiplying in Any Order

R 12-5

2 rows of 4 — 2 × 4 = 8
4 rows of 2 — 4 × 2 = 8

Circle each row. Write the multiplication sentences.

1.
2 rows of 3 — 2 × 3 = 6
3 rows of 2 — 3 × 2 = 6

2.
3 rows of 4 — 3 × 4 = 12
4 rows of 3 — 4 × 3 = 12

3.
5 rows of 3 — 5 × 3 = 15
3 rows of 5 — 3 × 5 = 15

4.
2 rows of 6 — 2 × 6 = 12
6 rows of 2 — 6 × 2 = 12

Use with Grade 2, text pages 355–356.

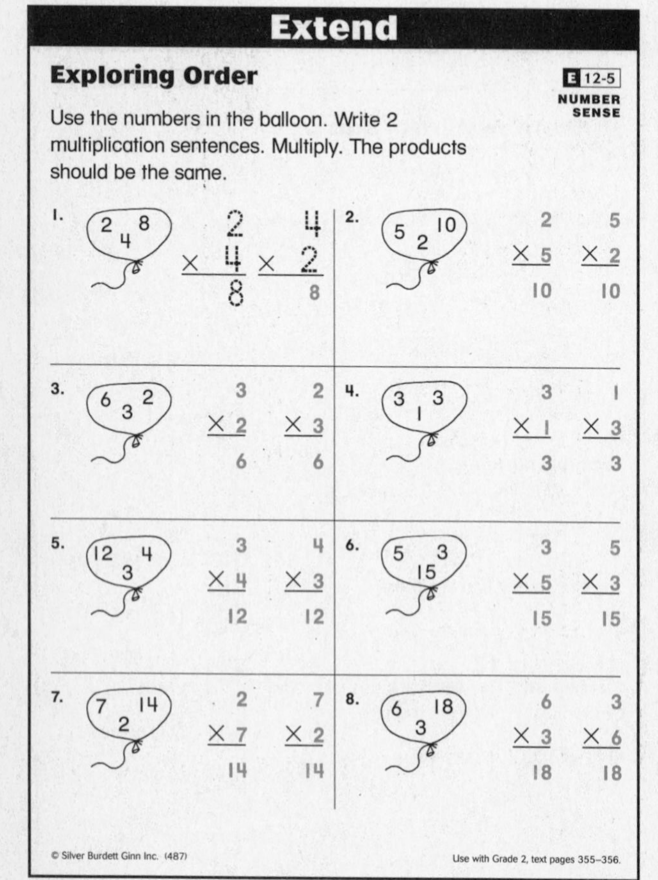

Extend

Exploring Order

E 12-5 NUMBER SENSE

Use the numbers in the balloon. Write 2 multiplication sentences. Multiply. The products should be the same.

1. Balloon: 2, 4, 8 — 2 × 4 = 8; 4 × 2 = 8
2. Balloon: 5, 2, 10 — 2 × 5 = 10; 5 × 2 = 10
3. Balloon: 6, 3, 2 — 3 × 2 = 6; 2 × 3 = 6
4. Balloon: 3, 1, 3 — 3 × 1 = 3; 1 × 3 = 3
5. Balloon: 12, 4, 3 — 3 × 4 = 12; 4 × 3 = 12
6. Balloon: 5, 3, 15 — 3 × 5 = 15; 5 × 3 = 15
7. Balloon: 7, 2, 14 — 2 × 7 = 14; 7 × 2 = 14
8. Balloon: 6, 18, 3 — 6 × 3 = 18; 3 × 6 = 18

Use with Grade 2, text pages 355–356.

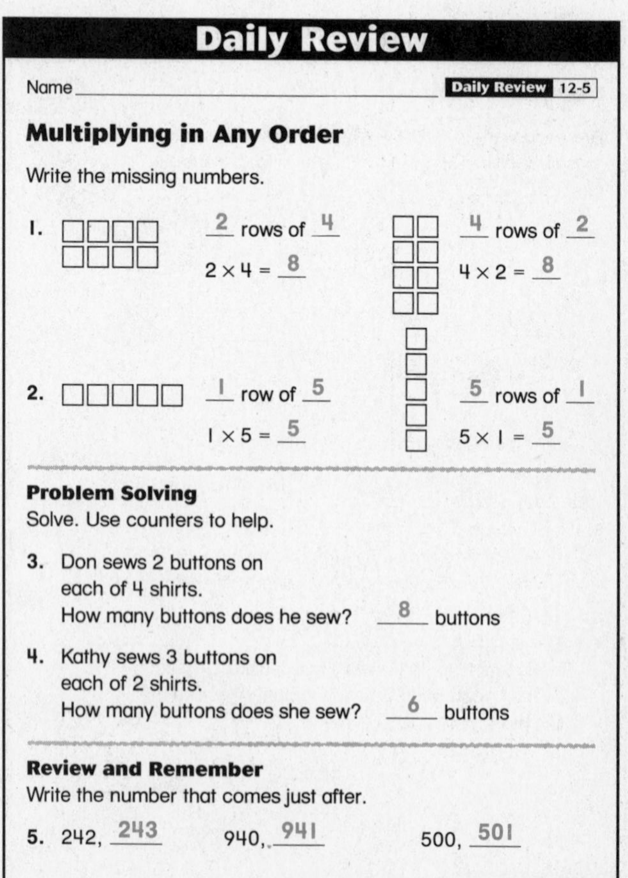

Daily Review

Name ____________________

Daily Review 12-5

Multiplying in Any Order

Write the missing numbers.

1. 2 rows of 4 — 2 × 4 = 8
4 rows of 2 — 4 × 2 = 8

2. 1 row of 5 — 1 × 5 = 5
5 rows of 1 — 5 × 1 = 5

Problem Solving

Solve. Use counters to help.

3. Don sews 2 buttons on each of 4 shirts.
How many buttons does he sew? 8 buttons

4. Kathy sews 3 buttons on each of 2 shirts.
How many buttons does she sew? 6 buttons

Review and Remember

Write the number that comes just after.

5. 242, 243   940, 941   500, 501

Chapter 12 • Lesson 6

Practice

Problem Solving P 12-6

Draw a Picture Check students' drawings.

Draw pictures to solve each problem.
Write the multiplication sentence.

1. Circle which is less.
   3 groups of 6 birds or (2 groups of 8 birds)

   3 × 6 = 18   2 × 8 = 16

2. Circle which is more.
   (the total number of legs of 5 cats) or the total number of legs of 7 people

   5 × 4 = 20   7 × 2 = 14

3. Elle picked 4 flowers with 5 petals on each. How many petals were there on all the flowers?

   4 × 5 = 20   20 petals

4. Maggie needs to buy wheels for 6 toy cars. How many wheels does she need to buy?

   6 × 4 = 24   24 wheels

 Use with Grade 2, text pages 357–358.

Reteach

Problem Solving R 12-6

Draw a Picture

There are 4 kites. Each kite has 3 ties.
How many ties are there in all?

Write the multiplication fact.
4 × 3 = 12 ties

1. Draw 2 stripes on each balloon.

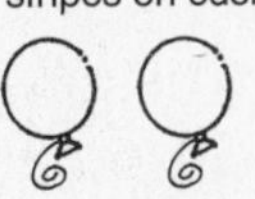

   Write the multiplication fact. 6 × 2 = 12 stripes

2. Draw 4 spots on each ball.

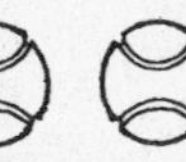

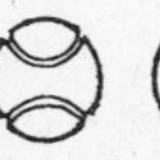

   Write the multiplication fact. 5 × 4 = 20 spots

3. Draw 8 eggs in each basket.

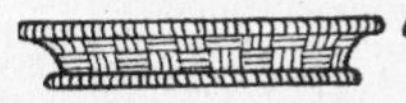

   Write the multiplication fact. 3 × 8 = 24 eggs

 Use with Grade 2, text pages 357–358.

Extend

Collections E 12-6 NUMBER SENSE

Which pile will fill the box with none left over?
Make a guess. Circle the pile. Possible answers are circled.

1.

2.
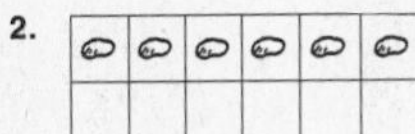
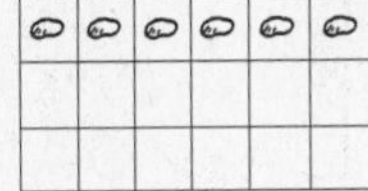

3.
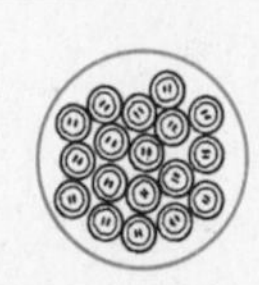

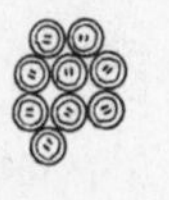

4.
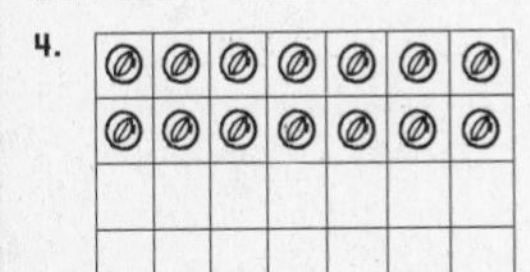

 Use with Grade 2, text pages 357–358.

Daily Review

Name________________ Daily Review 12-6

Problem Solving

Draw a Picture

Draw pictures to solve each problem.
Write the answer. Check students' drawings.

1. There are 4 books.
   Each book costs $2.
   How much do all of the books cost?

   $8

2. There are 3 small pizzas.
   Emily cuts each pizza into 3 slices. How many slices does she have?

   9 slices

3. Todd mailed 2 postcards to his family.
   He kept 4 postcards.
   How many postcards did he start with?

   6 postcards

Review and Remember

Add.

4. 351 + 234 = 585   260 + 89 = 349   593 + 184 = 777   624 + 359 = 983   472 + 8 = 480

Chapter 12 • Lesson 7

Practice

Ways to Multiply

P 12-7

Think about ways to solve each problem. Write the letter of the way you choose. Then solve.

A. counters B. pictures C. repeated addition

Check that students have solved according to their choices.

1. $6 \times 2 =$ 12

I used ____

2. $4 \times 4 =$ 16

I used ____

3. $3 \times 5 =$ 15

I used ____

 Use with Grade 2, text pages 359–360.

Reteach

Ways to Multiply

R 12-7

I would use counters.

How would you solve this problem?
There are 3 cats. Each cat has 4 legs.
How many legs in all?

You could draw pictures.

4 legs 4 legs 4 legs

$3 \times 4 = 12$

You could use counters.

3 groups of 4

$3 \times 4 = 12$

You could use repeated addition. $4 + 4 + 4 = 12$

Write each multiplication sentence. Solve.
Then circle the way you solved the problem.

1. There are 6 spots on 2 butterflies.
How many spots in all?
2 × 6 = 12 spots
pictures / counters / addition

2. There are 2 children. Each child has 3 balloons.
How many balloons in all?
2 × 3 = 6 balloons
pictures / counters / addition

3. There are 6 trees. There are 3 nests in each tree.
How many nests in all?
6 × 3 = 18 nests
pictures / counters / addition

 Use with Grade 2, text pages 359–360.

Extend

Watch the Birdy

E 12-7 PROBLEM SOLVING

The Bird Club members saw robins and sparrows.

Circle the questions that you can answer by using the chart. Then find the answer.

Cross out the questions you cannot answer.

	Robins	Sparrows
Monday	7	22
Tuesday	16	15
Wednesday	3	4

1. How many robins did they see in all?
26 robins

2. How many sparrows did they see in all?
41 sparrows

3. On Thursday, did they see more robins or more sparrows?
____

4. On Tuesday, did they see more robins or more sparrows?
robins

5. On which day did they see the most birds?
Tuesday

6. How many birds did they see on Friday?
____ birds

 Use with Grade 2, text pages 359–360.

Daily Review

Name ____________________

Daily Review 12-7

Ways to Multiply

Choose a way to find each product.
Draw or write to show your choice.

Use counters.
Use addition.
Draw a picture.

Methods will vary.

1. $4 \times 4 =$ 16

2. $5 \times 2 =$ 10

Problem Solving

Solve. Draw a picture or write to show how.

Check students' methods.

3. There are 3 sandwiches on each plate.
There are 3 plates.
How many sandwiches are there?
9 sandwiches

Review and Remember

Subtract.

4. $34 - 8 = 26$ $81 - 40 = 41$ $46 - 27 = 19$ $29 - 11 = 18$ $55 - 36 = 19$

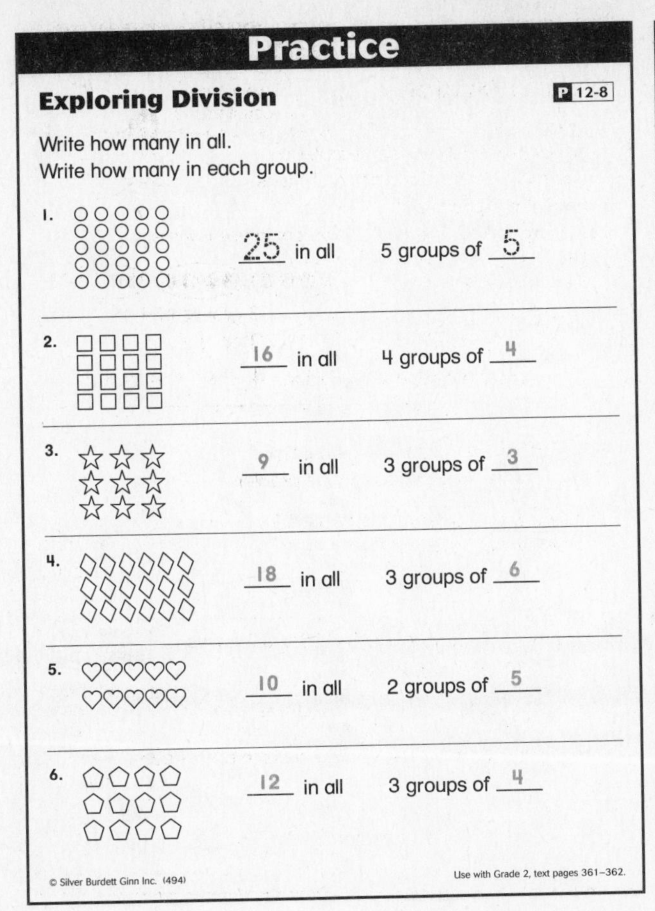

Practice

Exploring Division

P 12-8

Write how many in all.
Write how many in each group.

1. 25 in all — 5 groups of 5
2. 16 in all — 4 groups of 4
3. 9 in all — 3 groups of 3
4. 18 in all — 3 groups of 6
5. 10 in all — 2 groups of 5
6. 12 in all — 3 groups of 4

Use with Grade 2, text pages 361–362.

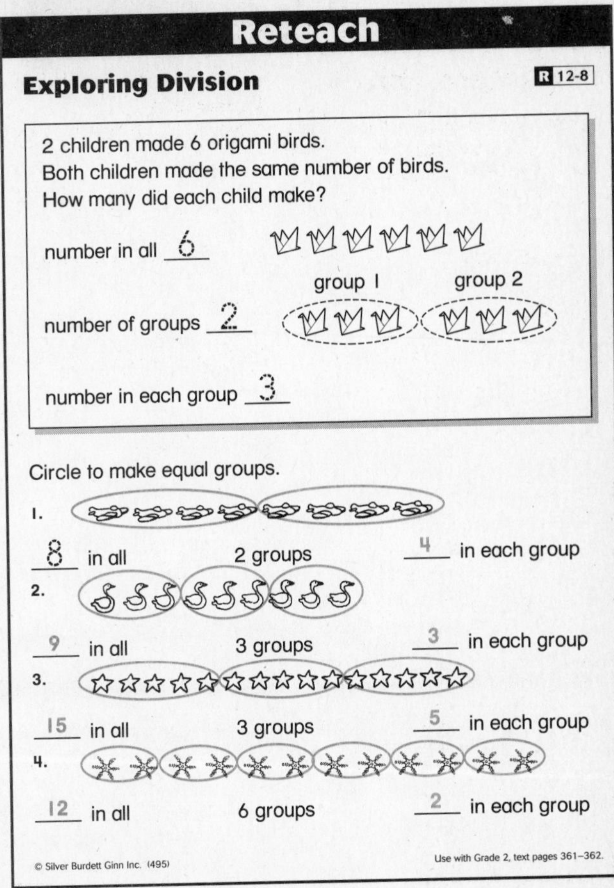

Reteach

Exploring Division

R 12-8

2 children made 6 origami birds.
Both children made the same number of birds.
How many did each child make?

number in all 6

number of groups 2 — group 1, group 2

number in each group 3

Circle to make equal groups.

1. 8 in all — 2 groups — 4 in each group
2. 9 in all — 3 groups — 3 in each group
3. 15 in all — 3 groups — 5 in each group
4. 12 in all — 6 groups — 2 in each group

Use with Grade 2, text pages 361–362.

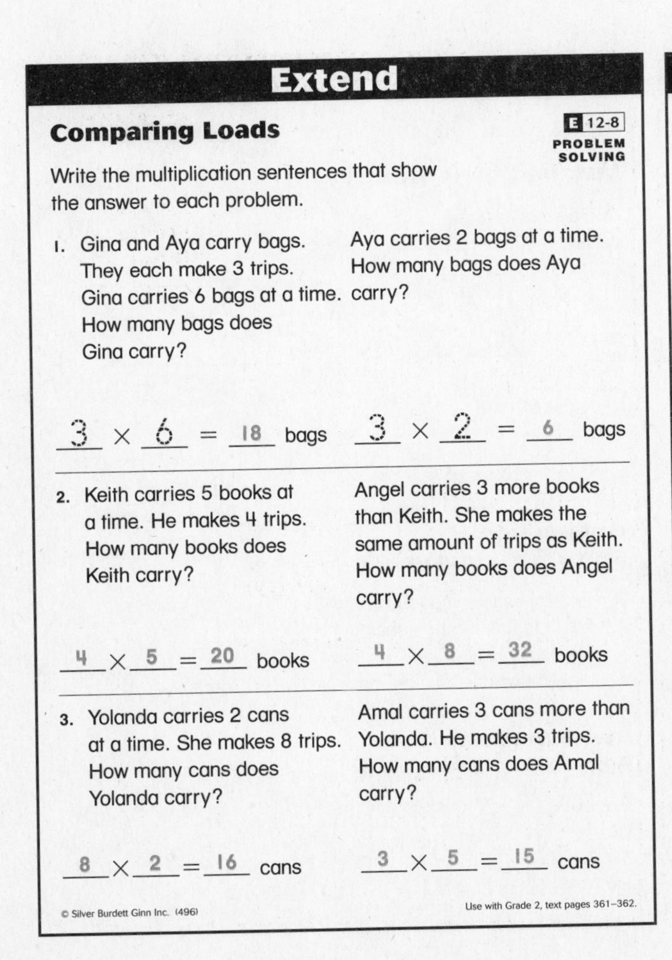

Extend

Comparing Loads

E 12-8
PROBLEM SOLVING

Write the multiplication sentences that show the answer to each problem.

1. Gina and Aya carry bags. They each make 3 trips. Gina carries 6 bags at a time. How many bags does Gina carry?

   $3 \times 6 = 18$ bags

   Aya carries 2 bags at a time. How many bags does Aya carry?

   $3 \times 2 = 6$ bags

2. Keith carries 5 books at a time. He makes 4 trips. How many books does Keith carry?

   $4 \times 5 = 20$ books

   Angel carries 3 more books than Keith. She makes the same amount of trips as Keith. How many books does Angel carry?

   $4 \times 8 = 32$ books

3. Yolanda carries 2 cans at a time. She makes 8 trips. How many cans does Yolanda carry?

   $8 \times 2 = 16$ cans

   Amal carries 3 cans more than Yolanda. He makes 3 trips. How many cans does Amal carry?

   $3 \times 5 = 15$ cans

Use with Grade 2, text pages 361–362.

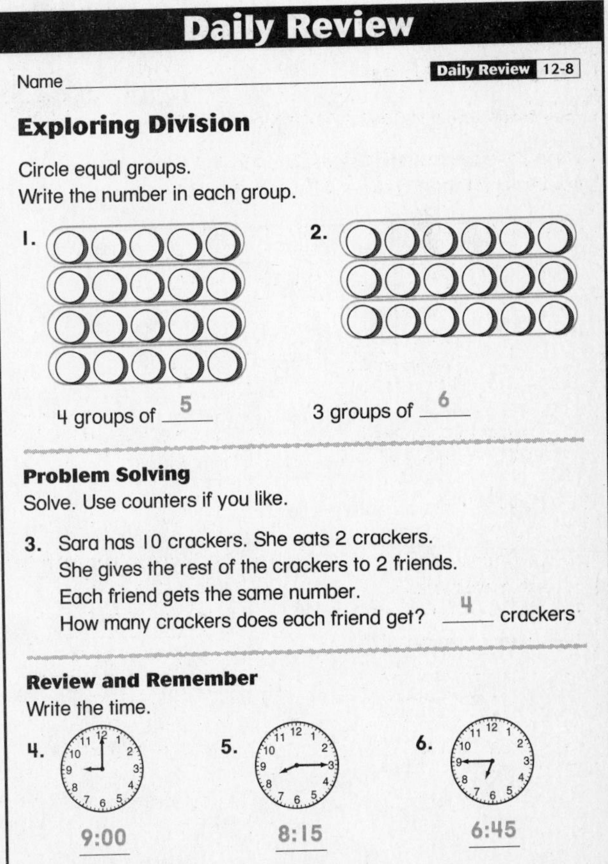

Daily Review

Name ____________________ Daily Review 12-8

Exploring Division

Circle equal groups.
Write the number in each group.

1. 4 groups of 5
2. 3 groups of 6

Problem Solving

Solve. Use counters if you like.

3. Sara has 10 crackers. She eats 2 crackers. She gives the rest of the crackers to 2 friends. Each friend gets the same number. How many crackers does each friend get? 4 crackers

Review and Remember

Write the time.

4. 9:00
5. 8:15
6. 6:45

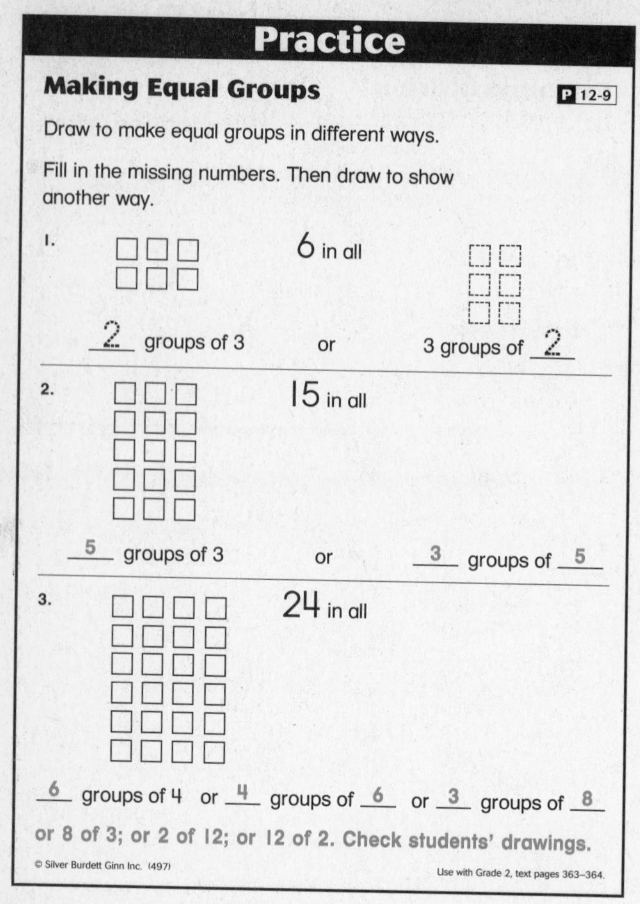

Practice

Making Equal Groups

P 12-9

Draw to make equal groups in different ways.

Fill in the missing numbers. Then draw to show another way.

1. 6 in all

2 groups of 3 or 3 groups of 2

2. 15 in all

5 groups of 3 or 3 groups of 5

3. 24 in all

6 groups of 4 or 4 groups of 6 or 3 groups of 8

or 8 of 3; or 2 of 12; or 12 of 2. Check students' drawings.

Use with Grade 2, text pages 363–364.

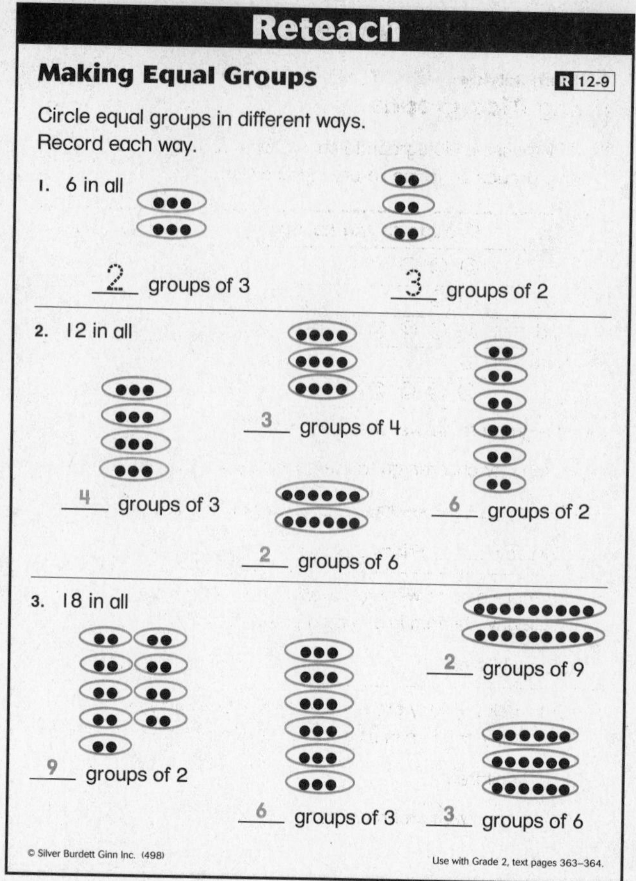

Reteach

Making Equal Groups

R 12-9

Circle equal groups in different ways.
Record each way.

1. 6 in all

2 groups of 3

3 groups of 2

2. 12 in all

3 groups of 4

4 groups of 3

6 groups of 2

2 groups of 6

3. 18 in all

2 groups of 9

9 groups of 2

6 groups of 3

3 groups of 6

Use with Grade 2, text pages 363–364.

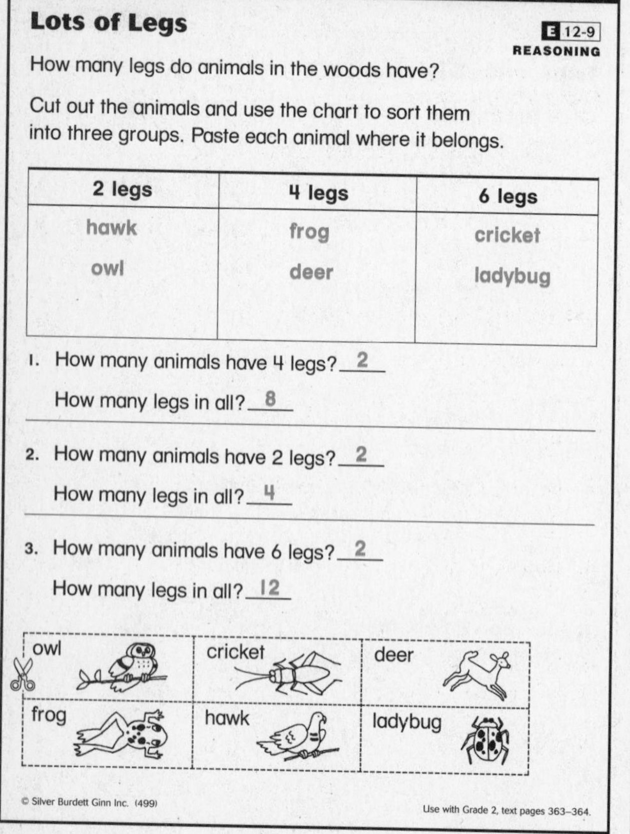

Extend

Lots of Legs

E 12-9
REASONING

How many legs do animals in the woods have?

Cut out the animals and use the chart to sort them into three groups. Paste each animal where it belongs.

2 legs	4 legs	6 legs
hawk	frog	cricket
owl	deer	ladybug

1. How many animals have 4 legs? 2

   How many legs in all? 8

2. How many animals have 2 legs? 2

   How many legs in all? 4

3. How many animals have 6 legs? 2

   How many legs in all? 12

Use with Grade 2, text pages 363–364.

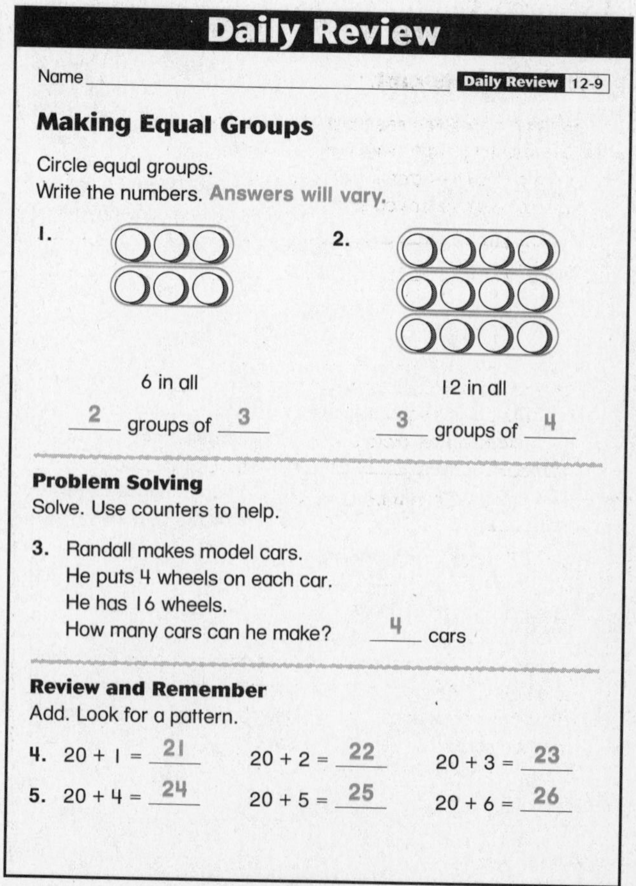

Daily Review

Name ______________________

Daily Review 12-9

Making Equal Groups

Circle equal groups.
Write the numbers. Answers will vary.

1. 6 in all

   2 groups of 3

2. 12 in all

   3 groups of 4

Problem Solving

Solve. Use counters to help.

3. Randall makes model cars.
   He puts 4 wheels on each car.
   He has 16 wheels.
   How many cars can he make? 4 cars

Review and Remember

Add. Look for a pattern.

4. 20 + 1 = 21   20 + 2 = 22   20 + 3 = 23

5. 20 + 4 = 24   20 + 5 = 25   20 + 6 = 26

Practice

Problem Solving
Using Pictographs P 12-10

Mr. Holtz uses a pictograph to show how many reading groups go to the library in the afternoon.

Day	Groups to the library ☺ = a group of 4 children
Mon.	☺ ☺ ☺
Tues.	☺ ☺
Wed.	☺ ☺ ☺ ☺ ☺
Thurs.	☺
Fri.	☺ ☺ ☺ ☺

Use the graph to answer the questions.

1. How many children go to the library each day?
   Monday 12 Tuesday 8 Wednesday 20
   Thursday 4 Friday 16 in all 60
2. If 3 more groups went to the library on Monday, how many children in all would go on Monday?
   24 children
3. Last week 2 Friday groups switched to Wednesday. How many children in all went to the library on Wednesday?
   28 children
   How many went on Friday? 8 children

 Use with Grade 2, text pages 365–366.

Reteach

Problem Solving
Using Pictographs R 12-10

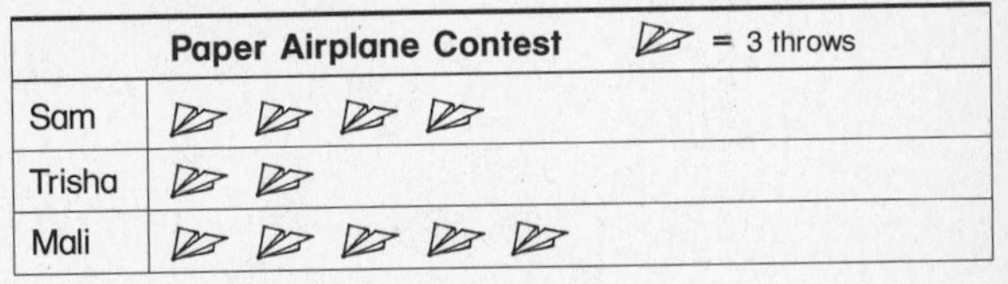

Use the graph to answer the questions.

1. How many throws did each child make?
   Sam 4 × 3 = 12 throws
   Trisha 2 × 3 = 6 throws
   Mali 5 × 3 = 15 throws
2. How many more throws did Mali make than Sam?
   3 more throws
3. How many more throws did Sam make than Trisha?
   6 more throws
4. How many throws did all 3 children make?
   33 throws
5. Who made the most throws?
   Mali

 Use with Grade 2, text pages 365–366.

Extend

Make a Pictograph E 12-10 DATA

1. What colors do you see most often in clothing? Guess whether red, blue, or green is the most common. Look at clothing around you. Mark how many of each color you see.

Red	Blue	Green

2. For every 5 marks, color a square below. Then cut out the squares and put them where they belong on the pictograph.

Clothing Colors ☐ = 5	
Red	Check that students' marks and graphs match.
Blue	
Green	

 Use with Grade 2, text pages 365–366.

Daily Review

Name ________________ Daily Review 12-10

Problem Solving
Using Pictographs

Second Graders Who Ride the Bus	
Room 10	웃 웃 웃 웃 웃
Room 12	웃 웃 웃 웃
Room 14	웃 웃 웃
Room 16	웃 웃 웃 웃 웃

웃 = 2 children

Use the graph to answer each question.

1. How many children in each room ride the bus?
   Room 10 10 Room 12 8
   Room 14 6 Room 16 10
2. How many second graders ride the bus altogether?
   34 second graders
3. How many more children in Room 16 ride the bus than in Room 14? 4 more children

Review and Remember
How many cups does each hold?

4. 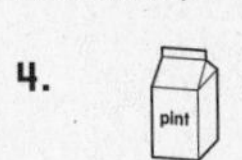

2 cups

5. 

4 cups

Practice Workbook Answers

Practice Workbook

Understanding Addition

Count on to find how many in all.
Use cubes if you like.

1. 6 + 3 = 9   8 + 2 = 10

2. 7 + 2 = 9   5 + 1 = 6

3. 8 + 1 = 9   9 + 3 = 12   6 + 0 = 6

4. 5 + 3 = 8   3 + 2 = 5   4 + 1 = 5

5. 6 + 2 = 8   9 + 0 = 9   4 + 3 = 7

6. 4 + 0 = 4   3 + 1 = 4   9 + 2 = 11

Review and Remember

Draw more apples to make each number.

1. 6

2. 12

Practice Workbook

Number Combinations

Tell how many in all. Use cubes if you like.

1. 5 + 4 = 9   4 + 5 = 9   1 + 5 = 6   5 + 1 = 6

2. 0 + 3 = 3   3 + 0 = 3   4 + 2 = 6   2 + 4 = 6   3 + 5 = 8   5 + 3 = 8

3. 3 + 2 = 5   2 + 0 = 2   0 + 4 = 4
   2 + 3 = 5   0 + 2 = 2   4 + 0 = 4

4. 1 + 2 = 3   5 + 2 = 7   1 + 0 = 1
   2 + 1 = 3   2 + 5 = 7   0 + 1 = 1

5. 4 + 4 = 8   1 + 1 = 2   5 + 5 = 10

Review and Remember

1. Circle the one that is more.

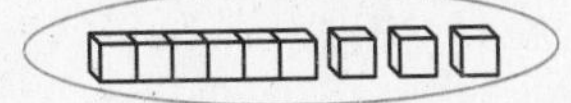

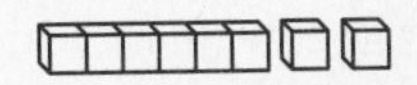

2. How did you know without counting?
You begin with 6, but you add on more for 6+3 than for 6+2.

Practice Workbook

Using Order in Addition

Count. Write how many in all.

1. 3 + 2 = 5   2 + 3 = 5   2 + 3 = 5   3 + 2 = 5

2. 6 + 1 = 7   1 + 6 = 7   6 + 1 = 7   1 + 6 = 7

3. 3 + 2 = 5   6 + 2 = 8   3 + 7 = 10
   2 + 3 = 5   2 + 6 = 8   7 + 3 = 10

4. 1 + 8 = 9   5 + 6 = 11   2 + 9 = 11
   8 + 1 = 9   6 + 5 = 11   9 + 2 = 11

Review and Remember

Write the number.

1. two 2   ten 10   six 6   nine 9

Draw more hats to make the number.

2. 5

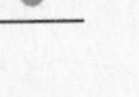

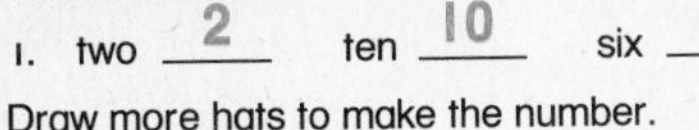

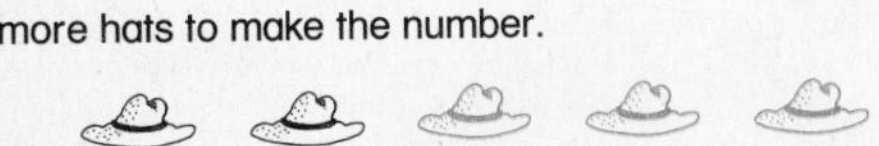

Practice Workbook

Using Doubles to Add

Write the addend to make a double.
Find each sum.

1. 3 + 3 = 6   4 + 4 = 8   2 + 2 = 4   0 + 0 = 0   5 + 5 = 10   6 + 6 = 12

Circle doubles. Add.

2. 3 + 4 = 7   (1 + 1 = 2)   2 + 1 = 3   3 + 7 = 10   1 + 9 = 10   2 + 6 = 8

3. (4 + 4 = 8)   (3 + 3 = 6)   3 + 6 = 9   2 + 9 = 11   (2 + 2 = 4)   0 + 1 = 1

4. 3 + 8 = 11   (0 + 0 = 0)   9 + 1 = 10   2 + 7 = 9   1 + 6 = 7   3 + 9 = 12

Review and Remember

Write two number sentences for each picture.

1. 2 + 6 = 8
   6 + 2 = 8

2. 3 + 7 = 10
   7 + 3 = 10

Chapter 1

Practice Workbook

Three Addends

Add.

1. $5 + 1 + 4 = 10$ ($5 + 1 = 6$; $6 + 4 = 10$) $5 + 1 + 4 = 10$ ($1 + 4 = 5$; $5 + 5 = 10$)

2. $3 + 1 + 3 = 7$ $7 + 0 + 4 = 11$ $3 + 3 + 3 = 9$ $5 + 2 + 3 = 10$ $1 + 4 + 1 = 6$

3. $0 + 4 + 5 = 9$ $3 + 2 + 6 = 11$ $6 + 3 + 3 = 12$ $4 + 2 + 3 = 9$ $4 + 4 + 4 = 12$

4. $4 + 2 + 1 = 7$ $6 + 2 + 2 = 10$

5. $9 + 0 + 2 = 11$ $6 + 2 + 4 = 12$

Review and Remember

1. Circle the greater number. 6 (8) (4) 1
2. Write the number. seven 7 two 2

Chapter 2

Practice Workbook

Counting Back

Subtract. Count back. Use the number line if you like.

0 1 2 3 4 5 6 7 8 9 10 11 12

1. $5 - 2 = 3$ $6 - 3 = 3$ $4 - 1 = 3$
2. $7 - 2 = 5$ $12 - 2 = 10$ $11 - 1 = 10$
3. $7 - 3 = 4$ $11 - 2 = 9$ $12 - 1 = 11$
4. $10 - 2 = 8$ $7 - 3 = 4$ $11 - 3 = 8$ $6 - 2 = 4$ $9 - 1 = 8$
5. $12 - 3 = 9$ $11 - 0 = 11$ $8 - 2 = 6$ $5 - 3 = 2$ $9 - 3 = 6$

Review and Remember

Add or subtract.

$8 + 2 = 10$ $6 - 3 = 3$ $9 + 1 = 10$ $8 - 4 = 4$ $7 + 1 = 8$ $4 + 5 = 9$

Chapter 2

Practice Workbook

Related Addition and Subtraction

Write an addition fact.
Then write a related subtraction fact.

1. $4 + 5 = 9$ $9 - 5 = 4$
2. $1 + 6 = 7$ $7 - 6 = 1$
3. $4 + 8 = 12$ $12 - 8 = 4$

Add or subtract.

4. $10 - 6 = 4$ $4 + 6 = 10$ $11 - 5 = 6$ $6 + 5 = 11$ $3 + 5 = 8$ $8 - 5 = 3$

Review and Remember

What double facts are missing?
Complete each fact.

1. $2 + 2 = 4$ $5 + 5 = 10$ $3 + 3 = 6$
2. $1 + 1 = 2$ $6 + 6 = 12$ $4 + 4 = 8$

Practice Workbook

Make a Graph

The pictograph shows how many pets the children in Mrs. Hope's class have.

1. How many cats do the children have? 4
2. How many dogs do the children have? 5

Make a bar graph to show the total numbers.
Sarah had 1 stone and 4 acorns.
Jimmy had 3 stones and 2 acorns.

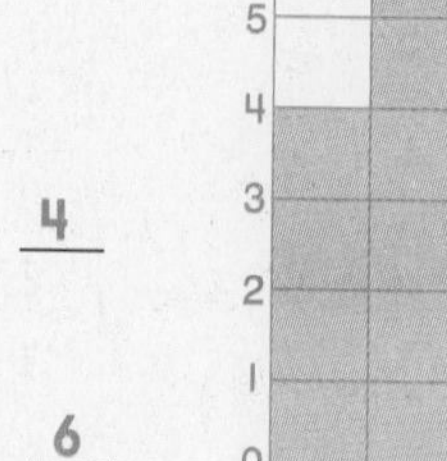

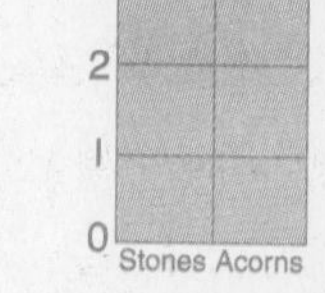

3. How many spaces do you color for Sarah and Jimmy's stones? Color them. 4
4. How many spaces do you color for Sarah and Jimmy's acorns? Color them. 6

Review and Remember

Add or subtract.

$3 + 0 = 3$ $0 + 10 = 10$ $6 - 2 = 4$ $14 - 7 = 7$ $8 - 7 = 1$

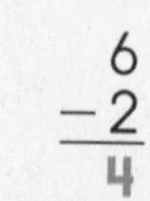

Chapter 2

Practice Workbook

Fact Families to 18

Subtract.
Circle the related addition fact.

1. 13 − 4 = 9 5 + 9 = 14; 4 + 8 = 12; (9 + 4 = 13)
2. 14 − 6 = 8 6 + 9 = 15; (6 + 8 = 14); 6 + 7 = 13

Add or subtract.

3. 15 − 6 = 9; 3 + 7 = 10; 16 − 9 = 7; 14 − 7 = 7; 7 + 8 = 15; 3 + 8 = 11

Circle names for 10.

4. (7 + 3) 5 + 6 (12 − 2) (16 − 6)

Review and Remember

Add or subtract.

1. 12 − 5 = 7; 11 − 8 = 3; 4 + 8 = 12; 6 + 6 = 12; 10 − 4 = 6; 8 + 7 = 15
2. 9 − 6 = 3 10 − 8 = 2 1 + 6 = 7

Practice Workbook

Identifying Names for Numbers

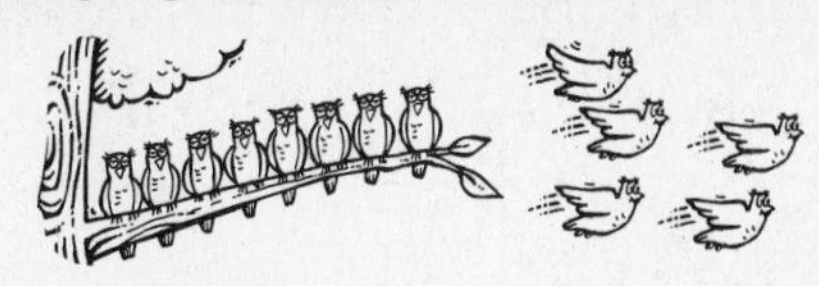

Look at the picture.

1. Write two addition facts.
   8 + 5 = 13
   5 + 8 = 13
2. Write two subtraction facts.
   13 − 5 = 8
   13 − 8 = 5

Circle names for each number.

3. 7 (1 + 6) (14 − 7) 5 + 3 (16 − 9)
4. 9 (18 − 9) (9 + 0) (15 − 6) (13 − 4)

Write four names for 5.

5. Answers will vary.

Review and Remember

Solve.

11 − 4 = 7; 3 + 4 = 7; 0 + 7 = 7; 7 + 9 = 16; 15 − 6 = 9; 16 − 7 = 9

Chapter 3

Practice Workbook

Exploring Regrouping

Draw tens and ones models to show each number.

1. Show 16 ones.

Regroup 16 ones.
Make a group of 10.
Show 1 ten and 6 ones.

Show each number. Regroup when you can.

2. 16 ones — 1 ten 6 ones
3. 14 ones — 1 ten 4 ones
4. 1 ten 10 ones — 2 tens 0 ones
5. 1 ten 16 ones — 2 tens 6 ones
6. 1 ten 19 ones — 2 tens 9 ones
7. 2 tens 19 ones — 3 tens 9 ones
8. 5 tens 12 ones — 6 tens 2 ones

Review and Remember

Find the correct name. Fill in the ◯.

1. 16: ◯ 1 + 6; ◯ 7 + 7; ● 9 + 7
2. 9: ◯ 14 − 6; ● 13 − 4; ◯ 17 − 9
3. 8: ◯ 4 + 5; ◯ 9 − 2; ● 16 − 8
4. 15: ● 8 + 7; ◯ 1 + 5; ◯ 6 + 8

Practice Workbook

Skip Counting and Patterns

Skip count.
Write the numbers as you count.

1. 5, 10, 15, 20, 25, 30, 35, 40
2. 3, 6, 9, 12, 15, 18, 21, 24
3. 10, 20, 30, 40, 50, 60, 70, 80

Look for the pattern.
Then write the missing numbers.

4. 12, 14, 16, 18, 20, 22, 24, 26
5. 3, 6, 9, 12, 15, 18, 21, 24
6. 5, 10, 15, 20, 25, 30, 35, 40
7. 30, 40, 50, 60, 70, 80, 90, 100

Review and Remember

Circle the odd numbers.

1. 2 (5) (47) 56 (99)

Circle the even numbers.

2. (4) (18) 21 (72) 89

3. If a number ends in 0, is it odd or even?
   even

Chapter 3

Practice Workbook

Numbers to 99

Circle the number that is greater.

1.  (18) 17 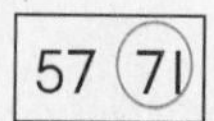 57 (71) 33 (43)

Circle the number that is less.

2. 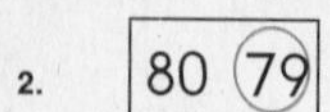 80 (79) 22 (9) (98) 99

Compare. Write the numbers to make each sentence true.

3. 14 21 — 21 is greater than 14. 21 > 14
   14 21 — 14 is less than 21. 14 < 21

Write > or < in each ◯.

4. 85 > 10 20 < 40 30 > 29 89 < 98

Review and Remember

Add or subtract.

1. 12 − 7 = 5 18 − 9 = 9 14 − 6 = 8
2. 9 + 6 = 15 4 + 9 = 13 4 − 4 = 0

Practice Workbook

Ordering Numbers

Write the number that comes **after**.

1. 18, 19 23, 24 44, 45 12, 13
2. 63, 64 94, 95 39, 40 57, 58

Write the number that comes **before**.

3. 60, 61 46, 47 78, 79 52, 53
4. 81, 82 14, 15 20, 21 37, 38

Write the number that comes **between**.

5. 93, 94, 95 87, 88, 89 40, 41, 42
6. 10, 11, 12 68, 69, 70 55, 56, 57

Review and Remember

Add or subtract.

4	11	8	3	5	6
+0	−7	−4	+8	−5	+6
4	4	4	11	0	12

Chapter 3

Practice Workbook

Ordinal Numbers

first second third fourth fifth sixth seventh eighth ninth tenth

1st 2nd 3rd 4th 5th 6th 7th 8th 9th 10th

Circle the place where each student is found.

1.  first / (third) / fifth 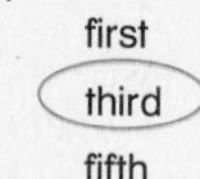  ninth / seventh / (eighth)   (second) / third / fourth

2. sixth / fifth / (seventh) third / second / (first)  (tenth) / twelfth / ninth

Write the number and the word.

3.  6th sixth

Review and Remember

Write the number.

3 tens 8 ones 38 8 tens 3 ones 83

Chapter 4

Practice Workbook

Counting Sets of Coins

Count the money. Write the amount.

1.    

25 ¢ 30 ¢ 31 ¢ 32 ¢

2.     

50 ¢ 60 ¢ 70 ¢ 71 ¢

Circle the coins you need.

3.  38¢    

Review and Remember

Circle the odd numbers.

1. (25), 14, 36, (99), (27), (43), 8, (71), (1)

Write the number.

2. 2 tens 7 ones 27 7 tens 2 ones 72

Practice Workbook

Ways to Show Amounts

Match the amounts of money.
Write each amount. Then draw a line.

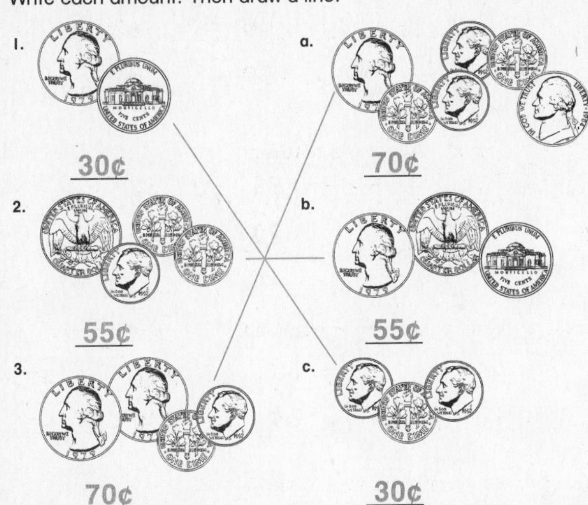

1. 30¢ — a. 70¢
2. 55¢ — b. 55¢
3. 70¢ — c. 30¢

Review and Remember

Jessie read 3 books about bears.
She read 8 books about dinosaurs.
How many books did Jessie read? 11 books

Practice Workbook

Exploring Dollars

Write how many coins there are.
Write each amount.

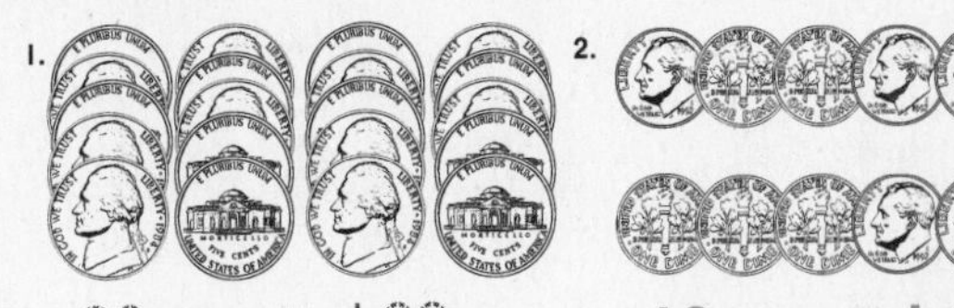

1. 20 nickels = \$ 1.00
2. 10 dimes = \$ 1.00

3. 4 quarters = \$ 1.00
4. 2 half dollars = \$ 1.00

Review and Remember

Write the missing addends that give each sum.

1. 17
   9 + 8
   8 + 9
2. 16
   7 + 9
   9 + 7
   8 + 8
3. 15
   8 + 7
   7 + 8
   9 + 6
   6 + 9

Chapter 4

Practice Workbook

Using Data From a Picture

Find how many in all.

1. 6 + 4 = 10
2. 2 + 7 = 9
3. 4 + 3 = 7
4. 4 + 6 = 10
5. 5 + 6 = 11

Review and Remember

Add or subtract.

1. 12 + 5 = 17; 8 − 7 = 1; 11 − 6 = 5; 6 + 6 = 12; 14 − 8 = 6

2. 1 + 2 + 7 = 10 4 + 7 + 1 = 12

Practice Workbook

Making Change

Count up from the price. Write the change.

	You pay	Price	Count up	Change
1.	40¢	29¢	30 ¢ 40 ¢	11 ¢
2.	70¢	57¢	58 ¢ 59 ¢ 60 ¢ 70 ¢	13 ¢
3.	50¢	23¢	24 ¢ 25 ¢ 50 ¢	27 ¢

Review and Remember

Write the missing numbers.

1. 2, 4, 6, 8, 10, 12, 14, 16
2. 3, 6, 9, 12, 15, 18, 21, 24

Practice Workbook

Deciding When to Regroup

Do you need to regroup?
Circle **yes** or **no**. Then add.

1. (yes) no — 23 + 48 = 71 | yes (no) — 53 + 14 = 67 | yes (no) — 71 + 22 = 93 | (yes) no — 19 + 54 = 73 | (yes) no — 63 + 29 = 92
2. (yes) no — 38 + 18 = 56 | (yes) no — 13 + 47 = 60 | yes (no) — 51 + 12 = 63 | (yes) no — 25 + 65 = 90 | yes (no) — 43 + 52 = 95

Review and Remember

Compare. Write > or <.

1. 45 (>) 44   77 (<) 78   64 (>) 46
2. 22 (<) 62   21 (<) 61   83 (>) 82
3. 23 (<) 32   29 (<) 30   74 (>) 47
4. 15 (<) 51   40 (>) 39   52 (>) 49

Practice Workbook

Modeling Addition

Find each sum. Use tens and ones cubes if you like. Regroup if you need to.

1. 16 + 25 = 41 | 48 + 11 = 59 | 21 + 39 = 60 | 38 + 53 = 91 | 24 + 53 = 77 | 44 + 37 = 81
2. 70 + 19 = 89 | 35 + 28 = 63 | 26 + 42 = 68 | 78 + 16 = 94 | 33 + 39 = 72 | 64 + 26 = 90

Rewrite and add.

3. 45 + 47   25 + 62   71 + 18   14 + 28

	tens	ones
	4	5
+	4	7
	9	2

	tens	ones
	2	5
+	6	2
	8	7

	tens	ones
	7	1
+	1	8
	8	9

	tens	ones
	1	4
+	2	8
	4	2

Review and Remember

Write the missing mystery numbers.

32 + 2[8] = 60   5[5] + 17 = 72   [2]8 + 27 = 55   24 + 4[8] = 72

22 Use after Grade 2, text page 144. © Silver Burdett Ginn Inc.

Chapter 5

Practice Workbook

Adding Two-Digit Numbers

Do you need to regroup?
Circle **yes** or **no**. Then add.

1. yes (no) — 81 + 8 = 89 | (yes) no — 35 + 8 = 43 | (yes) no — 56 + 6 = 62 | yes (no) — 72 + 7 = 79
2. (yes) no — 43 + 47 = 90 | yes (no) — 16 + 71 = 87 | yes (no) — 63 + 20 = 83 | (yes) no — 24 + 18 = 42
3. yes (no) — 75 + 20 = 95 | (yes) no — 55 + 29 = 84 | yes (no) — 44 + 53 = 97 | (yes) no — 64 + 18 = 82

Review and Remember

Write the number.

1. 6 tens 4 ones 64   5 tens 9 ones 59

Write > or < in each ◯.

2. 16 (<) 61   72 (>) 27   98 (>) 18

Practice Workbook

Adding Three Numbers

Add. Regroup if you need to.

1. 63 + 23 = 86 | 35 + 36 = 71 | 42 + 29 = 71 | 3 + 10 = 13
2. 34 + 19 + 2 = 55 | 7 + 18 + 4 = 29 | 50 + 9 + 24 = 83 | 3 + 71 + 9 = 83
3. 43 + 25 + 30 = 98 | 40 + 9 + 29 = 78 | 24 + 26 + 19 = 69 | 11 + 44 + 33 = 88

Review and Remember

Match. Draw a line.

1. twelfth — 12th; tenth — 10th; first — 1st; sixth — 6th; third — 3rd

Solve.

2. June's favorite number is even. It is less than 6. It is greater than 2. What is it? 4

Chapter 5

Practice Workbook

Getting Data From a Table

Use the table to answer each question.

Class Birthdays		
Season	Boys	Girls
Spring	1	2
Summer	3	5
Fall	5	0
Winter	3	4

1. Are there more boys or girls in the class? **boys**
2. What time of the year do most students have birthdays? **summer**
3. What time of the year do the fewest students have birthdays? **spring**
4. How many boys are in the class? **12**
5. How many girls are in the class? **11**
6. How many students are in the class? **23**
7. When is your birthday? **Answers will vary.**

Review and Remember

Add.

8 + 9 = 17, 5 + 5 = 10, 6 + 7 = 13, 9 + 5 = 14, 8 + 5 = 13, 7 + 9 = 16, 1 + 9 = 10

Use after Grade 2, text page 158. 25

Chapter 6

Practice Workbook

Deciding When to Regroup

Use tens and ones models.
Complete the chart.

	Do you need to regroup?	How many are left?
1. Show 1 ten and 5 ones. Subtract 3 ones.	yes (no)	1 ten 2 ones
2. Show 3 tens and 9 ones. Subtract 6 ones.	yes (no)	3 tens 3 ones
3. Show 8 tens and 4 ones. Subtract 5 ones.	(yes) no	7 tens 9 ones
4. Show 1 ten and 1 one. Subtract 6 ones.	(yes) no	0 tens 5 ones
5. Show 6 tens and 7 ones. Subtract 3 ones.	yes (no)	6 tens 4 ones

Review and Remember

Estimate.

Today 18 planes fly from New York to Boston. Then 11 planes fly from Atlanta to Boston. About how many planes fly from New York and Atlanta to Boston?

about **30** planes

Chapter 6

Practice Workbook

Subtracting Two-Digit Numbers

Subtract. Regroup if you need to.
Circle the problems in which you regrouped.

1. (63 − 7 = 56), (63 − 27 = 36), (57 − 9 = 48), (57 − 39 = 18), 39 − 28 = 11
2. 42 − 41 = 1, (42 − 38 = 4), (90 − 12 = 78), 88 − 66 = 22, (38 − 29 = 9)

Rewrite and subtract.

3. 32 − 18 = 14, 50 − 37 = 13, 41 − 14 = 27, 76 − 48 = 28

Review and Remember

Add or subtract.

23 + 19 = 42, 23 − 19 = 4, 50 − 40 = 10, 29 − 0 = 29, 30 + 60 = 90

Practice Workbook

Checking Subtraction With Addition

Subtract. Add to check.

1. 57 − 28 = 29; 29 + 28 = 57
2. 87 − 53 = 34; 34 + 53 = 87
3. 89 − 16 = 73; 73 + 16 = 89
4. 74 − 47 = 27; 27 + 47 = 74

Review and Remember

Add.

1. 6 + 3 + 4 = 13, 8 + 2 + 2 = 12, 9 + 0 + 7 = 16, 5 + 5 + 4 = 14, 1 + 1 + 6 = 8, 3 + 5 + 3 = 11, 7 + 1 + 6 = 14
2. 10 + 6 = 16, 8 + 10 = 18, 3 + 10 = 13
3. 10 + 7 = 17, 4 + 9 = 13, 8 + 8 = 16

Chapter 6

Practice Workbook

Adding and Subtracting Money

Add or subtract. Regroup if you need to.

1. 48¢ − 9¢ = **39¢**   63¢ + 36¢ = **99¢**   44¢ − 44¢ = **0¢**   71¢ − 17¢ = **54¢**
2. 57¢ + 38¢ = **95¢**   57¢ − 48¢ = **9¢**   98¢ − 69¢ = **29¢**   34¢ + 17¢ = **51¢**
3. 25¢ + 15¢ = **40¢**   30¢ − 15¢ = **15¢**   35¢ + 30¢ = **65¢**   55¢ − 5¢ = **50¢**
4. 85¢ − 59¢ = **26¢**   93¢ − 26¢ = **67¢**   54¢ + 45¢ = **99¢**   83¢ − 38¢ = **45¢**

Review and Remember

Add.

43 + 18 = **61**   16 + 38 = **54**   74 + 12 = **86**   57 + 21 = **78**   16 + 39 = **55**

Use after Grade 2, text page 188. 29

Practice Workbook

Choosing the Operation

There are 23 students in Miss Gonko's class. Mr. Brisk has 20 students. How many students are there in all? Do you add or subtract? Circle the example that makes sense.

(23 + 20 = 43) circled   23 − 20 = 3

Write each sum or difference. Circle the example that makes sense.

1. How many more students does Miss Gonko have than Mr. Brisk?

   (23 − 20 = **3**) circled   23 + 20 = **43**

2. Mrs. Rodgers has 19 students. Mr. Wong has 6 more students than Mrs. Rodgers. How many students are in Mr. Wong's class?

   (19 + 6 = **25**) circled   19 − 6 = **13**

Review and Remember

Count up to find the change.

1. Monica has 60¢. She spends 44¢.

   45¢ **50¢** **60¢**   **16¢** change

2. Barry has 80¢. He spends 69¢.

   70¢ **80¢**   **11¢** change

30 Use after Grade 2, text page 190.

Chapter 7

Practice Workbook

Minutes

Draw each missing minute hand. Write the time for the fourth clock.

1. 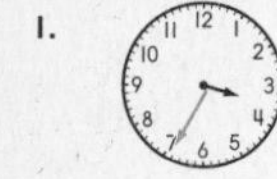   

   3:35   3:40   3:45   **3:50**

2.    

   7:00   7:20   7:40   **8:00**

Review and Remember

Estimate. Then solve. Compare your estimate with your answer.

Accept all reasonable estimates.

1. Two buses come to the station. Each one carries 38 riders. About how many riders are there in all?

   Estimate ______

   Answer **76 riders**

2. One day 29 campers park in lot A and 33 park in lot B. About how many campers park in both lots?

   Estimate ______

   Answer **62 campers**

Use after Grade 2, text page 206. 31

Practice Workbook

Telling Time

Write the time.

1.   

   3:00   **2:25**   **6:30**

2.     

   12:00   **10:10**   **5:55**

Show the time.

3.  

   11:30   4:45   6:00

Review and Remember

Subtract. Regroup if you need to.

86 − 13 = **73**   95 − 26 = **69**   21 − 10 = **11**   43 − 17 = **26**   58 − 41 = **17**   67 − 29 = **38**

32 Use after Grade 2, text page 210.

Chapter 7

Practice Workbook

Elapsed Time

Draw the missing hands. Write the time.

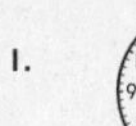

1. Bill's game starts in 2 hours.

It is 2:00 now. The game starts at 4:00.

2. Laura's party is in 4 hours.

It is 9:00 now. The party is at 1:00.

About how long does each take? Fill in the ◯ for the correct answer.

3. reading a book
   - ● 1 hour
   - ◯ 1 minute

   playing a baseball game
   - ● 2 hours
   - ◯ 6 hours

   flying across the United States
   - ● 6 hours
   - ◯ 6 minutes

Review and Remember

Add or subtract.

45¢	62¢	38¢	53¢	49¢
+49¢	+ 9¢	−18¢	−14¢	+13¢
94¢	71¢	20¢	39¢	62¢

Practice Workbook

Reading Schedules

Morning

Room	9:00–10:00	10:00–11:00	11:00–12:00
Art	Puppets	Clay	Painting
Science	Dinosaurs	Bugs	Fish
Gym	Tumbling	Singing	Running

Afternoon

1:00–2:00	2:00–3:00
Painting	Clay
Birds	Dogs
Kickball	

Use the schedule to answer each question.

1. In which room do you learn about dinosaurs? science
2. At what times could you paint? 11:00 and 1:00
3. Singing starts at 10:00.
4. Can you play kickball or learn about birds and dogs in the afternoon? yes

Review and Remember

Solve.

1. The pig picked turnips at 5:00. The wolf came by 1 hour later. At what time did the wolf come by? 6:00
2. The pig went to the fair at 2:00. The pig stayed for 3 hours. At what time did the pig leave? 5:00

Chapter 7

Practice Workbook

Using a Calendar

Sunday	Monday	Tuesday	Wednesday	Thursday	Friday	Saturday
		1	2	3	4	5
6	7	8	9	10	11	12
13	14	15	16	17	18	19
20	21	22	23	24	25	26
27	28	29	30	31		

Use the calendar above.
Write the day of the week.

1. The first day of the month is on Tuesday.
2. The 12th day of the month is on Saturday.
3. The last day of the month is on Thursday.

Write each date.

4. the second Monday 14
5. the fourth Sunday 27

Review and Remember

It is 11:00. The play starts in 8 hours.
Write the time the play starts. 7:00

Chapter 8

Practice Workbook

Inches, Feet, and Yards

Guess how long each object is.
Then use an inch ruler to measure. Answers will vary.

1. your shoe
   Guess: about ______ in.
   Measure: about ______ in.
2. your little finger
   Guess: about ______ in.
   Measure: about ______ in.
3. your pencil
   Guess: about ______ in.
   Measure: about ______ in.
4. the width of this book
   Guess: about ______ in.
   Measure: about ______ in.

Circle the better estimate.

3 feet = 1 yard

5.

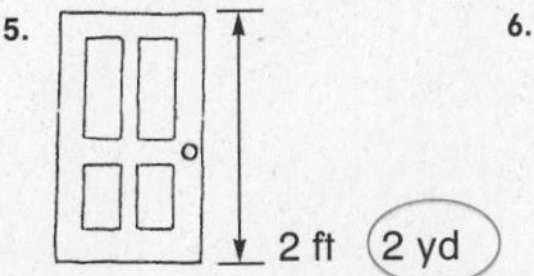

2 ft (2 yd)

6.

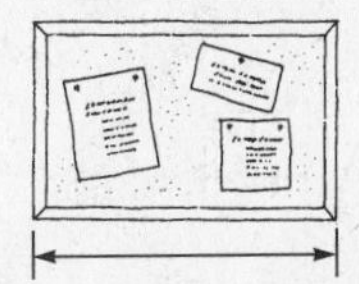

1 ft (1 yd)

Review and Remember

Circle the coins to show each amount below.

57¢

23¢

Chapter 8

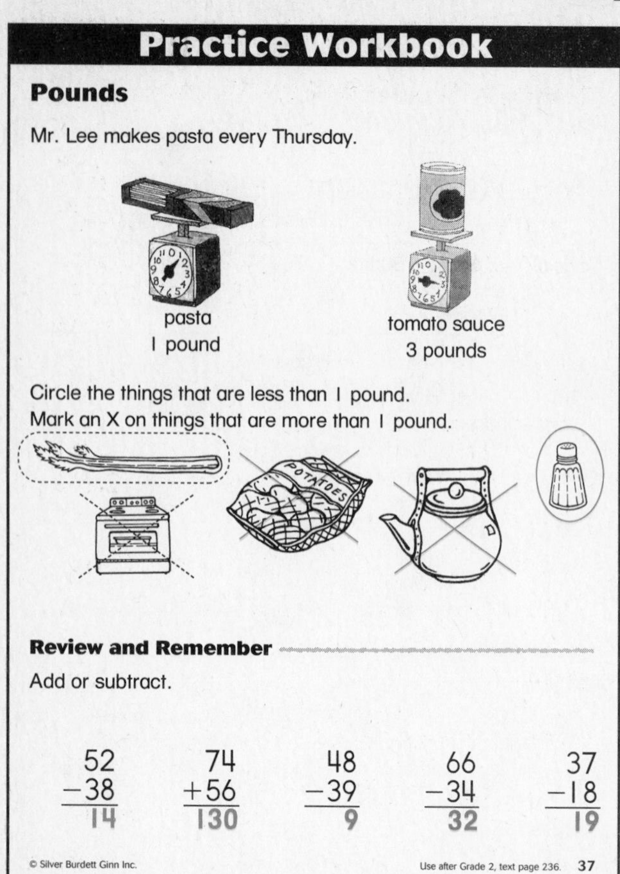

Practice Workbook

Pounds

Mr. Lee makes pasta every Thursday.

pasta
1 pound

tomato sauce
3 pounds

Circle the things that are less than 1 pound.
Mark an X on things that are more than 1 pound.

Review and Remember

Add or subtract.

52	74	48	66	37
−38	+56	−39	−34	−18
14	130	9	32	19

© Silver Burdett Ginn Inc. Use after Grade 2, text page 236. 37

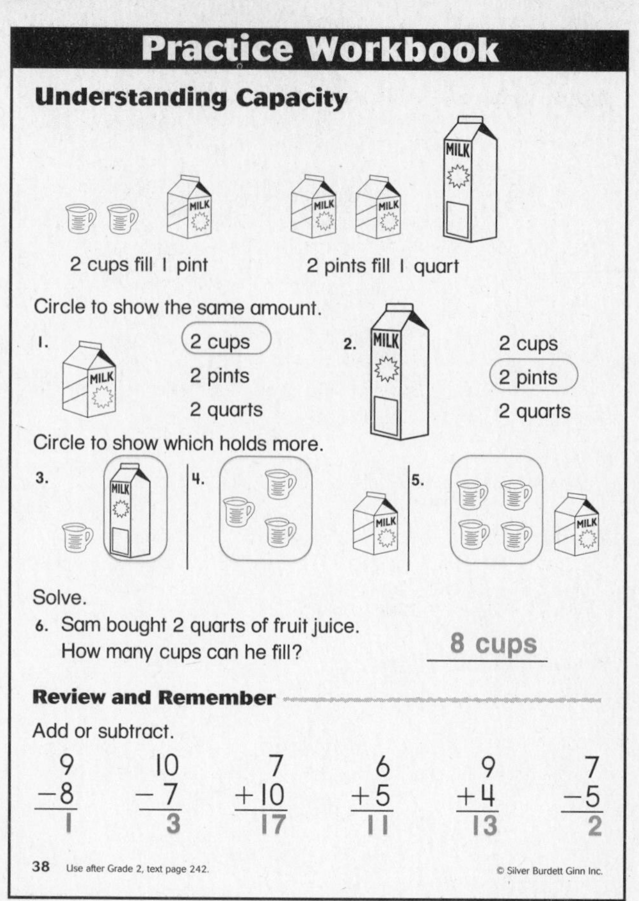

Practice Workbook

Understanding Capacity

2 cups fill 1 pint 2 pints fill 1 quart

Circle to show the same amount.

1. 2 cups / 2 pints / 2 quarts
2. 2 cups / 2 pints / 2 quarts

Circle to show which holds more.

3. 4. 5.

Solve.

6. Sam bought 2 quarts of fruit juice. How many cups can he fill? 8 cups

Review and Remember

Add or subtract.

9	10	7	6	9	7
−8	−7	+10	+5	+4	−5
1	3	17	11	13	2

38 Use after Grade 2, text page 242. © Silver Burdett Ginn Inc.

Chapter 8

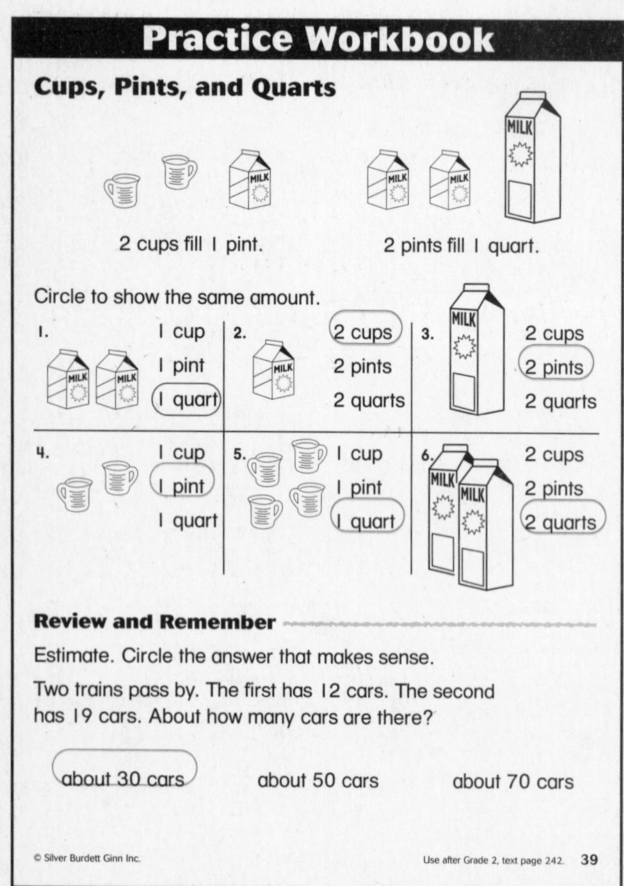

Practice Workbook

Cups, Pints, and Quarts

2 cups fill 1 pint. 2 pints fill 1 quart.

Circle to show the same amount.

1. 1 cup / 1 pint / 1 quart
2. 2 cups / 2 pints / 2 quarts
3. 2 cups / 2 pints / 2 quarts
4. 1 cup / 1 pint / 1 quart
5. 1 cup / 1 pint / 1 quart
6. 2 cups / 2 pints / 2 quarts

Review and Remember

Estimate. Circle the answer that makes sense.

Two trains pass by. The first has 12 cars. The second has 19 cars. About how many cars are there?

about 30 cars about 50 cars about 70 cars

© Silver Burdett Ginn Inc. Use after Grade 2, text page 242. 39

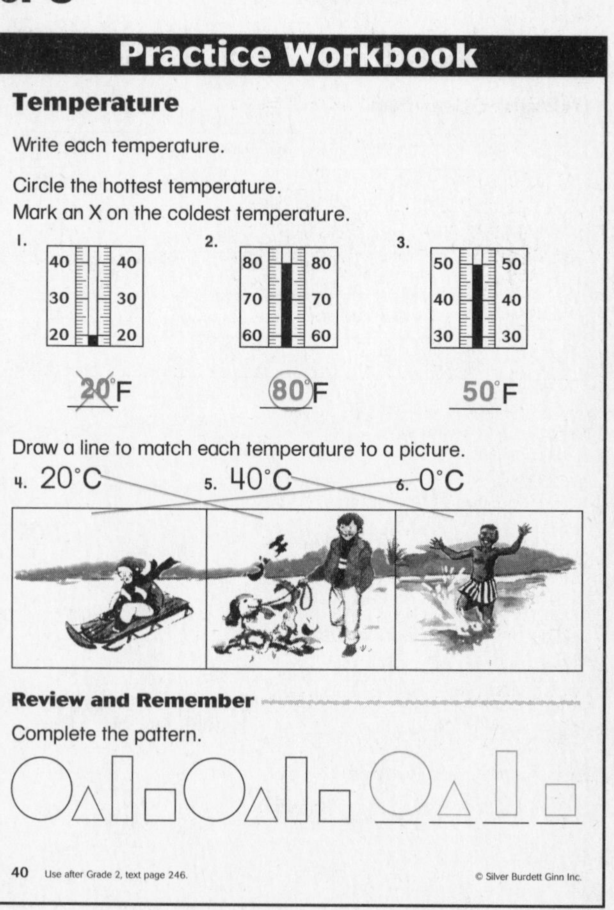

Practice Workbook

Temperature

Write each temperature.

Circle the hottest temperature.
Mark an X on the coldest temperature.

1. 20°F
2. 80°F
3. 50°F

Draw a line to match each temperature to a picture.

4. 20°C 5. 40°C 6. 0°C

Review and Remember

Complete the pattern.

40 Use after Grade 2, text page 246. © Silver Burdett Ginn Inc.

Chapter 9

Practice Workbook

Understanding Hundreds, Tens, and Ones

Write the number.

1.

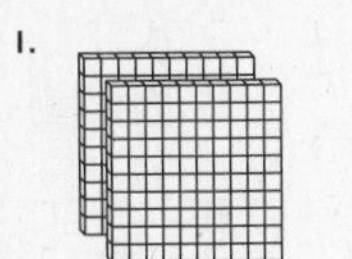

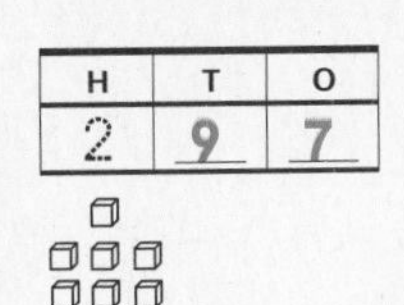

H	T	O
2	9	7

Write how many.

2. 569   5 hundreds   6 tens   9 ones
3. 902   9 hundreds   0 tens   2 ones

Circle the correct number.

4. 8 hundreds 2 tens 0 ones   82   802   (820)
5. 3 hundreds 0 tens 9 ones   (309)   39   93

Review and Remember

Write the time or draw the clock hands.

1.

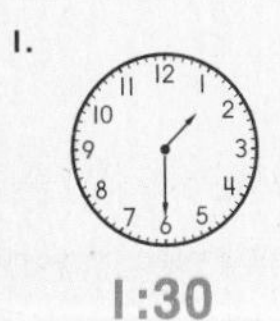

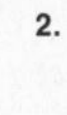

1:30

2.

2:55

3.

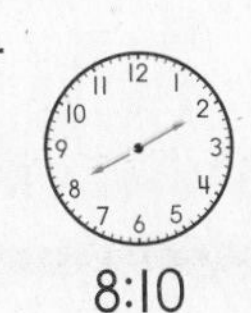

8:10

Practice Workbook

Understanding Three-Digit Numbers

Write each number.

1.

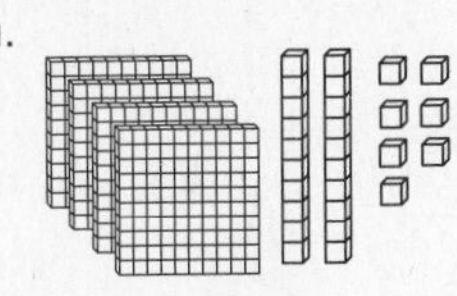

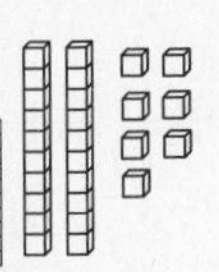

427

2.

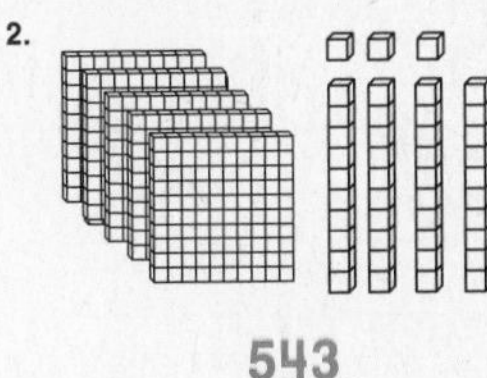

543

Write the numbers.

3. Before
   - 376, 377
   - 599, 600
4. After
   - 419, 420
   - 899, 900
5. Between
   - 542, 543, 544
   - 929, 930, 931

Write > or <.

6. 598 < 604   352 > 325   616 < 661

Review and Remember

Which fact is not needed?
Cross out. Solve.

~~A pig can run 11 miles in an hour.~~
A cheetah can run 70 miles in an hour.
A rabbit can run 35 miles in an hour.
How much faster can a cheetah run than a rabbit? 35 miles an hour

Chapter 9

Practice Workbook

Understanding Place Value

What does each number mean?

Write how many.

1.

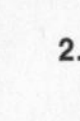

865 pounds

8 hundreds 800
6 tens 60
5 ones 5

2.

920 pounds

9 hundreds 900
2 tens 20
0 ones 0

3.

427 pounds

4 hundreds 400
2 tens 20
7 ones 7

4. 376
   - 3 hundreds 300
   - 7 tens 70
   - 6 ones 6
5. 185
   - 1 hundred 100
   - 8 tens 80
   - 5 ones 5
6. 601
   - 6 hundreds 600
   - 0 tens 0
   - 1 one 1

Review and Remember

Read. Cross out the fact that is not needed. Then solve.

The black bear eats 9 loaves of bread.
~~The black bear weighs 300 pounds.~~
The brown bear eats 8 loaves of bread.
How much bread do both the bears eat? 17 loaves

Practice Workbook

Comparing Numbers to 1,000

Compare. Write > or <.

1. 465 < 492   347 < 362   537 > 527
2. 613 < 704   464 > 332   194 < 202
3. 858 > 829   550 < 560   396 > 388
4. 251 > 250   729 > 721   343 < 347
5. 401 < 410   162 < 182   724 > 714

Review and Remember

Write the facts in each family. Order of answers may vary.

1. $6 + 3 = 9$ $12 - 7 = 5$ $15 - 7 = 8$
   - $3 + 6 = 9$ $12 - 5 = 7$ $15 - 8 = 7$
   - $9 - 6 = 3$ $5 + 7 = 12$ $8 + 7 = 15$
   - $9 - 3 = 6$ $7 + 5 = 12$ $7 + 8 = 15$
2. $6 + 8 = 14$ $9 + 6 = 15$ $14 - 9 = 5$
   - $8 + 6 = 14$ $6 + 9 = 15$ $14 - 5 = 9$
   - $14 - 6 = 8$ $15 - 9 = 6$ $9 + 5 = 14$
   - $14 - 8 = 6$ $15 - 6 = 9$ $5 + 9 = 14$

Chapter 9

Practice Workbook

Ordering Numbers to 1,000

Write the numbers in order.

1.	501	502	503	504	505	506	507	508	509	510
2.	511	512	513	514	515	516	517	518	519	520

3.	851	852	853	854	855	856	857	858	859	860
4.	861	862	863	864	865	866	867	868	869	870
5.	871	872	873	874	875	876	877	878	879	880
6.	881	882	883	884	885	886	887	888	889	890

Look at the charts. What patterns do you see?

Review and Remember

Which kitten is Gremlin? Cross out pictures that do not fit the clues. Circle the correct picture.

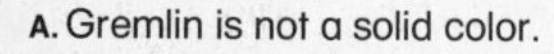

A. Gremlin is not a solid color.

B. Gremlin does not wear bows.

C. Gremlin is sleeping.

Use after Grade 2, text page 272. 45

Chapter 10

Practice Workbook

Space Shapes and Plane Shapes

Circle three shapes that are the same.

Circle the space shape that could make each plane shape.

Write how many sides and corners.

5. △ A triangle has 3 sides and 3 corners.

6. □ A square has 4 sides and 4 corners.

Review and Remember

It is 10:00 in the morning. The game starts in 4 hours. At what time does the game start? 2:00

Draw hands to show when the game starts.

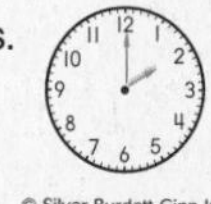

46 Use after Grade 2, text page 290.

Chapter 10

Practice Workbook

Exploring Perimeter

Each •–• is 1 unit. How many units around is each shape?

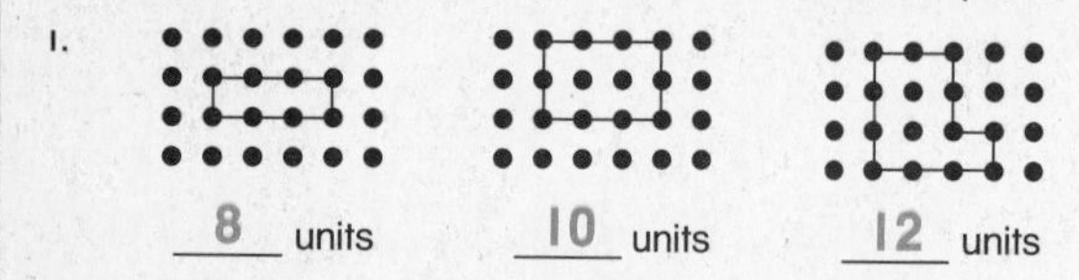

1. 8 units   10 units   12 units

Draw each perimeter. **Drawings may vary.**

2. rectangle 6 units around   square 8 units around

3. square 12 units around   rectangle 10 units around

Review and Remember

Count by 100s.

1. 300, 400, 500, 600, 700, 800, 900

Write the number between.

2. 213, 214, 215   499, 500, 501   789, 790, 791

Use after Grade 2, text page 294. 47

Practice Workbook

Congruent and Symmetric Shapes

Look at the first shape. Circle shapes with the same size and shape.

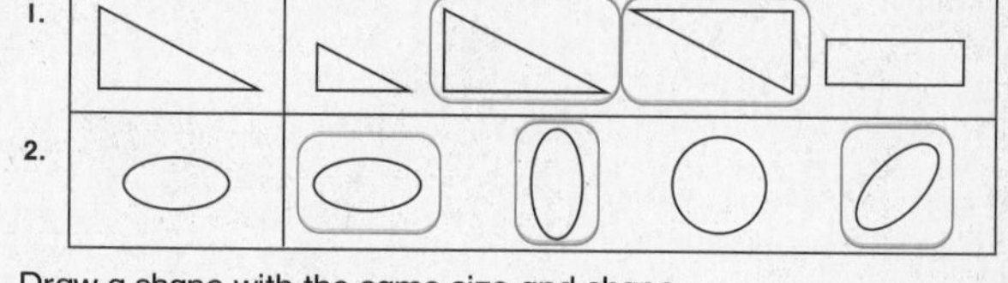

Draw a shape with the same size and shape.

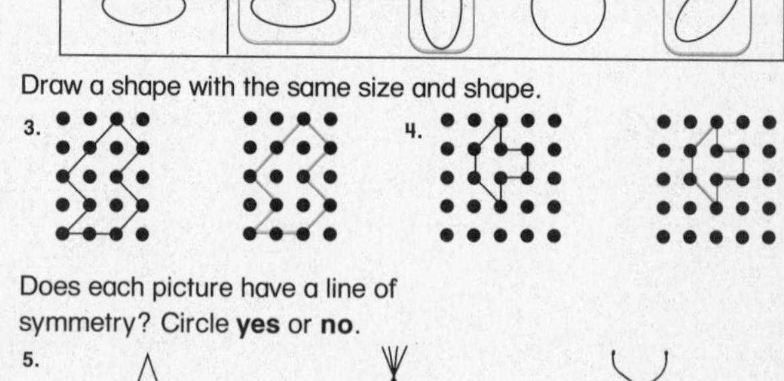

Does each picture have a line of symmetry? Circle **yes** or **no**.

5.

yes no   yes no   yes no

Review and Remember

Write the number.

1. before 99, 100   2. after 77, 78   3. between 9, 10, 11

48 Use after Grade 2, text page 297.

Chapter 10

Practice Workbook

Understanding Fractions

Write $\frac{1}{2}$, $\frac{1}{3}$, or $\frac{1}{4}$.

1. 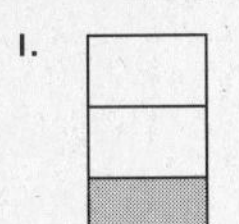 $\frac{1}{3}$ 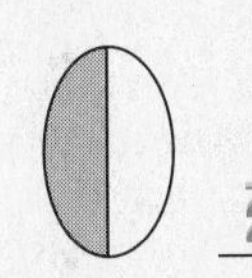 $\frac{1}{2}$ 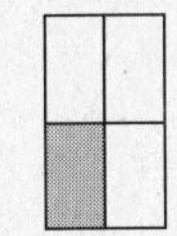 $\frac{1}{4}$

Circle the shape that shows each fraction.

2. $\frac{1}{4}$ 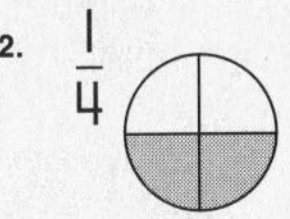 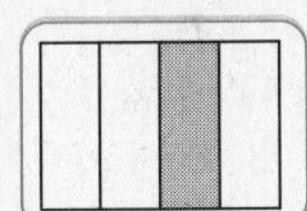 $\frac{1}{3}$  

What part is shaded? Fill in the ○.

3. 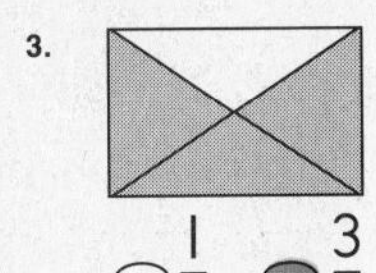 ○ $\frac{1}{4}$ ● $\frac{3}{4}$ 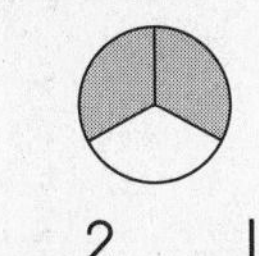 ● $\frac{2}{3}$ ○ $\frac{1}{3}$ 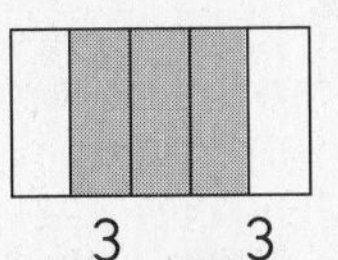 ○ $\frac{3}{6}$ ● $\frac{3}{5}$

Review and Remember

Find the perimeter of each shape.

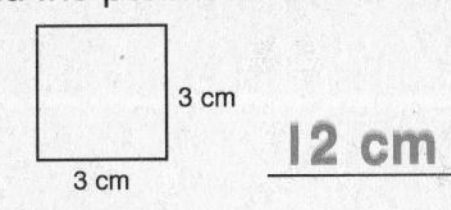

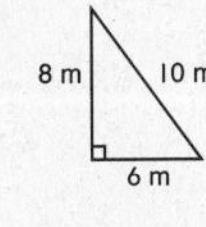

24 m

Practice Workbook

Working With Fractions

Color to show the fraction.

1. $\frac{2}{6}$ two sixths 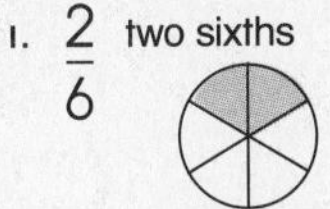
2. $\frac{4}{5}$ four fifths 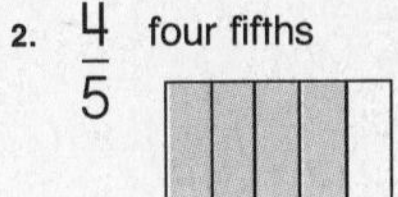
3. $\frac{7}{8}$ seven eighths 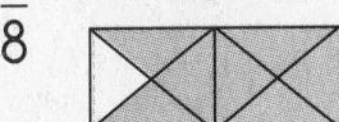
4. $\frac{1}{5}$ one fifth
5. $\frac{5}{6}$ five sixths 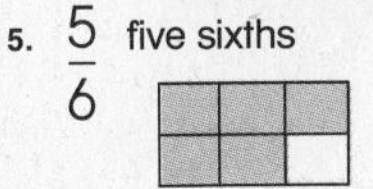
6. $\frac{1}{6}$ one sixth
7. $\frac{6}{8}$ six eighths 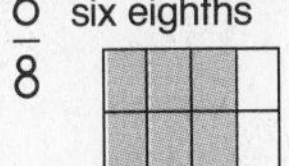
8. $\frac{3}{8}$ three eighths 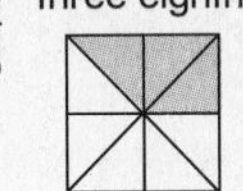

Review and Remember

Read. Cross out the fact that is not needed.
Then solve.

Boat A is 30 feet long.
Boat B is 45 feet long.
~~Boat B has a crew of 10.~~
How much longer is boat B than boat A? 15 feet

Chapter 11

Practice Workbook

Practicing Addition

Add. Regroup if you need to.

1.	102 + 639 = 741	429 + 265 = 694	326 + 43 = 369	432 + 459 = 891	216 + 546 = 762
2.	411 + 128 = 539	645 + 27 = 672	150 + 729 = 879	29 + 721 = 750	308 + 541 = 849
3.	528 + 42 = 570	111 + 157 = 268	364 + 528 = 892	719 + 38 = 757	483 + 13 = 496
4.	418 + 275 = 693	360 + 541 = 901	947 + 27 = 974	108 + 212 = 320	782 + 46 = 828
5.	574 + 161 = 735	111 + 473 = 584	302 + 136 = 438	265 + 607 = 872	426 + 368 = 794

Review and Remember

Estimate. Do you have enough money to buy the card? Circle **yes** or **no**.

yes (no)

Practice Workbook

Practicing Subtraction

Subtract. Regroup if you need to.

1.	564 − 428 = 136	393 − 219 = 174	941 − 237 = 704	668 − 343 = 325	840 − 137 = 703
2.	983 − 538 = 445	796 − 426 = 370	572 − 359 = 213	865 − 34 = 831	693 − 417 = 276
3.	870 − 428 = 442	351 − 151 = 200	487 − 168 = 319	685 − 57 = 628	700 − 700 = 0
4.	463 − 237 = 226	690 − 375 = 315	507 − 285 = 222	753 − 271 = 482	964 − 794 = 170

Review and Remember

Count the money. How much in all?

    36¢ in all

25¢ 30¢ 35¢ 36¢

Chapter 11

Practice Workbook

Adding and Subtracting Money

Write the numbers.

1. 6 dollars 9 cents $6.09
2. $6.93, $6.94, $6.95, $6.96, $6.97, $6.98

Compare. Write > or < in each ○.

3. $8.98 < $9.89 $2.10 > $2.01 $5.99 > $5.00

Add. Regroup if you need to.

4.

$5.14	$4.32	$0.21	$3.29	$0.12
+ 2.06	+ 3.91	+ 0.49	+ 0.91	+ 0.60
$7.20	$8.23	$0.70	$4.20	$0.72

Review and Remember

Circle the number.

1. 7 hundreds 1 ten 5 ones: 751 (715) 705
2. 3 hundreds 6 tens 0 ones: (360) 306 603

Write the missing numbers.

3. 477, 478, 479 565, 566, 567 798, 799, 800
4. 301, 302, 303 912, 913, 914 629, 630, 631

Practice Workbook

Too Much Information

Which fact is not needed?
Cross it out. Then solve.

1. An Indian elephant has 19 pairs of ribs. ~~An elephant's tusks can be 5 feet long.~~ An African elephant has 21 pairs of ribs. How many more pairs of ribs does an African elephant have? 2 pairs
2. A polar bear ran 35 yards. A cheetah ran 35 yards farther. ~~The cheetah had 8 cubs.~~ How far did the cheetah run? 70 yards
3. An elephant was 80 years old. ~~Each of its tusks weighed about 35 pounds.~~ A lion was 25 years old. How much older was the elephant than the lion? 55 years

Review and Remember

Look at the string of beads.
Write a fraction for each kind of bead.

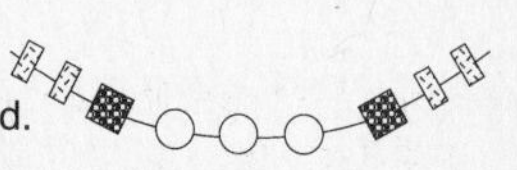

1. ○ $\frac{3}{9}$
2. ■ $\frac{2}{9}$
3. ▯ $\frac{4}{9}$

Chapter 11

Practice Workbook

Using Estimation

Think about the underlined words.

Circle the best answer.

1. Which number is about 500? 435 600 (502)
2. Which number is a lot less than 534? (248) 535 529
3. Which number is nearest to 199? (201) 113 315
4. Which number is a little more than 579? 499 (581) 876

Write your own number for each. Answers will vary. Possible answers are shown.

5. Write a number that is about 500. 499
6. Write a number that is close to 200. 202
7. Write a number that is a little less than 234. 232
8. Write a number that is a lot more than 468. 768

Review and Remember

Solve. Read one clue at a time and cross out. Circle the answer.

Which sweater belongs to Mel?

A. Mel does not wear stripes.

B. Mel's sweater has a picture on it.

C. It does not have a ball on it.

Chapter 12

Practice Workbook

Exploring Multiplication

Circle groups of 2. Multiply.

1. 3 groups of 2

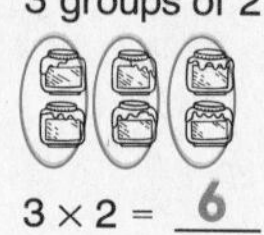

$3 \times 2 =$ 6

2. 2 groups of 2

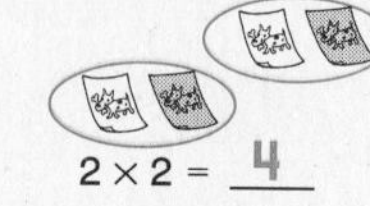

$2 \times 2 =$ 4

3. 4 groups of 2

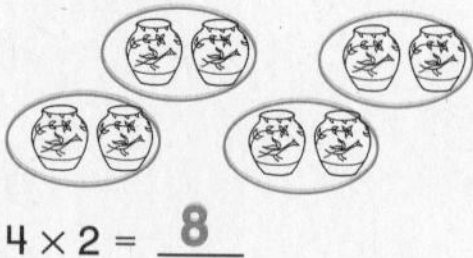

$4 \times 2 =$ 8

4. 1 group of 2

$1 \times 2 =$ 2

5. 5 groups of 2

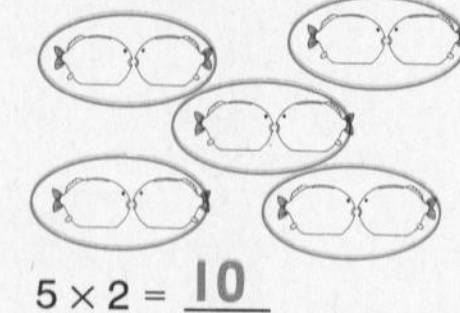

$5 \times 2 =$ 10

6. Make your own.

___ × ___ = ___

Review and Remember

Two classes get on the school bus. There are 21 children in each class. About how many children get on the bus? Circle the best estimate.

about 20 children about 30 children (about 40 children)

Practice Workbook

Addition and Multiplication

Add. Then multiply.

1. Henry gathers 5 chicken eggs every day. How many eggs does he gather in 2 days?

   $5 + 5 =$ 10

   $2 \times 5 =$ 10

2. Teresa writes 3 letters every week. How many letters does she write in 4 weeks?

   $3 + 3 + 3 + 3 =$ 12

   $4 \times 3 =$ 12

3. Shawn needs 6 flowers for each vase. There are 2 vases. How many flowers does she need?

   $6 + 6 =$ 12

   $2 \times 6 =$ 12

Review and Remember

Add or subtract.

43	231	211	430	567
+77	−107	+563	−179	+258
120	124	774	251	825

Practice Workbook

Multiplying Across and Down

Multiply across and down.

Write the numbers.

1. 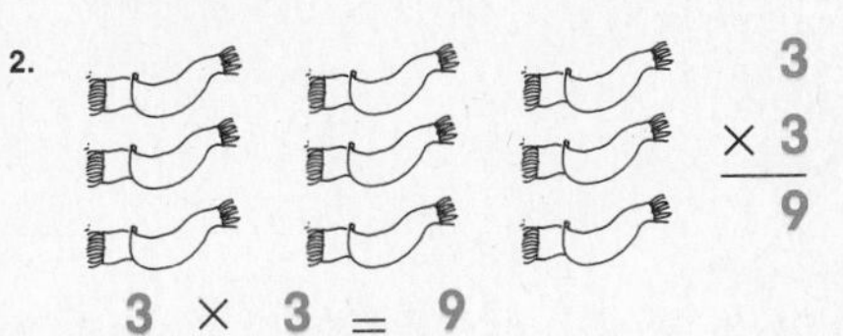

   $2 \times 3 = 6$

   $$\begin{array}{r} 3 \\ \times 2 \\ \hline 6 \end{array}$$

2. $3 \times 3 = 9$

   $$\begin{array}{r} 3 \\ \times 3 \\ \hline 9 \end{array}$$

3. $4 \times 3 = 12$

   $$\begin{array}{r} 3 \\ \times 4 \\ \hline 12 \end{array}$$

Review and Remember

Circle the best estimate.

Milk in a baby's bottle:	1 gallon	(1 pint)
The weight of a large book:	1 gram	(1 kilogram)
The weight of a watermelon:	(more than 1 pound)	less than 1 pound
Temperature of ice:	(0°C)	30°C

Practice Workbook

Multiplying in Any Order

Find each product.

1. $3 \times 5 = 15$ $\quad 5 \times 3 = 15$
2. $2 \times 6 = 12$ $\quad 6 \times 2 = 12$
3. $4 \times 5 = 20$ $\quad 5 \times 4 = 20$
4. $6 \times 1 = 6$ $\quad 1 \times 6 = 6$
5. $2 \times 4 =$ 8, $4 \times 2 =$ 8
6. $2 \times 3 =$ 6, $3 \times 2 =$ 6
7. $2 \times 1 =$ 2, $1 \times 2 =$ 2
8. $2 \times 5 =$ 10, $5 \times 2 =$ 10

Review and Remember

Write each time.

 1:30

 11:15

 2:15

Practice Workbook

Exploring Division

Circle equal groups.

Write the number in each group.

1. 2 groups of 3
2. 2 groups of 4
3. 4 groups of 4
4. 5 groups of 3
5. 5 groups of 4
6. 5 groups of 5

Review and Remember

Add or subtract.

18	72	87	29	45
+ 9	− 5	− 4	+63	+468
27	67	83	92	513